FROM APES TO WARLORDS

FROM APES
TO WARLORDS

The Autobiography
(1904-1946) of
SOLLY ZUCKERMAN

COLLINS
8 Grafton Street, London W1
1988

William Collins Sons & Co Ltd
London · Glasgow · Sydney · Auckland
Toronto · Johannesburg

BRITISH LIBRARY CATALOGUING IN PUBLICATION DATA

Zuckerman, Solly, Zuckerman, *Baron, 1904-*
    From apes to warlords 1904-1946.
    1. Science. Zuckerman, Solly Zuckerman,
    Baron, 1904-. Biographies
    I. Title
    509'.2'4

    ISBN 0-00-215246-0

First published by Hamish Hamilton 1978
This trade paperback edition published 1988
Copyright © Solly Zuckerman 1978

Made and printed in Great Britain by
William Collins Sons and Co Ltd, Glasgow

For Joan
who came to dinner

CONTENTS

Contents

FIGURES

(Maps drawn by Patrick Leeson)

A SPAN OF YEARS

THE BEGINNING lies so far in the past, and the view from my Norfolk window is so different from the scene in which I grew up, that it scarcely seems credible that the present emerged from what went before. But that it clearly did, however unpredictably, and however much chance played a part. I came to England as a medical student fifty years ago, having left South Africa with no serious intention of becoming a practising doctor, and with an undeclared resolve never to return. Those last two or three months stand out vividly in my memory. From our home on the lower slopes of Table Mountain there was a view over Cape Town into Table Bay where, because of a shipping strike, a number of vessels were lying at anchor. The house still stands, but today the view has been obliterated by skyscrapers, and even the shoreline and docks have changed. But this was at the end of 1925, and at the time I was reading for an examination. In the warm, early summer days I would take my books onto the verandah which opened from the bedroom floor, and every now and then would scan the sea and count the ships. I had persuaded myself that once they had all left, my own chances of leaving would vanish. Happily, a few were still there when the examination was over, and little more than three weeks later I was on my way to London in a small, slow boat, the *Garth Castle*.

When I sailed I did not know that I was to become a kind of renegade, and indeed it took some years before this was driven home to me. Soon after I had settled in London I met Edward Wolfe, then a young, and I suppose what one would call, struggling painter. He, too, had been born in South Africa, but had made England and Morocco his homes. Then I ran into Roy Campbell, who also had abandoned his native heath, and who was making his way as a poet. So was William Plomer, another poet and writer. There were others. I remember meeting Laurens van der Post, and thinking, incorrectly, that he, too, was a deserter. But it was only years later, many years later, that I really understood that I had become one.

South African passports had brown covers—perhaps they still do— and in the custom of the day all native South Africans were simply described as 'British subjects by birth'. Some years later, I was issued in

London with the familiar dark-blue British passport. But changes were afoot in the old Empire. When, after the war, I needed a new passport, I was referred by the British Passport Office to the South African High Commission, where I was told that because I had been born in what was then the Cape Colony, it would be contrary 'to the spirit of the South African Citizenship Act' if I held a British rather than a South African passport. The concept of citizenship had taken shape during the first post-war Conference of Commonwealth Prime Ministers, and had then become enshrined in legislation in all the countries concerned. But in accordance with the new laws, people who had been born in what had been a British Territory, but who were resident in the United Kingdom, could, by a simple process of registration, change their citizenship. This I promptly did.

The occasion on which I was made to feel a renegade came several years later. In 1961 there was another Commonwealth Prime Ministers' Conference in London, at the end of which South Africa formally left the Commonwealth. At the time I was Chief Scientific Adviser to the British Minister of Defence, and during the course of the Conference my wife and I were invited by Harold Macmillan, the Prime Minister, to lunch at Chequers. When we arrived I spotted among the other guests the late Dr. Verwoerd, the head of the South African Government, whom I had not met before. We were well separated at the luncheon table, but when Lady Dorothy led the ladies from the room at the end of the meal, the Prime Minister suggested that I move to the chair next to Dr. Verwoerd. There was a slight pause after I had sat down, and I opened the conversation by remarking politely that in spite of the British reaction to South African apartheid policies, he himself had enjoyed a warm and friendly reception during the course of his visit. He let my remark drop like a stone, and then said something like, 'I know about you, and what you are doing now. Where would you suggest that I look for someone to stand in the same relation to me as I see you do to the British Prime Minister?' I hardly knew how to reply, and did not feel easy until we were in the car driving back home. It was on the following day, the Monday, that it was announced that South Africa was leaving the Commonwealth. My tenuous national connection with the land of my birth was now completely broken.

In 1930 I went back to South Africa for three months. After that I did not return until nearly fifty more years had passed. I found the country as vast and as beautiful as it had ever been, but Cape Town had shrunk. The site at the end of the Avenue which had been shared by my old school and by Cape Town University, seemed minute. The old buildings were still there, but they were now in other hands, for both the University and the school had been moved out of the town, and both had grown enormously. I knew just a handful of people by name, and there was practically no-one whom I knew even by sight. I met unknown cousins whom I would never recognise again, and strangers introduced themselves to me and invested me with an apocryphal past. Compared with the kind of world I remembered from my childhood, there seemed to be wealth everywhere. Vast buildings and motorways had spawned and spread, and the physical trappings of a modern industrial society had replaced the quiet of a land which once depended on its agriculture and on distant mines. The only things that had not changed were the country's political problems. They had merely become more acute. I felt like a foreigner, and was glad to leave and return to what was, when I had first seen it, the heart of Empire. Impoverished, small and crowded, engulfed in economic storms and torn by industrial dispute, with no concerted vision of where it now stood in the world, England nonetheless still beckoned with a far greater promise than did the backwood from which I had come.

This book takes me to the end of the Second World War, and in it I have traced the steps by which my own beginnings led to the present, or at least part way to the present, a task on which I embarked in order to satisfy the curiosity of friends who wanted to know how it came that the two ever connected. Sadly, I find that I have outlived most of the people who come into my story. All the hopes which they personified, all their needs, all that pleasure enjoyed and given, all that pain endured, all that knowledge stored in so many heads, gone forever.

No doubt we all have a story to tell, perhaps more than one. As I see it, I was moved along by one accident after another, with little or no idea of who I was, or of what I would become, and with little or no notion of what the morrow would bring. We were all young then, young and unknown in an unknown world. Nothing was planned, nothing was seen in advance through a crystal ball. Life was full, and the world seemed peopled only by men and women who wrote books or music, or painted, or were in the theatre, or made scientific discoveries. All was excitement, and all personal. Up to the time of the Second World War, I should have laughed if anyone had suggested that in the years ahead I would become involved in public events which would become part of official histories, or that I could read other people's memoirs to 'cross-reference' some of what I say here. Even if I have had to do this, the story I tell is simply a record of turning-points in my own life. It is neither an exercise in self-analysis, nor an anatomical account of friendships and romances. And even if I did become involved in some moments of history, I do not pretend to write history. Some of what I have to say may supplement history, but history is the domain of the professional historian.

Forgetfulness can make one ungenerous to the past. At one moment

I thought that I would embark on this book in the easy way, and begin by saying that all which could be of any interest to others emerged from a dinner party in the early spring of 1942, at a time when London was being bombed, and that until then I had never dreamed that I might become a scientist at large in the public arena. The dinner party was real enough. It led me to the staff of Combined Operations Headquarters. But I can now see clearly that it could not have been a turning-point if there had not been others before.

I am still active as a scientist, and have never ceased writing papers, reports and reviews. I therefore have a considerable amount of published and unpublished material, and much correspondence, from which to check what I have related in this book about the first phase of my academic life. Half of my chapters, however, concern the years from 1939 to 1945. My initial involvement with war-work was through the Ministry of Home Security, for which, as a free-lance research worker, I had undertaken to make enquiries into the biological effects of explosions. It was from this that all the rest stemmed. I never became formally part of any of the various organisations with which I then worked, but partook of events rather as Pierre Besoukhov does in Tolstoi's *War and Peace*; as a civilian observer who happened to stray into a military camp. Because my links were all unofficial, many of my personal papers of the war period were still available when I started working on this book a few years ago.

In addition to these papers, I was fortunate to have at my disposal the unpublished autobiography of a wartime colleague, Air Vice-Marshal E. J. Kingston-McCloughry, C.B., C.B.E., D.S.O., D.F.C. The voluminous daily Historical Record of the Allied Expeditionary Air Forces (A.E.A.F.), where I worked during the first half of 1944, was brought to my attention by Lady Freeman, who at the time was Personal Assistant to Air Chief Marshal Sir Trafford Leigh-Mallory, the Commander-in-Chief of A.E.A.F. Numerous histories, official and unofficial, autobiographies and biographies, as well as the Public Record Office, were also there to consult so as to make sure that my memory was not at fault. Needless to say, I have also conferred with friends who have survived the events which I describe.

Cross-referencing has entailed a great deal of work, none of which would ever have been possible without the unstinting help of Gillian Booth, my special assistant, and of Deirdre Sharp, whom I like to call my archivist. Their appointments were made possible by a grant to the University of East Anglia from the Wolfson Foundation. My indebtedness to the University, and in particular to its Vice-Chancellor, Dr. Frank Thistlethwaite, is great. After a post-war life divided between Whitehall and an active professorship in the University of Birmingham, I retired from that University as Professor Emeritus. The University of East Anglia then appointed me 'Professor-at-Large', and after five years in that capacity continued to give me 'house-room' as its own Professor Emeritus. Had it not been for the indulgent way that I have been treated over the years by the Universities of Oxford, Birmingham and East Anglia, I would never have been able to cultivate the range of interests that I have.

In order not to burden my main text, I have made liberal use of appendices and notes where these seemed appropriate. References to published works are in the usual form. Those to unpublished official documents are made in a way which should allow them to be identified in the Public Record Office. Copies of private papers which relate to some of the public matters discussed in Chapters 6 to 18 have been deposited in the Library of the University of East Anglia.

S. Zuckerman
University of East Anglia
Norwich.
February, 1977.

CHAPTER I

COLONIAL BEGINNINGS

IN MY childhood Cape Town was still a city of ox-wagons and carts; of fish-sellers who heralded the arrival of their carts by sounding a small tin trumpet; of coloured fruit-sellers who went from door to door with vast baskets on their heads. Its population, including that of the suburbs which reached beyond the Cape Peninsula, was no more than about a quarter of a million, of whom somewhat fewer than half were Europeans. The people of Dutch descent outnumbered the British, and Jews were relatively few. The large coloured population consisted mainly of Cape Coloureds—indigenous natives in whose veins flowed some white blood; of some pure blacks; of a brightly-clad community of Malays; and of some Indians—even a few itinerant snake-charmers, complete with pipes, baskets and cobras. In those days apartheid was not spoken about; it simply existed. But to a child there was a sense of fear of the blacks and, if one wandered into 'District Six', the coloured section of the town, especially at weekends, one gained a knowledge of violence from seeing mounted police charging into mobs of black people, some of them drunk on cheap drink or dazed with the smoking of 'dagga', a kind of marijuana which grew everywhere.

Both sides of my family had emigrated from Eastern Europe to South Africa at various times during the latter part of the nineteenth century. Those were the days when vast numbers of Jews were fleeing westwards to escape Tsarist oppression in Poland, the Baltic States and Russia. I do not have the slightest idea why both my father's and my mother's families chose South Africa rather than England or America, which were then the chief goals of that particular exodus. Nor did I ever hear of any relatives who had stayed behind, although Isaiah Berlin, whose family came to England at the time of the Russian Revolution in 1917, once thought that he and I were kinsmen. Our great grandparents would be laughing in their graves, he said, if they saw how the fates had treated us. My mother's family, the Glasers, had all gone to South Africa, and only two of my father's family settled in America. I vaguely remember my mother's parents—both died when I was a child—and I knew my father's stepmother. All I knew about his father, who had died before I was born, was that he was, as my father put it, a very gentle person;

no-one had ever heard him raise his voice. Whatever else he was, he was
certainly biblically minded. My father, his eldest son, was named Moses,
the second Joseph, the third Samuel, and the youngest David. For the
rest, the story of my forebears is a blank. I once tried to find out something about them. My parents had died by that time, but with the help
of my uncle David (now in his nineties) and of an uncle on my mother's
side, I managed to track both sides back some five generations into the
late eighteenth century, to add to what I already knew. But there the
trail petered out. Wandering Jews were not in the habit of carrying their
genealogical records with them. I discovered nothing about how they
had lived but, from circumstantial evidence, it would seem that they had
shuttled between Prussia and Western Russia as political circumstances
changed during the course of the last century.

My parents married in 1902, the year the Boer War ended, and I was
born in Cape Town two years later, a daughter having been born in 1903.
I have practically no memory of my father until I was, I suppose, about
six, when he returned from what was then German South West Africa,
where he and my mother's younger, unmarried brother had gone to seek
their fortunes. It must have been about this time that I remember the
town being draped in purple and black to mark the death of Edward VII.
The brothers-in-law must have had an interesting time. My uncle David
has a story that my Glaser uncle invented some kind of washing table to
sift the diamond gravels of South West Africa, but that while he and my
father were back in Cape Town trying to arrange for some financial
backing, the De Beers mining company obtained a restrictive concession
over the whole area. I have a photograph of my uncle proudly standing
in the doorway of his room in South West Africa, clearly unaware that
on the floor behind him can be seen a heap of empty wine and beer
bottles. The bottles no doubt reflect the fact that in those days drinking-
water had to be distilled from sea-water. The look on his face suggests
that at that moment riches seemed to be just around the corner.

My father then set up a furniture and hardware business in Cape Town,
I believe under the wing of his brother Joseph, who had rapidly become
a prominent merchant of the town. The family business which he established goes on unchanged to this day. Writing to me not so long ago,
my uncle David observed that it mattered not at all that others had
pushed on while they had stood still—Joseph was well satisfied with
what had been done. Whether his son, Bertie, who is now the chairman
of the company, shares this view, I do not know. When I last saw him,
in 1975, he seemed to regard himself as representative of a class of
merchants who had allowed themselves to become extinct in a world of
mail-order stores and supermarkets. In 1926, the year I left South Africa,
the Zuckerman building of about ten floors was all but the tallest in Cape

After going to the University of Cape Town, my elder sister embarked on a career as a pianist, studying in London and Vienna. We shared no common interests, and even in South Africa very rarely did anything together. She failed as a pianist, married unhappily, and became very eccentric in the years before she died. I was followed by identical twin sisters, both of whom are still living in South Africa. Then, after a gap of some years, the last member of the family, a son, was born. He was still a boy when I left South Africa, and we are like strangers on the rare occasions that we have since met. During the war he became harbour master in Tel-Aviv, and at its end he remained behind, and in due course became an Israeli citizen. Such contact as I have maintained with my family has been through my twin sisters, both now widows, and both tough and courageous women.

Apart from the uncles whom I have mentioned, there was another, whom I seem to remember was often the worse for drink. There were two aunts whom I particularly liked. One was my 'rich' uncle's wife, Aunt Dinah, an elegant woman who died when I was in my early teens. She helped to introduce me to the world of novels. She had made a scrapbook of a mass of newspaper cuttings about Oscar Wilde's trial, which she felt that I should read. The other aunt was my mother's sister Martha, who lived in a small town in the Karoo where her husband had a general store, and an ostrich farm nearby. In those days it took a day and a night's railway journey to reach them, but from time to time I was taken there for a holiday. I remember Aunt Martha mainly because she would tell me that I was 'the best boy of all the girls', a remark which I took as a major piece of praise.

If I found my mother a taskmaster, she, I suppose, must have found me an unresponsive child. I mostly walked alone, and sometimes did odd things. One evening when on holiday at a small seaside resort near Cape Town where we had rented a small house, I put myself to bed and was found to be fully clothed under the bedclothes. I had worked it out that it was silly to undress at night only to have to dress again next morning. I never tried that again. If birds could fly, so could I—so flapping my arms as I jumped off a small ledge, I defied the laws of gravity, and then had to have my scalp stitched. That was not the only time when as a child I defied those laws, and suffered mild concussion as a result. I hated learning to read, and still recall the torture of being made to struggle through Ballantyne's *Coral Island*. But once I had overcome an initial reluctance, I found myself wanting to open books, provided I chose them myself, and discovered the joy of reading illicitly at night by the light of a secreted candle. I also found pleasure in collecting books, even as a boy. For a time Henty was my passion, and I responded to his stories, as no doubt did all his young readers, not only by sharing the adventures of his heroes, but also by being proud that South Africa was part of an Empire that had spread across the whole world. I discovered that lead piping could be melted in the flame of a candle, and that the strange shapes the molten drops took as they fell into a bowl of water were those of animals and people. And I remember my puzzled humiliation when I demonstrated the experiment to a boy whom I had told of my discovery, and who looked at me strangely and went off laughing. I was believed to be 'delicate' because after the extraction of a milk-tooth I had once bled as though I were a haemophiliac. I must have been even more of a nuisance when the reaction to my music lessons took the form of a swelling of my finger joints. A tentative diagnosis of bone tuberculosis led to my being taken away from school for a couple of months. The whole thing was, in modern parlance, psychosomatic, but it got me off my music lessons. During this self-generated school holiday I wandered into a small second-hand bookshop and bought for a few pennies what turned out to be a first edition of Edmund Burke's *Enquiry into the Origin of our Ideas of the Sublime and Beautiful*. Why I should have wanted this book at the age of twelve or so I cannot think, but I did not part with it till years later, long after I had settled in England.

I have no vivid memories of my school-days at S.A.C.S. (The South African College School), one of the oldest educational establishments in the country, and I suppose not a bad school by the standards of the day. I went there as a day-boy during the First World War and, as in most schools, day-boys were in general regarded as a lesser breed than the boarders. I disliked competitive sports and managed to avoid playing either cricket or rugger, both main elements in the life of the school. Table Mountain was on our doorstep, and when a mountaineering club was started, I became an enthusiastic climber. Indeed, when I left school for University, I joined the South African Mountain Club, and continued rock-climbing almost until the time I came to England. My usual climbing partner, Jackie Whitworth, was somewhat older than me, and well before we had exhausted the most difficult classified climbs up Table Mountain, we used to go—sometimes just the two of us, sometimes in a bigger party—and climb the mountains of the surrounding countryside. The custom in those days was to build a small cairn of rocks on peaks which were not already so adorned, and to leave a note in a bottle giving the date of the climb deemed to be the first, and the names of those who had made it. Whitworth wrote up a few of our climbs for the Club journal. He was by far the better rock-climber; I was willing enough to follow, but never to lead. And while I would be exhilarated at the end of a strenuous day's climbing, at times I was not a little frightened as we found our way to the top. Fatal accidents among our climbing friends were fortunately very rare, but they were not unknown.

Dry-rock climbing in those days was, of course, a far less specialised sport than it is today. Our equipment consisted only of a rope and clinkered boots. Jackie occasionally carried a revolver, but he used it only rarely, firing once at what, in the faint dawn light, I took to be a leopard in the nearby rocks. When we climbed in the country we filled our rucksacks with the bare essentials we felt we needed for the number of days we were going to be away. We slept in the open on ground-sheets, and were fairly skilled in making ourselves comfortable, although finding water to put in our Boer War army-surplus water bottles was at times a problem. Climbing in the country provided ample opportunities to observe baboons and other wild animals, without at the same time gaining the impression, somewhat prevalent today, that watching animals in the wild constitutes 'high' science. There were exotic birds, too, and wonderful wild flowers. The rare red and blue Disa orchids were already protected plants, but we often found them on our climbs.

The school curriculum was simple enough, but I find it odd that in a primitive country like the South Africa of those days it included both Latin and Greek, neither of which filled me with enthusiasm. Yet I chose to take both subjects, for the class was small. Mr. Le Mesurier, the Classics master, held that no-one could be counted a 'gentleman'—a word he never defined—if he did not know at least one book of the *Aeneid* by heart. He was able to teach both Greek and Latin without making us realise that the culture of Athens and Rome underlies a significant part of our own civilisation. For him it was enough to follow Xenophon as he marched so many parasangs across Asia Minor—or wherever it was that he marched.

Chemistry and physics, which I also took, were elementary, and only years later did I realise that the master was teaching both subjects between 1915 and 1920 without ever referring to the atom. But I liked chemistry sufficiently to fit out a laboratory in a small glasshouse at home, and to do simple routine experiments just for the pleasure of seeing things happen. Sometimes I shared these interests with David Bean, a friend who was regarded as the brightest boy in the school, and who everyone knew would in due course be awarded the school's Rhodes Scholarship to Oxford—for S.A.C.S. was one of the four schools to which Cecil Rhodes had allocated their own annual scholarships.

Only one of the masters, Mr. Hanton, who had returned from the war and who seemed rather withdrawn, made any real impression on me. He took a small class for English and for some reason he singled me out and fed me books which I read at the back of the form. Most were new novels. I remember those of E. F. Benson and particularly Alec Waugh's *The Loom of Youth* which had just come out. He also introduced me to Bernard Shaw's writings. When I visited S.A.C.S. after nearly fifty-five years, I was shown some old issues of the school magazine, and discovered that I had once spoken in the Debating Society on the subject of alchemy, and that I had also contributed a short and ostensibly 'funny' article on infinity. But being allergic to competitive games, I can hardly imagine that I was popular in a school where the good cricketers and footballers ruled the roost.

South Africa was seriously affected by the 'flu epidemic which spread across the world at the end of 1918, and which in the course of a few months carried away more than twenty million people. More than one in fifty of South Africa's population died, and Cape Town was particularly badly hit. I forget whether the disease came to the Cape during the school holidays, or whether the schools had to be shut as a precaution. I would walk alone through the town, and a vision of heaped bodies wrapped in sacking being carried on wagons to be buried in the nearby country still sticks in my memory. One would sometimes pass a corpse at the side of the road, and once there was a small old black woman, walking in front of me, who just collapsed and died. But I do not remember being frightened, or feeling that there was anything unnatural in people 'dying like flies'. Death as a concept was not one of my preoccupations.

The 'flu epidemic occurred at the end of the war, of which we were reminded every day by a constant stream of South African, Australian, and New Zealander troops who passed through the town. The school had a cadet corps, which I think we all had to join, and it also had its old-boy heroes. One of them, a young flying officer called Beauchamp Proctor, had won the V.C., and when home soon after the end of the fighting, he paid a visit to the school. As the small figure walked into the classroom he inspired a sense of awe and pride in all of us. Proctor was killed flying soon after he returned to England. When Armistice Day came in 1918 I felt that I had been cheated of the chance of taking part in great adventures.

I went to the occasional party with my sisters, but what little social life there was for a schoolboy I shared mainly with two or three school friends. There was no rich society that I was aware of, and no social barriers within what society there was. But in retrospect I can see that I met some extraordinary people. One of my contemporaries was Ernst Bohle, who later became Hitler's Gauleiter for the Ausland Deutsch. For a time I was keen on his sister, with whom I first danced at a party at the home of Dr. Malan, deputy to General Hertzog, the leader of the Nationalist Party. This was a few years before the latter helped overthrow General Smuts. But in those days I did not know what politics meant.

When, at the age of sixteen, I took the national matriculation examination, it was rumoured that I had come out not only first in the school, but also near the top of all the schools in the country. Whether or not this was true I do not know, but I never did get over my surprise that I had come out ahead of David Bean and a few others, with whom it would hardly have occurred to me to compete—at least partly because of the conviction that they were far cleverer than I was. Perhaps the rumour was false, but anyhow, on the strength of my success, I was awarded what in those days was the biggest prize scholarship to Cape Town University.

The University was literally next door to the School, both having been spawned by the South African College, which was the first major educational institution to be founded in the country. Going to the University was as to a new-found liberty. One could attend lectures or avoid them, one could idle or work, play games or not play games. I walked out in the middle of one of my first lectures—one on ethics— just to see whether it was true that attendance was not obligatory. No-one appeared to notice. I had registered as a medical student which, at the time, implied that while I could study the basic medical sciences in South Africa, I would have to go abroad for my clinical work. The custom was to spend a first year on general subjects, and then two more, on anatomy and physiology, before taking a B.A. degree. I was certainly not a hard worker, and for a time I found the business of dissecting the human body somewhat 'offputting', and as we operated in pairs, I left most of the work to my partner, Eric van Hoogstraaten. He constantly chided me for distracting him and wasting time, always complaining that while learning was no effort for me, it was hard going for him. He was one of the few of my contemporaries whom I met on my return visit in 1975, when I was told that only five of the thirty-nine in my class were still alive. Eric regaled me and my wife with recollections which seemed like fairy-tales. In those days, he reminded me, we never had two pennies to rub together but nonetheless had a marvellous time. According to him, I was an inveterate party-goer and, in spite of never appearing to work, always seemed to know what we were expected to know. One of his stories was that on an occasion when some students were standing around a cadaver having an abstruse piece of anatomy explained to them, I walked in with a doughnut in my hand. When the Professor had finished, with no-one much the wiser, I then demonstrated the matter much more clearly, moving the doughnut from hand to hand as I pointed to various parts of the body until enlightenment had spread through the dissecting room. Eric refused to agree that his story was sheer invention, and I had to accept that, given a favourable sequence of events which add up to success, time can be relied upon to provide its own embellishments. But in the end, once again, I did far better in the final examinations than I had expected, and gained First Class Honours in both main subjects.

I continued with my climbing and, with a few others, joined the national militia, or defence force, in a regiment called the Prince of Wales' Own Rifles. In a sense this served as a kind of Officers' Training Corps. I enjoyed the drills, the rifle shooting and the occasional camps. All-in-all, I treated this venture more seriously than did most of the others who had joined, and became one of the two sergeant-majors of our company. My military fervour at times provided unforeseen amusement for those under my 'command'. Once I had to march my platoon from the University at the upper end of the main Avenue of the town to the Drill Hall about a mile away. Two of my 'men', who were well-known buffoons, arrived with umbrellas as well as rifles, and the amusement this caused encouraged them to refuse to put them down. All I could therefore do was tell them to fall out, and to make their own way to the centre of the town. This they did by marching with open umbrellas about fifty yards ahead of my column-of-fours. As we passed the two sentry boxes in front of the Governor-General's Residence, which opened on to the Avenue, they stepped out of the boxes, smartly presenting arms with their umbrellas, to the bewilderment of passers-by, the amusement of my platoon, and to my embarrassment. On another occasion when 'defending' a mountain ridge near Simonstown, I had posted my sentries at various points which I visited every four hours to change the guard. Hardly one of my sentries was not asleep at his post, and one had even mislaid his rifle in the dark. It was not found until next morning. They were an undisciplined lot, 'my men', or I was very bad at keeping discipline.

For a time I interested myself in amateur theatricals, under the tutelage of a woman lecturer in drama. Another of her pupils, Ena Burrill, later became a well-known actress on the English stage. Not long ago she wrote to me out of the blue to remind me that I had played the part of Everyman in the fifteenth century Dutch morality play of that name. 'I see you', she said, 'rising up centre-stage—in a full spotlight—covered in yards of bright red butter-muslin, and making a long speech full of foreboding for mankind'. I had forgotten. I read a lot and, possessed by now of my first dinner jacket, went to dances. Often I would play cards with two friends who were close neighbours. They were the sons of a surviving brother of Jan Hofmeyr, the nineteenth-century politician who had consolidated the South African Dutch as a political force through the Afrikander Bond, or Brotherhood. Both Karl and Steve became Rhodes Scholars and Rugger Blues at Oxford, and rumour has it that both later became passionate members of the Nationalist Party and of a near fascist, anti-semitic movement. In my boyhood the Afrikaners were the very reverse of anti-semitic—they were too devoted to the Old Testament for that. In so far as I was ever conscious in my youth of anti-semitism, its source was more likely to be some narrow-minded descendant of English settlers. Today this no longer seems to be the case; I have heard that the sentiment is more frequently found in some sections of the Afrikaner world. I also now know that even at the turn of the nineteenth century there were many people, not just politicians, who were worried about the racialist structure of South Africa, and who were already asking what the upshot was going to be—in a society in which white battled against white, where whites were lined up against blacks, and where 'coloureds' and blacks were divided amongst them-selves. The basic issue remains what it was when the problem was debated by statesmen such as John X. Merriman and Cecil Rhodes in the years before the Act of Union of 1910. How can the vastly more numer-ous black population of the country become politically integrated with the whites? South Africa's answer for the moment is apartheid and unrest. No-one knows what the morrow will bring.

I made new friends at the University. There was H. E. S. Fremantle and his daughter Isabella. Just before the start of the Boer War, when he was only 25, Fremantle, an Etonian who had been an Oxford don for a few years, had been appointed Professor of English and Philosophy in the South African College. He soon gave up academic life for politics, unexpectedly turning against those politicians of English descent who at the time were arguing for a federal constitution for the Union of South Africa. After the Union was formed, and on the outbreak of war in 1914, he helped General Hertzog set up the Nationalist Party as the official opposition to the ruling party led by Botha and Smuts. Fremantle used to feed me tales of the duplicity of these two Generals, both of whom cooperated with the British to end the Boer War. In the end, of course, he was regarded with suspicion by both the English and the Botha/Smuts Afrikaner politicians. Shortly before his death in 1932, I unsuccessfully tried to help him publish some articles he had written about the part he had played in South African politics. Fremantle was the first person who made me aware of the fact that some Englishmen educated in the Humanities regarded the Sciences with disdain. 'So you've decided to become a scientist', he said one day, and picking up a copper ashtray, he added, 'I suppose that means that you'll be able to tell me why this turns green'. He seemed to be implying that knowledge of that kind was not for academics. One of my other friends, a cricketer who was reading law, was the brother of Sarah Gertrude Millin, the novelist and biographer of Rhodes and of Smuts. We once stayed with her in Johan-nesburg. She was the first novelist I had met and I was greatly impressed.

I took my B.A. degree soon after I had turned nineteen, and I then

had to decide what to do next. Since my parents did not have the money
to send me to England, the obvious thing was to enter the clinical
school which was about to be established in Cape Town. But England
was where I was determined to go. At my father's suggestion I went to
see his 'rich' brother, but he turned me down. The Professor of Anatomy,
a Scot called M. R. Drennan, then approached me and two other students
who had just graduated, with the suggestion that we became Demon-
strators in the dissecting room, at the same time as we embarked on a
two-year course of study and research leading to the M.A. degree. A
stipend went with the job, and if I saved, it would all help if I was ever
to go abroad. And so I embarked on my first academic job.

I do not recall doing much teaching, but I started systematically reading all the literature about evolutionary theory that was available in Cape
Town. It was then that the casual observations which I had been making
of baboons in the wild started to crystallise. Man is the only fully-
upright member of the mammalian order of Primates, in which we are
classified together with the great apes, monkeys and lemurs. The overwhelming majority of sub-human primates live in the trees, but the
baboons with which I was familiar lived on the ground. To my unin-
formed mind this posed the question: given that the terrestrial habit was
a factor in man's evolution, why had baboons, also a terrestrial primate,
not evolved further than they had? Why had they remained quadrupeds?
I decided to study every aspect of the animal in order to find an answer
to this question, in the mistaken belief that this was not too ambitious
a project in the time at my disposal. What I had in mind was a detailed
study of the creature's anatomy and growth, behaviour, and so on.
Drennan left us very much to our own devices, and he did not point out
that my plan was not only wildly ambitious but also scientifically silly.

I covered reams of paper with records of the observations I made on
the general anatomy of the baboon (the bulk of it remains unpublished)
and, as opportunity offered in the course of climbing expeditions, I tried
to learn more about the way the creature's social life is organised. I had
a friend, Marcus Cole Rous, whose father owned a vast farm near Graaf
Reinet in the Cape, and on whose land there were several packs of
baboons which roamed within their recognised territories in a range of
low mountains.

Marcus had set out to be a surgeon, and we decided that it would be a
good idea if he polished his anatomical knowledge by helping me with
my dissections of baboons. Several weeks of two long vacations were
spent in this way. Having shot and 'pickled' our specimens, we spent two
or three hours most days dissecting and recording. On other days I
would sally forth alone on horseback, laden down with haversack, field-
glasses, camera and rifle. I would ride for some five to ten miles, tether

my horse to a bush, and then take up a position in the hills to keep watch on the baboons and to photograph them when possible.

Marcus's stocky father was a bully, never without a sjambok hanging from his wrist. The sight of him striding around in his riding breeches and leather leggings, driving his black farm-hands to work, inspired me with fear. We had prayers before breakfast every morning, and ate springbok, a deer with nice flesh when taken in moderation, but which palled when served at almost every meal. On some evenings I would ride across the veldt with Marcus, or with a young Englishman who was learning about farming in Africa, to sheep compounds some miles away. Here we separated ewes which had been automatically marked with dye when they had been covered by the prize stud rams, from those whose turn was yet to come. Every day Marcus's father made one or other of us keep watch for an hour or so on his bee-hives. We would sit about eight feet away, in the full glare of the sun, waiting for the pirate wasps which alighted on the landing ledges ready to pounce on bees as they returned with their forage. In those days I was a fairly good shot, but I now find it incredible to think that the holes the small air-gun slugs made in the wood in most cases implied a dead wasp. Sometimes I took a gun and went after the meerkat, a small carnivorous creature, rather like a stoat, which lived in burrows that interlaced with those of a rodent called the spring-hare. Once I had the rare chance of seeing a giant ant-eater, but it rapidly disappeared into the earth when I made towards it. On a very hot afternoon—the temperature must have been about 104°F—I asked one of the native hands where they buried their dead, and helped him disinter for me a magnificent human skeleton, the skull of which is now in the Medical School at Birmingham.

But what really stands out from those two visits to the Cole Rous estate are conversations I had with another guest, who was the widow of the Principal of what was then, at Fort Hare, the only College of Higher Education for black people in South Africa. Almost all the men who worked on our host's farm wore the scantiest of European clothes, and most were totally illiterate. Around us were the kraals of native huts many of whose inhabitants still wore animal skins. The widow had only a sad tale to tell—of a total lack of opportunity for blacks who wished to be educated. She wrote to me several times after I had settled in England, but they were always sad letters.

In my childhood it was still possible to run across the occasional Hottentot, a primitive indigenous native people, but by then Bushmen were a curiosity. In my climbing days I had been lucky enough to discover in a tight rocky overhang some Bushman cave-paintings which had not been recorded before. It was only by a narrow shave that I then escaped becoming a professional physical anthropologist. About fifteen miles from Cape Town is a small coastal village called Fish Hoek, from which an arid valley runs horizontally across the Cape Peninsula. In the drift sea-sand by which much of the valley was covered, one occasionally came across the bleached bones of 'Strandloopers', the Afrikaans name for an extinct race of Bushmen who had lived on what food they could gather near the water's edge. I had an undergraduate friend who lived on the outskirts of the village at the eastern end of the valley, and facing her house was a large open rocky cave. Knowing that the area had once been the hunting ground of Bushmen, I got it into my head—at the latest this would have been the summer of 1924—that the cave had once been inhabited, and that it would be interesting to dig in it for human remains. One hot day I gave a few pennies to a black man to help me cut a trench some six to eight feet long and about four feet deep. We turned up ashes, shells and animal bones, but no human remains, and after a few hours I returned to my friend's house to tell her of my fruitless quest.

Two or three years after I had settled in London, my sisters sent me some newspaper cuttings which reported that a Mr. Peers and his son, local animal dealers, had visited the cave, and having noticed a trench which suggested to them that someone had thought that there must be something to find, had started to dig systematically. This was in 1927. Some human skeletons and implements were disinterred, and descriptions of the remains are now to be found in most textbooks on physical anthropology. Some regard 'Fish Hoek Man' as having been an ancestral Bushman, others as representative of a vanished people called the Koranas. Much later I learnt that when the famous French anthropologist the Abbé Breuil visited the cave, which was by then widely known as the 'Skildergat', he noticed on its walls Bushmen paintings which had been missed both by me and by the Peers, with whom, together with a Mr. van der Poll, I later discussed the finds during a visit to South Africa in 1930. I was also interested to read that a Mr. Goodwin had investigated the cave in 1925, and that he had dug a trench, abandoning his work when he too found nothing. Anyhow, it was fortunate for me that it was a hot day, and that instead of going on digging, I had returned to my friend's house and so escaped falling into the anthropological pit I was unwittingly digging for myself. Had I gone on I might have ended up in a field of science which later I realised was mainly concerned with conjecture and speculation.

My last year at Cape Town University was a busy one. Mrs. Ruth Bisbee, an exchange lecturer in zoology from Liverpool University, had come that year to Cape Town, and for the first time in my life I learnt what it was to be lectured to in an inspired way, and what a fascinating field of study zoology is. She encouraged me in my ambitious idea of carrying out a comprehensive enquiry into the baboon, and my dissections and other research went on apace. I studied the way the rounded skull of the infant baboon is transformed into the long-snouted skull of the adult, and in the course of my work discovered that some of the statements that had been made on the subject by T. H. Huxley, Charles Darwin's great contemporary, were wrong. I therefore decided to concentrate on this particular piece of work, a report of which in due course became my first published scientific paper.

I also had to make quite sure that I knew my systematic human anatomy, since that also was going to be reviewed in the final examination. Drennan had been brought up in the Edinburgh tradition, and according to him one could not afford to neglect any detail of anatomy, however trivial.

Towards the end of the year I turned night into day, staying in the Anatomy Department until dawn, before returning home for a few hours of sleep. I soon realised that there was no way in which I could be sure of remembering every anatomical fact. Rather than stop at the end of a page to see what I had absorbed, I therefore read first one textbook from cover to cover, and then repeated the exercise with another major text, and so on with a third. But on my recent and belated visit to South Africa, I was reminded that in spite of all the work I was doing I still kept up an active social life. How, I do not remember. One of my twin sisters had agreed to type my paper on the growth of the skull of the baboon, and according to her there was more than one night when I left her typing in the Anatomy Department while I went off to dance. One of my dancing partners, who was 'studying art', did the drawings which illustrate the paper. I remember returning one night in the early hours, still in a dinner jacket, and sitting in the deserted dissecting room, morbidly communing with the dead.

My two examiners in my final year were Drennan and Raymond Dart. Dart had come to South Africa about two years before to fill the Chair of Anatomy in the new University of the Witwatersrand in Johannesburg. Within months of arriving he had got himself very much into the news. One of his colleagues had brought him from Bechuanaland, now Botswana, a fossil ape-like skull which, presumably by divine guidance, Dart immediately recognised as the 'missing link' in the line of man's evolution from ape-like precursors. The Taungs Skull, as it became known, was Dart's first essay into the field of sub-human primate anatomy. What stands out most clearly in the memory of my first meeting with him was a moment, before my examination took place, when he and Drennan asked me whether the skull of a young ape, one of a very small number of ape skulls which were then available for study in South Africa, was that of a gorilla or chimpanzee. At the time I was at my bench chipping limestone from a fossil baboon skull—for by then I had added fossil baboons to my studies. Neither Drennan nor Dart had ever studied the anatomy of apes or monkeys before, and their views about the Taungs fossil obviously differed. The question they put to me was a real eye-opener. Even though he could not tell one great ape from another, Dart had known straight away that the Taungs Skull represented a unique ape-man. Another thing I remember about Dart was his reaction to an examination essay I wrote in answer to the question: 'Discuss the evidence that man is the product of a process of evolution'. I was taken aback that so broad a title had been set, when for three-quarters of a century, ever since Darwin, volume after volume had been written on the subject. So for three hours I elaborated an ironical reply. When our papers were returned after the examination, I was not surprised to find that every page of my long essay had been crossed through, with an angry comment added here and there. Nonetheless, I was awarded Honours in the examination, and given the University's senior zoology medal. A geologist graduate and I were also elected to its scholarship for overseas study. This, when added to the little that I had managed to save, and to what my parents scraped together, made it possible for me to go to England.

In the light of the life-long experience of the educational world which I have enjoyed, it is not unfair to say that neither school nor university in the South Africa of my day provided the kind of intellectual stimulus that is expected today from one's teachers. I was not taught to realise how much the advance of natural knowledge depends on carefully controlled experiment. I knew nothing of the revolution that was beginning to transform genetics. And I certainly was not encouraged to be wary of established wisdom. There is nothing so exciting for a student as discovering for himself that something he reads in a learned book is not necessarily true.

On the other hand, I did enjoy the advantage of being left to myself. The master who at school fed me new novels helped me to independence. Mrs. Bisbee transformed into an excitement what was otherwise rote-learning. And Professor Drennan, by leaving me to my own devices, whether or not he did so by intent, forced me to develop my own critical sense.

Early in 1925 a surgeon, who was a part-time lecturer in anatomy, spoke to a few of us about blood-groups, then a relatively new discovery, and asked if we would volunteer to be 'tapped'. I donated a pint of blood and, like the others who did, was rewarded with £5—a lot of money in those days. I spent it on books, among them Bergson's *Creative Evolution*, which I read meticulously and, as was my habit, annotated in the margins. I have just looked at my old copy. The opening sentence reads: 'The history of the evolution of life, incomplete as it yet is, already reveals to us how the intellect has been formed, by an uninterrupted progress, along a line which ascends through the vertebrate series up to man'. Against this I wrote: 'It does nothing of the sort'. There are many notes in the same vein, one of which expresses my doubt that 'a screening' of 'all missing links' would ever reveal to us the exact path of man's evolution—as Bergson implied it would. I have since provided ample reason why I continue to doubt this particular proposition. But I can also now see that my scepticism was a form of intellectual arrogance. However it happened, I certainly had learnt not to be fearful of authority. Nonetheless, I am sad that it was only after I had left South Africa that Lancelot Hogben came to Cape Town as Professor of Zoology. That outstanding and unhappily neglected scholar turned the place upside down, and revealed the excitement of the experimental method in biology. He provided much pleasure for a few by stirring intellectual controversy, even challenging in polemical debate South Africa's number one citizen—General Smuts—on his own ground as a philosopher of holism. I wish I had been there at the time.

When I left Cape Town there was the usual boat-leaving ceremony of those days, with parents and friends coming to bid farewell when I embarked on the *Garth Castle*. We were about three and a half weeks at sea, with stops at St. Helena and Teneriffe. Those were the days of gold sovereigns, and I had something like a hundred in a small leather purse to see me through my first few months in England. And I also had under my supposed charge another medical student, the son of family friends, who it was thought would benefit from my sober care. He was going to London to join an elder brother who was already at St. Thomas's Hospital Medical School. I felt no wrench at leaving, only a sense of great things waiting to be savoured. I was abandoning no loves, and it did not occur to me that once I had gone there might be someone who might miss me, or whom I would miss. By the standards of today, and indeed by those of many of my friends of fifty years ago, I was certainly naïve about personal and sexual matters. It never occurred to me to question my feelings about my parents or about people in general. I was not consciously aware of what I knew; I was certainly not competitive. I took things as they came, and to myself I was an ordinary man-in-the-street, going off to new things. In short, I was an unabashed, unfrightened, independent young man leaving one country for another where he sensed that the horizon, if not as beautiful as that of South Africa, was certainly wider.

CHAPTER 2

THE MEDICAL STUDENT

I SPENT my first night in London with the family with whom Jessie, my musical sister, was staying. We had extraordinarily little to say to each other, and I played patience most of the time. The next day I made my way to St. Thomas's Hospital, which I had thought of joining so as to be with my South African friends. Times have certainly changed. It was then easy to get into any medical school. But when, on the following day, I presented my first letter of introduction to Professor Grafton Elliot Smith at University College I changed my plans. No-one could have been more welcoming, and on the incorrect assumption that University College Hospital Medical School—U.C.H. as it is usually called—was part of the College, I agreed to get myself admitted there. The letter which Drennan had written referred to my draft paper on the baboon skull, and this Elliot Smith asked to see. I showed it to him next day, and after glancing at it he suggested that since I had arrived out of season for the introductory course to clinical medicine, I should try for one of the Medical School's two open exhibitions, the examination for which was due to take place a few months later. He also suggested that I should sit for the primary examination for a Fellowship of the Royal College of Surgeons, not only because I might end up as a surgeon, but because he felt that since I had spent so much time on anatomy I was already prepared for the examination. This suited me very well, because even though it meant my signing on for a 'cram course' at another London medical school which specialised in preparing students for the F.R.C.S. examinations, I now had time to look around before committing myself.

I found a room in a small hotel in Gower Street, literally next door to the Medical School, and started to savour the life of London. Mill's Hotel consisted of two houses which had been knocked into one, together with two on the opposite side of the road. The house in which I had my room had once been Charles Darwin's home, and was one of those which had to be demolished when University College's new Institute of Biological Sciences was built in the late fifties on to the side of Elliot Smith's Institute of Anatomy.

When I met him, Elliot Smith was at the peak of his powers. He was not only Britain's most prominent anatomist, but also one of the most influential of British scientists. He was the recognised authority on the structure and evolution of the brain. He had distinguished himself as an egyptologist, and had become the leading exponent of the diffusionist anthropological school, whose basic doctrine is that all the major ideas that have transformed society have emerged as unique events in only one part of the globe. For Elliot Smith, this mainly meant Egypt. He was also greatly interested in problems relating to man's physical evolution—a subject almost as controversial as that of man's cultural evolution—as well as in a variety of other 'hot' anatomical problems.

In addition to a central Department of Anatomy, his Institute comprised a sub-department under the direction of a celebrated embryologist, J. P. Hill, and one of cultural anthropology, presided over by W. J. Perry, a quiet man who was the author of many books on the spread of early civilisation. Diffusion was W. J. Perry's sole preoccupation. H. H. Woollard, a man with a first-class mind and a scathing tongue, was the leading anatomist in the Institute. In due course he succeeded Elliot Smith as its head. Woollard was then setting a framework for the study of the comparative anatomy of the most primitive sub-human primates, the Tarsiers, at the same time as he was promoting the experimental approach to the whole subject of anatomy, which in England had at the time all but become a dead discipline. His position in the department was, however, always being challenged by H. A. Harris, a somewhat superficial 'know-all', who was styled Professor of Clinical Anatomy and who later became Professor of Anatomy in Cambridge. Harris appeared to have a hold over Elliot Smith, who was obviously only too ready to leave to him the main burden of departmental administration. There was a lecturer whose only interest was the way the four chambers of the heart go through their orderly contraction during each heart beat, and another who was laboriously investigating the structure of a minute part of the brain.

There were some who did not fit into the mainstream of the Institute's interests. There was Charles Singer, an outstanding medical historian. There was also Sir Bernard Spilsbury, then the country's most illustrious forensic expert. It was in his room, which was adorned with bottles containing bits and pieces of murder victims, that I was later to perch. There were also a number of young research students, among them Daryll Forde, who was charged by Elliot Smith to look after me. Daryll later became head of the Department of Anthropology in University College, and a considerable authority on the cultures of West Africa. Everywhere one turned in the Institute, there was someone at work on a riveting problem.

Popular writers, like H. J. Massingham, and amateur scientists like

John Layard, were in and out of the department in search of the last
word about the diffusion of culture. And then there was a constant stream
of visitors who were also drawn to the high priests of diffusionist
philosophy. But while that subject was the dominant intellectual interest
of the department, it did not by any means overshadow the other concerns of the community of vigorous minds over which Elliot Smith
quietly presided.

Before long he summoned me to say that he proposed to submit my
thesis on the baboon skull for publication in the *Proceedings of The
Zoological Society*. He also thought that I should attend some meetings of
the Society so as to get an idea of what it would be like to address a
scientific audience. At the same time he suggested that I should become
a member of the Anatomical Society, and that while I was waiting to be
admitted to the Medical School and preparing for the Primary F.R.C.S.
I should extend my study of the baboon skull to the chimpanzee. Collec-
tions of the skull of this ape were in the Natural History Museum in South
Kensington, and in the Hunterian Museum of the Royal College of
Surgeons, to whose Curator, Sir Arthur Keith, I also had a letter of
introduction. Elliot Smith said he would arrange for me to work in
South Kensington.

The horizon of my world of a few weeks before had now shrunk to
trivial proportions. In one university department I was being admitted
to the company of men whose disciplined minds were far more sophisticated than any I had ever encountered before, and who illuminated
intellectual worlds of whose existence I had previously been totally
unaware. The critical sense which I had cultivated in isolation was now
to be sharpened in a company where accepted belief had to bend before
enquiry, and where what was likely to turn out to be true, even if only
for a moment, had to emerge from the flames of controversy. For under
Daryll Forde's tutelage, it did not take more than a few days to discover
that the world of Elliot Smith was a highly controversial one. Elliot
Smith's and Perry's diffusionism was hotly contested by Bronislaw
Malinowski, the functional anthropologist of the London School of
Economics, at the same time as Elliot Smith and Arthur Keith were all
but mortal enemies when it came to the assessment of the significance
of human fossil remains. I felt as if I were being reborn.

Sir Arthur Keith was every bit as welcoming as Elliot Smith had been,
even though I sensed some disapproval that I had already 'signed on'
under the wrong colours. He was even better known than Elliot Smith
as an authority on man's physical origins, and it was easy to see why his
had become so prominent a name in the anatomical world. His voice was
soft, gentle and persuasive, and no glimmer of doubt coloured anything
he said. At one time he and Elliot Smith had been friends and scientific

allies, but they had fallen out in a bitter public debate about the significance of the famous Piltdown Skull—history was to reveal that both had
been wrong. Keith showed me a plaster cast he had recently made of the
inner surface of a piece of skull. Stroking it and pointing to some irregu-
larity on the surface of the cast, he said: 'This is unique, I have never
seen anything like it'. Whether it was unique did not matter; to Keith it
was. But I had already learnt to beware of *ex cathedra* pronouncements.
Keith took me round the Hunterian Museum, of which he gave me free
run, and in which he provided me with a little room at the top of the
building to which I could take the skulls I wished to study. Keith was
an odd man. In his well-known *New Discoveries relating to the Antiquity
of Man*, which appeared in 1931, I was surprised to discover that he had
qualified something I had said in a published paper, with the words
'Dr. Zuckerman would be the first to acknowledge that his observations
had been made on captive animals', etc. But Keith had never discussed
the matter with me, and I should certainly not have necessarily agreed
with the qualification.

The Curator of Mammals in the Natural History Museum was a small,
slightly hunch-backed man, called Pycraft, who readily allowed me access
to the skulls I wanted to study. Like Elliot Smith and Keith, Pycraft
had concerned himself with the problem of man's evolution, and had
taken part in the debate on the significance of the Piltdown Skull. All
three appear in the much reproduced painting of a group of anatomical
experts who are shown gazing at the Piltdown remains. Today we know
that all had been taken in by a hoaxer who apparently knew enough
anatomy to mislead the foremost anatomists of the day, and also enough
of human nature and vanity to know how to stimulate a controversy in
which each of the participants in the debate used his special knowledge
to try to outdo the others. The only face missing from the portrait, but
which might have been included at the time, was that of an obscure
Scottish anatomist called Waterston. He had dared to raise his voice
against the acknowledged leaders of the subject, only to be crushed for
his pains. If anyone was right in this silly story, it was Waterston.

So there I was, within weeks of arriving in London, accepted and
welcomed into a scientific society of which I had been aware only by
name. I had also embarked on a new piece of research. No-one could
have had a more fortunate scientific start. And, as it also turned out,
no-one could have had a better introduction to the kind of social life for
which I must have been secretly yearning.

This came about partly through Daryll Forde, and partly through a
young painter, Doris Chapman, who had also lighted upon Mill's Hotel
before settling into a studio of her own.

Daryll, who was a little older than me, had studied geography and anthropology at University College, and had then been given a junior post under Perry. Daryll was extrovert and noisy, and always leapt at the chance to make new friends. He lived with a group, of which he must have been almost the youngest, which had taken over a house in Taviton Street, off Gordon Square in the heart of what I soon discovered was Bloomsbury. Of the people who lived at 19 Taviton Street, an address that everyone seemed to know, the ones I remember were Janet Vaughan, later to become the Principal of Somerville College in Oxford; David Gourlay, the man whom she married and who seemed to manage the establishment; Dick Lythgoe, who had been an artillery officer in the 1914–1918 war before qualifying in medicine, and who was now a sense physiologist; Ka Tansley, also a young sense physiologist, who later married Dick; John Hope-Johnston, once the tutor of Augustus John's children, and a dilettante and aesthete who later disappeared 'somewhere in the East'; and Hedley Briggs, who for a time was a well-known ballet dancer. Daryll introduced me to this circle, through whose frequent and noisy parties I was led towards an even wider circle of acknowledged or would-be writers, poets, actors and painters, and where once again I was accepted as though I had always belonged. Daryll also introduced me to the inexpensive Italian, French and German restaurants in Charlotte Street, on the fringes of Soho, where I soon became an habitué.

But it was through Doris Chapman that I met, and got to know well, the painters and writers of that bustling world. John Armstrong and Bernard Meninsky had their studios in the same street—Meninsky for a time in what had been Constable's studio. The Fitzroy Tavern—better known to us as Kleinfeld's—at the corner of Percy Street, was treated as a club to which one repaired after dinner (a few years later it was to become one of Dylan Thomas's favourite haunts). I often went there, at first timidly if I was alone, looking to see if any of my friends were there, and then with the not entirely assured confidence of a would-be regular. The real regulars seemed giants, most of whom I took to be brilliant writers or painters or composers. Here I met Constant Lambert, the composer, and first saw Nina Hamnett, the artist and writer, and one of Charlotte Street's best-known figures, and Betty May, the 'Tiger Woman' of Aleister Crowley's life. And here I first met Hugh Gaitskell, who had recently come down from Oxford to become a junior lecturer in economics at University College, and Dora, whom he later married, and who is now the sedate Lady Gaitskell of the House of Lords. No-one could then have sensed that Hugh was to become the great politician he was destined to be. At that time the only contact I had had with the world of British politics was when I delivered my final letter of introduction to H. E. S. Fremantle's brother, a Tory M.P., and was invited by him to lunch at the House of Commons. All I remember of the conversation was being told how hard times were, and being shown a small darn in his shirt as illustration of the fact.

Doris introduced me to John Armstrong, the painter, and it was through him that I met Charles Laughton and Elsa Lanchester, who were then at the beginning of their acting careers, and who lived in a small flat off Charlotte Street. All three became close and life-long friends. In only two or three months, South Africa had become lost to a new world, of which Sir Henry Wood's 'Proms' and the Diaghilev Ballet very quickly became an essential part. I had no time for sight-seeing, for going to Westminster Abbey or the Tower of London, and it was some months before I visited the National Gallery. Life had become too full for that.

Such work as I did in my first two or three months was devoted to the Primary F.R.C.S. examination, which I successfully passed at my first attempt, and to my studies of the chimpanzee skull. In April I formally registered for a course of introductory classes to clinical work at University College. From snatches of conversation and from the occasional newspaper which I read, I was vaguely aware at the time that all was not well with the country, and on 3 May, as I was making my way to the first class I had decided to attend, I bought a paper which gave the news that a General Strike had been called. I stopped to read the paper, and then drifted into a class where a lecturer was explaining how cancer of the tongue spreads to the lymphatic glands of the head and neck. I listened for a moment at the back of the classroom, only the front two rows of which were filled, and then, believing that I knew as much as did the lecturer about the structures he was explaining, put my head down on the desk and started wondering what a General Strike implied. Some moments later I became conscious of a dense silence. I looked up and saw that everyone was looking in my direction, and heard the lecturer saying: 'Stop reading that newspaper, or leave the room'. I truthfully replied that I had already read the paper. When he angrily repeated his demand, I picked up the paper and left.

The strike, the reasons for which I did not understand at the time, totally disrupted the work of the hospital, but this did not affect me since I had already decided to keep away. All I remember of it now is wandering alone one night to Piccadilly, and becoming involved in a wild rush near Hyde Park Corner, from which mounted police were moving into a violent fighting crowd. I had no idea who was on whose side, and just clung to a lamp-post as the police swept by. There seemed to be quite a few civilians around who had obviously been officers in the war which had ended only eight years before. Some of them appeared to be enjoying themselves.

Attendance at classes was not obligatory, and it was some weeks before

I again appeared at one. The intervening time I spent in the studios and restaurants of Charlotte Street, and carrying on with my studies of the chimpanzee skull. Since the examination for the School's Scholarships was soon due, I also devoted some time to re-reading texts on anatomy and physiology, which were the main subjects on which candidates were to be tested. To my great surprise and pleasure I was elected, happy that the lecturer whom I had affronted was not one of the examiners. One of the small number who were also trying for the scholarships was George Pickering, later to become Regius Professor of Medicine in Oxford, and then Master of Pembroke College. In retrospect, I feel it would have been more appropriate to the medical profession if he had won.

After the preliminary course was finished, I was assigned as a member of a team of 'clerks' to one of the hospital's consultant physicians, who made little impression on me, and as a 'dresser' to Wilfred Trotter, one of its surgeons. Trotter was the outstanding member of the staff of University College Hospital, in a period when it was graced by some of the most distinguished clinical scientists of the day. If he can be described as such, he was the Hospital's 'intellectual' and was known to a much wider public for his *Instincts of the Herd in Peace and War*, a book which had gone through many impressions since its appearance in 1916. In those days it was the habit to be overbearing and scornful with students, and Trotter was no exception. 'Sixpence for the boy who can tell me what this is', he would say as he held between forceps a muscle or a vessel during an operation on the neck. By that time I had learnt that the wise thing was to remain silent. My first encounter with him had been when he was examining a young woman who had suffered since birth from a split collar-bone. Singling me out from the back row of the students around the bed, he said, 'You're supposed to be an anatomist. How do you think this came about?' I was well into a learned dissertation about the way the bone develops during embryonic life, and how the two centres of bone formation from which it is made might not have united, when he cut me short with the sarcastic comment, 'Have you never heard of a birth injury?'—I had not—'That is what it is, but thank you for the lecture'. Near the end of my time as a medical student, and long after I had ceased to be Trotter's dresser, another such case turned up in the hospital. This time the history was that one of the patient's parents had also been born with a divided collar-bone. I lay in wait for Trotter, reminded him of his comment of a year or so before, told him the new story, and asked whether it did not imply a congenital abnormality. 'Well', he said, 'birth injuries to the clavicle occur once in so many thousand times. For it to occur in two successive generations means a chance of one in a million'—or some such figure. 'I suppose it is just possible you are right'. I never again tested Trotter's well-known sarcasms, of which accounts were legion.[1] 'Mr. X', he would say to his regular anaesthetist (those were the days of the chloroform or ether mask), 'If the patient can stay awake'—implying that not enough anaesthetic had been given—'could you try to do the same?' And then, about a patient on whom he was about to operate and whose X-rays had been examined by H. A. Harris, 'Professor Harris tells me that the trouble is at the base of the brain. That confirms my view that I shall find it at the top'. Now that I began to realise what the life of a budding doctor was likely to be, I was becoming certain that I did not want to make medicine my career.

My paper on the baboon skull[2] was to be read at a meeting of the Zoological Society about two months after I started as a clinical student, and I had been told to be prepared to speak for twenty minutes, and to answer any questions which might be put. I was also provided with lantern slides of the illustrations I had brought from South Africa. I was more overawed than nervous, and was relieved to see from the printed agenda that I was to be the last speaker of four, of whom two were well-known zoologists. This would give me an opportunity to see how a public scientific discussion proceeded. In the chair was Sir John Bland-Sutton, a stumpy and elderly surgeon whose renown dated from Victorian times, and who also had something of a reputation as a comparative anatomist. The paper before mine was by the country's leading expert on worms, and just before he had finished, Sir Peter Chalmers Mitchell, the formidable character who was then the Society's Secretary, came down from the dais and whispered that, since the meeting had to end by 7 p.m., and because the previous speakers had overrun their time, I would have to confine myself to ten minutes.

When called to the speaker's desk, I therefore skipped the introduction I had prepared, and leapt straight into the body of my paper, calling for my first lantern slide. The lights went out, and pointing to the essential features of my diagram on the screen, I began by saying that Huxley—meaning the great T. H. Huxley—had said this and this, but as the next slide would show, he was wrong, and this is what really happens, when the rounded skull of the baby baboon becomes transformed during growth into the long skull of a snouted adult. Before the audience realised that I had finished, and before the lights went on, I slipped back into an empty seat in the front row—I had been sitting next to Elliot Smith before. Someone moved to the neighbouring seat and said, 'My name's Huxley; I'd like to talk to you about what you've just told us'. It was dark, and for a mad moment I thought, 'Good heavens, which Huxley?' And that is how I began a close friendship with T.H.'s grandson, Julian, who soon introduced me to a world of science that went even wider than University College, and much later to those matters of public concern in which he was interested. Julian was then Professor of Zoology at Kings College and was busy writing his classic work, *Problems of Relative Growth*.[3] Figure 18 of his book is one of the illustrations which had been drawn for me by my art-school friend in the early hours of one of my last days in Cape Town.

The belief that I was headed for a career of scientific research and not of practical medicine soon became general in the Medical School. In consequence, my failure to abide by the usual routine was looked upon tolerantly by the authorities. I also made a number of new friends amongst the house surgeons and registrars, who seemed to like having someone around who did not fit into the usual category of medical student. When the time came for me to cram for my qualifying examination in medicine, no people could have helped me more than they did. One of them was Philip D'Arcy Hart, who later devoted his life to the study of pulmonary diseases, and who became an intimate friend. He had had a somewhat formal social upbringing, and encouraged me to go to a tailor to be fitted with a coat of tails so that I could attend a deb dance in a white tie and starched shirt. But deb dances were not really for me. I preferred Bloomsbury and Charlotte Street, and moved happily from one social circle to the next—they rarely overlapped. Some largely apocryphal stories about the way I behaved when a medical student, which I have heard recounted publicly by contemporaries, among them Harry Himsworth who later became head of Britain's Medical Research Council, have made my ears burn. I may not have been set on a medical career, but I certainly did not spend all my time playing cards and engaging in some of the strange adventures that have been attributed to me.

Only occasionally did I run into South Africans. Once some visiting Rugger celebrities introduced me to the London night-clubs. On another occasion, I went to Oxford to see old friends, most of them Rhodes Scholars, including David Bean, the academic star of my schooldays. Two or three of them had become fervent adherents of the Oxford Movement, which was then in its infancy. Most of the day I spent with Karl Hofmeyr, by then a Rugger Blue, who finally put me on to a train back to London slightly the worse for alcoholic wear. Later he and I with two others spent a week in the Cotswolds on a presumed reading holiday, during which I read nothing.

By now I had moved from Gower Street to one of Bloomsbury's big squares. Here I enjoyed myself furnishing a large and pleasant room, which I left when my landlady, who at first was tolerant of my ways, began to object that I had too many guests. I then found a flat in Wyndham Street off the Marylebone Road. In theory I had enough money to live modestly, for without counting anything else, there was the Medical School Exhibition which I had won, and my South African scholarship.

But I was constantly all but broke through overspending, a habit which I fear I never made any great effort to overcome. Living from hand to mouth came naturally to me, and I clearly was convinced that the Lord would provide for His children. My conscience suffered no twinges when I borrowed from friends, even from Mrs. Bisbee, whom I occasionally saw on her visits to London. She knew only of the scientific work I was doing, not of the way I spent the rest of my time (I am happy to say that in the end I returned to her what I borrowed). I was enjoying my new intellectual and social life to the full, without giving a thought to what I should do once I qualified as a doctor.

My future was settled by Elliot Smith. One day he sent for me, and after a few introductory words, enquired what I proposed to do with my life. I assumed, no doubt correctly, that he had been told that I was hardly taking my clinical studies seriously. He then asked, 'Do you want to be a surgeon or a research worker?' to which I could only reply, 'What do you advise Sir?' He looked at me, hesitated for a moment, and then said, 'I don't think a surgeon'. I agreed that I did not seem to be cut out for a clinical career, and we left it at that.

I spent the next weekend at Grantchester with the Tansleys. Ka Tansley had invited me to stay with her parents before, and I had been taken up by her father. A. G. Tansley was a botanist with very wide interests, and I enjoyed a close friendship with him until his death at the age of 84 in 1955. If anybody deserves the distinction, 'A.G.' can be called the father of the science of ecology. He was the first Chairman of the Nature Conservancy when it was established in 1949, and I have a feeling that he would turn in his grave if he realised how what was once a respectable scientific discipline has been vulgarised into an almost meaningless field of propaganda by the antics of some latterday environmentalists. A.G. had been one of Freud's disciples, and was the author of a book called *The New Psychology*, which had helped to introduce Freud's teaching to British psychologists. He also had a fine, even if specialised palate for wines, particularly the German wines of the Rhine and the Moselle. And it was from him that I first heard about Bertrand Russell. Their friendship had been broken at the beginning of the First World War, when Russell realised that Tansley did not share his pacifist convictions.

During the course of a long walk that weekend, I told Tansley of Elliot Smith's concern about my future, and was greatly encouraged when he turned out to be more positive than Elliot Smith had been. Although at the time Tansley's judgment could have been based only on the general talks we had had, and on my evident fascination with all the matters which interested him, he was confident that I would succeed as a research worker, whether or not I was cut out to be a surgeon.

Within days, Daryll Forde sought me out with the news that the

Anatomical Research Fellow at the Zoological Society, who was known as the 'Prosector', was about to resign, and that Elliot Smith wanted me to apply for the post. Elliot Smith soon confirmed this himself. With some help—I had never written such a document before—I drafted a short application, and in due course presented myself at the Society's offices in Regent's Park with the other candidates who had been short-listed. When my turn came, I was called into the Council Room—a room which many years later I was to get to know all too well—and was asked a number of questions by a committee which was chaired by the same Sir John Bland-Sutton who had presided over the meeting when I presented my paper on the skull of the baboon. References were made to this paper and also to the fact that my new one on the chimpanzee skull had now been accepted for publication. I was questioned about what I proposed to do next, and was also asked my age. Knowing that the man who had resigned the post was moving to a professorship, and that his two predecessors had been well-known zoologists, I thought it was unlikely that I would be appointed if I said that I was barely twenty-three. I therefore added a year, in the belief that that would help. I was then asked to wait outside the room. When I was recalled, I was told that I had been selected, and that the appointment was for three to five years. The committee felt, however, that I should complete my medical course before taking up the post, since one of the responsibilities of the Prosector was to attend to any minor accidents which befell visitors to the Zoo. When going over some of the Society's records many years later, I was amused to see noted at the head of my application form: 'Age not stated, but apparently quite young', and then the incorrect figure of 24 which I had given.

I ran the mile or so from the Zoo to Doris Chapman's studio in Charlotte Street, with the glad news that I was now 'fixed up' with a job which I wanted, and one which assured me complete freedom in the future. There was no need to hedge any more when asked what I proposed to do after I qualified.

But the final medical examinations, the passing of which had all but been set as a condition by the Zoological Society, were only three and a half months away. The problem was serious. I had managed to get 'signed up' for the courses I was supposed to have followed, but this was very largely with the help of the Medical School's porter. In all the time I had been at the Hospital, I had bought only one elementary introductory book, and I knew practically no clinical medicine. This was when the friends I had made amongst the Hospital's junior staff rallied round. I furnished myself with the necessary texts, and was then put through an intensive and personal crash course of the kind that would see me through the Conjoint examination of the College of Physicians and Surgeons. I slept little, read hard, and was taught as much as the time allowed about the signs and symptoms of disease.

Obstetrics was a serious obstacle. The regulations of the period demanded that every medical student had to be signed up for twenty deliveries which he himself conducted. These were carried out in the homes of expectant mothers who lived within a given radius of the particular medical school with which they were registered. In those days there was no National Health Service, and home deliveries were part of the charitable services provided by the hospitals for people who could not afford, or who did not want to pay for, the services of a doctor.

Before a student was sent out on 'the list' or 'district', it was assumed that he had attended lectures on the subject, and that he had also witnessed some deliveries in hospital. There was, however, little control, and I had done neither. The only book that I had read which bore on the subject was a small essay entitled: *Lysistrata, or Woman's Future*, which had been published by C. K. Ogden in his 'To-day and To-morrow' series of avant-garde writings. Ludovici, the author, was a 'nature-man' whose message was that childbirth was a natural event which doctors should not mar by their ministrations. Armed only with this doctrine, and a black bag, I set out to deliver my first baby at the address I had been given. When I arrived the expectant mother was in bed in the front of the two rooms she and her husband occupied on the first floor of a run-down small terrace house. With her was the local midwife, or 'gamp', totally different from the uniformed district nurses of today. I expressed my pleasure at being with them, congratulated my pregnant patient and, true to Ludovici, said that there was nothing that either of us had to worry about or to do.

On my way to the house I had noticed a small secondhand bookshop on the ground floor of a neighbouring house, and told the gamp that I would be there till she wanted me. I spent a happy two hours turning over the pages of books and buying a few. Among them was a copy of a course of lectures on obstetrics which had been delivered by Professor David Davis, the first U.C.H. Professor of the subject, and which had been annotated by a medical student of nearly a hundred years before.

When I was called back to the house, I allowed nature to take its course, but the labour was difficult and there was nothing I could do to alleviate the mother's pains. Apprentice accoucheurs were not provided with anaesthetics. The father had returned by this time, and in response to his wife's cries had started to shout angrily and to bang on the door which, lest he should burst in and fall on me, I promptly locked. After what seemed a very long delay, the baby was born, and with the gamp's help, I then did what was necessary. But when I left I was feeling pretty exhausted. On the following day I returned with a bunch of flowers, and my patient could not have been more charmingly grateful.

The next ten deliveries were easier, and adequately upheld the Ludovici doctrine of 'do nothing'. Then disaster struck. I had told John Layard of my doings, and he begged me to take him on my next case since, as he put it, childbirth was the one experience which he had not enjoyed, even at second- or third-hand, in a lifetime in which he had tried to experience everything.[4] I knew of no regulation which said that I could not take him with me, so off we went. The expectant mother was most impressed that she had two, not just one, 'doctors' in her small room, and the gamp was equally welcoming. Labour, however, was slow in starting, and even slower in its progress, and I soon realised that I did not have any idea of what to do. Still believing in Ludovici, I did not telephone the hospital, nor indeed would I have known where to find a public telephone. My first delivery had occurred in the afternoon, but it was already almost midnight and I was beginning to fear not only for the life of the baby, but also for the well-being of the mother. Then, without warning, the door burst open and in came Trevor Jones, the obstetrical registrar at the hospital. He was on his way from a party, and was wearing evening clothes and carrying a collapsible opera hat—an article of wear most of us possessed in those days. He had checked at the hospital where I was, and had come round on the off-chance that I was free to go on with him to another party. When he saw what was happening, he threw his hat into a corner of the room (for all the world like someone on a music-hall stage), and got to work. But the baby, which was enormously overweight, was dead when delivered.

As we left the house, Trevor did his best to console me, saying that even if he had been there from the start, he could not have prevented the tragedy. He made no comment about the presence of John Layard. Next day and the day after, I called on the bereaved mother and was deeply moved by the resignation with which she accepted the fact of a still-birth. My visits and my flowers merely added to her gratitude and to the pride she felt in having been attended by three 'doctors'. If anything like that were to occur today, there would be no gratitude, and no doubt an action of malpractice would be brought against the hospital and the 'doctors'. But I am sure such things can no longer happen.

I was much shaken by the experience, and was given permission to 'assist' at my next deliveries in the hospital, as opposed to going out 'on the district'. I attended two or three, and by a horrible coincidence the first, which was presided over by a very experienced obstetrician, also resulted in a still-birth. Of course, only potentially difficult deliveries were taken into hospital; but that made it no better. Ludovici from now on was to be forgotten. The remainder of my twenty deliveries were fortunately completed without incident.

The only member of the senior staff of U.C.H. whom I met during my final and intensive months at the Hospital, and whom I got to know fairly well afterwards, was a man called Barrington. 'Snorker', as he was familiarly known, was the senior surgical urogenital specialist and, because of his eccentricities, was avoided by most medical students, to whom he seemed allergic. I was advised to attend one of his teaching clinics, and when I saw that I was on my own, I timidly asked whether he minded my being there. 'Not if you don't get in the way', was the reply. I liked this. Snorker was a real scientist who had carried out some meticulous experimental researches on bladder-control. He was a bachelor, and wore clothes which were cut as though he was still in the Navy, in which he had served during the First World War. He was also known for his hard-drinking habits. There were a host of stories about him, among them that old chestnut of the house-surgeon going to the house where he had his rooms and asking the housekeeper whether Mr. Barrington lived there. 'Yes', she replied sadly, 'carry him in'. But Snorker was much more than a hard drinker. When we later became friends, I discovered that he was a considerable naturalist, and that he always carried a volume of a pocket edition of Gibbon's *Decline and Fall of the Roman Empire* with him. Once or twice he may have encouraged me to drink more than I could happily carry, but he also opened for me a number of doors to an intellectual vista wider than the surgery of the kidneys.[5]

Three months later, I presented myself for the finals. The written papers did not bother me; that was book learning. But I was distinctly uneasy about the practicals, at which candidates had to see patients in the presence of their examiners. Having made a diagnosis of one case, I was asked why I had reached my conclusion, and what therapy I would advise. I was sure enough about the diagnosis, but had to give my imagination full rein when it came to the treatment. I was a little disturbed by the smiles on the faces of my two examiners as I improvised. When I had finished I was asked the name of my medical school. I was then asked whether I had learnt what I had just told them from my Hospital teachers. My only possible reply was that I could not have learnt it anywhere else, which at least was truthful.

One of the examiners then enquired whether I would be returning to the Hospital, and added: 'You might tell whoever taught you what you've just told us that it's the kind of treatment that was abandoned about the time of Waterloo!'

I was therefore more than surprised when I learnt that I had passed my final examinations. Today a medical student has to spend four full years doing clinical work before he can qualify for practice. It seems strange that in my time it was possible to complete a full clinical course in less than two. Yet from the moment I passed, I had the legal right to embark on medical practice without even doing a statutory year as a house physician or house surgeon. Fortunately for an unsuspecting public, no such thought was in my mind.

CHAPTER 3

THE ZOO'S PROSECTOR

THE PROSECTORSHIP of the Zoological Society was established in mid-Victorian times at the instigation of T. H. Huxley, who, as one of the foremost biologists of his day and as a member of the Council, then played almost as big a part in the affairs of the Society as did his grandson, Julian, some seventy years later. The responsibilities of the post varied over the years in accordance with the qualifications of its holder. At times, one of the duties of the Prosector was to see that a diagnosis was made of the causes of death of the animals in the Society's Gardens. He also had to ensure that the best scientific use was made of the remains of dead animals, on the understanding that he could keep for his own anatomical researches whatever he wanted, distributing the rest, as required, to other scholars. When called upon by the Secretary, and in order to 'fill in' the agenda at the Society's fortnightly scientific meetings, the Prosector also had to give brief accounts of matters of interest which he might have noted in the discharge of his duties. The post had a certain prestige, not only because of the prominence of the Zoological Society in the world of science, but also because the main emphasis of zoology during the nineteenth century and the early part of the twentieth had been on comparative anatomy.

I was the seventh, and last but one, comparative anatomist to be given the job. In keeping with the times and with fashion, and also because there was now a full-time pathologist on the Society's staff, the title had been changed in my predecessor's time to Anatomical Research Fellow. The first Prosector, Dr. James Murie, who had held the post between 1865 and 1870, died only three years before I took over. By the time my own term of office ended in 1932, experimental biology had moved to the centre of the zoological stage. Partly because the Society's one laboratory of those days provided no opportunity for experimental work, and partly because of the need to economise, the Council then decided to use the salary which had previously provided for the post, to cover that of the Society's Curator of Reptiles, a Dr. Burgess Barnett, whose field of interest was snake venom. After his retirement in 1937, the Prosectorship was suspended for almost twenty years, when it was revived for W. C. Osman Hill, a considerable writer on monkeys and apes. The post was abolished in 1962.

The small gas-lit one-storey building which for five years became my main workplace was called the Prosectorium. It still exists, although it is no longer used for its original purpose. In essence, it was a two-roomed animal mortuary, and when I first saw it, it must have been just as it was in Murie's day. There was a white-tiled room with skylights, in which the dominating piece of furniture was a large lead-covered table on which animals were post-mortemed and prepared for anatomical study. To the side was a long narrow room, with a bench down one side and shelves on the other. A steep staircase in the neighbouring bird-house led to three communicating rooms which had been assigned to the Prosectorium as additional laboratory space and offices. Big animals, such as sea-lions or giraffes, and on rare occasions an elephant, had to be autopsied in a covered area outside.

However primitive, the Prosectorium had its charms. Billy Lawrence, the main technician, had been there for years, and had a good idea of what would be seen when he opened up the belly of even the most exotic animal. Corbett, his young assistant, prepared material for microscopic study. Then there was Mrs. Kelly, big, fat, lumbering and kindly, who never objected to cleaning up each day's bloody mess, and who imperturbably made tea in an environment of flesh, flies and bottled specimens. And finally there was Pincher Moss, a small bent old man whose job it was to clear the bins into which unwanted remains were put. He never did this without going through them to see if there was any tasty-looking piece of meat which could be salvaged for a meal. I found nothing surprising in this, and certainly did nothing to stop the practice. After all, Frank Buckland, the Victorian naturalist and writer whom posterity regards as having been sufficiently important to merit a commemorative plaque on the house where he lived near the Zoo, used to visit the Prosectorium regularly in search of new species of animal which might add to man's normal larder. He was the founder, in 1860, of a short-lived British 'Acclimatization Society', which was a sister institution to a corresponding body in France. Why those of us who worked in the Prosectorium did not die a thousand deaths from obscure infections I cannot think.

Very soon after I was appointed, it was announced that Dr. H. H. Scott, the Society's pathologist, was resigning to take up an appointment in the Government's Colonial Service. Chalmers Mitchell then asked me whether I would, or rather told me that I was going to, act as pathologist until a replacement was found. This took some six months. Billy Lawrence showed me how to do the post-mortems and how to fill in the pro-forma which had to be completed for every animal that died. In my brief career as a clinical student, I had paid less than scant attention to pathology, and because of a certain squeamishness had attended very few human post-mortems. It was not blood that I minded, but the smell. Fortunately, the far more varied smells of the Prosectorium never bothered me at all. I soon became sufficiently interested to spot a few out-of-the-run cases of disease and, with some help in their study, to write them up for publication.

Indeed, it was just chance that prevented me from throwing myself whole-heartedly into the subject. In those days tuberculosis was still rampant, not only in human beings, but also in cattle and in zoo animals, and it was customary in the Prosectorium to make a microscopic study of any lesion that was suspected of being tubercular. Corbett taught me how to stain for the tubercle bacillus—a simple technique which I should have learnt at U.C.H. One day I realised that tubercular lesions were much more common in birds whose respiratory passages were relatively clean than in those that had been blackened by the dust which they had breathed in; those were the days when London was still famous for its fogs. In spite of the absence of obvious tubercular lesions, I discovered that 'smears' of the lungs of birds which had been blackened with dust sometimes contained bacilli which reacted positively to the stain which was specific for the tubercle bacillus. I 'collected' some London sparrows with the help of an air-gun, and observed the same correlation. *Ergo*, and knowing nothing about the subject, I argued to myself that coal-dust in some way weakens or inactivates the tubercle bacillus. I searched the literature and read that coal-miners were an occupational group with a relatively low incidence of tuberculosis (as opposed to silicosis, a pulmonary disease caused by the inhalation of hard stony particles). Philip D'Arcy Hart, my U.C.H. friend who was about to embark on the study of tuberculosis, warned me that my sup- posedly inactivated T.B. bacillus might be just a common and unharmful 'contaminant' called the 'Timothy Grass bacillus', which also reacted to the stain that picks out true T.B., but which unlike the latter grows readily on almost any medium. Undeterred, I reported my findings to the Society's Prosectorial Committee. This Committee consisted of eminent scientists, and was responsible to the Council for assuring the quality of the Society's scientific work. I was then instructed to send any specimens in which I found my presumably inactivated tubercle bacillus to a Dr. Stanley Griffith in Cambridge, who was one of the country's experts on the subject, and who had agreed to try to grow my bacilli in hens and guinea- pigs. None of his cultures proving positive, his diagnosis was that the apparent T.B. bacillus in my specimens could not be the germ which caused the disease. In that case, I then argued, it must either be Timothy Grass, which would be expected to grow readily but which in fact did not or, as I supposed, a T.B. 'bug' which had somehow or other become enfeebled in the presence of coal dust. Griffith succeeded in culturing one specimen I sent him, and this case he diagnosed as true T.B. Logic got me nowhere, and soon after a professional pathologist had been appointed to the Society's staff, I lost interest in the problem. Some years later, however, my attention was drawn to an article by one of the country's authorities on tuberculosis, reporting that tuberculin, the 'principle' that can be extracted from the tubercle bacillus, is inactivated by media that have been 'doctored' with coal dust. While later work has cast doubt on this observation, and also on the belief that as an occupational group coal-miners suffer less from tuberculosis than might be expected, there was nevertheless something in my original observation, since it is now established that many strains of the tubercle bacillus which affect birds will not multiply except in the presence of a specific growth factor.

There were other moments when it seemed as though I was becoming over-interested in animal pathology. Some two years before I had joined its staff, the Zoo, and especially the Prosectorium, had been much in the news because an elephant had died of anthrax, and because six people, including four of the Zoo staff who had helped in the post-mortem examination, and then in the disposal of the carcass, had contracted the disease. Unfortunately the diagnosis was made after Gerrard's, a firm of taxidermists which used to buy the skeletons and skins of creatures that had died in the Zoo, had moved the remains of the elephant from the Gardens. This was done in an old horse-drawn wagon which leaked. It must have been a miracle that the disease was not spread throughout London, which in those days had a much larger population of horses than it has today. Billy Lawrence was the only one of the prosectorial staff who contracted the disease, and he had to spend a very unpleasant three weeks in hospital. The net effect of this experience was that the Zoo became highly sensitive to the dangers of anthrax.

Not surprisingly, Billy and Corbett had learnt how to recognise the anthrax bug under the microscope. There came a day when we diagnosed anthrax as the cause of death in a wild boar. Knowing the trouble which the elephant had created, and realising the dangers of any spread of the disease, we spent hours burning the carcass and, for good measure, the white coats we had been wearing, together with our shirts and ties. This done, and with our jackets over our bare chests, we then reported our suspicions to Dr. Geoffrey Vevers, the Superintendent of the Gardens, only to be told that as the carcass had been disposed of, the cause of death could not be checked. Moreover, if it had been anthrax, the part of the Gardens in which the animal had lived would have to be closed to the public, and 'we'd had enough of that'.

I decided that the next time that I suspected something really unusual in the Prosectorium, I would be careful about proceeding before drawing conclusions and taking action. I became interested in the causes of paralysis in monkeys, and in their investigation managed to secure the help of one of the country's leading virologists of the time. With recent developments in our knowledge of the lethal power of some of the viruses which can attack the monkey brain, I doubt if today I would be quite as eager as I was then to pursue such a line of enquiry. Using the primitive techniques of those days, I also introduced to the Zoo tuber-culin-testing of monkeys, and in my enthusiasm allowed a big male Mozambique monkey to get its head out of the net in which it was being held while I was injecting tuberculin into its skin. Warwick, the sana-torium attendant who was helping me, was in bed for a month recover-ing from the bites he received. I fortunately escaped, and learnt to be more careful next time. The trouble with working in the Prosectorium was that almost everything one saw was new and exciting, and every observation cried out to be followed up. I had forgotten the interest I found in all this work until I recently came across the quarterly reports I had to prepare for the Prosectorial Committee. But it was a good thing for me when the Council appointed as full-time pathologist Colonel Hamerton, a man who had recently retired from the Royal Army Medical Corps. I then became free to turn my attention to the unspecified duties of Research Anatomist, which meant being free to follow any line of enquiry that I wished.

The London Zoo was, and still is, a unique organisation. It is as much a national institution as is the National Gallery or Kew Gardens, but, unlike them, and unlike national zoos in other countries, it does not receive an annual subsidy from the public exchequer. It, and the large zoo-park at Whipsnade, thirty miles from London, are administered by the Zoological Society of London, which is an educational charity. The Society is still the premier institution of its kind in the world, not only because it is the custodian of the British national zoos (as the *Oxford Dictionary* explains, the word 'zoo' was coined as an abbreviation for the Zoological Gardens in London), but because of its research activities, and because it publishes a series of international scientific journals on zoological matters. The main executive officer of the governing body, which is an elected and unpaid Council, is the Secretary. Sir Peter Chalmers Mitchell, who occupied that office during the five years when I was a member of the Society's staff, was not only the Society's un-questioned ruler, but also a well-known character in the life of London. In his time the secretaryship was a highly paid full-time post, which enjoyed a number of privileges, including a luxurious flat on the upper floor of the Society's main office. Mitchell ruled his domain with a rod of iron, and while his chief administrator was Dr. Vevers, he himself seemed to be ruled by Joan Proctor, the Curator of Reptiles, a young

woman of powerful personality. Once I was commanded to go to see her
in her house near the Zoo. This was an unnerving experience, since she
kept as a pet a wild Serval cat, on which I had to keep a wary eye as she
spoke. She ordered me to relieve some giant tortoises of the constipation
from which she supposed them to be suffering. I did not have the slightest
idea what to do but, in my anxiety to get away, said that I would attend
to the matter. Later that day I joked about my impending task with
Malcolm Pearson, a medical student friend. Malcolm had a nice sense
of humour, and after we had discussed the matter, I sent a message
to Joan Proctor's staff to have the affected animals strung up in tennis
nets by 9 o'clock the next morning, and to have pails of soapy water and
syringes prepared for a visit which I and another doctor would be
making. There was no need for any enemas by the time we arrived.
Excitement alone had done the trick, and the centre of the new Reptile
House was a terrible mess. Apart from asking me to give anti-venom
serum to a keeper who had got himself bitten by a snake, Joan Proctor
never bothered me again. Malcolm and I dined out more than once on
the story.

Chalmers Mitchell was not the only member of the Society's Council
who had fallen under Joan Proctor's spell, and when she died in 1931
at the early age of 34, a medal, one side of which bore her likeness, was
struck in her honour. The intention was that it should be presented each
year to a distinguished expert on reptiles, but I can find no record that
it was ever awarded. Perhaps she was not sufficiently outstanding
scientifically to be commemorated in this way. The one copy of the medal
that I know still exists is among the Society's memorabilia.

As Research Anatomist, there was no shortage of topics to pursue,
and I soon learnt to respond to Chalmers Mitchell's requests to lay on
demonstrations for scientific meetings. Two stand out in my memory.
The only known exceptions to the general rule that the red blood cor-
puscles of mammals are circular are the camel and the llama. Chalmers
Mitchell got it into his head that the oval shape of their blood-cells
would interest the Society, and I was told to prepare a demonstration.
Getting just one drop of blood from unanaesthetised camels and llamas
proved almost as difficult as getting blood from a stone, and far more
nerve-racking. My second demonstration was much better received than
were the microscopic slides of camel and llama blood. It was of the
ability of a young baboon, which I had trained, to differentiate colours
in the way that human beings do, for monkeys and apes are the only
mammals other than man which are known to have true colour vision.

The fact that these animals had always been my main interest was by
this time well-known to my friends, and it was also one which the Zoo
provided ample opportunities to pursue. When I became Research

Anatomist, zoos were still in a sense living museums, and the London Zoo housed an extensive collection of different species of monkeys and apes. There was also a large colony of Hamadryas (Abyssinian) baboons which lived on what was called Monkey Hill, a big construction of artificial rock which was demolished in the mid-fifties. The only other captive colony of corresponding size was in Munich. I realised that here was an opportunity to make a detailed study of the family life of the animal, which could be set against the background knowledge I already had of the way baboons lived in the wild. As I saw it, the results of such a study might also be interesting when viewed against what I had learnt from the anthropologists at University College about the structure of primitive human food-gathering societies.

From the start it was obvious that male dominance determined the way the London baboon colony was subdivided into families. I then had the luck to discover from post-mortem study that ovulation in mature females occurs in the middle of the monthly sexual cycle, and that this event determined the order of female precedence in the harems of those few males who shared, in unequal numbers, all the females of the colony. Unlike what happens in the vast majority of mammalian species, and even though the fertility of baboons varies seasonally, it was also clear that, like man, monkeys and apes are sexually active throughout the year. I read as much as had been published about the social behaviour of animals, and it was not long before I had a story to tell.

In January 1929, only a few months after I had been relieved of the responsibility for the routine post-mortem work of the Zoo, Elliot Smith therefore suggested that I should talk to the Anthropological Society of University College on the subject of the social life of the monkey in relation to what was known of its reproductive physiology. It must have been he who passed the word around, because the lecture hall was full, and while I can find no notes of the occasion, I can only imagine from the outcome that my talk was a success. My audience comprised not only interested undergraduates and members of staff, including Elliot Smith, Perry and Daryll Forde, but also people from outside, among them Bronislaw Malinowski and Gerald Heard, a well-known figure of the contemporary cultural world of London and a friend of Aldous Huxley. Both Malinowski and Heard introduced themselves to me when the meeting ended, Malinowski to offer me an invitation to his school, and Heard to ask me to write up my lecture for *The Realist*, a journal which had just been launched, and which he edited. I accepted the first and undertook to do the second. In the final paragraph of my first quarterly report of 1929 to the Zoo's Prosectorial Committee, I wrote: 'The greater part of this quarter has been devoted to a study of the social life of the Primates and its bearings on Human Sociology. This study has been largely stimulated by the interest of Professor Elliot Smith, Mr. W. J. Perry, and Professor B. Malinowski, and has resulted in the preparation of a book, the scope of which is roughly the physiological basis of the family.' 'Roughly' was certainly the right word, but I was clearly launched on a major task.

It must have been Gerald Heard who had introduced me to C. K. Ogden. In the circles in which I moved, Ogden, the inventor of Basic English, was already a legendary name. This was partly because of his exploits in publishing an anti-Government paper in Cambridge during the First World War; partly because of his editorship of several series of widely-read books which were issued by Kegan Paul; partly because of his catholic interest in almost everything; and partly because of the eccentric way he lived. At the dinner at which we met, he suggested that in addition to the article for *The Realist*, I should write a book, to the theme of The Social Life of Monkeys and Apes, for his 'International Library of Psychology, Philosophy and Scientific Method', in which such works as Wittgenstein's *Tractatus Logico-Philosophicus*, and Koehler's *Mentality of Apes* had already appeared. I accepted the flattering invitation, and in a sense of ambitious euphoria thought I could get the job done within a year. It took more than two.

I was, of course, already deeply immersed in the subject, but the interest which my talk aroused must have stimulated me to double the time that I was already devoting to the work. Malinowski was very encouraging. For some reason which I never understood, he seemed to feel that the generalisations to which I had been led were relevant not only to his own studies of primitive human societies, but also to his continuing battle against Elliot Smith's and Perry's views about the diffusion of culture. He gave me two of his books, one inscribed in different coloured pencils to 'my comrade in arms'—but in arms against whom he did not say. I have lost that one. The other one, his *Family among the Australian Aborigines*, was inscribed 'with best regards for the apes and baboons who practice a strict Family Life'. Strict was hardly the word for the violence which characterised Monkey Hill.

Gerald Heard also urged me on, and within a few months I had my paper ready for him. But there was a slight hitch before it was delivered into his hands. Elliot Smith had gone to the Far East soon after the meeting, and H. A. Harris was acting-head of the Department. Following the usual custom, it was to him, therefore, that I took my typescript for the professorial blessing or 'imprimatur' before submitting it for publication. Harris was not only a bit of a bully, but also something of a prude. It immediately emerged that he disapproved of the paper because it discussed matters relating to sex. When he added that he was sure that Elliot Smith would also disapprove of what I had written, I could only reply that if it had not been for Elliot Smith I should never have given the lecture or written the article. After Harris had again expressed his displeasure, he gave me back my text. Believing that the denial of approval by the head of a University department meant that it could not be published, I disconsolately went to see Dick Lythgoe.

I told him what had happened and began to tear up the pages, saying, 'so much for this lot'. Dick's reaction was immediate. He grabbed my text, put on his jacket, and said that Harris was a so-and-so who always exceeded his authority. More than that, he himself was going to see that I gave my paper to Gerald Heard. So off we went. My article appeared in July, in an issue of *The Realist*[1] that included articles by such well-known people as Sigmund Freud, Arnold Bennett, J. B. S. Haldane and R. A. Fisher. I had not quite realised the honour that Heard was paying me when he asked someone in his early twenties to contribute to his short-lived journal. When I now read the names of the contributors to the ten issues that he published, I can see—although I certainly did not recognise it at the time—that I was being admitted to the company of some of the best-known intellectuals of the day. Re-reading my article I can also see that my unbending critical attitude to attempts to explain human behaviour by analogies from the animal world must have been acquired at a very early age. This is how the article starts:

'Until recently, the study of animal psychology was pursued mainly in order to obtain evidence supporting the Darwinian hypothesis by demonstrating mental continuity between the animal and human worlds. Its point of view, however, was anthropomorphic, and its extravagant exposition provided some animals with an intelligence little less than human and many with a code of morals which would have sustained them in any civilised community. From this plight it was rescued at the beginning of the present century, and to-day the study of animal behaviour is one of the more stimulating and useful branches of psychology. On the other hand, animal sociology stands to-day where animal psychology stood thirty years ago. Its method is still mainly anthropomorphic description, either in the older blatant form or in a new guise, provided with a crude behaviouristic formula which explains all behaviour as the product of an instinctive nucleus and experience. In the hands of its exponents animals share with man a common classificatory scheme of social conduct. However sound this formula may be, one can see in it no justification for such purely speculative assumptions as that made by Alverdes in maintaining that human monogamy and the monogamy of birds are comparable, and can be discussed in identical terms.'

For Alverdes, I would today write Konrad Lorenz, Desmond Morris,

and Robert Ardrey, three writers who are equally adept at devising superficial analogies.

Since the essential part of my story depended on an understanding of
the reproductive physiology of apes and monkeys, I extended the review
that I had made of what was already known by embarking on a further
series of studies of the breeding seasons and sexual cycles of mammals.
Here again I was immensely lucky, because among the friends I had
made at University College were A. S. Parkes and G. P. Marrian, both
of whom were at the start of important research careers in the field of
reproduction. At that time the chemical nature of the hormones which
are secreted by the ovaries of the female and by the testes of the male, and
which were known to control the main reproductive organs, had not been
elucidated. But Marrian, a biochemist, was well on the way to the identi-
fication of a female sex-hormone which finally proved to belong to the
class of substances which today is a main constituent of 'the pill'. Parkes
was busy on an experimental analysis of the sex cycle in rodents and other
laboratory animals, and he agreed to join me in corresponding studies of
baboons and monkeys.

I knew too little chemistry to do more than follow Marrian's work
with a kind of awe, but by chance I was able to put him in touch with
Desmond Bernal, about whom I shall say more later, who was then
digging deep into the field of X-ray crystallography at the Cavendish
Laboratory in Cambridge. When we met, I told Bernal, who was then
known as 'the Sage', about the work I was doing, and about that of my
colleagues at University College. His reaction was that if only biologists
had the sense to consult people like him, their chemical problems would
very quickly be solved. He particularly had in mind Marrian, who had
isolated a small number of pure crystals of what was clearly a sex-hormone, and who was literally racing against other teams of scientists, both
in England and abroad, to determine their chemical constitution. Bernal
had been working on the structure of what he was sure was a related
substance, and he told me that if he could get hold of only one or two
of Marrian's minute crystals, he was sure that he would be able to help.
I arranged a meeting between them, at the end of which Marrian sadly
parted with a few of his precious crystals. I walked with Bernal from the
College to Euston station, where to my surprise he had to borrow ten
shillings to pay his fare back to Cambridge. It took only a few days
before he was able to provide some powerful new information about the
molecular nature of the unknown hormone. As it turned out, he was
clearly on the right track, but he was temporarily diverted from the view
which he had reached by the contrary findings of certain other workers.
Not many months later the problem was solved, more or less simultaneously, by Butenandt in Germany, Doisy in America, and by Marrian and

some other workers in London. The three groups had been working on three very closely related molecules, all of them different phases, as it were, of the same sex-hormone. But Marrian and Bernal were not included in the Nobel Prize which was later shared by the German and American chemists. I never did understand why.

The twenties and thirties were halcyon days for those who were carrying out experimental research into reproductive physiology. There were vigorous, even if small, schools at work in the United States, France and Germany, against whose findings those of us in England, still fewer in number, could judge the adequacy of our own work. I was the only one in England who was primarily interested in the reproductive mechanisms of monkeys, and by the time my appointment in the Zoo ended in 1932, I had published a number of papers on the subject, a few of them in collaboration with Parkes. These formed the foundation of a longer series of reports which I published over the next few years, mainly in the *Proceedings of the Royal Society*, and which provided experimental justification for an hypothesis, which I had formulated at the start, to explain the hormonal control of the sexual cycle in monkeys and apes.[2] I had the good fortune to advance my understanding almost in parallel with that of two American friends, George Corner and Carl Hartman, who were then studying much the same set of problems, but on the rhesus monkey.

The sex-ratio of the inhabitants of Monkey Hill in the London Zoo was manifestly abnormal. But it was nonetheless clear from the observations which I made there, and also at the Zoo in Munich, as well as from those which I had made in the wild in South Africa, that a family group consisted of a male overlord, one or more females, their young, and some 'bachelor' hangers-on. Fights on Monkey Hill were frequent, since its size did not permit of dispersal. In the wild, as I well knew, each pack of baboons kept to its own territory, within which it followed a fairly regular routine of daily activities. Since the Zoo was unable to provide all the anatomical material I needed for my analysis of the reproductive cycle, and because I also wanted to refresh my knowledge of the way baboons lived in their native state, I was then granted three months' leave, as well as the necessary funds, to return to South Africa. I made careful preparations, and my trip in the early part of 1930 proved both enjoyable and rewarding. I spent most of my time in the field, and in particular in two areas, one of them the Cole Rous farm, where I had studied wild baboons before. My hosts organised baboon hunts— baboons had for years been officially declared a pest to be destroyed if possible—and I was able to collect sufficient material not only to establish that breeding occurs at all times of the year regardless of seasonal variations in fertility, but also the fact that adult females far outnumber adult males in the normal family party or harem. I was much helped in my field work by Captain Shortridge, the Director of King William's Town Museum, and by Mr. J. Hewitt who was in charge of the Grahamstown Museum. Shortridge lived alone on the outskirts of his small town, and had devoted the better part of his life to the collection and classification of the wild animals of South Africa. I spent many evenings listening to his tales as we drank Cape brandy, and wondered at his dedication. I was given a permit to shoot in the Pirie Forest, which had already been declared a game reserve, and especially remember riding back into a nearby town with some of my collection tied to the back of a rickety car, partly with the help of a long green snake which my hunting companion had killed. But I declined the head ranger's invitation to stay on for a few more days to take part in a 'hunt' of the men of the local Xhosa tribe who poached the forest, once one of their hunting grounds. On one occasion I returned to Grahamstown, tired and thirsty after some days in the field. My companion on that occasion was the son of the editor of the local paper, and in the bar he introduced me to some of his friends who were merry with a tale of a white man and a black woman who had been up before the current assizes, having contravened a newish law which forbade sexual relations between the races. On the previous day the judges had found the woman guilty and sentenced her to nine months' imprisonment. That day her white companion had been declared not guilty. The judgment was properly reported in the local paper.

It was in one of my camps on this trip that I first met Dr. Robert Broom, the only 'F.R.S.' South Africa could then boast. Broom was a Glasgow medical graduate who had pursued an eccentric and chequered career, and at the time he was practising as a doctor somewhere in the neighbourhood. He was also a palaeontologist whose study of the fossil record has contributed greatly to our understanding of the evolutionary relationships of the earliest known mammals to a certain group of reptiles which had become extinct tens and tens of millions of years ago. But his critical sense had become warped by an irrepressible belief that almost everything he found was unique. From this point of view he was just like Arthur Keith. Having heard through the 'bush telegraph' that a scientist from England was in the field studying and collecting baboons, he decided to come and see for himself what I was up to. He found me near some farm buildings which were then my base, cutting up baboons which had been shot in a drive that dawn. I was being helped by a black man and was surrounded by a number of naked children who were looking on in amazement as they sucked the ends of the wrists and feet which had been cut from the baboon carcases. I was told that children regarded these as a delicacy, but that after boys had gone through their initiation ceremonies, they no longer put baboon meat to their mouths.

Broom proved to be only vaguely interested in the observations I was

making and in the purposes for which I was preserving pieces of tissue—
that was not his kind of science—and ended his visit by giving me as a
gift the broken skull of a baboon, with the suggestion that I should
describe it as a new species or sub-species of South African baboon. I
asked where it had come from, and he pointed vaguely to some neighbouring hills. The skull was that of a creature that must have died fairly
recently, but I had to accept the offering. The only baboons which lived
in those hills belonged to the species that I was studying, and Broom was
talking nonsense. Distinguished as he was, he knew little about, or was
little concerned about, the relatively enormous amount of physical varia-
tion one finds in all animal species. Some years later I became involved in
what, I must admit, was a not unduly intellectual controversy with him
and Raymond Dart, and others who accepted their views about the
evolutionary significance of the growing number of fossil ape-like
remains which started to turn up in South and East Africa after the initial
find of the Taungs Skull. The main reason for the argument, which has
still not completely died down, has been my continuing inability to
agree that purely visual impressions can be the basis of diagnoses in
classifying animal bones and assessing their relationships. I was definitely
the 'odd man out' when the argument started, and I now derive some
minor satisfaction from the fact that as more and more fossils have been
uncovered, my scepticism about the views of Broom and Dart has been
justified, in the same way as the methods of analysis which I insisted
should be followed in assessing the significance of fossil bones have
become commonplace amongst younger research workers.

I shall never forget the journey back from Grahamstown to Cape
Town at the end of my time in the field. In addition to my bottled and
pickled specimens, I had a considerable collection of live reptiles of
various kinds, for wherever I went I had offered the little back boys, who
seemed to spring up everywhere in the veldt, a penny for every 'lizard'
they brought me. I also had two baby baboons, whose mothers had been
shot in the course of my hunts, and the younger of which had been
slightly wounded in an arm. The train journey took a day and a night,
and the babies and I shared a sleeping compartment. I was very tired,
and while at first I did not mind taking them from their boxes to give
them milk every hour or so, in the end I felt like strangling them. At one
point I remember holding the smaller one out of a window and wondering whether to kill it in order to get some sleep. My patience did not in
fact crack but I had regretfully to give the creature a lethal dose of anaesthetic when we got to Cape Town because its wound had become too
septic for adequate treatment.

Leaving Cape Town was a frantic business. On my arrival more than
two months before, my twin sisters had arranged a meeting between the

young Mr. Peers and me. I not only wanted to talk about the cave in which he and his father had unearthed 'Fish Hoek Man' but also to see whether, in his capacity as an animal dealer, he could get together a collection of South African snakes, including puff-adders and the even more venomous spitting-cobra or Ringhals, for me to take back to London. He had also undertaken to get me some baboons. He was as good as his word, and had also seen to it that not only his snakes, but my lizards and baboons as well, were securely caged for the voyage. Another task which I had undertaken, this time for the British Natural History Museum, was to bring back with me a skeleton of a false killer whale. A school of more than a hundred of these sea mammals had stranded themselves some two years before on the beach of a village called Kommetjie on the west side of the Cape Peninsula, more or less at the same time as similar strandings of the same species had occurred in the Shetlands and on the shores of Ceylon. Before starting on my pursuit of the baboon, I had driven out to Kommetjie and had arranged for a local native to disinter one of the larger of the carcases which lay half-buried in the sand, and to remove all the flesh that remained on the creature. He had done his part of the job, but now I had to arrange for the still smelly and large skeleton to be securely packed in an air-tight zinc-lined box. My sisters helped me with this and other matters, including collecting a few more live baboons which I wanted to take back to London.

I must have seemed a strange ship-companion to my fellow passengers, what with my caged snakes, lizards and baboons, and having to exercise and play with my remaining baby baboon. Fortunately, nothing untoward happened on the voyage, and I delivered my live creatures to the Zoo and the skeleton to the British Museum, from which in spite of its size, it has since mysteriously vanished.

I kept the baby baboon as a pet in the flat in Ormonde Terrace, close to the Zoo, to which I had moved not long before I had gone to South Africa. She became a favourite of my friends, to whom she was known as Chastity. For a time she lived in the house of Clough and Amabel Williams-Ellis, whose children adored her, although Clough, in his book *Architect Errant*[3] incorrectly calls her Betsy. Chastity was the animal I used in my experiments on colour vision. In addition to the demonstration that I gave at the Zoological Society, I delivered what turned out to be a slightly hilarious lecture on the subject of animals and colour vision at University College. On that occasion Chastity was much more concerned to amuse the audience than to show off her ability to differentiate hues of different wavelength regardless of their brightness—dogs and bulls can only differentiate degrees of brightness. Chastity also provided another distinguished performance of her abilities. Francis Meynell, the famous typographer, lived with his wife Vera in Bloomsbury's

Gordon Square. They had a son, then about a year old, and they thought that it would be amusing to test his ability to differentiate colour against Chastity's already proven skill. On the first occasion, the baboon proved far quicker in mastering the 'multiple discrimination' test-box that I had had made. When his turn came, little Benedict crawled towards the wrong colour signal. Very soon, however, as a worthy representative of the human race, he demonstrated his superiority over his far-distant sub-human cousin.

I was reminded of this incident in an unexpected way some forty years later when in 1970, shortly after Edward Heath became Prime Minister, I was a member of the party which accompanied him to Washington for his first talks with President Nixon. We arrived late, and after dinner at the British Embassy, we sat down to be briefed about the matters we were due to discuss next day at the White House. Just before the meeting started, our Foreign Office expert on American affairs came over to me and said, 'You know, we've met before. I'm Benedict Meynell. When I was a baby you pitted my intelligence against that of a baboon of yours.'

About the same time, the idea of comparing the learning ability of monkeys with that of humans cropped up in quite a different context. I had met Lionel Penrose, later to become Galton Professor of Eugenics at University College, shortly after he had qualified as a doctor at St. Thomas's Hospital. Lionel's personal wealth allowed him to pursue a number of what seemed to be eccentric intellectual interests, including psychoanalysis and the writing of musical scores which sounded equally interesting when the treble and bass were inverted. He also had a passionate interest in the possible genetic nature of mongolism, and had managed to get himself appointed as Research Director of the Royal Eastern Counties Institution in Colchester, which housed a number of mongoloids. I visited him there a few times, and was fascinated by the Hogarthian picture presented by the twenty or so unfortunate victims of the disease which he was sympathetically studying. In the end we decided not to proceed with an experiment we had designed to compare the learning ability of human mongoloids and baboons, lest news of it were to stimulate hostile comment. Later Lionel was to write the first comprehensive analysis of the aetiology of mongolism. This was the precursor of an authoritative series of studies of other presumed hereditary diseases.

After a time Chastity became too lively and obstreperous to continue as a house-pet, and had to be moved to University College, where at night she occupied a cage on a big flat roof. During the day she was attached to a post by a longish chain which was clipped to a belt round her loins. One day she was found hanging dead from her post; the chain had got entangled round her neck when she was swinging in her usual happy way.

During my prosectorship, I did not have a licence to carry out experiments which involved operations on living animals. Here my collaboration with Alan Parkes at University College proved invaluable. When I was working on my first and lengthy monograph on the general nature of the menstrual cycle in monkeys and apes, we had purchased two female baboons in order to check by experiment whether the conclusions to which my direct observations were leading me were on the right track. As soon as I was back from my South African trip we set to work on the new material I had collected, and well within a year had completed for publication a detailed microscopic study of the changes which take place in the baboon's reproductive organs during the course of the menstrual cycle. We also decided to embark on a corresponding study of a vicious species of primate called the Green Monkey, but this got nowhere.

Facilities for keeping monkeys and baboons at University College were poor. A few baboons once escaped, and their recapture provided some excitement. The animals clambered over roofs to a busy nearby street, causing considerable consternation as they made their way along, with a group of us in hot pursuit. As Alan Parkes recalls in his book of reminiscences,[4] the last animal was cornered in the carpet department of a large furniture store not far from the College. Customers and salespeople behaved as though a lion had got loose.

One of my few regrets of that phase of my researches is that I failed to interest Sir Thomas Lewis, the chief heart physician at U.C.H., in the physiological mechanisms that might be involved in the cyclical swelling and coloration which every month transforms the buttock region of the non-pregnant female baboon. Sir Thomas was well-known for his researches into the processes that lead to the retention of fluid in the body; for example, into the causes of the dropsy which is associated with heart failure, and the leakage of fluid into tissues which are bruised. I already knew that the 'sexual skin' swelling in the baboon was caused by a hormone that is secreted by the ovaries, and that it is due to the localised retention of excess body water. The body-weight of one somewhat unusual baboon which I had under investigation used to increase by as much as a third during the first half of every cycle, due to fluid which was held back in her buttock region, and which her kidneys excreted in a rush after ovulation had occurred. Lewis sent one of his assistants to see and discuss the strange phenomenon, but there it ended. It proved to be one of my premature scientific interests. We now know that the hormone which is responsible for the swelling belongs to the same class of compound as does 'cortisone', in which doctors have for so long been interested because of the part it plays in water retention. In those days we knew nothing about the category of adrenal hormones to which cortisone belongs.

While all this work was proceeding, I was pressing on with the book on the social life of monkeys, which I had promised to C. K. Ogden. As each chapter was finished I sent it for comment to Mrs. Bisbee at Liverpool University. She is the R.C.B. to whom the book is dedicated. As I have already said, she had taught me more during her year of lecturing in Cape Town than I had learnt from any of my other teachers, and I had got in touch with her before my appointment to the Zoo. I had also sent her the manuscript of my paper on the skull of the chimpanzee. She was tireless and ruthless in her criticism. Draft after draft of the chapters would come back scored through, marked with alterations, and often with sarcastic comment. On one occasion I could bear it no longer, and literally started to weep with frustration. But that was the way to learn, and if I later passed this lesson on to my own pupils, it was only because I knew no better way to make a young scientist ask himself what it was he was trying to say.

My work was becoming fairly well known, and I was often asked to lecture on the social life of monkeys and apes. Just before my visit to South Africa, I addressed the Psychoanalytical Society, with the doyen of the British profession, Ernest Jones, in the chair. I was so carried away by my subject that I went on for well over an hour, followed by another hour or so of questions. Then there was the 'Heretics' in Cambridge, a club which had been started by C. K. Ogden in 1909, and which had provided a forum for many of the advanced thinkers of the day. Richard Braithwaite of King's College, already prominent as a philosopher, arranged a dinner party for the occasion, and among my fellow guests were Joan Robinson and Richard Kahn, two young economists who, in due course, were to reach the top of their profession, and with whom I have enjoyed an enduring friendship. There was also our mutual friend, Margaret Gardiner, the daughter of a leading egyptologist who had tried to involve me in his interests in the origins of speech and language. I was far too excited and drank too much and, not unexpectedly, spoke too fast, too volubly and too long, to an audience in which I recognised Roger Fry and other Bloomsbury notables. Julian Huxley, whose interests were wide, also introduced me to a company which had been gathered together by a Lord Charles Hope to investigate scientifically the claims of a well-known medium, Rudi Schneider. I went to a few séances, and enjoyed the in-between talk, but Rudi, alas, passed no scientific tests. In July 1930 I gave three evening talks over the radio on different aspects of the biology of monkeys and apes. In the days of the B.B.C.'s Savoy Hill studios, broadcasts were usually on serious topics, and I was put on at the peak time of eight o'clock. But most of the lectures I gave were to conventional scientific societies, and since my researches were not confined to primate reproductive physiology and social behaviour, I was sometimes asked to speak on matters relating to other aspects of human evolution. The days were full, but there then seemed to be time for everything.

A month or two before my collecting expedition in South Africa, Elliot Smith had got it into his head that I should offer myself as a candidate for a chair in Social Biology which the London School of Economics proposed to establish. Since his advice had led me to the Zoo, I agreed with this further suggestion, being enthusiastically supported by him and by Tansley, who described me to the authorities as a man of 'ruthless critical faculty'. This was all very flattering, but I had no regrets at all when, fortunately for me, Lancelot Hogben was chosen. I say 'fortunately', partly because I was then fully immersed in what I was already doing, and therefore did not want a new job; partly because I knew nothing about organising a University Department; but most of all because it brought Lancelot into my life. On the one earlier occasion when I had met him, I had experienced some of his caustic wit, but equally I had read his *Nature of Living Matter*, an outstanding example of clear-thinking, and at the time a necessary antidote to a mass of writings on vitalism and holism and other woolly 'philosophies'. Lancelot had a lot to teach me, but the man who was still to write *Mathematics for the Million* failed to make me appreciate certain principles of statistics which he felt would help me establish whether breeding times were cyclical or random in nature.

Towards the end of 1930 I had combed all the daily records of births and deaths which the Zoo had kept uninterruptedly since 1828, in an effort to differentiate those species which breed throughout the year from those that have their young in a restricted season. There was no problem about extreme cases. For example, scores of polar bears have been born in the Society's Gardens in the 150 years of its existence, and all in the short period from early November to the middle of December. On the other hand, the Axis Deer of India has bred at all times of the year. The distinction here is sharp. But in other species, where seasonal variations in frequency of birth occur, the difference is anything but clear-cut. I consulted Hogben, who sat me down and gave me tutorials in probability statistics. I consulted other authorities, but all to no avail. I wrote to most of the world's better known zoos, and particularly to those in the Southern Hemisphere, to ask for their breeding records, because I also wanted to know if seasonal breeders changed their habits to accord with the new seasons when they moved across the equator, and if so, how speedily. In my second quarterly report for 1932 to the Prosectorial

Committee I had to write that I had spent much time during the quarter attempting unsuccessfully a 'mathematical exercise (a task for which I am unfortunately not well equipped)' of the Society's breeding data. Twenty years were to pass before I published a monograph on the subject, and then I used empirical methods of analysis which I had to devise myself.[5]

The office of Prosector carried with it a part-time lectureship in anatomy and physical anthropology at University College, for which a small honorarium was paid. The duties were light, but the attachment meant that I was in constant touch with all the work that was going on in the Department, and in particular with the researches of Parkes and Marrian in the next door building, and also with those of Dick Lythgoe and Ka Tansley, who were both hard at work on the physiology of vision in a laboratory a few doors from the room which I shared with Sir Bernard Spilsbury. Elliot Smith also got me to give courses of lectures on anatomy at a girl's art school in Chelsea. Although I was only in my mid-twenties, I was used by then to a much more mature society, and the students seemed incredibly young to me. I did not get to know any of them, and I cannot remember what my lectures were about. But what I do remember is waiting absent-mindedly at the underground station at Euston for a train to take me to Chelsea, and dropping my pipe on to the rails. I jumped down from the platform, and as I looked for the pipe in the shadows I became aware of shouts of 'You bloody fool, you'll be killed'. Looking up, I could not see the person to whom the message was addressed, but keeping a wary eye open for trains coming in from the tunnels at either end, I continued my search. Having found the pipe, I jumped back on to the platform, only to see the station master coming towards me through a crowd of shouting people. He did not speak for a minute, and then said: 'Do you realise what could have happened? Don't you know you could have been electrocuted?' I stupidly replied that I had forgotten, but that it didn't matter because I had stepped over the live rail. At that moment my train drew in and I leapt aboard. It was only after a few moments that I started to feel frightened.

New friends kept coming into my life, and I never knew what it was to be bored. I met more and more people of the inner Bloomsbury circle. Adrian and Karin Stephen became close friends. He was Virginia Woolf's brother, and Karin was a stepdaughter of Berenson, the art historian and connoisseur about whom so much has been written. Once, having accepted an invitation to dine with the Berensons, I rang Karin to cry off because I was so busy with the final stages of my *Social Life*. 'You can't do that to B.B.', she cried in horror. 'No-one does'. So neither did I. There were Vanessa Bell, Virginia's painter sister, and Duncan

Grant, and the great Virginia herself and her husband Leonard. In his *Downhill all the Way*,⁶ Woolf quotes from Virginia's diary an entry about a party given by Adrian Stephen in May 1932. I do not believe that either Virginia or her husband really knew what the party was about. It was held in Duncan Grant's rooms in Fitzroy Square, not, as one would imagine from the printed word, in Adrian's house in Gordon Square. Virginia writes of Adrian dwelling on his past, instead of realising 'there's his present and his future all round him'. She writes of Karin as deaf (which she certainly was) 'twisted, gnarled, short, stockish, baffled' (which she was not, at any rate not to me). She mentions Duncan Grant, James and Alix Strachey, 'Dick' Strachey, Hughes—was that Richard Hughes?*—Doris Chapman and me, to whom she refers with much disdain. She clearly disliked or disapproved of me, and I must confess that her conversation was too precious for my liking. She writes that the party broke up at 11.20, and that we were all courteously thanked for coming by Adrian. But, she asks, what pleasure can such parties conceivably give, 'all these old elements of a party not mingling'. The answer is that Adrian arranged the party precisely in order to try to get the old elements to mingle, in order, as he had told me, to reconstruct the atmosphere of pre-war Bloomsbury. More than that, he hoped that part of his future was before him—he had fallen for Doris, who was still on-and-off with me, and he wanted to impress her. Clearly his sister Virginia realised this, but I do not know whether Adrian ever succeeded in his aims. Doris was an odd girl.

In order to practice psychoanalysis, both Adrian and Karin had qualified in medicine after having started out in different professions. Adrian had been admitted to the Bar, and Karin had begun as an academic philosopher. Under the title of *The Misuse of Mind*, she had written one of the first volumes published by Ogden in his 'International Library'. I spent many a weekend at their country cottage—I think it was a converted inn—in a minute village on an estuary in Essex close to Thorpe-le-Soken. Sir William Gull, one of Queen Victoria's physicians and the man who had first recognised the syndrome of thyroid deficiency in adults, was a native of the place, a fact which was recorded on a crudely painted board on the cottage where he was born. Sometimes we sailed, often we bathed, and there was always talk. It was there that I first met Patrick Blackett and his wife—Patrick was already renowned as one of the outstanding young men working with Rutherford in the Cavendish Laboratory. I particularly remember a day when I was sitting in the sun reading Virginia Woolf's *The Waves*, which had just been published.

* The author of many well-known works, among them *A High Wind in Jamaica*. I always thought that the children whose adventures it recounts were modelled on the Williams-Ellis young.

Adrian drifted over to see what the book was. 'I can't follow a word of it', was his comment. I pretended that I could.

Was it through Adrian and Karin that I met the Williams-Ellises, or was it the other way round? Clough's model village of Portmeirion on the Welsh coast was then only half built, and Amabel was busy, as she probably still is, on good works and writing books. I sometimes stayed with them in Wales, and also at Newlands Corner in Surrey, where Amabel's mother, Mrs. St. Loe Strachey, lived. Here I first met John Strachey, Amabel's politician brother who was then working with Oswald Mosley to form the New Party, from which Mosley in due course moved to his British Union of Fascists. It was there too that I first met Cyril Joad, England's popular philosopher of the day, and to me a colossal bore with all the tales of his sexual prowess. More importantly, it was there that I first met Desmond Bernal, with whom I was later to work closely, and for whose intellect I had an enormous respect. The Laughtons had a country cottage—Stapledown—in the woods a few miles from the Strachey house, and I sometimes stayed with them. One weekend, when John Armstrong and Benita Jaeger, whom he was to marry, were there, Elsa shot a short film to the theme of 'the salacious parson', with John in the title role, and Elsa—or was it Benita—as the country girl, victim of the parson's wiles, and me as an extra and some kind of country yokel. Before he died, John told me that the film had not been destroyed, and Charles Higham refers to it as 'The Sleeping Clergyman' in his book on Charles Laughton, although he does not mention my one and only appearance on the silver screen.[7]

The Williams-Ellises introduced me to Alex and Diana Spearman, he a rising Tory politician, and she a student of politics, and I stayed several times with them at Rolls Park, their home in Epping Forest to the northeast of London. Rolls Park was a late seventeenth-century mansion which was demolished shortly after the war. It had been the home of the Harvey family, and a portrait of William, the discoverer of the circulation of the blood, was one of a family group in rococo plaster frames set into the wall of one of the grand rooms. There were always interesting people there, mainly writers and politicians, and the food and wine were excellent, even if guests occasionally complained of the cold.

I had told the Spearmans about Bernal's amazing knowledge and ability to discourse learnedly on any subject, and since they had also heard of him from John Strachey, I was asked to bring him along one weekend. Bernal always travelled light, and arrived with just the clothes he was wearing, carrying a briefcase which, in addition to papers, contained only a razor and a slide-rule. The maid who unpacked his bag was puzzled, but thought that the slide-rule, an object which she had never seen before, was some multipurpose instrument which served as hairbrush and toothbrush combined. She would not have thought this if she had seen Desmond's enormous head and shock of hair. The news of the strange visitor spread before dinner, and he fully lived up to his reputation in a large party which included Evelyn Waugh, whom I had met there before. When the ladies left the room after dinner, and the port had begun to circulate, what was a general discussion soon became a dialogue, sometimes heated, between Bernal and Waugh, the former a defecting Catholic, the latter at the time an aspirant. The main topic of conversation was the way Christianity had spread from its source into Europe and Africa; a dreary topic, one might imagine, but one which riveted everyone's attention as the wine passed. About 10.30 one of the abandoned females was sent in to ask Alex and the other men to join the ladies. No-one stirred, and the highly attractive messenger sat down and remained till the argument—it was more a lecture from Bernal—came to an end at about midnight. I cannot recall that Evelyn Waugh persuaded Bernal about anything.

I have some other memories of Evelyn Waugh at that house—in his Diaries he refers to me as a member of the Spearman Circle. For some inexplicable reason I had apparently gained something of a reputation as an explorer after my collecting trip to South Africa, and Waugh asked me to join him on his first visit to North Africa. Much as I enjoyed his novels, I did not think this a good idea. Peter Fleming, who was then literary editor of *The Spectator*, and for whom I wrote several reviews, extended a similar invitation when he went off to the Matto Grosso in Brazil in search of the remains of Colonel Fawcett. That invitation I also declined. But I did take him to see Chalmers Mitchell, who agreed that the Zoo would pay the cost of collection and transportation of any rare animals that he might chance upon. Peter refers to his attempt to collect otters in his *Brazilian Adventure*, the book he wrote about the trip.[8] And I also declined to be the senior member and medical officer of a team of 'explorers' which Tom Harrisson was taking to Borneo. Tom settled there for a time both before and after the war. He had also been parachuted into the island when it was still in Japanese hands.

Tom, who with Charles Madge later founded 'Mass Observation', was more than a little eccentric in those days—with age he became only somewhat less so—and the manner in which he conveyed his invitation, and the night he spent with me instead of, as he claimed, spending it in his usual way in a public lavatory for the cost of a penny, were almost as bizarre as was the ending of his first Borneo trip. I was on my way to a party in Putney which was being given by Herbert Sidebotham, a political and diplomatic journalist who wrote for the *Sunday Times* under the pseudonym 'Scrutator', and had arranged to meet Tom beforehand at the Café Royal to discuss the proposed expedition.

When he told me that he spent his nights in London in public lava-
tories, I offered him instead the divan in my sitting-room, at the same
time warning him that I would be back late. 'Thank you,' he said, 'but
I think I'll do what I usually do.' When I got back after midnight, I
found Tom fast asleep on the landing outside the front door. I got sheets
and blankets for the divan while he looked at the books on my shelves, a
few of which he pulled out, saying that he would rather read than sleep.
He then asked whether I had anything to drink. I gave him a half-full
bottle of whisky, and having expressed the hope that he would be comfortable, went to bed. The next morning I found him still sleeping,
having neither touched the whisky nor opened a book. I judged him to
be a kind of Walter Mitty and poseur. When he got up, I once again, but
more firmly this time, declined to go to Borneo.

When Tom and his party returned from the expedition, Banks, the
Curator of the Sarawak Museum, wrote to me: 'Never again will I
encourage the Rajah to allow in a pack of schoolboys and undergraduates. They behaved disgracefully'. Yet Tom ended up years later as
Curator in Banks's place. One of the party, a boy named Shackleton,
nearly forty years later became Leader of the House of Lords in Harold
Wilson's Government. Another is today Air Chief Marshal Sir Christopher Hartley. I do not know what happened to the others.

The Williams-Ellises, the Stracheys and the Spearmans gave me my
first introduction to politics. I did not have the slightest idea why there
had to be a 'New Party', but in March 1931, I went, as if to the opera,
to the opening meeting of the Party at the Memorial Hall in Farringdon
Street. Mosley, who was to have been the main speaker, had fallen ill,
but his wife Cynthia spoke, as did John Strachey. I was no wiser at the
end than I had been at the beginning, but very much enjoyed the supper
party for the would-be government which took place afterwards at the
Spearmans' London house in Tite Street.

The Zoo opened up yet other kinds of social and intellectual life.
Philip D'Arcy Hart had introduced me to his cousins, Godfrey and Nancy
Samuel, whose father was the Liberal politician Sir Herbert Samuel. One
night in 1931 when Godfrey and I had dined together at his house in
Porchester Terrace, a maid came to his sitting-room to say that his father
had returned from the House of Commons with some of his colleagues.
We looked over the bannisters into the hall and saw Sir Herbert, fol-
lowed by Lloyd George, Sir John Simon, and a few others, moving
into the library. The Liberal Party, more powerful then than now, was
debating whether or not to join the National Government which Ramsay
MacDonald saw as the only way out of the difficulties which then beset
England. The decision they took that night all but destroyed the
Party.

When Godfrey came down from Oxford, he studied at the Architectural Association School in Bedford Square. After qualifying, he joined some other young architects in a firm called Tecton, under the leadership of a young Russian, Berthold—'Tolik'—Lubetkin. I never knew how much to believe of his stories. Tolik was a refugee from Russia, and had had no formal architectural training. He had worked in Paris with an architect cousin, Jean Ginsburg until, according to his account, he was, as it were, exiled. When I asked why, he told me that he had entered a competition for the design of a war-memorial on the site of the Trocadero, and that the judges had thought his entry blasphemous, or some such thing. What he had suggested was a clear site with a big plinth in its centre, and mounted on it a vast, tall cylinder of glass filled with red fluid equal in volume to all the blood that had been spilled in the war. I wonder what truth there was in this tale.

Tolik had a colleague, a Polish architect, who had a secret recipe for a miraculous yoghurt. Those were the days before this dairy-product was on sale everywhere in the United Kingdom. On the first day after it was 'brewed', the Pole's concoction had a slight aperient effect. On the second day it was neutral, and on the third, costive. What better as a household dish, and would I therefore go with them peddling samples, and try to sell the idea to one of the big dairy/restaurant chains? I innocently accompanied them to a corner dairy, and was not surprised when we were shown the door. In the end Tecton became famous, not for its yoghurt, but for its designs. Some of its buildings, two of them in the London Zoo, are now scheduled for preservation as architectural monuments.

One day in the middle of 1932, Tolik, Godfrey and I were lunching together. This was shortly after the Zoo had acquired two young gorillas for what in those days was a considerable sum. For want of better, the animals were kept in a small building, long since demolished, that had been put up hurriedly some years before to house baby chimpanzees. When I told them about the gorillas, we saw that this was where Tecton could come in with its first significant assignment. 'It's ridiculous,' said Tolik, 'that two gorillas for which so much has been paid should be housed in a building that was not designed to meet their needs. If you tell us what is required, we could design a building, provided you get the authorities to call us in.' I spoke to Geoffrey Vevers who in turn spoke to Chalmers Mitchell, who was as beguiled as I was when he met Tolik and Godfrey next day. He agreed to put the idea to the Society's Council, which was due to meet on the following Wednesday. But it would help, he said, if Tecton could have ready by then a model of the building they proposed. So for the next few days I was bombarded with endless questions, which I could answer only by reference to the literature, about the temperature and humidity preferred by gorillas, about their agility, about the food they ate, and so on. I knew about chimpanzees, but the two new gorillas were the first that I had ever seen. The result is the Gorilla House in Regent's Park, now inhabited by a breeding colony of chimpanzees. Tolik then designed the Zoo's famous Penguin Pool, the Elephant House at Whipsnade, and one or two less important Zoo buildings. The war broke up the association between Tolik and the Zoo, but the original Tecton had broken up long before. Most of those who had been associated with it, except for Tolik, joined the services, and one was killed. Godfrey became Secretary of the Fine Arts Commission when he came out of uniform, and Tolik eventually retired to a small farm in the country.

It was in the Zoo, too, that my path crossed and then joined that of a group of young and at the time unknown painters and sculptors. From the day of its foundation in 1826, artists have come to the Zoo to paint or sculpt 'rare and curious subjects of the Animal Kingdom', to quote the words of the Society's Royal Charter. The list includes such names as Alexander Agassiz, Burne-Jones, Gould, the two Landseers and Gaudier Brzeska. Within weeks of becoming Prosector, I had the luck to meet John Skeaping, Barbara Hepworth, Ben Nicholson and Henry Moore, and from that moment on I spent hours in their studios in Belsize Park, north of Regent's Park, talking, watching them work, and absorbing the sense of what they were doing. Doris Chapman was a more conventional and certainly less dedicated artist than any of them, and indeed was bored by their work. Once we went with them to Paris, and while they all spent the days working in a studio, I sat on the terraces of those two famous cafés, the Dôme and the Rotonde, sometimes reading, sometimes talking to French artists whom we had met, sometimes writing amateurish poems, and sometimes just idly looking around. These new friends had nothing to do with the world of Charlotte Street, whose artists I had once found so interesting, but whose work had started to pall in comparison with the abstract art to which I was now being introduced. Some of my first pictures, and certainly my first sculpture, came from Barbara and John Skeaping, and from Ben Nicholson. Then, as now, artists banded together in groups, and I remember helping the Belsize Park Group to formulate in words, for publication in a new journal, what they believed were their aims. Years later, I helped Barbara to give titles to her operating-theatre paintings before they were hung for public exhibition. Later still, after I had become the Zoo's Honorary Secretary, I decided to resurrect the practice of giving prize awards to zoologists. With Sidney Bernstein, the head of Granada Television, I conceived the idea that instead of medals or books, contemporary sculptures or paintings should be the prizes. Sidney suggested that since

Henry Moore was a friend of mine, I should ask him to help. The result
was that Henry presented the Zoo with the full edition of seven of each
of three small sculptures; Sidney provided the money to pay for the
casting. When, a few years later, 'Henry Moores' became so sought-
after, we realised that the Zoo prizes were probably more valuable than
any awarded by any other scientific society.

But to go back to my years at the Zoo. In my third report for 1931,
I informed the Prosectorial Committee that my *Social Life* had been
completed, simply observing that 'It is a study of the correlation between
the reproductive physiology and the socio-sexual behaviour of the sub-
human primates'. It had taken more than two years to write, and it took
little more than three months to publish. There is a remark attributed to
H. G. Wells to the effect that while scientific papers write themselves,
books are always a heavy undertaking. Even if I would not be ready to
subscribe completely to the first part of this proposition, I can endorse
the second wholeheartedly.

The book[9] appeared simultaneously in America and in the U.K., and
was favourably reviewed in both countries. But, appearing as it did in
the depths of the Depression, it sold anything but well. Nonetheless,
I demurred when, after the war, the publishers asked whether I would be
willing to have the book reprinted, either as it stood or in a revised
edition. I was reluctant to agree, partly because my attention was then so
focused on my experimental work that I did not want to spare the time
to bring up to date two or three chapters dealing with the physiology of
reproduction, and partly because, at that time, I had good reason not to
like the chairman of Kegan Paul. I was also reluctant to allow the book
to appear as a Penguin paperback. The work, which is often spoken of as
a classic—whatever that may imply—has now been out of print for more
than forty years, and it rarely crops up, even in antiquarian lists. Most
practitioners of what is now called Primatology are much more confined
in their outlook than were students of monkeys and apes in my young
days. Indeed, I find myself asking how any biologist can restrict his
concern to a single family of mammals, as so many now do. Biological
interests have changed strangely over the years, and specialisation has
been a mixed blessing. When the book is referred to in some new
scientific paper or book, written by a so-called primatologist or ethol-
ogist, the reference usually turns out to be second-hand, and occasionally
views are attributed to me which I would be the first to deny. My
obstinacy about republication makes me at least partly to blame for this.
Practically every field-study published since I wrote the book bears out
the basic generalisations to which I was led, and I now hope that one day
there will be a second edition. Over the years, I have had to force myself
to smile at the joke about my having written a book about the sex-life

of Primates—to wit, the sex-life of archbishops. I myself invented the joke, but it simply will not die. The French gave a simpler title to their translation—*La Vie Sexuelle et Sociale des Singes*.[10]

I differed in no way from most newly-fledged authors in the pleasure which the sight and feel of my first book gave me. But its appearance did not mean any let-up, either in the pursuit of my professional scientific interests, or in the wider life I was leading. Parkes and I decided to extend the range of animals whose reproductive physiology we were studying, but here I got no further than helping in the collection of moles, squirrels and bats, a few of the species which later formed the subject of valuable monographs published by Ruth Deanesly, a research worker at University College who later married Parkes. I collected moles with an old mole-catcher in Surrey. I had met him when staying with Mrs. St. Loe Strachey, and he was the first person to make me realise how valuable country-lore is. He knew the runs in which his father had set traps, and could point to the spot where his grandfather had caught an albino specimen. Parkes and I collected grey squirrels in the woods of Kenwood above Hampstead, where they had become a pest. The foresters arranged drives soon after first light, and we shot the little creatures as they leapt through the branches. There was a memorable occasion when we collected bats. We were led along the subterranean passages of the Cheddar Gorge caves by members of the Bristol University Speleological Society, picking the creatures like fruit from the dripping roofs and walls. The Society's hut was desperately cold that night, and after a second day's collecting we went to Bristol, with our catch in two wooden boxes. There we found a boarding house in which to spend the night, but we slept very little. There was a continuous scuffling noise which we thought would rouse our landlady who would surely have thrown us on to the street had she realised that we had brought bats into her house. When we got back to University College next day, we discovered what the trouble was. We had mixed in our boxes members of two different sized species of bats, the larger of which had systematically killed all the smaller ones. A cold room had been prepared before we left, with wires stretched across its ceiling, to which we then attached the survivors. We thought we would leave them to get acclimatised to their new surroundings before starting on the experiments we had in mind. We inspected the creatures from time to time, and one day picked one from the wire as a test. It was dead, and so were all the others. But both Parkes and I had enough other work on hand not to shed many tears.

My two main lines of research continued to be the reproductive physiology of monkeys and apes, and the bearing of any evidence on the evolutionary inter-relationship of monkeys, apes and man. I was not only

deeply involved with my artist and actor friends, but also much immersed
in the wider intellectual interests which people such as Tansley, Ogden,
Bernal and Hogben stirred. The world-wide economic depression was at
its most intense, and one could not avoid its intellectual reverberations.
The general atmosphere of the times encouraged me to organise a small
dining club which became known as 'The Tots and Quots', an abbreviation and inversion of the well-known phrase in Terence's *Phormio*: 'Quot
homines, tot sententiae'—'so many men, so many opinions'. This happened shortly after I had been invited to join, in fairly quick succession,
two dining clubs that were then being formed. One, which I believe still
survives, consisted of zoologists. The other comprised some fifteen or so
young men from all walks of life, who dined in dinner jackets, and
solemnly sat around discussing the way the world was going. I doubt if
that one still exists.

One day when I was telling Dick Lythgoe about the two clubs and
how I found their dinners both dreary and at the same time quaint, the
thought struck me—why not form our own dining club; we'd only have
ourselves to blame if it proved a bore. Dick thought this a good idea,
and as a start we discussed the idea over lunch with two other friends,
Hugh Gaitskell and G. P. (Gip) Wells, H. G. Wells's eldest son, who was
a member of University College Zoology Department. They too thought
the idea worth pursuing, and so we canvassed further names. I have only
scrappy notes about the meetings of that first phase of the Tots and
Quots, and at this distance I cannot remember how we 'collected' our
first members. Each of the four of us must have suggested possible names
as 'starters'. I imagine that Desmond Bernal, J. B. S. Haldane, Lancelot
Hogben, Philip D'Arcy Hart and Godfrey Samuel were my nomina-
tions, and that Hugh Gaitskell put forward the names of M. M. Postan,
the Cambridge economist, Roy Harrod, an Oxford economist whom I
had already met through Godfrey Samuel, H. D. Dickinson and J. L.
Gray, also economists, as well as that of Sebastian Sprott, the psychologist and philosopher. Gip Wells suggested Julian Huxley, with whom he
and his father were then collaborating in writing their monumental *The
Science of Life*. I. A. Richards, the author of the *Principles of Literary Criticism*, Patrick Blackett, and Lionel Penrose, my geneticist friend, did not
want to become members, but said that they would like to 'clock in as
guests' whenever they were in London. A letter survives from Sir
Herbert (later Viscount) Samuel, declining to open one of our early discussions because of the amount of preparation it would take him, since
he did not want 'to give the Club merely casual ideas in view of the eminence of the members', referring to J. B. S. Haldane and Lancelot Hogben by name.

After much hectic work arranging the first dinner, I fell ill. It was on a

Saturday morning. I had left my Primrose Hill flat and walked the hundred yards to the Zoo, where the sun shone and everything seemed marvellous. As the morning wore on I became more and more euphoric, until I realised that something must be wrong. I walked back to my flat, took my temperature, and found it was well above 100°F. I had arranged to go that afternoon to a preview of one of the first exhibitions which Barbara Hepworth was having in a London gallery. But I did not go. It was well into the evening when I next became aware of the world around me. I was awakened by the continuous ringing of my door bell. Philip Hart and Margaret Gardiner had come to see what was wrong. By then my temperature had risen further, and the next morning, the Sunday, Philip and one of his fellow registrars took me, protesting, in a taxi to University College Hospital, where broncho-pneumonia was diagnosed.

My mind was only on the dinner that was due to take place the following Wednesday, and I made a colossal nuisance of myself by proclaiming that I was not sick, that my temperature would be normal next day, and that I would be out at the latest two days later. And so I was. But I paid for my obstinacy by having to take two weeks off recuperating after the dinner which inaugurated the club.

Elliot Smith had by now returned from the Far East and had started to draw me more and more into those of his anthropological interests which concerned man's physical origins. Dart continued to press his claims that the Taungs Skull was the 'missing link' in man's descent from some ape-like ancestor, but here neither he nor Broom succeeded in convincing Elliot Smith that they were right. In his *Adventures with the Missing Link*,[11] Dart gives an account of a visit he paid to London early in 1931 to demonstrate his fossil skull, and describes his failure to carry conviction with those whom he most wanted to impress—including me. He then returned to South Africa, leaving the skull with his wife in order that adequate plaster casts could be made of the fossil. He tells how, on the night before she was due to return home, she called on Elliot Smith, with whom the skull had been left, and who accompanied her back to her hotel with the precious specimen. When they got there, the taxi was dismissed and Elliot Smith and Mrs. Dart went on with their conversation. Only after Elliot Smith had departed did Mrs. Dart realise that the skull had been left in the taxi. It was safely recovered by the police next day.

I remember the incident well because Mrs. Dart had not just called on the Elliot Smiths. I was at the small dinner party which they had arranged to say farewell to her. When, the next day, the news of the missing skull started circulating, there were more than a few smiles and raised eyebrows. Whatever the incident implies about Elliot Smith's

views of the significance of the fossil, I am still convinced that not only
was he justified in his scepticism, but that the claims that the Australo-
pithecines of the Taungs variety were missing links in the direct line of
man's descent, and creatures which walked and ran upright, and coursed
wild animals across the plains with the help of primitive weapons, are no
more than speculation.

The other argument about human ancestry into which Elliot Smith
drew me occurred towards the end of 1932. It concerned the significance
of the Chinese fossils which were popularly known as Peking Man, and
which had been brought to prominence by Davidson Black, the Professor
of Anatomy in Peking, who, like Dart, was one of Elliot Smith's disciples. Here I did not find myself on Elliot Smith's side of the debate. He
had written a number of papers and monographs in which he had
followed and defended Black's thesis that *Sinanthropus*, the new genus to
which the Peking remains were assigned, represented a form of man
generically distinct from all other known types, including the early ape-
man of Java, *Pithecanthropus*. One day Elliot Smith was asked to give a
lecture on the subject to the Royal Anthropological Institute, but as he
had written so much about the fossils, he asked whether I would undertake the task. And so as to ease it, he suggested that I could use whatever
statements on the subject he had made, and whatever other materials
were available, including Davidson Black's own papers, as well as the
casts of the remains which were in University College.

Having set about the job, I soon concluded that Elliot Smith's belief
was untenable, and I was inevitably driven to the conclusion that what
was wanted was a re-assessment of the inter-relationships of all fossil
men. A rational classification seemed to imply the subdivision of the
family Hominidae into two sub-families, the Palaeanthropidae and the
Neanthropidae, two terms that had been coined by Elliot Smith himself
to emphasise cultural contrasts in the industries associated with the
various human types that were involved. These names are not used today,
but the same idea is implicit in the presently accepted classification of the
genus *Homo* into the two groups, *Homo erectus*, my Palaeanthropidae, and
Homo sapiens, my Neanthropidae.

I gave Elliot Smith a draft of the paper I had prepared. Instead of
defending the views he had previously proclaimed, he wrote me a letter
which said: 'I think the manuscript is excellent and raises a most important issue in a way which points the satisfying solution of it. On the
enclosed piece of paper I have jotted down what it might mean for those
who have to name the various creatures. This leads to the somewhat
surprising result that after all some justification may be provided for
Keith's use of the term "Palaeanthropus palestinus"!'

The meeting at which I delivered my paper, and over which Elliot

Smith himself presided, remains in my memory for a much more impelling reason than any of the arguments that I put forward. When we left the Anthropological Institute just off Gower Street, Elliot Smith asked whether I would accompany him home. This was in the days when people were prepared to walk, or travel by public transport, and we had to change buses in Camden Town in order to get to his house in Albert Road near the Zoo. While we were waiting for the second bus, he took out a handkerchief and, as he wiped the side of his nose, remarked strangely: 'I am wondering which blood vessels in my brain are leaking. All day I have felt as though I've a cold on the right side of my nose, and there's been a slight tingling in my fingers. I wonder how serious a stroke it's going to be.' I was much shaken, but he seemed very calm. I took him home, told his wife that he was not well, and called next morning to see how he was. Two or three days later he was in University College Hospital following a stroke, from the effects of which he never fully recovered.

It must have been at about the same time as I had undertaken to interest myself in the Peking fossils, the whereabouts of which are no longer known—they disappeared during the Second World War—that I accepted an invitation to take part in a debate on 'Primates and Early Man', which was due to take place early in September in York, at the 1932 meeting of the British Association for the Advancement of Science. I planned to base my contribution, not on the usual arguments derived from comparative anatomy, but on what was known about such matters as blood relationships, reproductive physiology and behaviour patterns. I knew of no previous attempt to pull together all the diverse functional studies to which I wished to refer, and much work was therefore involved in my self-imposed task. There were also my other researches, and at the time I was under some strain from a personal relationship which was going wrong. My contribution to the York meeting was nonetheless a success, and I committed myself to writing it up as a book.

But I just could not get going. A knowledgeable friend suggested that I should simply part from my girl-friend, but having neither the courage to do this nor to embark on marriage, I decided instead to take myself to University College Hospital. The diagnosis of extrasystoles—irregular heart-beats—was no more than I already knew. The suggested therapy was that I should rest, give up smoking, and drink only one glass of wine when I would prefer to drink two.

A day or two after my visit to the doctor, I was lunching alone and miserably in the Zoo restaurant, when H. G. Wells, whom I knew slightly, walked in. He looked around to see who was there, and then asked if he could join me. We had a pleasant lunch, during which we argued about which technological developments had been most far-reaching in the emergence of civilised life; whether the wheel or fire, or the key-stone, or clay pots. I forgot entirely about my extrasystoles until he lit a cigar and offered me one. His reaction to my saying that there was something wrong with me, and that I had been told not to smoke was that he'd never heard such nonsense from a young man. 'You won't blow up if you smoke,' he said. So I took the cigar, smoked it with pleasure and suffered no ill-effects. Instead of returning to the Prosectorium, on the impulse of the moment I went to my travel-agent and said that I wanted to go abroad for a few days. Where was I going, he asked. 'I don't know, what do you suggest?' I replied. 'Well, last time you went to Italy, what about Spain?' Next day, I fell asleep in a chair on the deck of a cross-Channel boat before it had even started to move, and I again fell asleep in a corner seat of a compartment of a train before it left Paris for San Sebastian. It was not till we reached Biarritz the next morning that I woke up.

After a day in San Sebastian, I moved to Zaraus, a small seaside resort nearby, where I fell in with two rowing 'hearties' who were enjoying a late holiday in the same hotel. I was still 'missing' those heartbeats, and continued to treat myself as an invalid. But on about the third day, I agreed to go with them to the Post Office, provided we walked slowly. Letters posted, we sat down on the terrace of a restaurant, and I gingerly drank a glass of vermouth while they imbibed something stronger. My second glass went down a little less gingerly, and a third followed. The wine flowed at dinner, and by midnight the three of us were drunk—and noisily drunk. In due course we had to pay for some trivial damage that we had caused. I do not remember getting to bed, but I certainly remember waking up the following mid-day with a terrific hangover. But the extrasystoles had gone, and never came back again. Two young American girls who were in the hotel were disgusted, or pretended to be disgusted, by our behaviour. One of them was Martha Gellhorn, later for a time Mrs. Ernest Hemingway. That is how another life-long friendship began.

On my return to London I found no difficulty in getting on with the book. At about the same time I received letters from Yale saying that John Fulton, the head of the Department of Physiology, wanted to see me to ask whether I would accept an invitation to become a member of an institute which had just been set up for the study of the great apes. The director was Robert Yerkes, whose name was well-known to me as a student of animal psychology, and in particular of the behaviour of apes and monkeys. I knew of Fulton from his writings on the physiology of the brain.

John used to give an apocryphal account of our first meeting. His story was that he found his way to the Prosectorium at the Zoo, and having asked Billy Lawrence where I was, was greeted by the sight of me lifting my head from the bowels of an elephant to enquire what his business was. However little truth there was in his tale, we got on well from the start, and at dinner that night I agreed to seek Elliot Smith's approval to my spending a six-month probationary period at Yale. This Elliot Smith gave, although it had been his plan that I should join his staff at University College as soon as my five-year appointment at the Zoo came to an end. My exchanges with Fulton took place early in October 1932. Yerkes, however, wanted me at Yale no later than the beginning of January, and I still had to prepare the lecture which Elliot Smith had asked me to give on the Chinese fossils. I was also determined to get my book on the *Functional Affinities of Man, Monkeys and Apes*[12] into the publisher's hands before taking on new duties. Not surprisingly, my little engagement book for the next two and a half months shows few entries of a purely social kind.

The preparation of the lecture on the Peking fossils was fairly straightforward, even if it led to what in those days was a novel conclusion. But the book, which I had innocently assumed I could just reel off, turned out to be an arduous task. I had arranged to sub-let my Ormonde Terrace flat to Gordon Childe, the archaeologist, whom I still regard as one of the most lucid writers there has ever been on the subject of man's social evolution from the phase of food gathering and hunting to that of settled agriculture and village life. As December drew on with the book still unfinished, I had to move with my papers and clothes into Philip D'Arcy Hart's flat around the corner. There had been occasions in the past when I had worked non-stop for twenty-four hours or even more, but the last four days before I handed in the manuscript proved to be the only time that I did not go to bed in normal fashion for three nights in a row. Anyone who came to see me—which included, as the two of us remember with a smile, Joan Robinson—was put to work helping with the index or correcting typescript. That was how the book got finished.

In my dealings with Kegan Paul over the publication of *Social Life* I had met Fredric Warburg, with whom I was and still remain on friendly terms. Not long before, he had asked whether or not his firm should publish a translation of a short book in German called *Do You Speak Chimpanzee?* While I did not discourage him, I warned him that the book was highly speculative. Many of the author's theories were unacceptable, and from the scientific point of view they were based on far too few data, most of them anyhow questionable, and on an acceptance of 'authorities' who had been discredited by careful students of animal behaviour. When I recently re-read the letter which I wrote to Fredric forty-five years ago, I was interested to see that what I said then about the author, one Gerry Schwidetzky, is precisely what I have since said about some

present-day popular exponents of the ethological school of Konrad
Lorenz. At my suggestion Margaret Gardiner translated the book. The
exercise gave us much amusement, and all I can hope now is that the
venture did not cost Kegan Paul too much. I have not heard of Schwidetzky from that day to this. He may have been a totally mythical
character, or merely a phony scientist like Eugene Marais, a drug-ridden
South African who wrote fanciful stories about baboons and ants in the
early part of the century, and who, because he was one of the fathers of
Afrikaans as a written language, has all but been canonised in the land
of his birth.

Unfortunately, Warburg was away on the day I proudly arrived at
Kegan Paul with my manuscript, completed well ahead of the contract
date. It was the day before I was due to sail for America. I was ushered
into the room of the senior partner, C. P. Franklin, whom I had not met
before, and whom I never saw again. What happened then made me vow
never to write another book. I handed over my manuscript but, instead
of being congratulated, or whatever it is that publishers do at such
moments, and then being given the advance of £40 which I had been
promised, Mr. Franklin pulled a piece of paper towards him, looked at
it, and said: 'You owe us thirty something pounds for proof corrections
on your first book; so that makes us all square.' I looked at him in
amazement, and said that no such transaction was implied in the contract
or letters that had been exchanged about the new book. 'That is neither
here nor there,' he replied, 'you are not going to get any money for this
book.' 'In that case,' said I angrily, pulling my typescript from his desk,
'you are not going to get this.' As I got up to leave, he slipped out from
under his blotter a cheque already made out to me for the agreed sum
and handed it to me. I gave him the text, took the cheque, and left the
room in cold anger.

The cheque went immediately to my typist, and in due course the
book came out. It was well received by the critics, but again sold poorly,
partly no doubt because of its specialised nature, and partly because the
Depression was still on. Two years after the start of the war, when I was
heavily immersed in war-work, I received a letter from Mr. Franklin
saying that he proposed to 'remainder' 23 bound copies of the book and
all the unbound sheets, and offering me the author's usual option of
buying whatever number I wanted at a reduced price. Incredible as it may
seem, he went through the same drill about what was still owing for
corrections as he had when I brought him the manuscript. Fortunately,
this time our exchanges were in writing. Only a sum of £6 was involved,
but I decided to have the matter settled by an agent. In the ten years that
the book had been out it had not earned me a single penny in royalties.
Presumably the sum I handed over to my typist was more than what the

book made. Be that as it may, no-one has since attempted to write a similar book; whereas enough time has passed for me to regard my experience with my first publisher as a manifestation of the kind of treatment some authors of the Victorian era—I have George Gissing in mind—must have regarded as normal. But although for a long time the experience discouraged me from any further adventures with book-writing, it did not stop the stream of scientific memoirs I continued to pour out.

CHAPTER 4

DISCOVERING AMERICA

IN ADDITION to finishing *Functional Affinities*, there were a number of other urgent matters to which I had to attend before sailing. I had to pack a large collection of anatomical and microscopic specimens on which, mistakenly as it turned out, I thought I would continue working once I got to America. There was the 'Tots and Quots', my small dining club, to be put into secure hands while I was away. I also wanted to get any assurances I could about the post which Elliot Smith intended to arrange for me at University College, given that I returned from America within a year or so. This was not easy, since after Elliot Smith's stroke I had to deal with Harris, who was certainly not as keen as his master that I should join the Institute's staff as Reader in Physical Anthropology. And in between I fitted in a final and vigorous social whirl.

The moment of departure was an enormous relief, and in spite of heavy seas, the crossing on the German boat *Bremen* was a peaceful break of five days during which I was able to keep entirely to myself. At the New York docks the customs officer did not know what to do when I told him he was free to open a dozen or so small packing cases to check my word that they contained anatomical specimens, and in order to decide whether or not they were dutiable. In the end he looked at me wryly and did nothing. Having arranged for their transport, I got into a taxi and looking neither to right nor left, was driven to Grand Central Station where I took a train for New Haven. Following the instructions he had given me, I telephoned Professor Yerkes when I got there. He seemed pleased to hear my voice, and asked how he was to recognise me when he came to pick me up. I replied that there would be no difficulty since, so far as I could see, I was the only man in the United States who at that moment was carrying an umbrella. John Fulton had not warned me that Yerkes lacked all humour, and from the tone of his voice when he answered, he seemed to have taken my remark as some kind of denigration of American manhood.

He drove me to the newly-built Harkness Institute of Human Relations, where he listed the people to whom he thought I should be introduced, and at the same time suggested a programme of what I should do in New Haven before going to his Anthropoid Experimental

Station in Florida. After taking me to see John Fulton, whose laboratories were in the same building, we returned to his room, where I was
left alone for a moment. I moved to a small table on which was a smartly-
bound book in which were pasted the reviews of *The Great Apes*,[1] a
volume which he and his wife had published some three years before.
This encyclopaedic compendium of all that had ever been written about
the creatures had been acclaimed as a considerable work of scholarship,
which it certainly is. As I turned over the pages I found the unsigned
review of the book which Peter Fleming had got me to write for *The
Spectator*.[2] Some of its passages had been underlined because they were
not entirely laudatory, and when Yerkes returned to his room I had a
feeling that he had guessed that I was the author.

I spent the night at his house, and soon realised that he was a much
drier and more austere character than his letters had given me to suppose.
Even if it had not been the era of Prohibition, I felt sure that there would
never have been anything alcoholic to drink in his house. At breakfast
the next morning, I politely had to swallow some almost raw eggs
because he assured me that they were good for me. At the same time,
I could only nod my head when he advised me to buy a razor which did
not make as much noise as mine did when it was being stropped. He had
obviously had his ears open while I was having my bath.

Later in the morning, when Yerkes was showing me over his Department, John Fulton came in search of me. Having taken me off, John
said that he was sure that I would find a second night in the Yerkes's
household heavy going, and that I 'would die of thirst'. He therefore
tactfully arranged that I should spend the next few days in one of the
new colleges that were then being built in the University. This made life
much easier. I was well entertained and lionised, without realising at
the time what this must have meant to poorly-paid young research
workers in the depths of a great economic depression. Somehow or other
they seemed to be able to provide themselves with bootleg liquor,
slightly toxic but nonetheless useful in making a party go. What my new
friends lacked in the sophistication to which I had become accustomed
in London, they certainly made up in kindness. They were greatly
impressed by the fact that I had a second book coming out. All of them
seemed to have read my first.

Yerkes was due to go to Florida a few days after my arrival, the
arrangement being that I would follow in a week or so to see whether
I would fit, and if so accept, the post of Resident Director of his Station.
Everybody seemed to know that this was why I had been invited to Yale,
but someone—I think it must have been John Fulton himself—then got
the idea that I should instead be asked to fill the vacant Chair of Anatomy
in the University. I was sent on a round of visits to the professors who

would have a voice in the appointment. I was also dined by Dr. Angell,
the President of Yale, in company with various heads of department—
again, I suppose, to see what sort of person I was. So excited was I by the
new world into which I had been thrown and by the new turn of
events, that I did not know whether I even wanted the job. The idea that
I should become the Professor of Anatomy fizzled out very soon.

The night before I had sailed from Southampton, I had been at a cocktail party given by J.B.S. (Jack) and Charlotte Haldane. Later that evening we went on to dine at the *Gargoyle*, a new club in Soho which was
then much frequented by the writers and theatrical people who lived on
the fringes of Bloomsbury. Jack had recently returned from America,
and when he heard that I was going there, he pulled from his pocket a
slip of paper on which was written the name of someone whom he
described as 'a blonde who was a journalist and not bad company'; he
suggested that I should telephone her if I went to New York. I had also
been given a letter of introduction by Elliot Smith to an American
couple, John and Maria Rogers who, while not professionally involved,
were following with close interest the debate on the diffusion of culture.

It must have been some ten days after I had arrived in New Haven that
I decided to go on a voyage of discovery to New York, armed with my
two 'letters of introduction'. About a day or so after I had arrived, I
telephoned the number that Jack had given me, and a sad voice asked
whether I would care to come round for a cocktail. When I arrived, I was
offered a tiny glass of some unknown South American liqueur, and for
the first time I really understood what the Depression and Prohibition
meant. Our conversation was dull, and as it dragged on I suddenly
realised that my hostess expected me to ask her to dine. My invitation
was accepted, but she asked whether I would first go with her to Carnegie Hall to hear Gieseking play Beethoven's 'Diabelli Variations'. It
turned out that she had a job as a music critic for one of the New York
papers, but I never did make out whether she liked or even knew about
music. During an interval she suggested that we should have a few words
with Gieseking, and then leave. I fell in readily with the idea of going to a
speak-easy called *Tony's*, of which she was a member, and which she
described as 'the hide-out of the *New Yorker* crowd'—the weekly was
then in its infancy—and of a lot of theatrical people.

Tony's was a poorly-lit and not over-large basement, in which a representative selection of the world she had described was sitting drinking,
with only a few eating. My depressed blonde seemed to know everybody.
I could not have imagined a more extraordinary introduction to a new
city. After a few months I settled down to a routine of spending nearly
every weekend in New York, and *Tony's* doorman, after scrutinising my
face through the peep-hole in the door, accepted me as an habitué and

would always let me in. What happened to *Tony's* after the repeal of the Prohibition Act I do not know. *Twenty-One* was another speak-easy close to *Tony's*, and although it has continued to this day as a popular meeting place and restaurant, it is now only a pale reflection of what a sophisticated speak-easy was like.

I stayed long enough in New York on that first visit for me to realise that the vitality and interests of the people to whom I was introduced made up for the professional narrowness of the majority of those I had met in New Haven. It was not until years later that it dawned on me that I never encountered another scientist or academic in the New York circles that opened up to me after that first visit to *Tony's*.

I returned to New Haven wondering what was in store now that I had been paraded around the Yale ring as a potential professor of anatomy, only to discover that while I had been away, the Dean of the School of Medicine, who really had the power of appointment, had been searching for me. When he was told that I had gone off to New York in quest of pleasure, he had decided, not surprisingly, that I was too young, and no doubt too unreliable a character, to be entrusted with the charge of a big university department. At the time I had no regrets, and in retrospect I feel enormously grateful to him for having judged the situation so well. It did not matter at all to Yale that Edgar Allen, the man who was then appointed, had not been brought up, as I had been, in the classical tradition of anatomy. Allen was a first-rate student of reproductive physiology.

After a few more days in New Haven, I took the train to Jacksonville in Florida, where I was met and driven to Orange Park, then a small village some thirty miles to the west. My memory is mainly of a wooded area with moss hanging from the trees, of hundreds of red cardinal birds, and of the big, slow St. John River. The Anthropoid Experimental Station, which was on the outskirts of the village, consisted of a number of animal buildings, each cage with its own outer enclosure. There was also a small office building, and a number of 'hides' in which Yerkes, his wife, and one or other of the few resident workers, would sit for hours watching the animals, and making notes. There were enough apes to satisfy the most avid researcher, but absolutely no real scientific purpose that I could discern in the endeavour. I stayed with the Yerkes', with whom also lived his secretary, Mrs. Morton.

On the first night, after an early and severely simple dinner—it was my introduction to pumpkin pie—I again tripped up. We had moved to the fire, and Yerkes asked whether I liked reading aloud. My reply, that I could think of nothing I liked less, was greeted with silence, and after some general talk, we all went to bed. The following day Mrs. Morton told me that Mrs. Yerkes usually read to her husband every evening, and that I had broken a ritual. The book of the moment was Aldous

Huxley's *Point Counter Point*, passages of which she would skip when she thought them to be in questionable taste.

I had not intended to be rude. No-one had warned me about the way my hosts spent the evenings in that outpost of civilisation. Since I knew that their manners were too good for them to suggest the next night that we should try reading aloud, I therefore pretended I had letters to write, and that I also wished to commit to paper certain observations which I had made that day. Mrs. Morton then confided that she had been suffering these reading sessions in silence, and she suggested that the Yerkes' would not mind if she drove me to see Jacksonville the next evening. Instead of doing that, we went to the dog races about ten miles away, a performance we repeated several times. I had only once before been to a dog race, and enjoyed not only the betting, but also the excitement of the last race, when the dogs were ridden by South American capuchin monkeys dressed like jockeys. That was a sight to be remembered, with the little monkeys clinging hard to their mounts with their tails curled round those of the dogs.

To get away from the Station, where I found very little to occupy me, I also invented an interest in cigar factories, which in those days formed a considerable industry in northern Florida. As she drove me round the country, Mrs. Morton must have thought me no less eccentric than did the Yerkes'. I also visited an empty tumble-down house near the Station where a couple called Kellogg had for a year or so brought up their child with a young chimpanzee, only to discover that while the ape failed to learn to speak and behave like a human being, their own infant started to pick up some of the not very hygienic habits of its companion. The Kelloggs wrote a popular and widely-read book about this 'experiment';[3] I never did discover what this had to do with science, and I was left no wiser when someone else repeated the experiment many years later. The day someone teaches two chimpanzees a conceptual language, and then records their conversations—as opposed to getting the animals to respond to, or even repeat, human sounds or signs—I shall sit up and take notice.

Florida was very hard hit by the Depression, particularly because of the collapse of a building boom that had been going on during the twenties. However beautiful the countryside, it was impossible not to be saddened by an environment in which poverty was so widespread. Old men waiting to die sat rocking in their chairs on the wide verandahs of their 'lodges', and everywhere were the miserable shanties of the black people. There was no mental stimulus; just trees and trees. Someone at the Station introduced me to a supply of illicit corn-liquor, which I kept openly in glass-stoppered hair-lotion bottles on my chest-of-drawers. That seemed a less offensive way of going against the habits of a teetotal

and non-smoking household than hiding bottles among my clothes. On
nights when Mrs. Morton could not drive me to the race-track or to some
other local attraction, I would go to my room, sometimes straight to bed,
and with a glass of corn-liquor and a cigar by me, I would either read a
book or write crazy verse to send to one of the new friends I had made
in New York. I was in Orange Park for only three weeks, but it seemed
an eternity. I made it clear that the proposal that I should spend six
months there as resident director, and the remaining half of the year in
New Haven, was not acceptable to me unless Yerkes was prepared to
transform the station into a real experimental, as opposed to an observational, laboratory. And there we left it, the only tangible result of my
visit being a paper which I published some time later showing that what
was then the new A–Z pregnancy test for women also worked for the
chimpanzee.[4]

My departure must have been as great a relief to Yerkes as it was to
me. It was not until the mid-sixties that I saw Orange Park again, on an
occasion when Jacksonville University was giving me an honorary
degree. Yerkes had long since died, and the Station, while still there and
manned, was in a state of physical decay, and scientifically derelict. I
doubt whether it ever lived up to the dreams which led to its foundation.
Observing apes was one thing; studying them to test whether this or that
hypothesis is a valid explanation of some particular phenomenon, is
another. But that was not the way Yerkes proceeded in his scientific
life.

Back in New Haven, I joined forces with John Fulton and Gertrude
van Wagenen. John had charm and vitality, and what social life I enjoyed
in New Haven for the next eighteen months revolved round him and his
wife Lucia, and round Dr. van Wagenen. John had encouraged her to
come to the Yale Medical School on an honorary basis, and most people
had then incorrectly regarded her simply as a wealthy amateur scientist,
instead of, as time has proved, a most dedicated student.

John had graduated from Harvard before going to Oxford as a Rhodes
Scholar. There he had come under the influence of Sir Charles Sherrington, undoubtedly the greatest nerve physiologist that England has ever
produced, and of the legendary Sir William Osler, the Regius Professor
of Medicine and a historian of medicine. He then returned to Harvard to
qualify in medicine under Harvey Cushing, the man who revolutionised
brain surgery, and who also had a professional interest in medical history.
After that John returned to Oxford as a Fellow of Magdalen and as a
member of Sherrington's Department. Our meeting at the Zoo had
taken place only two years after he had become the Director of the Yale
Department of Physiology, which he had transformed into a hive of
activity, attracting staff and research workers from far and wide. His new

Department imparted new life to neurological studies in America, and he himself added considerably to our knowledge of the brain. He also wrote extensively about the history of medicine and science. The Yale Library of Medical History was established on the basis of his collection of books, together with those of Cushing and of a Swiss bibliophile, A. C. Klebs. John poured out learned memoirs, but his indefatigable devotion to scholarship never seemed to be a brake on his zest for good living.

Gertrude van Wagenen, who was somewhat older than us, worked on the physiology of reproduction in monkeys, and when I arrived in New Haven she had already established the nucleus of a colony of rhesus macaques, the descendants of which still thrive nearly fifty years later. Because of my parallel interests, it was naturally to her laboratories that my steps turned.

After a number of somewhat superficial starts, the chief focus of my work became an enquiry into the possible interaction of the nervous and hormonal systems in the control of the reproductive organs. It was already known that most of the glands which produce hormones are under the influence of certain chemical substances produced by the pituitary, a small structure situated at the base of the brain, and that the chemical secretions of the ovaries in turn control the changes that occur in all the other reproductive organs. One of Fulton's chance observations was that damage to the spinal cord could affect the sexual rhythm in monkeys, an observation which had also been hinted at, but not followed up by Sherrington as far back as 1900. Gertrude van Wagenen had had her attention drawn to the matter, and I in turn became interested, assuming as a working hypothesis that some special nervous pathways connected the central nervous system, that is to say, the brain and spinal cord, with the ovaries. After some preliminary experiments to test this idea, which I carried out in collaboration with Dr. van Wagenen, I became more and more interested, and designed an extensive and systematic series of experiments to discover the nature of my presumed nervous connection. Alas, it turned out that I was pursuing a will-o'-the-wisp. The answers to my questions receded every time they seemed within reach. The work was arduous, but given that it did not prevent my getting to New York for the weekends, I did not mind working all hours. I did my experimental work by day, after which I would dictate a record of what I had done to a secretary provided by John Fulton. Mrs. Bundy was happy to put in two or three hours work in the evenings, but she did not like to see me doing post-mortems on monkeys, and the corridor into which our two rooms opened rang every night as I bawled dictation through an open door. I filled at least a dozen fat notebooks with the records of my experiments, but in the end had to conclude that the particular phenomenon which I had been investigating was a general reaction to damage to the central nervous system, and not some interference with a specific nervous network.

Most nights I was the only person at work in the building. On my way home at about midnight to the somewhat dingy block of flats where I was living, I used to stop at a sandwich bar which provided 'near-beer' and excellent thin steak sandwiches, and there I would speculate about the new observations which the following day would reveal, for my research had become my consuming interest when in New Haven. Apart from some experimental psychologists, I knew few people in the University, and fewer still in the town. The Fultons were always welcoming, and it was in their house that I had the good fortune to meet Thornton Wilder. His *Bridge of San Luis Rey* had been a success, but he then seemed to be somewhat in eclipse. It was heartening to get to know someone like him in my narrow academic environment.

My scientific interests took me out of New Haven on several occasions. John arranged that I should visit Harvey Cushing at the Peter Brent Brigham Hospital in Boston. It was a revelation to see the sophisticated way he operated on the brain compared with Wilfred Trotter's primitive techniques at University College Hospital. Later Cushing moved to New Haven to pursue his interest in the history of medicine, and there I met him again several times.

At the invitation of Professor Hooton, the head of the Department of Anthropology at Harvard, I paid a second visit to Boston to lecture to a special audience. I was met at the railway station and driven straight to a hall, where at two in the afternoon I was introduced by Hooton to an assembled class. After I had talked for a full hour, and been thanked, Hooton said that he had arranged for me to speak to another group on a different subject on which he knew I had been working. He added that I would have an hour in which to prepare my talk. Obviously there was nothing I could do but agree to the suggestion. He collected me just before my time was up, and whisked me off to a smaller lecture room where a group of Faculty members was waiting. After speaking, as I thought, rather well, for an hour to an audience whose attention I seemed to have captured, I sat down. Whereupon Hooton rose and said that they had enjoyed my lecture greatly, but by some misunderstanding of mine I had not spoken to the subject they had expected. Would I therefore mind continuing, say, not for a full hour since I might be a bit tired, but perhaps for three-quarters of an hour, on the topic on which he understood I had carried out some serious research. Slightly taken aback but nothing daunted, I stood up and launched myself on the third lecture of the afternoon. I vowed never to return to Harvard, and it was years before I did. But in response to his request, because he was a pleasant warm-hearted man, I did prepare for him a memorandum on the way I thought a university department of anthropology should be organised, since he assumed that I might come to Harvard if I did not stay at Yale. Whether anything came of that blueprint I never heard. I doubt it.

I was also occasionally invited to other universities and institutions, but only three such visits made any strong impression on me. The first was to Washington, to which I had been invited by Gerrit S. Miller Jr., the Curator of Mammals at the Smithsonian Institution, who wanted to discuss with me his theories about the evolutionary significance of the act of rape. In his way, Miller was as good an eccentric as I ever met. I spent some enthralling hours discussing his bizarre 'scientific' interests. After dinner that night, his domineering wife left the house to attend a midnight performance of Beethoven's 9th Symphony—why midnight I could not understand—and Miller and I sat looking at a file of original drawings by well-known modern painters to consider why they had selected what to him were highly abnormal subjects. Of one particular artist, he said, 'Can't you see that he was totally dominated by his mother, and that he had had incestuous relations with his sister?' After a time I joined in the game with zest, and tried to outdo him in imagination. I often wondered what became of those drawings. He had many which collectors of post-impressionist and surrealist paintings would now give much to own.

The second was to Baltimore, where I got to know many people who were attached in one way or another to Johns Hopkins University. On the first occasion, the invitation came from Carl Hartman, of the Carnegie Institution. He introduced me to a number of his colleagues, including Curt Richter, all of whom were studying the influence of sex-hormones on behaviour. In this way I came to know one of the most powerful groups in the world then engaged in the pursuit of knowledge in a field in which I had a primary interest. They were a remarkable and closely-knit group, many of whom enjoyed international reputations, and all of them full of vigour. In spite of my relative youth, they accepted me as one of their own, and we had long discussions about the research programmes on which we were engaged. One of the pleasures of visits to Baltimore was to be taken to a house known as 'the Hamilton Street Club', which was the meeting place of a select group which included H. L. Mencken, the writer and critic, Raymond Pearl, the demographer, and Lewis Weed, the Director of the Johns Hopkins Medical School.* Here I used to be encouraged to drink more beer than was my habit, and to get to my feet to speak on demand. It was not surprising that I came to feel that so far as the American academic world was concerned, the Baltimore crowd was the most outstanding.

* Lewis Weed later directed the American medical war effort.

The third was to Chicago, to meet Heinrich Klüver, a brilliant psychologist and student of animal behaviour. He had just published his *Behavior Mechanisms in Animals*, which revealed not only his skill as an experimenter, but also the fact that his European education had provided him with a much more powerful intellectual background for the kind of work that he was now doing than was possessed by the American animal behaviourists whom I had so far met. Klüver handled his monkeys fearlessly, and I learnt a great deal from our talks. He introduced me to some of the sights of Chicago, including the police mortuary where many gangsters had finished their days. After the war, Klüver was involved in the development of cybernetics, in association with the two renowned mathematicians who, more than any others, were responsible for its emergence as a science—John von Neumann and Norbert Wiener. When I last visited Klüver, in the fifties, he was still in his old quarters, where he had insisted on remaining while the rest of the building was demolished around him.

Before my probationary six months' appointment with Yerkes had expired, I had begun to wonder what came next, now that I had made it clear that what he had offered was not to my liking. Lack of funds made it impossible for John Fulton to do anything. Not knowing how Elliot Smith was, I wrote to Harris, who replied that he had been elected to the Chair of Anatomy in Cambridge, and that there was nothing for me at University College. One letter said that I should be patient, since the Lord would look after His own, and another ended with the words 'Thank Jehovah you are not in Germany'. Having received no encouragement from that quarter, it was arranged that I should be awarded a Rockefeller Research Fellowship to carry on my work in New Haven for another year. This suited me very well. Not only could I continue with my increasingly absorbing new field of research, but there was always the prospect of weekends in New York, where it was possible to clock-in without notice for a few dollars a night at the newly built Barbizon-Plaza Hotel, which in those days of the Depression always had room.

New York was wide open. There was first the world that *Tony's* had opened up to me, in particular the Gershwin world; George, his brother Ira, and Ira's wife, Lee. Then there were the Rogers'. I had been slow to look them up, but they introduced me to E. E. Cummings, then better known for *The Enormous Room* and *Eimi* than for his poetry. In a different circle, there was J. P. McEvoy, a popular writer of the day, through whom I met the denizens of the magazine world. Occasionally the Fultons and Gertrude van Wagenen would come to the big city and we would dine and go to the theatre or to a Harlem nightclub. And finally there were the occasional visitors from England. I flitted from one circle to the next, enjoying every minute between Friday evening and Monday morning, when once again I donned my white laboratory coat in New Haven.

Only one of these New York groups reached into my New Haven life, and that was by accident. Before I had ceased being the Zoo's Prosector, I was visited by a young American named Emily Hahn, who had already published her first novel to the title *Seductio ad absurdum*, and who was about to write a volume about her adventures in crossing the Congo alone on foot. That had the better title of *Congo Solo*. 'Micky', as Emily was and is still called, had a powerful amateur interest in monkeys, an interest which as her later writings show well, has never left her. Soon after we met, she had returned to New York where she became a kind of amanuensis to J. P. McEvoy, who at the time could command whatever space he wanted in the weekly magazines, and who later became one of the editors of *The Reader's Digest*. Some months after I had settled in New Haven, Micky wrote suggesting we should get together, and I was invited to join a weekend party at McEvoy's country retreat in Woodstock, in upper New York State. When I arrived I discovered a boisterous party in progress, helped along by the local red wine and by a kind of Calvados called 'apple-jack'. Among my fellow guests was the deputy-editor of *Vanity Fair*. I found her enormously attractive and reacted accordingly, without realising how much this amused McEvoy and some of the others. What I did not know was that on the Monday, he and Micky decided to immortalise the occasion in a short story for *The Saturday Evening Post*.

A few days before it appeared, Micky telephoned from New York to tell me what was about to happen, and to warn me that I would be recognisable to anyone who had ever met me. I was filled with horror at the thought that one of my Yale colleagues might discover what had happened that weekend. The day the magazine appeared, I was waiting at a street corner to buy a copy, and a quick glance justified my worst fears. I wandered from corner to corner round the Institute buying copies wherever I could, in the vain hope that I could exhaust the supply. After a time I gave up, and I then had the job of destroying all but two of the papers I had bought. Micky had been right. Apart from a few changes, the story was a fairly good account of my infatuation that weekend. But by good luck, as far as I could find out, none of my New Haven colleagues recognised me in the story, given that they even so much as saw it. Outraged as I was at the time, it did not stop me from seeing McEvoy, Micky or the *Vanity Fair* lady again. Nor did it discourage the latter from publishing her own, and somewhat more identifiable account, of the same weekend some three months later.

That same visit brought McEvoy's son Dennis to New Haven as my 'apprentice', the same Dennis who, after a career in the U.S. Pacific Navy during the war, successfully launched a Japanese edition of *Reader's Digest*. J.P. did not hold with conventional education, and Dennis, who was then fifteen years old, had been made to pursue an unusual school career, which had included a spell at Kurt Hahn's establishment at Salem in Germany. J.P. then got the idea that Dennis should join me as a kind of acolyte, doing whatever chores needed to be done in my laboratory, writing such essays as I might set him and, in general, learning from my example. I was not to be a paid tutor; it was to be an act of friendship, particularly as J.P. seemed to think that I shared his views about the restrictive effects of ordinary schooling. Odd as it was, the idea appealed to me, and in due course Dennis turned up in New Haven, where in the meantime I had obtained the necessary permission for him to spend the mornings with me in the laboratory. He was entertaining, and much more sophisticated than his years had led me to expect. He also wrote well, and was clearly interested in everything that went on. But the arrangement lasted for only about six months. Some mornings he would come to my flat and cook breakfast for me. I never gave a thought to how he spent his time when he was not with me, and it never occurred to me that eyebrows might be raised about our relationship. I was totally ignorant of the fact that while I was supposed to be his 'moral guardian', and in spite of his father's injunction that he should neither smoke nor drink, he not only managed to do both, but also encouraged the young girl technicians in the Department to share these pleasures with him. When I was politely informed about this aspect of his life, it was also gently suggested that the educational experiment should be ended. In writing to J.P. to explain the situation, I indicated that part of the reason for the apparent failure of the experiment was the fact that I had not given Dennis enough of my time. I wrote: 'My year here has been pretty profitable from the research point of view, and I have got into several new fields. It is incredible how much there is to be found out, but I'll be damned if I know why these things should be discovered.'

The Rogers's world was quite separate from that of the company which frequented *Tony's*. John Rogers was a wealthy figure in the insurance world, but it would have been impossible to guess this from his private life which, like the interests of his wife Maria who edited some 'way-out' sociological journal, was focused on literary and near-scientific matters. They entertained well, but the company never seemed to include anyone involved in politics, business, the theatre or journalism, and even by the standards of the day their circle was somewhat right-wing. The close bonds which we forged endured till their deaths in the sixties. The Rogers' knew of my friendships in the Gershwin circle, and usually gave an impression of silent disapproval, but not as obviously as did Cummings. I saw him and his new wife Marion constantly. I had met her before she came into his life, and on the occasion when I first saw them together at a party given by the Rogers', she drew me to one side and asked me to pretend that we had never met before. Marion was a beautiful woman who, I believe, had been in the Ziegfield Follies. The occasion to which she was referring was a party in a night-club at which she had been all but drunk. It was only rarely that I could entice either Cummings or Marion out of their small house in Greenwich Village. In all the thirty or more years that I knew Cummings, he always preferred his rocking-chair to the world outside, and much of the time he would sit declaiming his doubts about the way the human species was moving. It was the same years later, but without the rocking-chair, when he and Marion stayed with me in Oxford, and again when I was their guest at the farm-house in New Hampshire which he had inherited from his father. Here he was isolated from neighbouring farms and from everything else by a forest of trees which he wanted to grow right to his doorstep, so as to shut out the world beyond. I wish I had kept all the letters that he wrote, or copies of my own. His were a kind of poetry.

After his death a volume of his *Selected Letters*[5] was published. It included two that he had sent me. One of them, and another addressed to Freddie Ayer, to whom I had introduced Cummings in Oxford, contain references which might puzzle the reader. A letter dated 11 December 1950, ends with the sentence: 'c'est la saison de mistletoe et holly partout paraissent les *paysans* de solly'. Not long after the war when he was nostalgically talking about the past, and bemoaning the illiterate social changes which he saw coming, I told him that it was no use fretting— 'All over the world the peasants are on the move,' I said, 'and nothing will stop them.' In many a letter after that he referred to 'les paysans de solly'. The other reference is in a letter to Freddie Ayer, where Cummings talks of a 'selfstyled killerofAmericangenerals'. He sometimes referred to me like this in recognition of my war-time association with several American Service chiefs about whom, as a class, he still felt as he had about the military when he wrote *The Enormous Room*. Cummings ended another letter to me, not reproduced in the book, with a short paragraph: 'life in the 40odd states is dull. Listen. I dare you to slaybymistake an American general chez lui. Come on—et bonne chance'.

In another of his published letters, as a preface to a more profound observation, he wrote, 'all my heart is on a new hampshire hill gifted with blue mountains'. He gave me a water-colour of those mountains; it hangs in my dining room, and is treasured as are the copies of his books which he sent as they came out. Once I got him and Marion to come with me to see Martita Hunt in Giraudoux's *Madwoman of Chaillot*. He tolerated

Once, very soon after I first met her, I sat listening in silence to a sophisticated discussion about the different smells associated with people, and in a lull, I suddenly heard myself saying, in a room full of strangers, 'I think I smell like chrysanthemums'. All heads turned to me as Lee said: 'Well, that's all right, baby, if you like chrysanthemums'. I do not remember blushing, but I do remember making a vow not to make that kind of remark in public again. That did not stop her occasionally calling me 'the ovary kid'.

To a very slight extent, the Gershwin and Rogers circles were bridged by another lot of friends, whom I met through Esther Murphy, John Strachey's first wife. Esther was then married to Chester Arthur, a grandson of a forgotten President of the United States. She was a big woman, and a great talker, who always seemed to prefer re-enacting some piece of ancient history to engaging in current gossip or discussion about the regeneration of America, for which F.D.R.'s New Deal was designed. There were others whom I met with her—Dorothy Parker, Janet Flanner and Tallulah Bankhead. There was Virgil Thomson who had written the music for Gertrude Stein's opera, *Four Saints in Three Acts*. I went to Hartford in Connecticut for the opening night, and was pleasantly surprised to run into Freddy Ashton, who had been responsible for the choreography. If the occasion was not memorable on its own account, it certainly was from the point of view of the weather. During the performance it started to snow, and I was one of only a few who managed to return by car to New Haven. Most were stranded for days, and the snow lay thick on the ground for every bit of a month.

Life in New York was indeed very heady. Almost every one of my friends and acquaintances was in some way or other engaged in creative work, and I found myself made welcome even though I was the only professional scientist frequenting their circles. In that respect my American private life differed very much from life in London, where at least a few scientists were part of the social scene. The excitement engendered by the company of dramatists, writers, actors and musicians was so great that at times it all but drowned the background noise of the New Deal and of widespread poverty.

There was disturbing news from Europe. Hitler had come to power. But whatever concern I may have felt, even this I suppressed at the time. I saw only a few people from England. Richard Kahn was over on a Fellowship, and we met a few times. Once after we had stepped out of a taxi to enter a restaurant for dinner, I was so full of conversation that I absent-mindedly walked through a plate-glass door, without hurting myself as it shattered. Not knowing the local laws, we were both worried in case I was asked to pay for the damage. Equally, as I discovered later, the proprietor was concerned lest I sued him. A little shaken, we were led to a table, and the proprietor himself came and asked what he could bring us, no doubt thinking that I needed a glass of brandy. I asked for a dozen oysters, and was surprised when we were not given a bill.

Amabel Williams-Ellis and Aneurin Bevan were in a British party which visited the States in the summer of 1934 to raise money to help the victims of fascism. I lunched with the two of them when they passed through New York, and spent the rest of the day and most of the night with Nye. Their talk was disturbing, but still it did not quite touch me. By midnight my own remoteness from affairs seemed even to have infected Nye, who readily accompanied me to Gertrude van Wagenen's lush Park Avenue apartment, where we drank her brandy while he warned her of his awareness of what he called 'the Mayfair kiss'—the supposed process whereby a British socialist is corrupted by smart society.

I was beginning to feel increasingly nostalgic for England, and even though the Rockefeller Foundation had indicated that they would renew my Fellowship, I made it plain that I would not be interested in staying on when the year was up. The pleasures of New York had dulled even the excitement of my researches into the nervous pathways, especially since it seemed that my quest would never end.

Moments of depression, previously unknown, started to overcome me. In a letter I wrote to Philip Hart I said, 'Yale benighted, calcified and dull. Good for one thing—work. When I'm not in the lab or at a type-writer, I'm either asleep or eating. In the meantime all I hope is that England and Europe will not have gone up in flames before I return.' And in a letter I sent to Fredric Warburg replying to some criticism of the New Deal, I wrote that 'I see no reason to get excited by the dismal progress of the N.R.A.* or by the spectacle of a country getting through in a rush those reforms which have been in evidence in Europe for many years ... but I fear the consequences which the years will reveal. I am sure this country will not resist the growing tide of anti-intellectualism, and somehow or other, intellectualism does seem to be a value when everything else is crashing round ones ears.'

My main trouble was that I had no job to which to return. Le Gros Clark, Professor of Anatomy at St. Thomas's Hospital, was going to Oxford and wanted me to go with him, but not knowing how the University worked, he could not arrange the appointment. A few years before he had tried to get me to join him at St. Thomas's, but I had declined. Then Elliot Smith wrote to say that Davidson Black had died, and that the Chair of Anatomy in what was called the Peiping Union Medical College was now vacant. The College received its funds from the Rockefeller Foundation, whose directors, together with Elliot Smith,

* National Recovery Administration/Act.

had decided that I was the person to follow Black. In his trip to the Far East, towards the end of 1930, Elliot Smith had spent some months in China and had written to me about the charms of the place . . . 'one cannot avoid the use of superlatives in writing of Peking, whether of the filth and stench of the streets, the glories of the Forbidden City and the beauty of the private houses, of the ethnological survivals or the palaeontological treasures. There is a singular charm about the place and a mere month's experience is tantalisingly insufficient.' In his new letter he wrote, 'I hope that you will not think the Chinese proposal implies that we are not anxious to have you back here in July, for I heartily reciprocate the kind things you say at the end of your letter. It is only that you are the sole person I can think of who would be competent to take up the threads in China that I urged upon the Rockefeller Foundation the appointment of you as a solution of the difficulty. Their representatives in Paris were so enthusiastic about it that I felt sure I was doing the right thing. Your selection for this honourable office will put you in a class by yourself and will, I am sure, be to your eventual advantage.'

I could not have been more dismayed. Fascinating though it was to speculate about man's fossil ancestry, this no longer constituted science in the sense I understood the term. The final paragraph of my *Functional Affinities* had opened with the sentence, 'But in all the network of Tertiary forms [meaning the geological epoch which began sixty million years ago] it is impossible with even a pretence of certainty to indicate a point and declare "there stood the animal to whose evolutionary adventures man owes his presence on earth to-day".' I had ended the paragraph by saying that 'the available evidence cannot even deny the possibility of man's independent evolution from as far back as the Oligocene, and through the Miocene up to the present day'—sentiments which, with every stirring of the argument by new fossil finds, I would reiterate even more forcibly today.

In a strongly-worded telegram, Tansley advised me not to be diverted from the true path of science by the invitation to Peking. I wrote to Philip Hart, who, with Audrey Russell, a close mutual friend on the staff of the Anatomy Department, then got busy and put in an application on my behalf for a Beit Research Fellowship to be held in Le Gros Clark's Department in Oxford, where I was also to have a Demonstratorship. They succeeded, and I was saved. Philip added a postscript to one of the few of his letters of that time which have survived. 'You sound awfully hard up. Enclosed a cheque. Please do not be too proud . . . the hell you will. It's to be put on our long-distance debt, that is for when I am starving as a consultant in Gower Street and you are an academic king.' I was not too proud.

It was time to wind up my work in New Haven. Packing the papers and specimens I had accumulated in the New Haven laboratory, particularly my microscopic slides and the loose-leafed notebooks full of my typed observations, did not give much trouble. The Fultons threw a party for my thirtieth birthday, but being in a low state of mind I found it a sad affair. I determined to give a brighter goodbye party, and succeeded. I distributed my few possessions, including two small carvings, some cuff-links and a few treasured rare books, among my chosen friends. I could not have been more elated.

In New York I had to say my goodbyes, and also obtain the necessary income tax clearance which the customs officials would demand. That was a final illustration of the kindness I received on that first visit to America. In a dingy building near the docks I sat at the desk of an official who started to take particulars. Q: How long have you been here? A: A little more than eighteen months. Q: What have you been doing? A: For most of the time I was a Rockefeller Research Fellow. Q: What's that? Explanation, and then a puzzled look and the comment: 'That sounds like charity; I'll ask the boss'. He disappeared behind a dusty American flag in front of a door, and came back with a smile, saying, 'Yes, the boss says it's charity'. I then added that I had forgotten to say that I was an associate professor for the first six months. 'Say, you needn't tell me that. It doesn't sound like charity'. 'But I've told you', I replied, 'and I want a proper clearance as I'm coming back one day', proudly displaying an official card that I had been granted which said that I could return as many times as I wished without going through the formality of obtaining a visa. 'Hell, I'd better ask the boss.' He disappeared again, returning with a sad face to remark that the boss did not regard being a professor as a form of charity. 'How much did you earn?' I told him. 'Well,' he said, 'we've got to get rid of that. You must have had expenses. Let's say you spent $200 on books, $400 on instruments, so much on travel.' Every now and then he would add up his fictitious figures and say that there was still too much left on which to pay tax. And every now and then he would repeat, 'you needn't tell me about this'. In the end he won. His additions finally added up to 'nil income'. I was given a form to that effect, and he accompanied me to the street where he shook my hand, saying, 'please come again—you'll always be welcome'. And so, starting with a three-month visit in 1937, when I combined the pleasures of New York with some further research at Yale, I always have been.

A few days later I was on a boat on my way back home.

CHAPTER 5

OXFORD

I DO not remember on what day I left New York, or the boat on which I sailed, or what I did with those unopened cases of specimens that I had carried with me from the Zoo some eighteen months before. What I do remember is a mounting sense of excitement at the prospect of once again being in London, and at the same time a growing sadness at having left so many friends behind.

Gordon Childe was still in my flat in Ormonde Terrace when I got back. I therefore moved in with Philip Hart for a couple of weeks. When I returned to my rooms, I was amazed to discover from the empty bottles that Gordon Childe seemed to drink only Madeira wine—or was it Marsala? He appeared to have done all his reading and writing in an armchair, and I never did understand how he assembled the vast store of information for the books which he wrote. I liked Childe even though I found his appearance and habits strange. His squeaky voice came out from under a long wispy moustache, and in those days he always wore a very broad-brimmed hat. To the best of my knowledge he never married, and although he seemed to spend much of the time on his own, when I did see him he was always friendly and interesting.

I threw myself into a social round in London, seeing old friends, and making contact with those of my new American friends who were in London, among them Micky Hahn and Tallulah Bankhead. Tallulah had rented a house in Albert Road close to the Zoo, and here she held court from about mid-day until well after midnight. I whiled away pleasant hours there with a heterogeneous collection of stage celebrities, a writer or two, a new Wimbledon champion, and even politicians. There were also more serious engagements with scientific colleagues. The spectre of Mosley's fascism hung over England, and fascism was more than a spectre in other European countries. Murmurings of political unrest were widespread. But somehow or other I still did not feel as involved in what was stirring politically as did many of the people with whom I renewed contact, and who had been more exposed than I to the political and emotional shocks of the time. While I was in America, those of my friends who had been involved in President Roosevelt's 'New Deal' were more concerned with the domestic aftermath of the great Depression than they were with what was happening in Europe.

In September 1934 I moved to the Anatomy Department in Oxford as a Beit Memorial Research Fellow, and soon after was appointed a University lecturer. Sponsored by Roy Harrod, I also became a member of Christ Church. Tansley, whose professorial appointment carried with it a Fellowship at Magdalen, had wanted me to join his college, but I had not done so.

It was easy to find accommodation in Oxford in those days, and I obtained the lease of a quiet house in Museum Road, within a stone's throw of the Anatomical Department. It remained my home for nearly twelve years. I had to buy some furniture to add to what I already had, but everything from Ormonde Terrace seemed to fit into my new home, including my Ben Nicholson and John Armstrong paintings, my Barbara Hepworth carving and drawings, and a copy of a Sumerian relief which was in the British Museum, and which Barbara had given me. Above all there was room for my books. I already had several friends in the University, and from the moment I arrived I began to make more. What Oxford is like now I do not know, but in those days a bachelor could enjoy a rich social life on very little money and without ever penetrating the fastnesses of north Oxford where most of the married dons lived. I was constantly invited to lunch or dine in different colleges, and after a few months had the luck to 'inherit' a housekeeper from Micky Hahn. Mrs. Boyd, Elizabeth as she was known to all my friends, was also an excellent cook. Micky had come up to Oxford for a short time with Eddie Mayer, a script-writer who was escaping from Hollywood in order to write a play that really mattered. Only crumpled sheets of paper resulted from his efforts, and he then decided to give up the experiment. Elizabeth never minded when I gave her only an hour's notice to prepare a meal for four or even six guests. She adored the constant stream of visitors, particularly those who came to spend a night in my spare room. Over a period Tansley and I dined *à deux*, alternately in Magdalen and at Museum Road, in order to chat and to taste wines. Tansley never moved his family home from Cambridge. As a Professor, he preferred to live a somewhat solitary life in his Oxford college.

One day when it was my turn to have him to dinner, for which Elizabeth always made a special effort, I came home with Thornton Wilder, whom I had spotted in the buffet-car of the train from London. He was on his way to Oxford for no better reason than that he had twenty-four hours to spare. Even though I knew that Tansley often dried up in the presence of strangers, I asked Thornton to dine. Unfortunately he arrived first, and when Tansley came he was taken aback to find that we were not going to be alone. Thornton at first did all the talking, having just returned from Vienna and Switzerland, where he had visited both Freud and Jung. He was enthusiastic about psychoanalysis and, to give point to a story he was telling, started to describe the layout of Freud's study, laying particular emphasis on a picture of 'The David' which hung near Freud's desk. 'Do you see how the room was arranged?' he repeatedly asked Tansley. 'Do you see the picture?' 'Yes, I do,' came the reply in the end, 'I gave it to him.' Up to that moment Tansley had hardly spoken, and had certainly given no hint that he had once been a disciple of Freud. After that the talk became easier.

Charles Laughton, whose tortured emotional life has now been revealed to the world by Elsa Lanchester and Charles Higham,[1] was often a guest, and sometimes arrived with a gift of a bottle of whisky as his only piece of luggage. He was an enormous favourite with Elizabeth, to whom he used to bellow from one end of the small house to the other. The time I remember best was when he was making the film 'Rembrandt'. After we had eaten, he would lie on a divan, while I would encourage him to read out loud from the Bible, a passage of which he had to declaim in the film. I believe this was the start of his famous reading act. He obviously preferred male society, and that of intellectuals, and we got on very easily without enquiring into our respective lives. On two occasions I went abroad with him at a moment's notice. John Armstrong, who was more attached to Elsa than to Charles, also came to stay, accompanied by Benita Jaeger, whom he had now married. Another not infrequent guest was Michael Killanin* who, although up at Cambridge, found the Oxford of those days much more to his taste. But most of my guests were undergraduate and graduate members of the University.

The High Table and Common Room of Christ Church—the 'House'— were always bright and stimulating. I dined once or twice a week, and in the thirties it was rare for fewer than a dozen to be there on any evening. Professor Lindemann (later Lord Cherwell), better known as the 'Prof', had the habit of coming into the Common Room after dinner. As a vegetarian, teetotaller and non-smoker, it sometimes suited him to dine in his own rooms rather than in Hall, and there was always a sense of pleasure and interest when he entered the Common Room, stopping for a moment as he carefully laid down his bowler hat and coat on the table by the door. The Prof was invariably friendly, and never seemed to mind how much one disagreed with his views. And I never minded his sarcasms. I particularly liked an occasion when he said that he would have been inclined to agree with something I had said were it not for the fact that some of my friends—mentioning a few names—shared the same view. There was also J. C. Masterman and college personalities such as Roy Harrod, Robin Dundas and Canon Jenkins. Among the younger,

* Lord Killanin, now the President of the International Olympic Committee.

and then lesser known members of the Common Room were Gilbert Ryle and A. J. (Freddie) Ayer, the Common Room's philosophers. Frank Pakenham (now Lord Longford) and Patrick Gordon Walker, both in due course to become Cabinet Ministers, were there. So too were Hugh Trevor-Roper, the historian, and Bob Mortimer, later to become Bishop of Exeter.

The guests who came were also usually interesting, and I was never able to rid myself of the feeling that when I dined at the House I was going to a party. I was one of the Common Room's fairly regular bridge players, and since I had no duties such as undergraduate essays to read, and few lectures to prepare, I usually stayed till the end—which, as often as not meant midnight. In his fascinating book on the Prof,[2] Roy Harrod refers to the Prof's habit of always looking on when one played cards, fearful of joining in lest he made a mistake. While it is true that the Prof was an inveterate 'kibitzer', I did enjoy the unique distinction not only of playing bridge with him on one occasion but, what was more astonishing, a game of vingt-et-un, when Bob Mortimer, the Junior Censor of the College, was called from the game to the telephone. I can still hear one of our number urging the Prof to go on playing when Bob returned to the vingt-et-un game, and then teasing him by saying, 'We know why you won't go on, Prof. You've made 1s. 9d. and you're frightened of losing it.' We always played for low stakes, and it amused me that distinguished figures like Sir Farquhar Buzzard, also a member of the High Table and Oxford's Regius Professor of Medicine, kept a cumulative tally of his winnings and losses in his pocket diary. 'I'm not doing too badly,' he would say, 'I'm up 8/6 over the year.'

As the thirties wore on, the Civil War in Spain, the menace of Hitler and the possibility of a world war, began to dominate our conversation. Leo and Amethe von Zeppelin were friends whom I had met during the first phase of my London life. Their home was in Austria, and the story was that after the First World War Leo had become a Frei Korps leader, with his own private army to fight the communists and socialists who were out to destroy the 'old order', and that as a result he had in due course been banished from Germany. Amethe was the daughter of an English colonial civil servant, and a pupil of Bertrand Russell. Under her influence it seemed that Leo had become a liberal. During the thirties they spent more and more time in London, and Leo, who spoke out loudly against Hitler, whom he claimed to have known, often came and spent a few days with me in Oxford, making no demands, and endlessly reading thrillers.

One night Dick (R. H. S.) Crossman dined with us, and told how he had got caught up in a riot in Munich in the early twenties, and had taken refuge in a public lavatory. 'I remember that day,' commented Leo. 'I was out hunting communists. I might have killed you.' I was so impressed by Leo's anti-Hitler proagpanda that I put him in touch with Dick Plummer,* who was then Beaverbrook's right-hand man and manager of *The Sunday Express*. My idea was that Leo should write some articles which would expose Hitler as the menace that he was. It was Dick whom I had earlier unsuccessfully encouraged to publish Fremantle's articles on South Africa. Leo's pieces read impressively, but they, too, were never published. I also introduced Leo to the Prof, who both on his own account and as Winston Churchill's confidant was greatly concerned by the lamentably slow reaction of Britain to the threat which Hitler posed. One of the two occasions on which I took Leo to dinner at Christ Church turned out to be a disaster. Another member of the High Table had invited as his guest the senior naval attaché of the German Embassy, and the 'froideur' between him and Leo could have been cut with a knife. I took it that the two knew and mistrusted each other, and Leo told me later that he would never have dined had he known that one of Hitler's naval captains was going to be there. As a result of the Prof's interest, Leo was then put in touch with the Foreign Office, but what happened as a result of that I do not know. Then the story of our friendship took a curious turn. A few weeks before war broke out, Leo disappeared from London, but Amethe stayed on. One day she telephoned to say that she was passing through Oxford and asked if she could bring the so-and-so's to lunch—mentioning the names of a couple who were closely associated with Mosley's Fascist party. She explained that they were harmless, that they wanted to meet me, and that it would be interesting for me to talk to them. We had a neutral lunch. The last time I saw her was in London about a week before war was declared, when she tried unsuccessfully to sell me a car which she no longer wanted as she intended returning to Austria.

In those days one almost made a habit of listening to Hitler's rantings over the radio, and on the night after war was declared I was in a room where a radio was tuned to a German broadcasting station. And there, coming over the ether, was Amethe's voice, making an impassioned plea, urging England not to get into the war, but to come to terms with Hitler instead. For years she and Leo had fooled us, although whether they were spies in the strict sense of the term I never did discover. Some years after the end of the war, I learnt that Leo had been killed fighting for Hitler, and that she was living in hardship in Vienna. Then came a letter from her asking whether I was going to attend some congress or other which was due to take place in Austria, and in it she said that she

---

* 'Dick', later Sir Leslie Plummer, became the head of the ill-fated ground-nut scheme launched by John Strachey when he was Minister of Food in Attlee's post-war government.

had seen both Desmond Bernal and John Strachey on several occasions. I still sometimes wonder whether the Foreign Office or any other authority knew the true purpose of the Zeppelins's stay in England. It was an enormous shock to realise that they had been deluding me all the time. What was even more astonishing was to read much later, in Hugh Thomas's life of John Strachey,[3] that in 1932 John had parted from Leo because his leanings towards the Nazis were already apparent. John knew that the Zeppelins were living in London in the years before the war. How then did Leo get away with whatever game it was that he was playing?

I had more friends in non-scientific than in scientific Oxford circles. But I got to know the younger members of the Zoology Department— Billy Moy-Thomas, John (J.Z.) Young and E. B. Ford—and found that they were always worth listening to. John and I carried out a joint piece of research. In the background, but younger than the others, was Peter Medawar, whom I had first met in 1932 at a dinner party that Tansley gave for me in Magdalen. It must have been Medawar's first term as an undergraduate, but he more than held his own with Schrödinger, the theoretical physicist/philosopher, and with Harry Weldon, Magdalen's senior philosophy tutor, who were among Tansley's guests.

Freddie Ayer was a particular friend in those days, but after the war our geographical separation made it difficult to meet. During the period in which he was writing his first book, *Language, Truth and Logic*,[4] he was often in Museum Road, pacing up and down my sitting room, twirling a silver chain as he declaimed his views. It was arranged that I should review the book for *The New Statesman*. But the last sentence of what I wrote did not please him. I had referred to the final paragraphs of his book, in which he had, in effect, declared that philosophers had no real job other than to examine scientific propositions, and that what they therefore had to do was to become familiar with science and help clarify the scientist's thinking. 'The field of real knowledge', I wrote, 'is not divided into philosophy and empirical science; it constitutes a single record of experience, bound together by the same discipline of verification and statement. The scientist can therefore only wish the empiricist philosopher all success in the task he has set himself of understanding science and of clarifying its concepts.'[5] It was more than just success that I should have wished Freddie. I should also have wished on him the interest and energy necessary to become familiar with even a small part of science, for I do not recall that he ever made much of an effort to abide by the precepts with which he concluded his book. Indeed, I find it difficult to believe that the growth, or the directions of growth, of the natural sciences have been much influenced over the past forty to fifty years by the deliberations of academic philosophers. Nor can I see where these have affected those practical applications of science which have so transformed the social, economic and political environment of our times.

Another friend was the young Isaiah Berlin, whom I first met on an evening when I had been invited to dine at All Souls. He, Freddie and I were much in demand, and on one occasion when Isaiah and I were walking home after a dinner party, he remarked, 'I can just hear them saying now, "those two were very bright and amusing, but where did they come from?" ' Isaiah, I remember, used to feel uncomfortable in the presence of the Prof. I never did understand why.

There was also my life in London, where I had rented a small and cheap flat near Paddington Station. There were meetings of scientific societies where I read papers. Occasionally I gave more general talks. There was one eccentric occasion, the only one of its kind that I remember, when I substituted for Julian Huxley at a drawing room meeting of 'The Babies' Club' in Enid Bagnold's house, and spoke on 'the maternal instinct' to an audience in evening dress, with the Austrian Ambassador in the chair. There were also frequent weekends away, at Ashby St. Ledgers near Rugby with the Wimbornes (Lord Wimborne was one of the last viceroys of Ireland), where the talk was sometimes about politics, but usually about music, since William Walton, who introduced me to them, was always there; at Colworth in Bedfordshire with Gwen and Henry Melchett (the second Lord Melchett), where one's fellow guests might include the Prof and H. G. Wells, and where conversation ranged over any and every topic; or at Buscot Park with Gavin Faringdon, whose purely social weekend parties became increasingly political as the Spanish Civil War dragged on, and where one's fellow guests included Labour Party figures such as Nye and Jennie Bevan, Ellen Wilkinson and Susan Lawrence. I forget how I met Gavin Faringdon, but my first meeting with Gwen Melchett stands out because it was the only occasion that I spoke to Chaim Weizmann, the Zionist leader. It was at a dinner party given by Sarah Gertrude Millin, my first novelist friend, whom I occasionally saw in London when she was over from South Africa.

And of course there were holidays on the continent—France and Italy frequently, a month in Austria with Henry and Gwen Melchett, and another with them on a yacht in the Adriatic. That month had a truly Ruritanian flavour. I joined Gwen and Henry in Venice where, after a few days mostly spent at parties, we embarked in the *Peau Brun*, an ancient boat of about 70 tons not quite a hundred feet long, which was skippered by a bearded Captain Towner and manned by a crew of about six sailors of different nationalities. Apart from the crew's quarters there was a saloon and four small cabins. I slept in the saloon. There was one primitive bathroom and one equally primitive 'loo' for the lot of us. We usually travelled under sail, and when there was no wind the stand-by engine as a rule failed to function. There was no difficulty about stopping to swim. And with royalty aboard—my fellow guests were Princess Aspasia of Greece and her young daughter Alexandra, later the Queen of Jugoslavia—it was a quasi-royal progress wherever we stopped; first at Brioni, where we visited Princess Helen, the divorced and exiled wife of King Carol of Rumania, and met her son, the young Crown-Prince Michael, then Split, Ragusa, Corfu and Athens. Princess Aspasia and I consumed a jugful of a potent cocktail every evening before dinner. Gwen had her own special brew, and Henry, who was recovering from a coronary thrombosis, remained cheerful on a more innocent concoction. Occasionally I would be deputed to take the wheel, and once I was bold enough to say that I would take the watch between midnight and 4 a.m. When the captain relieved me, he discovered that I was right off course. I had been told to steer towards the vast shadow of Mount Parnassus, and had slowly shifted towards another shadow. I was not allowed to forget the occasion. When Towner turned the wheel to get us back on course, he did so too sharply, and the whole boat all but came apart. When my royal fellow guests disembarked, I was given their cabin, which I then discovered was inhabited by a myriad of cockroaches. I had never heard the previous inhabitants complain—but I did.

My pre-war years in Oxford were also a period of intense and productive work. I did little formal lecturing, nor indeed was I an assiduous demonstrator in the dissecting room. But I met a number of keen undergraduates, and was fortunate in attracting several first-rate research students. I was not the first to discover that the easiest way to capture and then keep the interest of an undergraduate is to introduce him to one's own problems, and to reveal one's own doubts about particular aspects of accepted learning. It was in this way more than any other that in the end I gathered together a long line of brilliant scientists, several of whom continued to work with me, some for as many as twenty years.

I had returned from America still obsessed with the idea that there might be specific nervous pathways whereby impulses from the brain passed through the autonomic nervous system in order to control the release of the sex-hormones produced by the ovaries. When Le Gros and I came to Oxford, the Department of Anatomy was not equipped for experimental work, and Sir Charles Sherrington, who was still Professor of Physiology, allowed me to use his Department to complete the experiments which I had designed to prove whether my idea was right or wrong. But as I have said, the trail soon petered out. I reported the negative results of what had been a carefully contrived and extensive series of experiments in one short paper,[6] and for years used to look sadly at the rows of black loose-leafed notebooks that embodied the typed record of the abortive work I had done. Poor Mrs. Bundy, all that work for nothing.

As soon as I had fitted up a small operating theatre and a room for monkeys in the Anatomy Department, I returned to my other lines of research. The main one was the elucidation of the hormonal conditions which underlie the periodicity of the human reproductive cycle. This proved a successful line of enquiry, the steps of which it was not difficult to formulate logically and to pursue experimentally. The results of this work were written up in papers which I published in various scientific journals. I had been working on the problem before going to America, and had already stated the general hypothesis which my experiments were designed to test, and which in the event they upheld, as have all recent findings which bear on the problem.

A second line of work concerned the hormonal factors which might be responsible for enlargement of the human prostate. The fertilised egg in all vertebrate animals is potentially bi-sexual, that is to say, it can develop either in a male or a female direction, the course it takes being determined by the egg's genetic constitution. This applies as much to man as it does to rats. The point on which I focused was the presence in the prostate of a rudiment of the embryonic tissue from which the internal reproductive organs of the female are formed. Reports of earlier experiments in which male rats and mice had been injected with female sex-hormone had given me the idea that an imbalance in the production of hormone in the male, leading to the secretion of female hormone, could stimulate the vestigial female cells in the prostate and so make it enlarge.

I started to test this hypothesis by collaborating with Alan Parkes at the National Institute for Medical Research in London. We worked on monkeys, because the structure of their prostate is essentially the same as in man. But as soon as facilities became available, I transferred the work to Oxford, where by chance I discovered that dogs sometimes develop spontaneously the same form of enlarged prostate[7] that Dutch workers had shown could be induced experimentally by injecting them with female sex-hormone. But here it turned out that I was following a wrong trail or rather, that I was on the right trail but facing in the wrong direction. Because I was looking the wrong way, the inference I drew was that the treatment for benign enlargement of the prostate should be to inject male hormone to redress the imbalance. Dr. Charles Huggins of Chicago, who had also become interested in the dog prostate, took a different view of the signs which the Dutch work and my experiments [8, 9, 10] indicated, and suggested that the way to treat malignant enlargement of the prostate was to inject female sex-hormone. My eyes had been on the less serious condition of benign enlargement of the gland. In due course Dr. Huggins's work was rewarded by a Nobel prize, and his treatment, while it has not turned out to be quite the success it seemed at the start, is still in vogue.

But the work on the prostate led me into a far more intellectually stimulating field of research—the reaction of the tissues of the male to treatment with female sex-hormone, and of female tissue to male hormone. The experimental studies on which I had embarked were leading me to a general theory, the gist of which was that the variety of tissues which react to female sex-hormone are related embryologically. What was of more practical significance was that I was also being led to an understanding of the cause of what some authorities regarded as precancerous changes in the cervix of the uterus. The work had not been completed by the time war broke out, but I did manage to embody the story in a monograph which was published in 1940.[11] By then I was all but totally taken up in work on the effects of high explosive, and I doubt if many people ever read my final paper on the subject.

As my eye passes over the list of some ninety scientific papers and monographs which I published between 1934 and 1939, I note that I also did a fair amount of work on the influence which sex-hormones exercise on the retention of water in the tissues of the body, a phenomenon that was one of the starting points of my understanding of the 'monthly' sexual cycle of female monkeys and apes, and one of the several clues which led up to the now-established fact that in man and other Old-World primates (that is to say, the great apes and all monkeys other than those that are indigenous to the New World) ovulation usually occurs somewhere about the middle of the monthly cycle.

There was one monkey, a pig-tailed Macaque, which I kept more as a pet than as an experimental animal, and which helped me in this piece of research. 'Piggy', as all knew her, used to be let out of her cage to follow me round the animal room when I made my daily inspection of the other monkeys. At fairly regular intervals she was put under an anaesthetic, a procedure to which she was thoroughly accustomed, so that her ovaries could be examined. But one day a highly experienced hospital anaesthetist, one as renowned as any other in the country, asked me to let him put Piggy 'under' the next time she was due for ovarian inspection. I could hardly refuse, but Piggy never recovered from his treatment. That was one of a few experiences that taught me that medical men used to dealing with humans sometimes fail to appreciate the care which needs to be exercised in work on little animals. Experimental studies designed to advance our knowledge of the working of the body demand immense caution and skill. Months, even years of work, can be wiped out by a piece of carelessness, or by failure to appreciate that animal surgery needs to be at least as precise as the most meticulous human operation. I first learnt this lesson from the late Clifford Dobell, a great historian of science and in his time the world's leading expert on amoebic dysentery. He would not allow even a technician to handle or feed his monkeys. If any mistakes were going to be made, they were going to be his, and his alone.

By the time I resumed my researches in Oxford, it was well known that the reproductive cycle of rats and mice could be suppressed by injecting them with female sex-hormone. George Corner,[12] the American scholar, and I then found—independently and more or less simultaneously—that such treatment could suppress the menstrual cycle and ovulation in monkeys. As a chance observation made in the course of another of my studies, I then found that male sex-hormone can also do so. All this work on the suppression of ovulation provided part of the foundation of knowledge on which Gregory Pincus, in the 1950s, based the development of 'the pill'. It also opened up for me a new and exciting line of enquiry, on which I embarked after the war, into the processes whereby egg-cells are formed in the mammalian ovary.

In the 1930s few British Universities boasted Departments of Psychology, and fewer still Departments in which animal behaviour was studied experimentally. Cambridge was one of them, with an active and well-established Department of Experimental Psychology under the direction of Sir Frederic Bartlett. When I arrived in Oxford in 1934, the only professional psychologist there was a Dr. William Brown, a practising psychiatrist who enjoyed the title of Wilde Reader in Mental Philosophy. He was a member of the High Table of Christ Church, and once told me that if he could only have the opportunity of a two-hour talk with Hitler, he knew he could divert him from his mad course of destruction.

Having written a book on the social behaviour of monkeys and apes, and having spent some time in one of the many American laboratories which devoted themselves to the experimental study of behaviour, it was not surprising that I found that I was expected to continue to cultivate this other interest of mine. In those days there was less regimentation than now, and the authorities placed no obstacle in the path of a small group of interested undergraduates who wanted me to take the lead in creating the beginnings of a school of animal behaviour in Oxford. After we had got started, we were invited by some members of Bartlett's Department in Cambridge to tell them about our programme of work, and to hear about theirs. This was followed by a return visit. We were being treated seriously.

I had a particular interest in one piece of behavioural research on which I set two of my B.Sc. students. Its purpose was to discover whether monkeys are capable of making abstractions, such as number concepts, in the way we do. This interest derived from my excursions into the vast anecdotal literature which purports to show that animals can count and reason. One of the myths of my youth was that the way to deal with marauding baboons was for five men to enter an orchard, and for four to leave. The theory was that baboons could not count beyond four, and would therefore 'think' that all the men had gone, and that they would run no risk if they now entered the orchard. Instead they were slaughtered by the man who had remained behind.

With the help of two students—J. W. B. Douglas, who continued to work with me during the war, and who has since published several books on the educational capacity of children, and C. M. Whitty, now a consultant neurologist—I designed a set of experiments which I hoped would show in a definitive way whether monkeys can be trained to make the abstractions necessary to differentiate between the qualities of 'oneness', or 'twoness', or 'threeness', as opposed simply to discriminating between, say, one and two, or two and three apples. These experiments were carried out on monkeys in Oxford and on a tame chimpanzee in the London Zoo. Although other workers have since claimed that monkeys are capable of number 'abstractions', the results of our experiments were precisely the reverse. I have always believed that the ability to make verbal or numerical abstractions is among the significant characteristics which critically differentiate the human from the animal mind.

In order to satisfy myself about the design of the experiment, I first spent a weekend with Bertrand Russell at Telegraph House in Sussex. I wanted to make sure that the author of the *Introduction to Mathematical Philosophy* would be satisfied that if the results came out one way, the answer would be 'yes', and if the other, 'no'. Russell was then between marriages, his second wife, Dora Black, having left him. 'Peter' Spence, whom he was to marry next, was the only other person there that weekend. Much of the time was spent listening to Bertie reading from some work on comparative religion, but we also discussed the concept of number in the framework of animal intelligence, and I left satisfied that our experimental design was on the right lines.

I learnt something else that weekend. I had often been told that in spite of the vast amount he published, Russell's first draft was normally the definitive one for the printer. This always amazed me. Like many other people I usually wrote draft after draft, on occasions as many as twenty, before I allowed what I had written to see the light of day. I was sitting in a low armchair when my eye lighted on a pile of script at my side, which I took to be the manuscript of a book or of a long article. There were no corrections on the top page, and idly turning over some others I noticed that they too were practically free of corrections. Interrupting whatever he was saying, I remarked, 'It's true, then, Bertie. Your first draft is always your last. I can't write like that.' His reply was immediate. 'I spend time thinking about what I want to say before I put pen to paper. You clearly waste both time and paper finding out what it is that you think.' He was quite right, but I never have been able to change my habit. I did not know Russell well, but I was always fascinated by his conversation. Some time after my weekend with him, he came to Oxford for a year as a Fellow of All Souls, and I believe that it was in my rooms that Freddie Ayer, who has written so much about him, first met him.

Not long after starting my small unofficial Oxford school of animal behaviour, I got the idea that, in order to stimulate a wider interest in the subject, what we needed in the United Kingdom was a national society or institute for the study of the subject. There was no lack of support and an Institute for that purpose formally came into being early in 1936, with Julian Huxley as President, and James Fisher, the ornithologist, as Secretary. Although my main research interest was then in the hormonal basis of reproductive processes, I undertook to edit a *Bulletin of Animal Behaviour*, the first slender number of which came out in October 1938. It was printed by a minute press within a hundred yards of my Museum Road house. Three more issues appeared between then and the end of the war, with most of the letterpress provided by three of my students. After the war the Institute became the Association for the Study of Animal Behaviour, and in 1953 the *Bulletin* changed its name to the *British Journal of Animal Behaviour*. A few years later, this was shortened to *Animal Behaviour*, which today is a flourishing journal. Its present size certainly belies its slender beginnings.

Another scientific publication in whose birth I played a part in those pre-war Oxford days was the *Journal of Endocrinology*, today an equally, if not a more thriving publication. My selfish reason for wanting to launch it was that the work I was doing, together with what I was directing, was proving so fruitful that it was difficult to get the results published fast enough. Life with Le Gros Clark had its ups-and-downs, and since he was then Editor of the *Journal of Anatomy*, I had to submit to him those papers which I wanted published in that Journal or, as he was already a Fellow of the Royal Society and I was not, such papers as I wanted to appear in the *Proceedings of the Royal Society*. At times he encouraged and lauded my activities; at others, he tried to damp them down. Le Gros was a mixed-up character, and although he writes in his autobiography[13] that I was a considerable help to him in the reorganisation and replanning of the Oxford Department of Anatomy, and while he says other nice things about me, the fact is that my apparently endless energy and numerous activities aggravated the moods of depression to which he was subject. The parting of our ways at the end of the war belongs to another story. But long before then he had written to suggest that the solution to my publishing difficulties was to publish less. Rather than accept this advice, I therefore decided to see whether it would be possible to found a journal dedicated to what was then my main field of research—reproductive physiology and hormones.

In June 1937 most of the small group of U.K. scientists who shared this interest were invited by Professor Courrier of the Collège de France in Paris to take part in one of the first international seminars to be held on the sex-hormones. It was in the bus on our way to Croydon airport that I first raised the matter and became assured of the necessary support. But the task did not prove as easy as had the founding of the *Bulletin of Animal Behaviour*. This time we were talking about a full-sized scientific journal, which meant that finance had to be guaranteed before a publishing house could be expected to be interested. More than that, it could not be assumed that established British journals, such as the Journals of *Anatomy, Physiology* and *Biochemistry*, would welcome competition which might drain contributions from them. I therefore had to write to the editors of fourteen leading journals to allay possible suspicions. Only two wrote regretting our proposed project, and one of them, a brilliant man whom I knew well, made the strange observation that he saw no point in what we proposed doing since there were no more than six research workers in the country who were interested in research on hormones. His estimate was almost certainly wrong at the time, and it is a measure of the rate of growth of science that today there are hundreds, if not thousands of British 'endocrinologists'. We also had to face the problem that scientific journals were usually the organs of publication of properly constituted scientific societies, which we certainly were not. The solution was for ten of us to guarantee the financial backing that the venture would need. This done, Tansley then helped me arrange matters with the Oxford University Press, which became the publisher of the *Journal*.

The first issue appeared under the editorship of Charles Dodds in 1939. Not surprisingly, the *Journal* was only able to limp along during its first five years, and for the first two or three after the war we were in serious financial difficulties. In 1948, after I had moved from Oxford to the Birmingham Chair of Anatomy, I took over as Editor, and for some time my problem was to beat off takeover bids from publishing houses— among them Pergamon Press and the British Medical Association— which had begun to realise that scientific journals were bound to become profitable undertakings. Another problem which was with me all the time was the small number of scientific papers which were being submitted for publication in the *Journal*. Unless one could assure authors that their papers would be published without delay, which is what most scientists want because of their wish to establish priority over discoveries, real or unreal, there was no reason why anyone should choose the

Journal of Endocrinology rather than a better-established journal. Consequently I always had to have an adequate number of typescripts ready to assure a steady rate of publication. This meant building up a head of pressure. There were many times when I had to lash my colleagues and students in Birmingham, as well as friends in other universities, to write up work and to send in texts. The policy worked. The *Journal* is now a highly profitable possession of the Society for Endocrinology. I ceased being Editor in 1956.

It was the Munich Agreement of September 1938 that first pulled me out of my academic backwater—not the actual occasion itself, but a chance remark made a day or two later by someone in the Christ Church Common Room to the effect that there was bound to be war, and that there were no plans to use either the Universities or scientists in the necessary preparatory period. I immediately thought of Bernal, and next afternoon went to London to see him. He was not at home, so I waited until he returned from a meeting of Lord Robert Cecil's Peace Campaign. It was late when he came in, and before dashing to Paddington to catch the midnight train back to Oxford, I just had time to urge him to devote as much of his energies to help prepare for war as he was giving to the search for peace. Bernal was a member of the Cambridge Scientists Anti-War Group, a group which never missed an opportunity to criticise the Government for the inadequacies of its measures for civil defence. I also knew that he was in touch with several people who had gained some first-hand experience of fighting in the Spanish Civil War. He agreed to my suggestion, and in the next few days we met several times to discuss and to prepare a memorandum on 'Science and National Defence'. This I undertook to get into the hands of Leslie Hore-Belisha, then the Secretary of State for War, whom I had first met at the Wimbornes.

Before I could do this, Bernal had set out the general lines of our document in an editorial which was published anonymously in *Nature*,[14] about two weeks after the signing of the Munich Agreement. Unknown to me, he had also asked Basil Liddell Hart for his opinion of our draft document. Hart refers to this in the second volume of his *Memoirs*[15] in which I read with surprise that the document had been drafted not just by Des and me, but also in collaboration with Julian Huxley. This was the first time I knew that Julian had had anything to do with our memorandum. Liddell Hart was on the whole encouraging, but he did not suggest any practical steps which we might take. Later I took Des to a small dinner party at Hore-Belisha's home in Stafford Place. While interested, Hore-Belisha's comment was that the implementation of some of the memorandum's recommendations would require him to have authority over several Departments of State. But, as he went on to say— correctly as events after the outbreak of war were to prove—'I don't feel

I've got authority over my *own* Department'. Nothing specific emerged, therefore, from this initiative of ours.

In the light of what was to happen, the memorandum is not without interest. In the opening paragraph we said that it was 'of the utmost importance that the special character of scientific work in the service of national defence should be realised, and that the proper steps should be taken in time to see that the work of scientists is not wasted. Scientific workers have, in relation to national service, two special qualifications. In the first place, they are expert in the use of essential instruments and methods which are acquired only after long training, and it would be impossible under war conditions to replace them. But this is the least important of their potentialities. They also have a special training in the ability to deal with new or unexpected developments and to suggest new possibilities of action.'

We then went on to consider the need for scientific research under the following six headings: Maintenance of civil and military life; maintenance and extension of war production; defence against aerial attack; carrying out of military operations; caring for casualties; and maintenance of morale. In retrospect I find it interesting that what the memorandum did not consider was the use of scientists in the analysis and planning of actual operations, an omission to which Liddell Hart in fact drew attention, and which in the end was to be my main preoccupation.

A by-election in Oxford in which Quintin Hogg, the official Conservative candidate, opposed Dr. Lindsay, the Master of Balliol, who was campaigning on an anti-Chamberlain ticket, brought some immediate and local heat to the Oxford scene. One evening I found myself dining at *The George* with Randolph Churchill, whom I had first met with the Melchetts. He had come up to see how the fight was going, and after we left the restaurant, he suggested we went along to one of Quintin Hogg's meetings. We did so, but it was not long after Randolph began heckling from the back of the hall, standing with his thumbs stuck in the armholes of his waistcoat, that we were edged into the street by stewards. We then thought we could call on Maurice Bowra, the Warden of Wadham, but he sent a message to us at his front door saying that he had no wish to see us. So we repaired to my house in Museum Road and had not been there long before Frank and Elizabeth Pakenham, two of Lindsay's staunch supporters, dropped in. Randolph decided to telephone his father to report on the election. I can still see him holding the telephone out to us while the voice of Winston boomed out, saying that this was a turning point in history and that it was vital that Lindsay should win. He lost. The telephone call seemed to go on endlessly, and I became worried as I thought of what the trunk-call might cost.

Civil defence now became a hot issue in Oxford as well as in Cambridge. Some time in the early summer of 1939, Sir Arthur Salter, a Fellow of All Souls, who then sat as a Member of Parliament for Oxford University, and whose experience of Whitehall was considerable, arranged a luncheon party to discuss what should be done. One of his guests was Sir John Anderson who, as Lord Privy Seal, had the responsibility for introducing measures for civil defence, and who it was known would become Minister for Home Security on the outbreak of war. Salter asked me to bring along Bernal, by then thoroughly well-known as a critic of the Government's policies. On his return to London, Sir John gave an account of the discussion to Dr. Reginald Stradling, the Director of the Building Research Station, who had just been appointed his Chief Scientific Adviser. A couple of years later Stradling told me that all he knew of Bernal at the time was that he was one of the Cambridge scientists who were regarded as 'reds', and that he had warned Sir John Anderson to that effect. Sir John's view was that if he could help, Bernal had to be brought in as an additional adviser on civil defence 'even if he were as red as the flames of hell'. Stradling then arranged a time to meet Bernal, and when he entered his office at the appointed hour, he found Bernal already there, reading some of his, Stradling's, papers.

I was staying with the Wimbornes at Ashby St. Ledgers on the Sunday we went to war. William Walton had been there for some weeks putting the finishing touches to his violin concerto. But that particular weekend he was doing no writing. We were all somewhat aimless and anxious as we speculated about what was likely to happen. I had something else on my mind, too, but kept it to myself. After we had listened to Neville Chamberlain's broadcast of the declaration of war, I decided to return to Oxford immediately after lunch. William was staying on, but another guest dropped me off at Oxford on her way back to London.

The other thing that I had on my mind was my marriage to Joan Rufus Isaacs—who, as the daughter of the 2nd Marquis of Reading, had the courtesy title of Lady Joan. We had met some two years before, when her brother Michael, then Lord Erleigh, who was in his last year at Balliol, had invited me to help make up a party for a 'Commem Ball' at Balliol, partnering his mother, Eva Reading. At his suggestion, I had invited them all to dinner beforehand. All I remember of the meal is its atmosphere of gloom. Michael's partner did not turn up; the undergraduate whom he had invited to partner Joan had failed his examination that day, and by one of those coincidences which should never happen, I had been his examiner; and Joan was mostly silent and hostile. Only her mother prattled away, and she and I went on dancing long after her offspring had gone to bed. Eva told me years later that she had gained the impression that evening that my house, and presumably my income, were much larger than in the end she discovered they were.

Joan was very young when we met, and the idea that we should ever marry would have seemed highly improbable both to her friends and to mine. But neither her mother nor her uncle, Henry Melchett, whom I had told of my second meeting with his attractive niece, at a London theatre, thought it in the least improbable. Joan had had a conventional up-bringing, including spells at finishing schools in Paris and Rome, and a coming-out season as a debutante. But that was not really her world. She had set her sights on becoming an artist—an ambition which happily she has achieved—and when we met she was training at an art school and also working alone in a borrowed studio. She had also become a volun-tary worker in an organisation which was helping to resettle refugee children from Hitler's Germany, and had joined the H.Q. of the W.V.S. (The Women's Voluntary Service), the organisation which her step-grandmother, Stella Reading, had been charged to set up by Neville Chamberlain in anticipation of war. Stella was the widow of the Rufus Isaacs whose public career had culminated in his appointments, first as Viceroy of India, and then for a short time as Foreign Secretary in Ramsay Macdonald's National Government of 1931–1935. Joan was never meant for a purely formal social life. Nevertheless, the disparity in our ages, in our backgrounds, and in the lives we were leading, gave us good cause to hesitate. As a spoilt bachelor in his early thirties, I had evolved a pleasant way of life which I was fearful of having disrupted. Joan, too, had her fears, fears of an unknown academic world to which she felt she might not measure up, and a husband who, to her, was fan-tastically obsessed by his own work. Her father tried hard to convince her that she was not cut out to be the wife of an Oxford don, in an environment where women were still regarded as second-class citizens. But Joan's mother, Henry and Gwen Melchett (who had by now known me well for some years), and Stella Reading, kept urging us on. But I still hesitated, and it was mainly the declaration of war, which immedi-ately made travel and telephone calls difficult, that in the end—on an occasion when I had gone to stay at her parents' home in Sussex—decided us to take the plunge.

Joan's father was not at all pleased at the prospect of having me as a son-in-law. When I saw him formally in London, I found him unbending and austere, a disciplined teetotaller into whose world dons with catholic tastes seldom strayed. Indeed, it was only after 1957, when he ceased to be a Minister of State in the Foreign Office,* that we got on to easy,

* Lord Reading was replaced when Harold Macmillan took over from Anthony Eden as Prime Minister after the Suez affair, about which Gerald Reading later assured me that he had known nothing in spite of his lofty position.

friendly terms. He was angry when I said that I saw no reason to put an announcement of the marriage in the papers, and asked, somewhat scathingly, whether I was ashamed that it should be known that I was about to marry his daughter. Here he had his way. But whatever the nature of his misgivings, time has shown that he need not have worried.

Back in Oxford, I was awakened a morning or two before our wedding by the telephone at the side of my bed. It was the Prof. 'Solly,' he asked, 'is it true what I read in *The Times*; that you are marrying Gerald's daughter? How could you have kept this from me?' It had been only too easy. Until a few days before I went to London to be married, I had not even told my housekeeper. Joan likes to embroider the story by saying that I was so fearful of losing my wonderful Mrs. Boyd that on the way back to Museum Road on our wedding day I stopped at a jeweller's to buy her a present. Elizabeth and her husband, who had a job as messenger to an Oxford tailor, remained with us for only a few months, but they were stormy months. Happily for us, they returned after a few years. I learnt that housekeepers are prone to behave like this when their bachelor charges marry. With war declared and no idea about what was going to happen, we could not get away for a honeymoon, but some months later we did manage to spend a few days in North Wales with Clough and Amabel Williams-Ellis at Brondanw, the house whose destruction by fire years later Clough has described so sadly in his *Architect Errant*.[16] Before this, Sidney Bernstein had thrown a magnificent party to introduce Joan to some of our mutual friends, among them many leading theatrical figures and writers. He had arranged for a well-known jazz pianist to play, and in so doing had jeopardised his tenancy of a large and elegant apartment in Albany. He just smiled when the proceedings were interrupted by a telephone call from the manager telling him that he was breaking a clause of his lease which forbad music late at night. The party went on and so did the loud jazz player.

Marriage at that time also put an end to my exchanges with Birmingham University about becoming head of its Department of Anatomy. The invitation to offer myself for the post was made to me in October 1938, and in spite of my reluctance to put in a formal application before I had been assured that the University could provide me with the facilities I needed for my work, I was invited to present myself at a meeting of the Faculty Board of Medicine. There were two other candidates who had been short-listed for the post, and one of them was already the holder of a chair of Anatomy in another University. I was the last to be interviewed, and was then told that the Board was going to recommend to the Council of the University that I should be elected to the vacant chair.

I was taken aback. It was all too sudden, but in a few words I managed to indicate that while I appreciated the honour, I wanted to know whether what was a magnificent new Department (Birmingham had just opened its new Medical School) so far as accommodation was concerned, was going to be equipped for the kind of work I was doing. I was only 34, my researches were all-demanding, and in all truth I neither had the wish to leave Oxford nor to take on the administrative and teaching responsibilities which would fall to the head of a big University Department.

On the train back to Oxford, I became more and more miserable, and on the following day composed a letter to the Birmingham authorities in which I explained my hesitations. After two months of further exchanges by letter, I was informed that the Council proposed appointing me, and that it had agreed to provide the Department with some additional resources. I replied politely, but indicated that what they were proposing would not go far enough. Letters continued to flow until war broke out, by which time the Birmingham people had, not surprisingly, all but lost patience with me. Finally, some two months after war was declared, it was agreed that the University would regard me as its 'titular' Professor of Anatomy, and that I would take up my duties when hostilities ceased.

Joan came with me to Birmingham for the final discussion. The University was then far smaller than it is now—I doubt if it had more than about a thousand full-time students—and its predominantly lay Council saw in it one of the reasons for the civic pride for which the City was renowned. Almost all the Council members, plus wives, turned out to entertain us to lunch, and Joan, aged 21, sat on the right of the Vice-Chancellor, Dr. Raymond Priestley. It was her first experience of a company of university dignitaries, and all she knew was that I had no intention then of moving to Birmingham. Her memory of the occasion has always amused me. Priestley was a geologist who had been a member of both Scott's and Shackleton's expeditions to the South Pole, and he always spoke in a fascinating way about the Antarctic. But Joan, who was trying to make polite and intelligent conversation, did not have more than the vaguest idea where the Antarctic was, at the same time as she was bewildered by what she described to me afterwards as 'all those elderly ladies with fur tippets'. Her day was capped when, on our return to Oxford, we went to dine at *The George*, and Freddie Ayer and Isaiah Berlin came to our table. It was the first time she had met them, for she claims that until we married I resolutely refused to introduce her to any of my friends. She found their conversation every bit as bewildering as she had her day in Birmingham. As she put it, 'I've never met people like that before. They might have come from another planet.' Well, if they did, they also soon became her friends, as they were mine. Oxford was certainly a very different place from a debutante's London.

Seven years were to pass before I ceased being Birmingham's titular Professor, and assumed the duties of the office. The University authorities were very patient; but then, there was a war to be fought.

CHAPTER 6

BOMBS IN THE LABORATORY

FROM THE time of the Munich crisis in 1938, there had been all manner of talk about how scientists were going to be put on some kind of register,[1] and that given a war, all we would have to do was wait until told what our battle-stations were. Nothing happened. But I was more than occupied, introducing Joan to friends, and keeping my peace with Elizabeth, who was not the least bit reassured when I told her that Joan, who had arrived with only a minimum of personal possessions—apart from her clothes, a bicycle and a painting by John Tunnard—would not interfere with the running of our small house. For reasons which I found difficult to explain, and which I regretted afterwards, I had made it known that we did not want any wedding presents.

Like many others, I helped to fill sandbags and to stack them around the laboratories, and one day I also acted as a medical officer to examine potential recruits. A don of Worcester College, Wilkinson by name, a cheery extrovert who was prominent in the affairs of the Officers' Training Corps, asked me to put some undergraduates through their medicals before they joined up. When I told him that I had never practised medicine, his reply was: 'I know that. But you have a medical degree, and surely you have a stethoscope?' My answer was 'yes' to the first question, but 'no' to the second. 'Buy a stethoscope and just lay it on the table in front of you. That'll impress them', was the reply. 'See that they all get through, unless they've got flat feet.' I wonder what happened to all those undergraduates whom I passed as fit for military service that afternoon in Christ Church.

In the prevailing atmosphere of uncertainty, there was nothing to do but to carry on working in the laboratory. I had to finish the monograph on the histogenesis of the tissues which react by cell division when stimulated by the female oestrogenic sex-hormone. There were others I had to finish. My list of publications shows that fifteen of my scientific papers appeared in 1939, and four more in 1940, including the monograph to which I have referred. Among them was a long paper on the anatomy of intersexuality,[2] which I then also regarded as a significant contribution to knowledge. But it was my histogenesis monograph which I considered to be the most important embodiment of my scientific ideas of that period.

Obviously the war overshadowed everything else. Like some of my friends, I firmly believed that our elders and betters, those who today would be called the scientific establishment, were not as enterprising as they could have been in mobilising the country's scientific resources in the fight against Hitler's Germany. Indeed, rightly or wrongly, we did not believe that they had much idea of the vast potential that lay in the scientific approach, or in the applications of scientific knowledge, when dealing with the complicated problems of war. We had to have a platform from which we could proclaim our views. To this end, we decided to resurrect the Tots and Quots which I had started in 1930. The club had been dormant for a few years, but several of its members were still around. The enthusiastic way in which we resumed our meetings was at least partly due to an exaggerated view some of us may have had of the value of the discussions that marked the first phase of the club's existence (of which an account, together with the club's later history, is given in Appendix 1), and out of which had emerged a strong theme of the social responsibility of scientists. Reviving the club took a certain amount of doing. We were, of course, not the only scientists who had become concerned with the threat of war. The then Association of Scientific Workers had also decided to busy itself with a 'scientific register'. What became of this initiative I do not know, since after the Munich crisis the Association was divided in its views about what it should do. The British Association for the Advancement of Science was more definite, and shortly after its summer meeting of 1938, it established, under Sir Richard Gregory, the Editor of *Nature*, a Division for the Social and International Relations of Science. Among the members of the committee of this Division were several leaders of the then scientific establishment. But there were also eight of us from the old Tots and Quots. The committee met intermittently, but its meetings were somewhat formal, and it became too concerned for my liking with vague issues such as drafting a 'Charter for Scientific Fellowship', and general statements about 'Science and World Order'. Not long after the committee started, I gave up attending its meetings, and its papers seem to have petered out in 1943. At one point the Secretary of the Association had asked me to see if Lord Samuel could be encouraged to attend a meeting of the Division, and also to see if the Prof could arrange for the Prime Minister, Winston Churchill, to attend the same meeting. There is no record that I did either of these things, and I doubt if Churchill attended a meeting of the British Association during the war, if indeed ever.

The first dinner of the second phase of the Tots and Quots took place on 23 November 1939. By then the membership had been shuffled a bit and become less formal. Apart from some of the old members who attended, including Roy Harrod, Bernal and Haldane, there were a few

new ones, among them R. H. S. Crossman and Harry Lucas, a friend
who had given up his city interests and joined the Ministry of Economic
Warfare. Harry had started his career as a naval cadet, but ill-health had
put an end to that. He was a wealthy man and had helped launch Sieg-
mund Warburg on the London career that culminated in the City bank
that now bears his name. William Penney, then a young lecturer in
mathematics at Imperial College, of which he became Rector in 1967,
is listed as a guest. At that time none of us could have even imagined
the events which later made him a key figure in the development of 'the
bomb', and in due course the Chairman of the British Atomic Energy
Authority. Hugh Gaitskell, then a temporary civil servant in the Ministry
of Economic Warfare, wrote to say that he was kept at work till
8 o'clock every evening, and that he found himself too weary for dinners.
Dick Lythgoe, the other founder member, had died not long before
from a mysterious infection started by a bite from a pet squirrel.

The theme of our first discussion was 'The disorganisation of science',
and its keynote was the belief that scientists who wanted to help in the
war effort were being regarded by the scientific establishment as meddle-
some troublemakers. The leaders of science 'felt it their duty not to
disturb the equanimity of the politicians and civil servants who were
running the war'. Not only that, scientists who wished to take up war
research had to face the opposition created by the vested interests of
second-rate people in the Service departments. It must have been little
consolation for the rest of us to hear Roy Harrod say that none of this
was unique to the scientific world; economists were no better off.

But those were early days, and in retrospect it is remarkable how
rapidly the country's academic talent was in fact mobilised. The members
of the club had been discussing matters between themselves for months
before that first war-time dinner, and I suppose the majority of us had
become immersed in war work of one sort or another. Nonetheless, the
club decided to carry on with its crusade.

In February 1940, with a representative of the French Embassy
present, we discussed Anglo-French scientific collaboration and decided
on a plan of action which eventually led to the formation of an Anglo-
French Society of Sciences. Preliminary discussions were held in Paris
early in April between some members of the Tots and Quots—in particular Crowther—and leading French scientists, many of whom Bernal
and I met again later that month during the course of a visit we made to
France on behalf of the Ministry of Home Security. Crowther, one of our
members, and a historian of science as well as a scientific journalist, has
published a record of the negotiations he carried out,[3] and by the time
the club dined in June, the French had formed a provisional executive
committee, and we were trying to set up one of our own. Our idea had

been that Sir Charles Darwin should be the chairman, but he had to cry off from the dinner at the last moment. In order to give Darwin, who was a grandson of *the* Charles Darwin, and then the Director of the National Physical Laboratory, an idea of what we had in mind, Crowther had prepared an imaginary history of an Anglo-French society of scientists which, if it had been founded in 1936, would have been able to spring into rapid action when the war started.

However, this meeting was notable for producing what was undoubtedly the crowning practical achievement of this phase of our club's activities. This was the anonymous publication of a small paperback which appeared in July 1940 under the title *Science in War*.[4] Allen Lane, the publisher of Penguin Books, was a guest at the meeting. When we had finished talking about Anglo-French cooperation, we resumed the discussion of the proper use of scientists in the war effort. The point was again made that the first thing we had to do was to devise sensible propaganda directed not only at the scientific community, but also at the general public. Kenneth Clark,* another guest, who was then at the Ministry of Information, observed that since it was part of the Government, his Ministry could not assist in publicising any possible defects in the governmental administration of science. Blackett also advised caution, reminding us that scientists could not help in the immediate problems of war production. The club nonetheless re-emphasised its determination to press on with its crusade, and began to discuss the drafting of parliamentary questions and of articles for the press. At about midnight, Allen Lane remarked that it was a pity that no-one had made a verbatim record of the discussion since it would have made an excellent 'Penguin Special' as it stood. I immediately asked if he would undertake to produce a book in a fortnight if I could get a type-script to him in the same space of time. He agreed, although to this day I do not know whether he took my suggestion seriously at the time. Each of us kept his word.

We were extremely busy in the following two weeks. Bernal and I got together and drafted an outline of a book, telephoning our colleagues to seek their agreement. Then came the business of arranging who was to write what. I did most of this work, helped by Bernal and Crowther. Snippets came in from various people, and then came the job of editing and filling in, the brunt of which became my responsibility. A mass of paper survives, but I find it difficult to work out who contributed exactly what to the substance of the eight chapters that made up the small 150-page book. Among those who certainly contributed were C. D. Darlington, then Director of the John Innes Horticultural Institute and later Sherardian Professor of Botany in Oxford; E. J. (Bobby)

* Now Lord Clark O.M.

Carter, Librarian-Editor of the Royal Institute of British Architects and
later head of the Library Division of U.N.E.S.C.O.; L. F. Urwick, a
pioneer of scientific industrial management, and the author of many
books on that subject; Hugh Sinclair, the Oxford specialist on nutritional matters; William Slater, who was soon to be appointed one of the
Ministry of Agriculture's main scientific advisers, and who was Secretary
of the Agricultural Research Council from 1949 to 1960; Frank Yates,
the statistician; J. Z. Young; C. H. Waddington (who was then at the
Strangeways Laboratory in Cambridge, and who later became Professor
of Animal Genetics at Edinburgh); Louis Rapkine, a French biochemist
who had come to England on a scientific liaison job; and Hugh Cott, a
Cambridge zoologist who was an authority on animal coloration and
eamouflage. I did not move from London for the second of the two
weeks. Sunday, the 23rd of June was the deadline we had set ourselves, and
that day a few of us gathered in Jimmy Crowther's flat in Russell Square
for the final dotting of i's and crossing of t's. Miss Eunice Frost, Allen
Lane's special assistant, was on hand to prepare the typescript for the
printers. The story of the impact which the book had is told in Appendix 1.

Throughout the preceding weeks the news from France had been
worsening. There had been the tragedy of Dunkirk at the beginning of
the month. On Saturday, the 22nd of June, Petain signed Hitler's armistice terms. Some time during the course of our deadline day, we got a
telephone message saying that a group of our French scientist friends
had managed to escape, with the help of Lord Suffolk—a colourful
young man who had got himself appointed scientific liaison officer between our Ministry of Supply and the French Ministry of Armaments,
and who in England a year later blew himself and his blonde secretary up
when trying to defuse an unexploded German bomb of novel design.
They were carrying with them what was then the world's stock of heavy
water. We were told that among them were Laugier and Longchambon,
the two Directors of France's newly formed Centre National de la
Recherche Scientifique,[5] and that the whole party was under house-
arrest at the Great Western Hotel near Paddington Station. One of us
arranged that they should be excused for the evening and brought to us,
and just as we were putting the finishing touches to our text, Laugier and
Longchambon, together with the physicists Hans Halban and Kowarski,
walked in.[6] Halban and Kowarski were soon to become immersed in the
British project to develop an atomic bomb.

We started considering what could be done, because we all thought—
and this included John Cockcroft* who had now joined us—that it was

* Sir John Cockcroft O.M. He was a key figure in the development of radar, and
after the war became Director of Harwell and a member of the Atomic Energy
Authority. In 1952 he succeeded Tizard as Chairman of the Defence Research Policy
Committee, a post he held for two years. Later he became the first Master of Churchill College, Cambridge.

outrageous that our French colleagues were being treated as suspicious aliens instead of being welcomed with open arms. The obvious solution was to get the Prof to intervene. I was put down at the telephone, and first tried to get him at Christ Church, and then at 10 Downing Street. Failing to find him, I next tried to contact Herbert Morrison, then the Minister of Supply. Towards midnight I tracked him down to the small hotel where he spent the night when in London. He undertook to deal with the matter first thing in the morning. Exactly what he did, I do not know, but early the next day I received a telephone call from one of his senior scientists, only to be rapped on the knuckles for having interfered.

From the start of the war, Desmond Bernal had been formally attached to the new Research and Experiments Department of the Ministry of Home Security. The Department's headquarters were at the Forest Products Research Laboratory at Princes Risborough, about twenty miles from Oxford. During those first weeks, he drove over frequently to tell me what he was up to, but most of what he had to report related to the physics of explosions and to the resistance of structures to various types of shock, none of which I found easy to understand. One day he asked me to meet him at Princes Risborough. He had suggested to Dr. Reginald Stradling, the Director of the Department, that I could help to find out whether there was any risk that people in underground shelters might suffer from concussion as a result of shock-waves which passed through the earth when a bomb exploded nearby. That was the beginning of my active involvement in war work.

There was nothing remarkable about the experiment which I suggested might help answer the question. All that was necessary was to devise the harness and fixings with which to restrain some monkeys against a wall of a concrete-lined shelter, and to detonate a bomb which was buried in the ground nearby. The experiment was carried out on Salisbury Plain on 15 October 1939, as one of a series of tests of the effect of 'ground shock' on different designs of trench. A number of 'experts' were there, including the Home Office Inspector of Explosions. I had taken with me a technician and, as photographer, Peter Krohn, one of my old students. Desmond was already there, and since there was no restriction on travel in those days, Joan came along for the ride. About two minutes after the explosion, Des and I were in the trench. The wall closest to the bomb had been fractured, but none of the monkeys seemed at all affected. Against the advice of the Inspector, Des and I then sat in another trench while a second bomb was fired. I do not think we were as close as the monkeys had been, but to the surprise of the others who were stationed much further away, neither of us was aware that a second bomb had been exploded before anxious faces peered in to see if we were safe. In those days no-one seemed to know anything about the precise effects of bombs.

The result of this experiment was written up in a paper[7] for the Civil
Defence Research Committee (the C.D.R.C.), a body that had been set
up a few months before the outbreak of war by Sir John Anderson, by
now the Minister of Home Security. I was not present at the meeting in
January 1940 at which the paper was discussed. Stradling had circulated
it to various individuals and bodies, including the Government's Medical
Research Council (M.R.C.), which at the time did not seem at all keen
that freelance experimenters should enter into fields of enquiry which
it regarded as its own domain. The understanding of the M.R.C. was
that if a government department or any of the armed services wanted to
know about the effects of explosions on people, the M.R.C. was the
official agency to provide the information. That was certainly the view
of Sir Edward Mellanby, the M.R.C.'s powerful secretary. Indeed,
Professor Greenwood, who was the Council's chief expert on statistics,
took it upon himself to circulate in official circles a critical note[8] com-
menting on a proposal which I had included in my paper that further
work should be done on the effects of explosions on human beings.
Greenwood's view was that no light 'could be thrown on these matters
by laboratory experimentation', and he added that 'from the public
point of view, this is a case where ignorance is bliss'. This douche of
cold water did not, however, have any influence either on Stradling or on
the other members of the Civil Defence Research Committee, for in the
interval between sending in my paper and the meeting at which it was
considered, I had also prepared a review of as much published and unpublished work as I could find which dealt with the effects of explosions
on the human frame, and from which I had drawn the blunt conclusion
that we knew practically nothing.

Many popular books were then being written about air-raids and bomb
casualties, and every manner of rumour was rife. The Spanish Civil War,
and especially Guernica, had added their full quota to a uniform tale of
horror. Stanley Baldwin, when Lord President of the Council, had
declared in 1932 that 'the bomber will always get through',[9] and Cyril
Joad, who then had considerable influence as a radio propagandist, had
warned everybody that a single bomb might flatten about a square mile
of a city. Even J. B. S. Haldane, good scientist though he was, had
written, on the basis of his Spanish experiences, that when a big bomb
explodes (and they were not very big bombs in those days), the blast
becomes translated at a distance into a wave of sound like that 'of the
last trumpet which literally flattens out everything in front of it. . . . It is
the last sound which many people ever hear, even if they are not killed,
because their ear-drums are burst in and they are deafened for life. It
occasionally kills people outright without any obvious wound.'[10] A
corresponding story was told in a Government report of an enquiry that

had been carried out for Sir John Anderson into the protective value of small home shelters—the kind which later became known as 'Anderson shelters'. This study[11] was made in 1939 under the direction of that ancient body, the Ordnance Board, an institution which traces its origins to the beginning of the fifteenth century, and of which I was elected an Associate Member after the war. The study was monitored on behalf of the Medical Research Council by Sir Joseph Barcroft, a highly respected physiologist of the day. Its main conclusion was that blast exercises its effects on the body by forcing its way down the mouth and nose into the lungs, which burst as a result. To sharpen public disquiet about bombs and about the strength of the German Air Force, it was widely rumoured that casualties from air-raids were likely to exceed 100,000 a week. Everyone, of course, knew about the evacuation of children from the cities, and it was also no secret that innumerable sacks and cardboard coffins had been provided to remove, by special trains, the bodies of the thousands who it was assumed would be killed in air-raids on London and other big cities.

Stradling agreed that I should enquire further.

I began with the problem of blast, and straightaway ran into luck. My first experiments were carried out at the Road Research Laboratory near Slough, where facilities were available to allow small animals such as rabbits and guinea-pigs to be exposed to the 'explosion' of large gas-filled balloons. The pressure of the resulting shock-wave was not high, but it was high enough to cause the characteristic bruising of the lungs which was conventionally ascribed to 'blast'. But I also noticed that the injuries were always more severe on the side of the animal facing the explosion, and that the bruised patches often followed the lines of the ribs. If the damage were really due to a wave of pressure passing through the mouth and nose into the lungs, it should have been equal on both sides. But it was not. The observation that the spots of haemorrhage that could be seen on the surface of the lungs often followed the lines of the ribs also suggested that the blast wave had hit the body like some flat solid object. If that was really what happened, could the effect of the wave be lessened by protecting the chest of rabbits with sponge-rubber? Before testing that idea, I then asked myself what about birds, with their delicate air-sacs leading off from their lungs, and with their enormous thick breast muscles, which ought to protect their lungs from a sharp blow? If blast exerted its effects through the passages that lead to the lungs, the air-sacs ought to suffer pretty severely. I did not believe that they would.

In fact the idea of testing birds had struck me somewhat earlier, during the course of a visit which Bernal and I paid to France in April 1940. This trip was organised through the Ministry of Home Security, and as

I cannot recall having had anything to do with the arrangements, I presume that Bernal had indicated what we wanted to see, and with whom we wanted to talk. We were met at Le Bourget by Lord Suffolk, and spent two or three hectic days in Paris, during which we had meetings with Professors Laugier and Longchambon, and with a number of their colleagues. I saw Professor Jean Mayer, who was in charge of a programme of research into 'shock', and who wanted to establish an effective liaison with those who were working, or preparing to work, on the subject in the U.K. I met Professor Millot, who was directing such research as was being done into the subject of bomb casualties, and who complained that he had not had replies to two letters he had recently sent to Mellanby of the M.R.C. I saw other friends at the Collège de France, and gained the feeling that the French military were not at all keen on scientists 'muscling in' on their territory. A marvellous dinner was given us in the private room of a restaurant by a few of the older generation of established leaders of French science, including Jean Perrin and Paul Langevin, and some of its new leaders—Laugier and Longchambon and Joliot-Curie. We swore eternal friendship and committed ourselves to the closest cooperation in our efforts to defeat the common enemy. Lord Suffolk took us to meet M. Dautry, the Minister of Armaments. On his desk was a copy of *La Vie Sexuelle et Sociale des Singes*, the translation of my *Social Life*. He did not refer to it, and I took its presence either as a sign of good manners, or of the diligence of one of his private secretaries. That evening we met Suffolk at the Ritz bar, having arranged to go with him to some quasi-official social gathering. But there was nothing official or quasi-official about the parties to which he took us. And this was no more than a month before Paris fell to the Germans. There was nothing in the air to make one feel we were at war.

I spent most of the time in Paris in a haze which my limited command of French was unable to dispel. Bernal chatted away in his fluent and personal variety of French, and it was largely through him that I sensed what we were about. But I also learnt much, and more directly, from the visits which were the main reason for our trip. First, there was a day at the Bellevue Ballistics Laboratory, which was then directed by Colonel Libessart, a tall, thin, stooped figure of a man who came to work with me in Oxford after the fall of France. I was to learn an enormous amount from him. He took us to Modane, in the southern part of the Maginot line of fortifications, where I was less impressed by the test explosions we made outside gun embrasures in which we had placed rabbits, than I was by the fact that anything so vast could have been built underground. There was a mess luncheon in the fortress at which the most junior officer, the 'popotier' for the day, called out the menu we were going to enjoy, including the year of the Mâcon we were going to drink. After he had wished the presiding General and the rest of us 'bon appetit', we all went through the traditional ceremony of beating the table with the handles of our knives as we called out, 'Bon appetit, popotier'. Libessart had given us dinner the night before at the Gare de Lyon in Paris. Some fifteen minutes after we had steamed out of the station I realised that I had left my briefcase, which contained plans of the part of the line we were going to visit, in the station restaurant. Libessart told me not to worry, and left the compartment. The train stopped slightly longer than usual at the next station, and he again left us, to return with my case. I was more than a little impressed by the efficiency of the Deuxième Bureau or the Military Police, or whoever it was who had been tailing us. I am happy to say that that was the only occasion in more than thirty years of handling secret papers that I ever mislaid an official document or left a briefcase unguarded.

In those days I knew nothing about ballistics or fortifications. Nor did I know anything about big field guns, which I first saw fired on an artillery ground near Bourges, to which Libessart took us on our way back to Paris. We were behind a protective wall, furnished with slits, at some distance from the guns, when I noticed that birds were flying around, and that at the moment that one of the big guns fired, a bird which had alighted near its muzzle, just flew off. I immediately decided that when we returned to London I would see what blast did to birds as well as to rabbits. That was why I arranged that particular experiment at the Road Research Laboratory. It turned out that pigeons were not at all affected by the blast from the exploding gas-filled balloon. I then decided to see if rabbits provided with an additional layer of artificial breast muscle made of sorbo-rubber would be less sensitive to blast than were unprotected animals. They were.

By now I was convinced that the accepted view about the way blast acts on the body was wrong. But in order to prove that a blast-wave exercises its effects through its direct impact on the trunk, it was necessary to extend the work to the detonation of proper charges of explosive. For work of this kind the Ministry of Home Security had the use of part of the brick-fields at Stewartby near Bedford. But I needed help if I was to continue. I was still busily engaged on my normal researches, and writing scientific papers and reviews and correcting proofs. Up till then the only help I had in my new war work was provided by a technician whom I used to take with me from Oxford to Slough, and by Dr. R. B. Fisher, a friend who taught in the neighbouring biochemistry laboratory. Fortunately, Stradling was interested, and authorised me to build up a staff, the first member of which was Peter Krohn, who by now had qualified in medicine in London. That was the beginning of what became known as the Oxford Extra-Mural Unit (O.E.M.U.) of the Ministry's Research and Experiments Department.

We immediately started experimental work at the brick-works. If ever the word 'field-day' was justified, that was it. Carrying the animals across country from Oxford to Stewartby; arranging the lay-out of the animals in their cages, as well as of the pressure-gauges which measured the intensity of the blast at increasing distances from the explosions; detonating the charges; making immediate observations on the animals; and then packing the cages and equipment for the return journey to Oxford, where immediate post-mortems had to be done on those animals which had already died, or which it was decided would not be followed through a recovery period. The laboratory work after our return usually took us into the early hours of the morning, and weeks were spent on the subsequent microscopic study of tissues. But it was all new experience and exciting—and no-one minded. Even Joan assisted at those midnight post-mortem sessions, overcoming a natural squeamishness. The field-work, too, had its unintended excitements—chasing across the fields after monkeys which had got loose, staking goats, and heaven knows what. But most of that came in the second and immediately following phase of the work on blast, when I set about the task of scaling up the experiments in an effort to discover the range of shock-wave pressure which might be damaging to man.

I wrote an account of the first set of results which had shown that the lung injuries caused by a blast-wave were due to the impact of the pressure pulse on the surface of the body and not to a pressure or suction effect acting on the lungs through the air passages.[12] This paper was also taken by the Civil Defence Research Committee. The meeting was held at the National Physical Laboratory at Teddington at the end of June 1940,[13] just after the capitulation of France. Professor E. V. Appleton,* the Secretary of the Government's Department of Scientific and Industrial Research, was in the chair, and other distinguished physicists, including Professor Geoffrey Taylor,† Professor R. H. Fowler,[14] and Sir Charles Darwin were present. So were two representatives of the Medical Research Council who attended in place of Sir Edward Mellanby. I told my tale, and the two M.R.C. bigwigs, speaking to their brief, could only say that my interpretation of the cause of direct blast injuries differed from the M.R.C. doctrine. But as they could produce no evidence for the view that the lungs were affected by way of the mouth and nose, the physicists were not impressed. I was later encouraged to speak to the Royal Society of Medicine,[15] and soon nothing more was heard of the conventional explanation of blast injuries. For it was not long after

* As Sir Edward Appleton, he later became the Principal of Edinburgh University.
† Later Sir Geoffrey Taylor O.M.

the Teddington meeting that I was able to prove my hypothesis to everybody's satisfaction by exposing rabbits at a distance from the detonation of a big charge of bare explosive at which the blast pressure was so high that the creatures should have been blown to pieces. But my animals survived. Their bodies had been totally protected in steel boxes which were strong enough to withstand the explosion, and only their heads had been exposed. They suffered no internal injury and did not even lose consciousness. Their only injuries were ruptured ear-drums.[16]

At the same meeting of the Civil Defence Research Committee, I put forward proposals to investigate the wounding power of small splinters from exploding bombs or shells or grenades. The evidence that I had managed to collect in a rapid survey of men who had been wounded during the fighting when we were driven out of France indicated that, depending on their velocity, relatively minute fragments of metal could cause serious wounds. There was one incident which had impressed me greatly. A soldier had had both bones in his forearm fractured by a minute piece of metal which weighed no more than one-fiftieth of an ounce (about half a gramme).

But that was not the real reason why, with Stradling's and Bernal's foreknowledge, I had suggested that this study should be made. Without my realising it, my first piece of work on blast had begun to make people think that I was an authority on the biological effects of explosions. For example, the Director General of the Government's Emergency Medical Services had already issued a public statement about the practical implications of my work on blast.[17] Moreover, there was hardly anyone else working on the subject, and wherever one turned there were fascinating questions which, when clearly formulated, could lead to ready answers. Before the Teddington meeting I had been asked by the President of the Ordnance Board, Major-General Loughborough, to attend a meeting of the Board at Woolwich Arsenal, at which they were going to discuss the criteria for assessing the relative wounding power of fragmenting weapons. The standard procedure of the period was to explode a shell or grenade in a 'static test', and to count the number of fragments which penetrated one-inch-thick wooden boards set up at increasing distances from the burst. No attention was paid to fragments of less than a twenty-fifth of an ounce. The question put to me was whether I thought that fragments of lesser weight could cause injury. Without hesitation I replied 'yes', and added that I could see a way of getting a firm answer. Instead of trying to assess the wounding power of irregularly shaped fragments which are sent flying when a bomb or shell casing is shattered by the detonation of the enclosed explosive, I would begin by using a uniform shape of metal, such as a small ball-bearing, and standardise its wounding power at different velocities against a uniform target. I would then equate the results with the penetration power of small cubes or rectangular blocks of metal, before moving on to irregular metal splinters.

Even before the Ordnance Board meeting I had thought the problem worth tackling. In a letter which the *British Medical Journal* published in July 1940,[18] three weeks after the C.D.R.C. meeting at Teddington, I had suggested a new explanation, again not in accordance with current doctrine, for the fact that a minute fragment of metal travelling at high velocity could cause a wound whose size was out of all proportion to the weight of the missile. My view was that neither the spin nor the irregular shape of the splinters had much, if any, effect, and that the main cause of damage was the kinetic energy of the fragments when they struck, and the momentum they imparted to the tissues lying in their path. In effect, a high-velocity small fragment caused an internal explosion. In this hypothesis I was basing myself on work that had been done by two Germans on the penetration of clay by high-velocity bullets.[19]

When I put my proposals to the Teddington meeting, the representatives of the M.R.C. immediately objected that work on the subject was unnecessary. My argument—that information about the wounding power of small fragments could be useful in assessing the value, if any, of light-weight protective armour—was also received with displeasure, this time by Dr. H. J. Gough, the Director General of Scientific Research and Development of the Ministry of Supply. The General Staff of the Army held that troops were already carrying too much weight. In spite of strong support from Bernal, the Teddington discussion was thus not very encouraging, but nonetheless Stradling allowed me to embark on this new line of research, mainly because of the Ordnance Board's interest.

After the meeting, both Geoffrey Taylor, who had pointed out the difficulty of projecting small irregularly-shaped splinters of metal along a fixed path, and R. H. Fowler (I could not have had two more powerful supporters) told me that were they in my shoes they would pay no attention at all to the views of the M.R.C. representatives. At the same time they offered their help in devising a technique for shooting small ball-bearings. But in all truth it never occurred to me to worry about the attitude of the M.R.C. I was far too interested in my new world of exploration to lose any sleep because of Sir Edward Mellanby's objections.

The Council's attitude was only to be expected. The M.R.C. was, and remains, the Government organisation that has the responsibility for finding official answers to biomedical questions. At the start of the war there were many people in authority who vividly remembered the excellent work which the Medical Research Committee, the precursor of the Council, had directed during the First World War. Some of the men who had investigated shell-shock and the effects of gas warfare were still actively at work. Moreover, at the beginning of 1939 the M.R.C. had, at the request of the Air Staff, established a Flying Personnel Research Committee. The trouble was that the organisation did not move fast enough for a new Department such as the 1939 Ministry of Home Security. When I started to enquire into the biological effects of explosions, the Council had little or no interest in the problem. What was worse, I had committed the sin of embarking on researches into unfamiliar problems without the preliminaries of committee discussion, and without taking into account the views of men who were presumed to know more than I did.

It was not until the middle of 1940 that the M.R.C. set up a War Wounds Committee, with a rich array of sub-committees, to consider the medical aspects of wounds. Towards the end of that year, it also set up a Body Protection Committee, which transformed itself into a Military Personnel Research Committee, to which was then appended a sub-committee on body armour and steel helmets. By that time Stradling saw little point in papers from his Department being passed to a Committee whose members were unfamiliar with the concepts which underlaid the work for which he was responsible. After he had received a number of peremptory requests from the M.R.C. that I should prepare reports for them on the work I was doing for his Department, he instead insisted that Bernal and I should be made members of the sub-committee that wanted our papers. Another matter which had been resented in some quarters of the M.R.C. was the speed with which we had designed a helmet for civil defence (A.R.P.) workers without reference to them.

In the late summer of 1940, after the fall of France, and after Colonel Libessart had joined my growing Unit, Stradling had been asked to design a protective helmet for air-raid wardens, since supplies of the standard army issue were limited. This job was passed to me. Libessart held that helmets were hardly any use at all; his attitude seemed to imply that no self-respecting soldier would demean his profession by attempting to protect himself. Accordingly, I did not spend more than a day or two, or indeed focus much scientific thought, on the design of what became the standard issue of helmet for the A.R.P. (Air Raid Precautions) worker.

That was about the time that the M.R.C., instead of advocating the adoption of the new American helmet which had just made its appearance, had started to busy itself with the redesign of the British army helmet which had been inherited from the 1914–1918 war. Sir Hugh Cairns, the first Nuffield Professor of Surgery in Oxford, and the foremost British neuro-surgeon of the day—he was also in charge of the newly-formed head-injuries hospital at Oxford—was all in favour of the

American helmet, but his views did not prevail—perhaps because I sided with him. This was my first encounter with that almost universal reaction —that an article should be rejected simply because it has been developed or invented by someone else or, more significantly, by some other country rather than by one's own. This is now known as the N.I.H.— not invented here—syndrome. Cairns was more successful in his promotion of crash-helmets for motor cyclists. It was because of his determination that they became obligatory for army despatch riders, and in due course for all motor cyclists. It was Cairns who had tried to save the life of Lawrence of Arabia after his motor-cycle crash, and, knowing Cairns well, I always believed that it was this death that drove him into his crusade for crash-helmets. When I saw the final M.R.C. product being worn, I used to wonder if the considerable efforts to change the standard army helmet were ever justified. The information my own Unit was collecting about head wounds suggested that whatever changes could be made just in the shape of an ordinary steel helmet would be too trivial to have much practical value.

In order to stop the continuous sniping from M.R.C. quarters, I suggested to Stradling that he should ask Mellanby to set up an Air-Raid Casualties Committee. This was at the end of 1940, and again Bernal and I had to become members. This was a face-saving device, which in practice only meant that we had to attend occasional meetings, and that we arranged for the M.R.C. to have copies of some of our reports. The M.R.C., in the end, neither helped nor obstructed the work we were doing, the variety of which for a time became more and more beguiling.

There was first a follow-up to my ground-shock enquiry. A. N. Black,* a colleague in the Engineering Department in Oxford, collaborated in a series of experiments whereby a plate of metal to which a monkey was harnessed was instantaneously accelerated up to a maximum velocity of $10\cdot8$ ft./sec. by means of a blow from a large pendulum hammer.[20] No ill effects were observed. There were other experiments on concussion in monkeys which I carried out with Ritchie Russell, a neurologist at the Radcliffe Infirmary, and some related experiments on the elasticity of the skull, in which a young Ph.D. engineering student, D. G. Christopherson† participated. There was a macabre weekend in which Black and I tried to find an answer to a question put to me by the Navy about the level of force at which the human ankle is fractured. Ships were being mined and torpedoed, and as a result of the instantaneous vertical displacement of the decks, men were having their ankles broken, as were sailors who, when sliding down the exposed hull of a sinking ship,

* Later head of Southampton University's Department of Engineering.
† Now Sir Derman Christopherson, Vice-Chancellor of Durham University.

suddenly hit the bilge-rail. Someone had suggested that sailors should be provided with heavy rubber-soled boots to absorb the shock, and I was asked to find out whether such boots did any good. Clearly the first step was to find out how much force, in terms of g,* would break an ankle. Black arranged a very neat hangman's drop and, official permission having been given to use two human cadavers, we began by dropping one corpse a few inches, and then gradually increased the drop, X-raying the limbs between drops, so as to find out how big a fall was necessary before the ankle broke. We then put boots on the second corpse and repeated the experiment. We found that the boots did to some extent protect the ankle, but that the fracture that it might have suffered now occurred higher up the leg.[21] This was a totally inadequate experiment to provide a convincing answer, but circumstances made it impossible to do more at the time. It was often like that with the *ad hoc* enquiries which were addressed to us.

It was the wounding power of blast and of high-velocity fragments which continued to be the main preoccupations of my growing Unit, which had now been reinforced by Ben Delisle Burns, another medical graduate. A central question to which an answer needed to be found quickly was how close to an explosion a man had to be before he suffered directly from the shock-wave, as opposed to being wounded indirectly by being violently thrown, or by being hurt by flying debris. This entailed some very precise work in order to determine the levels of blast pressure which were either lethal, or which damaged internal organs or the ear-drums. The experiments were carried out on mice, guinea-pigs, monkeys and goats. These were exposed at different distances from the detonation of bare charges of explosive, the distances being calibrated in terms of the over-pressure, that is to say, in units of pounds per square inch above atmospheric pressure, as registered on pressure gauges. The animals had to be restrained in such a way that injuries due to violent displacement could not occur. This work showed that the pressure at which blast would either kill or wound increased as body weight increased, and that it was approximately proportional to the surface area of the body. By extrapolation we could then calculate the level of pressure at which a man had a fifty per cent chance of being killed when exposed to an explosion in such a way that he could suffer only from the direct effects of the blast. It turned out to be nearly 500 lb a square inch. There was some scepticism when I first reported this conclusion.[22] The prevailing doctrine was that a man could not tolerate even a tenth of that pressure. But as a study of the victims of subsequent air-raids was to show, my experiments had indicated the right value.

As the scope of the work of my Unit increased, there were many

* g = acceleration due to gravity, i.e. *c*. 9·8m/sec./sec.

nights when those of us who formed the post-mortem parties after the
return from Stewartby never got to bed at all. Every available pair of
hands had to be called in. Laboratory space was also at a premium, and
3 Museum Road had all but become an office. By this time, food was
being strictly rationed, with food coupons being the order of the day.
Meat having become scarce, we used to distribute the rabbits which had
been used in our experiments. Rabbit made a splendid dish. Goat was
different, and in the week it became available, some of my team decided
to entertain. A piece of high and hairy goat which a colleague put before
us at the last of those dinner parties was the final straw. Even Woolton
pie, named after the U.K.'s wartime Minister of Food, a strange concoction of which carrots were a prominent ingredient, was preferable.

The work on blast was much easier technically than the research into
the wounding power of small fragments, work in which Burns and
Libessart became mainly involved. Here, as I have said, my first task was
to analyse the X-rays of men who had been evacuated to England from
Dunkirk. I have already mentioned the man whose forearm was shattered
by a minute metal splinter. In another instance, a man was in hospital as
a result of a metal fragment weighing less than ten mg which lodged in
his kidney; in other words, he had been badly wounded by something
little bigger than a pin-head. But the basement of the Anatomy Department was no place for experiments on wound ballistics, and additional
quarters and staff were now urgently needed. With novel and potentially
useful observations being made at an increasing rate, there was no reluctance on the part of the Ministry of Home Security to provide both—and
for much more than just work on the wounding power of metal fragments.

The Low Countries and France had fallen to Hitler by about the time
my work on wound ballistics had started in earnest, and by then my
Extra-Mural Unit had grown into a staff of twenty-five young graduates,
about half of them old pupils of mine. The Unit also had a modest team
of secretaries and technicians, and a group of seventeen field workers who
were employed in the investigation of bomb incidents. Angèle Vidal-
Hall, an Oxford graduate who had previously worked in the Bursar's
office of Magdalen College, was superbly efficient in administering all our
varied activities. Through her connection with my work and my association with French scientists, she later became prominent in the affairs of
the Society for Visiting Scientists, and for a period was the head of the
French Embassy's scientific section, when this was set up after the war.
All the members of staff except me received their stipends either directly
or indirectly from the Ministry of Home Security; I alone continued to
draw my salary from the University. Our experimental studies of wound
ballistics were carried out in two large huts that were quickly put up for

us on the site of Oxford's present Department of Forestry. A house in Beaumont Street became the central office where information about bomb incidents was analysed, and additional office space was provided in the University's Agricultural Economics Institute. We also continued to work in my old quarters in the Anatomy Department.

In order to help define some of the unknown threats posed by air-raids, I had set out on my own into uncharted seas without any idea of how my journey would end. As the official History of the War relates,[23] the outcome was a unit which during the war became the main U.K. source for precise information about the wounding power of bombs and other fragmenting weapons. We were fortunate in that we were able to devise methods of enquiry, and so build a body of relevant knowledge on the subject, against the background of a host of studies of the physical aspects of explosions. For while we were not directly, at any rate at the start, on the staff of Stradling's Department, we were very much part of his organisation, with myself, almost by accident, responsible for that part of its duties as related directly to casualties and the new subject of wound ballistics.

The first work we did in our hut laboratory was to test the hypothesis that small bomb fragments were dangerous because of the momentum they imparted to the tissues through which they passed. My 'guns' consisted of bored steel blocks, into which a detonator could be slipped. Stuck to its tip was a small ball-bearing, a tenth of an inch in diameter, which was ejected at high velocity when the detonator was fired. This technique had been suggested to me by Geoffrey Taylor. The first targets we used were blocks of meat, which at that time could still be bought, the object being to measure the extent of damaged tissue in relation to the velocity of the missile. When Libessart joined me, he taught us about spark photography, and thus made it possible to obtain successive shadowgraphs of the target at intervals of fractions of a second or so after it had been struck. We also carried out experiments on anaesthetised rabbits, the small steel ball being aimed either at the thigh or the upper part of the forelimb. Shadowgraphs showed that in the split second it took the ball to penetrate, the limb ballooned due to the formation of an internal cavity. It returned to its normal size almost immediately after the ball had emerged. Recalling some pre-war research that I had been doing on variations in the concentration of water in the tissues, we then got the idea of using as target material, not rabbits or blocks of meat, but blocks of gelatine at a dilution corresponding approximately to that of the protein of the body. Shadowgraphs showed that immediately after it had been penetrated by a pellet, a gelatine block expanded until it was three to four times its original volume. This again was due to the formation of a temporary cavity. The block then went through a series of rapid pulsations before resuming its original size. The results of this experiment,[24] and those by which it was followed, were later confirmed in the United States, and gelatine blocks are still used as standard target material in the few laboratories which are concerned with this kind of work. It also turned out that our minute metal sphere could fracture the thigh-bone of a rabbit when it passed through the limb in a track half an inch from the bone. These experiments gave real meaning to the phrase 'blowing one's head to pieces', for a skull can also be shattered by a small fragment travelling at high velocity.

Once we knew why minute splinters caused wounds out of all proportion to their size, the way was open to tackle the problem in which the Ordnance Board was interested—how much of the wounding power of an exploding weapon is due to metal fragments smaller than a twenty-fifth of an ounce. Such fragments make up something like ninety per cent of the weight of a bomb casing. Whatever answer we derived was also clearly relevant to the question of assessing the value of body armour as protection against fragmenting weapons. This proved to be a long and arduous piece of research, in which Libessart was particularly helpful in devising photographic instruments and more sophisticated firing apparatus. In each experimental firing we had to have a measure of the striking velocity of the fragment or standard ball, and, if it penetrated fully, its residual velocity after it had passed through the target material. To measure the striking velocity, we used standard spark photography, but to estimate the residual velocity we were introduced to a neat technique. Standard steel balls as well as metal fragments of known weight were fired at different velocities into telephone directories, and the number of pages penetrated were then calibrated against the velocity and weight of the projectile. If a fragment of a given weight was shot through our block of gelatine and then penetrated a telephone directory behind it to a page beginning, say, with the name Dawkins, we could tell its residual velocity by referring to our standard tables and curves. Knowing its striking and residual velocities as well as its weight, we could then tell how much energy the fragment had lost when penetrating the target. In comparison with today's techniques of measurement and high-speed photography, those we used were extremely primitive. But they were adequate for the job.

We began our experimental enquiry knowing, of course, that wounds from fragments which struck the head, neck or trunk, were likely to be more dangerous than those that hit the limbs, and that they could be regarded as 'incapacitating'.[25] We then arbitrarily but conservatively decided that our criterion for a head wound which on average would be incapacitating, would be any perforation of the skull cap by a fragment. The criterion for a hit on the chest and abdomen we took as perforation of the breast plate; and for a limb, penetration half-way through. The next step was to determine the velocities at which the small steel ball satisfied these criteria, using as targets anatomical material taken from, and returned to, a hospital post-mortem room. In the circumstances of those days, this did not seem as gruesome as it does now. We had to do this to get a necessary base line. From then on our targets were always blocks of twenty per cent gelatine. Relating the weight, velocity and degree of penetration of irregularly shaped small fragments of the same relative parameters as the standard steel ball proved a tedious task.

Since only chance determines where a man is struck by fragments from an exploding weapon, or the position he is in when struck, another critical step was to determine what I called 'the mean projection area' of the body and of its main parts. Our models for this exercise were those members of the team who allowed themselves to be photographed in the nude—front, back and side, standing, kneeling and lying down. In this way we derived a figure for the mean projected surface area of the body; it measured 0·4 of a square metre, or just over four square feet. Ten to fifteen per cent of this area represented the projection on the surface of the body of vital organs such as the heart. Wooden panels of this size, which were dubbed 'zuckermen', were subsequently used by Army Operational Research groups in tests of wounding power. I did not know whether to feel flattered or irritated when I first heard that the dummy targets were called after me, and when I read statements to the effect that so many 'zuckermen' had been set up on a test-ground in order to determine the spread of lethal fragments from a grenade or shell.[26]

By combining our various results, we then estimated the probabilities of a man being incapacitated regardless of where he was hit or of the weight of the fragment that hit him, whether directly or in a glancing impact. By some yet further complicated steps which took in information about the numbers of fragments of different weight-ranges into which a grenade or shell shattered, and the rate at which the fragments lost velocity, we were able finally to obtain a standardised figure for the wounding power of a whole fragmenting weapon. Our stock of irregular fragments used to be provided by Dr. Payman of the Safety in Mines Laboratory in Buxton. He was an interesting man who knew a lot about the physics of what were called 'micro-explosions'.

The fact that the wounds caused by high-velocity fragments of metal could be totally disproportionate to their size also aroused my interest in the calibre of rifle bullets, which seemed to me unnecessarily large. When stalking deer in Argyllshire with Michael Noble, a friend who was married to one of Joan's cousins, I had been able to observe for myself that small bullets fired from a high-velocity rifle were lethal at ranges up to nearly two hundred yards. Michael, the stalker, and the pony-man were much interested in the post-mortems I made on the spot. I discovered that small 0·22 bullets killed, not because of a so-called 'dumdum' effect, or because they spun round after they had penetrated, but because of the destructive energy which they imparted to the tissues. But discussions which I started when back in London, about reducing the calibre of standard small-arm ammunition, made little progress, and it was not until years after the war ended that smaller calibre bullets became standard army issue.

We would have got nowhere without Colonel Libessart to guide us in the techniques which had to be developed as, in effect, we invented the subject of wound ballistics. Libessart was a 'polytechnicien' and very much a professional soldier. His English gradually improved, and he never changed his right-wing views. One day we were most surprised when he announced that he was going to marry. Joan and I, together with Lord Suffolk, were invited to the ceremony in a catholic church in the country. It was a warm day, and Suffolk was wearing a blue overcoat and a polka-dot scarf. At one moment when we had to stand up, Joan, who was seated between us, teased him about his unseasonal clothes, to which he reacted by unbuttoning his coat, revealing a bare chest covered with a blacksmith's leather apron—the uniform which he wore when dealing with unexploded bombs.

Libessart was a staunch Gaullist, and on one occasion he invited his hero to Oxford to meet exiled Frenchmen who were working there. A reception was arranged in Rhodes House, but before we went there Libessart had brought the General to 3 Museum Road. Years after, when recalling the incident to some friends, I had to remind Joan that Libessart had come to see us that day with another tall French officer. 'What,' she exclaimed, 'was that de Gaulle?' So many people came in and out of our house that I was not surprised that at the time he had made no impression on her.

Years later, I was reminded of the occasion by de Gaulle himself. During the period when Harold Wilson was Prime Minister, he paid a formal visit to de Gaulle, then President of France. I was having talks at the Westland Aircraft Company that day when I received an urgent message saying that an aeroplane was being sent to fly me to Paris. When we landed I was driven straight to the Elysée Palace and arrived just after the company had risen from the luncheon table. Geoffroy de Courcel, the French Ambassador in London, whom I knew well, had not been warned that I had been summoned to the post-prandial talks, and as I walked into the room, he came up to me to express his astonishment, and to say that I had to be presented to de Gaulle immediately. But before he could say anything, the President remarked that we had met before, and recalled the visit that he had paid us in Oxford in 1941.

It was no surprise to learn afterwards that he was noted for his phenomenal memory.

There were no examples to follow in our experimental studies. We had to rush ahead—rush, because there was no time to move slowly. Wherever we moved we were in new territory, with novel questions and problems arising every day, all of which demanded quick answers. What we learnt in the laboratory formed the background to my Casualty Survey when it was set up, not background in the sense that I had to wait for the completion of experimental studies before trying to understand what had happened in actual raids, but background in the sense that what we were doing in the laboratory helped to provide an understanding of what we learnt in the field. Our newly-gained knowledge was also called on frequently by the authorities who were concerned in assessing the effectiveness both of new weapons and of protective devices. Indeed, before the end of the war, the Oxford Extra-Mural Unit seemed to have links of one sort or another with all our armed services, and with all laboratories concerned with anti-personnel weapons. We studied the effects of blast in tanks and pill-boxes, and made several enquiries into the value of body armour. One continuing series of studies was carried out for Major-General Sir Millis Jefferis, who ran an establishment called M.D.1 in the village of Whitchurch, not far from Oxford. Jefferis was an interesting character whom I had first met when the Prof brought him to the Christ Church Common Room shortly after our unsuccessful foray into Norway in 1940. He was brimful with unconventional ideas which were always being resisted by the War Office, but through Winston Churchill's influence he had been allowed to set up his own experimental establishment, which became known as 'Winston Churchill's Toyshop'.[27] The 'shop' was a hive of activity, and for a period Peter Krohn, Ben Burns and I were fairly constant attenders at experiments, particularly those in which it was necessary to assess the risks to men in tanks that were hit by one of the many different shaped charges which Jefferis was designing. His most ambitious project was a bomb especially designed to sink the German battleship *Tirpitz*, scale models of whose decks were to be seen in the fields around the house at Whitchurch. This bomb was known as the 'Capital Ship Bomb' or 'Cherwell Special', a nickname which gave no pleasure to the eponym.

The O.E.M.U. was visited early in 1941 by a powerful team of American scientists who had come to England to discover what help they could give to Britain's war-effort. The group was led by John E. Burchard of the Massachusetts Institute of Technology (M.I.T.), and included in its number Dr. H. P. (Bob) Robertson, the Princeton cosmologist and mathematician who became one of my close friends, and Dr. John von Neumann, the mathematician and physicist who was to become a key figure in the development of 'the bomb', and who today is better known as the pioneer of game theory. Von Neumann and a few others of the team came to Oxford for a demonstration of the physical characteristics of under-water explosions—a problem which Colonel Libessart was then studying using detonators in a small water-tank. I believe that this was von Neumann's first practical demonstration of a phenomenon which was to become important in his later work. John Fulton also managed to pay us a visit.

The O.E.M.U.'s laboratory work continued until the end of the war, by which time we had produced some hundred and twenty reports of various studies.[28] A general account of the work that the O.E.M.U. carried out on the biological effects of explosions was later published in the official Medical History of the War,[23] and also in the *Textbook of Air Armament*,[29] which has long since been declassified. But in fact the cream of our new intellectual adventures had been skimmed in the first year or two after starting. This is so often the case with new fields of scientific enquiry. And it was not the work in the laboratory that in the end opened a door to the world of operations. That came from the study of bombs in the open.

CHAPTER 7

BOMBS AND BOMBING POLICY

ABOUT A year after the start of the war, just about the time when the scientific study of air-raids began in earnest, it was arranged that a record should be kept of every bomb that was dropped on the United Kingdom, with a note of the place struck, the nature of the weapon, and a statement of the casualties and damage caused. This was the beginning of what became known as the Bomb Census. Establishing the criteria for diagnosing a weapon from the damage it caused was one of the responsibilities of Stradling's department, which in this undertaking cooperated with other organisations, including the Bomb Disposal Service, which dealt mainly with unexploded bombs. It was also understood that once raids began, the conclusions of the experimental work which Stradling's staff had been carrying out would be checked against what happened in real life. It was out of this arrangement that my Casualty Survey was born. I had a permanent team that operated in London, with Guy's Hospital as its headquarters, a flying squad which investigated incidents in other towns, and a central analytical group in Oxford.

Bernal and I were with Stradling in a Civil Defence War Room in London when one of the first daytime raids was signalled. Anti-aircraft guns had been in action, and the news came through that St. Pancras Station had been closed because of bombing. 'That's for us', said Des, and off we drove to the station, where worried officials accompanied us to the end of a platform and pointed to some damage. Des diagnosed the cause as one of our anti-aircraft shells, and we left somewhat dashed and disappointed. I also went with him to the Luton area, where a factory had been hit, and where I saw my first real bomb damage. A few men had been blown to bits, and some small pieces of human flesh—I particularly remember a piece of brain—had not been completely cleared from the broken masonry. I was deeply impressed both by the incident and by Bernal's objectivity as he tried to reconstruct exactly what had happened when the bomb burst. To me, destruction was still destruction, and so far as I was concerned, it lent itself to no possible order. There were a few other rushed trips to other places, including one to Kent to watch Spitfires and Hurricanes in action against German raiders. Then an audaciously precise bombing attack occurred on Banbury, and this was to prove a vital turning-point in my work. It was the occasion when I first discovered for myself that a coherent story could be distilled from the debris of destruction.

The curious thing at the time was that I did not learn about the incident from Princes Risborough, which in those days of sporadic attacks normally let me know about incidents which it was thought might interest me. I had been away from Oxford, and on my return, a friend who was then pathologist to the Radcliffe Infirmary, telephoned to say that Banbury Station had been bombed, and that he thought that I would be interested in the casualties. Banbury being only some twenty miles away, I drove there to make a quick reconnaissance, before returning next day to investigate fully.

The attack was made by a lone German aircraft which in the early afternoon of 3 October 1940 had flown in over the East coast. It approached Banbury from a north-westerly direction, flying very low along the railway lines. It was so unhurried in its actions that it twice circled its targets before dropping its bombs. The first few were aimed at the gasometers at the side of the Banbury goods yard, and caused considerable damage. Then some more bombs were aimed at a signal box and at the main lines passing through the station. One of them destroyed a single-storey brick room at the end of a platform. Eight men were in it at the time. The aircraft, which presumably had a load of twenty 50 kg bombs, then flew on, and the pilot attacked what he took to be an aluminium plant, but which in fact was a dummy, before making his way back to the coast and to his base.

Shortly after the war the demolished room was rebuilt to the original plan. Whenever I passed through the station after the damage had been made good, I would look at the little building and think to myself: there is yet another place that has changed the course of your life. If Banbury had not provided the clue to the first reliable, even if empirical method that exists for comparing the relative effectiveness of anti-personnel weapons, on either a weapon-for-weapon, or a weight-for-weight basis, it is highly improbable that I would have moved, as I did later in the war, from laboratory and field work to strategic planning. I used to wonder what had happened to that pilot. When Herr Strauss, as the German Minister of Defence, visited London in the early sixties, I gave him a record of the incident and asked whether it would be possible to find out whether the pilot's cool performance had been noted at the time. I wanted to know what had happened to the man. But I never did find out. The Luftwaffe records had either been destroyed or removed by the Allies at the end of the war.

The room on which my enquiry focused measured twenty by fifteen feet. The bomb exploded about two feet from the floor, shattering the walls and roof. One man who was in the open just outside the door was killed instantly, as were two of the eight men in the room. A third died on his way to hospital, and two more during the course of the next day. But there were three survivors, of whom two had not lost consciousness when the bomb went off. All eight were wounded either by small fragments of metal from the bomb casing or by pieces of debris, and all also seemed to have suffered some direct blast damage to their lungs, although I could not rule out the possibility that their internal injuries had been caused by violent displacement, or by pieces of flying furniture. The blast pressure inside the room had been high enough to rupture everyone's ear-drums. What seemed incredible at the time was that all eight had not been killed.

The three survivors were 'walking casualties' about a fortnight after the incident, the last being discharged from hospital after nineteen days. They were only too eager to help me reconstruct a picture of everyone's exact position in the room at the moment the bomb exploded, and I also succeeded in piecing together a precise account of all the people who had been in the vicinity. This field-work took some time, but there was considerable interest in Princes Risborough in what was emerging from my enquiry, which was also helping to indicate an economical and routine way in which other incidents could be investigated.

A week after the Banbury attack I studied another isolated bombing at Woolwich in South East London, in which three small Anderson shelters had been hit by 50 kg bombs. I also investigated a few other incidents. Night bombing started in earnest not long after, and by the end of the year I had enough data to circulate a general summary and analysis of twenty-six incidents, each of which had been written up in detail. An analysis of a second series of twenty bombings followed six months later, and then, towards the end of 1941, a third report on a further thirty-five incidents. By the time a fourth and fifth general summary had been produced, the members of my Casualty Survey had made a detailed study of a total of 111 incidents,[1] most of them in London and Birmingham. No further general summaries of separate incidents were issued, but we continued to turn out papers on particular cases or on special categories of weapon such as the V.1 flying bombs.

My survey of casualties had begun as an attempt to discover whether blast injuries similar to those which I had observed in experiments on laboratory animals occurred in air-raids, and had taken the form of visits to hospitals and mortuaries, and of surveys, like the one I made in Banbury, of the actual scenes of incidents. These initial field enquiries suggested that while lung injuries resembling the blast lesions I had observed in experimental animals were occurring, many people who had been close to explosions escaped with relatively little injury, and apparently without showing any effects of blast. It was this unexpected finding that made it necessary to transform what was little more than a spot-check of raids into a systematic enquiry which could provide information about the casualty risks associated with different kinds of exposure to bombs, and about the value or defects of different kinds of shelter. And for this a field staff had to be rapidly recruited. The procedure for investigating incidents was refined as we went along, but obtaining precise information about all the people, hurt or unhurt, who had been in the vicinity of a particular explosion, never ceased to be laborious, any more than did visits to First Aid Posts, hospitals and mortuaries. For most incidents scores of people had to be traced and interrogated, usually after the scene of the disaster had been evacuated.

Increasing experience also helped determine the most useful ways of dealing with the mass of data we collected. What we were essentially concerned to discover was, first, the radius within which different weapons caused casualties; second, whether different conditions of exposure were associated with characteristic injuries; and third, what particular factors were responsible for air-raid deaths and disablement. So that 'like' could be compared with 'like', it was necessary to categorise various situations in which the growing numbers of people who came into our casualty survey had been exposed to risk. I also found it necessary to subdivide injuries according to whether they were 'primary', that is to say due to blast, or splinters or the flame from the explosion; 'secondary', when they were due to being violently thrown; 'tertiary', when they were due to flying or falling debris and other objects sent hurtling by an explosion; and finally, 'quaternary', that is to say due to events subsequent upon the actual explosion—for example, being buried under debris. Primary and secondary effects differed from those defined as tertiary or quaternary in so far as the casualties had not been shielded in any way from the explosion. By the beginning of November 1941 enough information had accumulated for me to draw up and publish a general report on our results.[2] It was known by its reference number, R.C.270, and became the standard work on the subject. It was declassified several years after the war.

By the time I wrote R.C.270, we had followed up individually more than 10,000 people (of whom about 1,000 had been casualties) who had been involved in 310 bomb explosions. The analysis of a large group of casualties caused in South-East England on the night of 16 April 1941 had not been completed by then, and had therefore to be excluded from my report, which nonetheless was able to provide the broad outlines of a picture, only details of which subsequently needed filling in.

The concept which turned out to be critical to the analysis was that of 'vulnerable area' or 'standardised casualty rate', to which I was introduced by Frank Yates of the Rothamsted Experimental Station. Frank was a colleague of R. A. Fisher, and later succeeded him as Britain's foremost statistician. From the outset Stradling had realised that statisticians were going to be necessary in the work of his Department. The two who worked there full-time, and whom I often consulted, were Drs. Garwood and Bradford Hill.* Frank Yates, who had been brought in by Bernal, was enormously inventive in devising new statistical techniques, and it was Bernal who suggested that he should come over to Oxford to discuss my findings. Des knew that I was extracting a lot of new information, but he also realised that Yates could help in my efforts to devise a standard way of comparing the effectiveness of bombs of different size and of different charge/weight ratio; that is to say, the ratio of the weight of the explosive-filling to that of the bomb as a whole. Standardising destructive power seems very simple now, but before Yates showed how it could be done, broken buildings and shattered bodies were only broken buildings and shattered bodies. Another of Bernal's recruits was Jacob Bronowski, then a geometer at the University of Hull, and already known as an interpreter of William Blake's art. Bronowski was a great talker and a great waster of time. He never did anything original, but impressed people by always suggesting some alternative mathematical approach to problems of analysis which had already been dealt with by simpler and perfectly adequate methods. But there was no denying that he knew how to write, and I was not in the least surprised by his later career as a popular expositer of 'la condition humaine', if it is legitimate here to borrow the title of André Malraux's famous book.

As I have already said, my immediate concern in starting a field survey of casualties had been to discover whether people suffered from the direct effects of blast and, if so, whether the indications which my experimental work had given of the danger levels of pressure were on the right side. I also wanted to find out the extent to which small bomb splinters caused air-raid casualties. That was why I always started out by making a reconstruction of the scene of an incident, marking the distance from the burst of the bomb of every person in the vicinity, noting whether they had been standing, sitting or sheltering, and the nature of the wounds which they had suffered. What Yates revealed to me was that this information could easily be generalised. Let us suppose, say, that we had records of a hundred incidents in which a total of 10,000 people had been exposed to risk in raids in which 100 kg bombs only had been dropped. Let us then suppose that of the 10,000 people, 1,000 had been within ten feet of the point of burst of one of these bombs, and that all

* As Sir Bradford Hill, he helped to establish the relationship between cigarette smoking and lung cancer.

had been killed. A circular area with a radius of ten feet would therefore be completely vulnerable; that would be an area of approximately 315 square feet. Let us then suppose that 3,000 people had been exposed to risk between ten and twenty feet of a burst, and that only half of them had been killed. That would mean that only half of the area of an annulus between ten and twenty feet from the bomb need, on average, be regarded as vulnerable; that is to say, half of 940 square feet, or approximately 470 square feet. Of the remaining 6,000 people who had been exposed to risk, let us suppose that 2,000 were between twenty and thirty feet from a bomb, and that only 500 of them—a quarter—were killed. The vulnerable fraction of the area of the annulus between twenty and thirty feet would then be a quarter of 1,570 square feet, i.e. 390 square feet. One would continue the sums in this way, until a distance was reached from the burst of the bomb at which no-one who was around at the time was killed. The sum of the successive vulnerable areas then represents the total vulnerable area for fatal casualties caused by the weapon in question.

Calculations could also be made for people who were seriously injured, or for all casualties, including those only slightly hurt. To convert the figure for vulnerable area into a 'standardised casualty rate' or 'standardised killed rate', we simply divided the vulnerable area in square feet by 1,000, on the arbitrary assumption that people were distributed at a density of one per 1,000 square feet (roughly 44 to the acre). It would have made no difference to the comparison of the differences of effect of different sized bombs if we had used any other arbitrary but standard figure for the density of the population that had been at risk when the bombs struck.

The standardised rates, for the calculation of which more sophisticated techniques were then devised, necessarily varied according to the way people had been exposed to risk. If one removed from the hypothetical population of 10,000 those who had been in well-built shelters, and did the calculations separately for them, one would end up with a smaller standardised casualty rate for the 100 kg bomb than would apply, say, to people who had been exposed to risk in the open, or in terrace houses. In short, the generalising capacity of the concept was an immensely powerful device for comparing the wounding powers of exploding weapons in different circumstances. Equally, the only way to obtain the data from which the standardised casualty rate could be reliably calculated was the form of casualty survey on to which I had stumbled as I puzzled over the Banbury incident. The provisos were that the incidents had to be representative of the circumstances being studied, and that the necessary and obvious adjustments had to be made to estimate the number of people who were at a distance from the explosion but who, having then been evacuated, could not be traced. Fortunately these were simple conditions to satisfy.

Some of the conclusions which emerged from our analyses were obvious, and others highly surprising and important. For example, it was not unexpected that in day-raids relatively twice as many people were in the open or in factory and office buildings as were at night, when one found about five times as many people in shelters as one did during the day. Nor was it surprising that the standardised casualty rate for bombs turned out to vary directly with the size of the weapon. But it was interesting that, ton for ton, 50 kg bombs produced significantly more casualties than did 250 kg or 1,000 kg bombs. This finding ran counter to a conclusion that had been derived from an earlier, more extensive even if less exact, series of data,[3] and it therefore obviously needed retesting. My inference proved to be correct. In a series of six categories of German bomb that we then studied[4] it turned out that in terms of the weight of bombs an aircraft could carry, the 50 kg bomb was the most potent casualty producer. Ton for ton it was every bit as dangerous as the V.2 rocket bomb—a weapon which later was to strike by day or night without warning.

The basic reason why smaller bombs were more effective in causing casualties was clearly the larger number of strikes that they implied for the same weight of aircraft load. Moreover, because of the smaller radius of effective action, a larger proportion of the people at risk when 50 kg bombs struck were exposed with little, or only light protection between them and the explosion. A bigger bomb might have a bigger radius of action, within which, however, thick walls might protect some people who would otherwise be at risk. It also turned out that the number of casualties caused by fragments of the metal casing decreased, aircraft load for aircraft load, as the size of the exploding weapon increased.

In the context of the studies we were doing this was a highly significant observation, and one to which the Germans were blind at the time. By then we were being called in fairly often to deal with the survey and analysis of the occasional fatal accident which occurred in army training centres, and were later able to extend our studies to cover a larger series of weapons, including mortar bombs and grenades. The analysis established beyond doubt that when fragmenting weapons are compared in terms of the total tonnage used, the efficiency of a missile, as measured in terms of the frequency of fragment wounds it causes, decreases as the weight of the missile increases. Biggest is not necessarily best, even in the irrational world where bombs play their part.

This was only one of the significant conclusions that were reached as a result of the air-raid casualty survey on which I had embarked. The concept of a standardised casualty rate made it possible to compare the relative risk of different sized bombs in different situations; for example, being out of doors or on the ground floor, as opposed to being in the cellar of a terrace house or in a small outside shelter. We were also able to find out whether there were differences in the spectrum of injuries associated with characteristic conditions of exposure in, say, daytime as opposed to night raids, or high-level as opposed to low-level attacks. Very soon, too, I had all the evidence which was necessary to reinforce the correctness of the extrapolations that I had made from my experimental studies about the levels of blast pressure that would prove directly fatal to men. As I have said, these were far higher than had been supposed being on average, about 500 lb per square inch. It followed that the threshold of blast pressure which was likely to be lethal would not be experienced except in the immediate vicinity of an explosion, where the danger of being fatally wounded by fragments of the bomb casing or by violent displacement would be overwhelming.

I am always reminded of man's tolerance to the direct effects of blast when I pass Broadcasting House at the end of Portland Place in London. One night in 1941 a parachute mine exploded after it had been stopped in its descent by a lamp-post about thirty feet from the building. Patches in the stone facade near the main doors of the building still show the spots where splinters from the casing hit the walls. When the bomb went off, a B.B.C. engineer was directly exposed in the open, lying in the gutter twenty-five feet from the point of burst. He managed to hold himself down by gripping the kerb, and to the best of his knowledge did not lose consciousness when the mine exploded. What was significant to me was that the injuries he suffered at a pressure of about 400 lb per square inch did not include any damage to his lungs, although, not surprisingly, his ear-drums were ruptured. His hearing was severely affected for some considerable time.

In general, it turned out that most air-raid casualties were caused not by the primary effects of explosions, but from such secondary consequences as violent displacement, and even more from what I had defined as the tertiary effects of an explosion—injuries due to flying and falling debris and other secondary missiles. This was because most people who were wounded in air-raids were in their houses, the frequency and severity of their injuries being proportional to the amount of structural damage that their dwellings suffered. There were, of course, pronounced differences in the effects of unconventional bombs, such as the V.1s and V.2s, which later were the subject of special study, as were the incendiary bombs which the Germans fitted with a small anti-personnel explosive device.

There was endless variety to our field experiences. One of the most peculiar was an occasion in the winter of 1940 when Sir John Anderson was told that a Coventry policeman had a special gift for 'divining' bodies under the rubble of bombed houses. Stradling was asked to investigate, and called on me to find out whether there was any reliable knowledge about this particular variety of divining. I thought of Eric Dingwall in Cambridge. He had made it his life's work to enquire into psychical phenomena and what he called 'other human oddities', about which he had written several books. I drove over to see him and discovered that this was not the first time that claims had been made for body-divining, and that it was worth investigating further. The matter was urgent, and I immediately set out in the dark on the return journey. But as I approached Princes Risborough, where Stradling and two colleagues were waiting for me, a girl ran into my car in the blackout and fractured her leg. I had to wait until an ambulance came to take her to hospital. It was nearly midnight before I could give my report. A few days later I was invited to witness a demonstration when a 'diviner' tried his art, or science, over a huge heap of rubble in the City of London. Alas, nothing was 'divined', and to the best of my knowledge that was the end of that method of trying to recover bodies.

Between us, Bernal and I had learnt as much about the effects of bombs as could be known at the time, short of having become victims ourselves. Two things then happened, which added a new dimension to the work we were doing. The first was that, a few months after he succeeded Admiral Sir Roger Keyes as Chief of Combined Operations, Lord Mountbatten recruited both of us as scientific advisers to his head-quarters. About that later. The second was that we became directly involved in the formulation of our own bombing policy. That story belongs to this chapter.

It began with a conversation with Lord Cherwell, as the Prof had now become, in the Christ Church Common Room on a Saturday night late in August 1941. In spite of the considerable amount of work I was doing, and the travel which was entailed, I still managed to dine occasionally at the House, and the Prof was often there. As was only to be expected, talk was usually about the war and bombs. During the winter of 1940 and throughout 1941, we had suffered the full weight of the German air offensive, while our own efforts against Germany seemed pretty in-significant. The news that the British public was constantly being fed about the effectiveness of our raids, particularly against the 'marshalling yards at Hamm', had ceased to carry conviction. Moreover, Churchill's belief that Germany could be defeated by bombing was being openly challenged in official quarters, where the policy to expand Bomber Command was seen to conflict with other more urgent national needs, for example, those of the navy. The most critical task which the Government faced was that of keeping our shipping-lanes open, and towards the end of 1941 Bomber Command necessarily had to join in the Battle of the Atlantic. This meant that fewer raids could be mounted against targets in Germany. Early in February 1942, Sir Archibald Sinclair, the Secretary of State for Air, nonetheless submitted a paper to the Defence Committee of the Cabinet, in which he argued that Bomber Command should be built up, and that heavy attacks on German cities, particularly incendiary attacks, should be resumed.[5] The paper was, in effect, agreed, and on 14 February 1942 a directive was issued authorising the C.-in-C. of Bomber Command to attack Germany 'without restriction', the objective being to destroy 'the morale of the enemy civilian population and in particular, of the industrial workers'.[6] This policy, however, conflicted so greatly with the need for the R.A.F. to continue its support of naval operations, and implied so much diversion of national resources, that the debate about Bomber Command became even sharper, not only in secret conclave, but also in the House of Commons and in the press. R.A.F. Bomber Command was running into formidable opposition.

From the start, and in spite of his awareness of the tactical short-comings of the attacks then being made against Germany, the Prof had been a powerful supporter of an area-bombing policy. He knew about the work of Stradling's Department, and about my own enquiries into the wounding power of German bombs. Quite early on, he had got the idea that our aircraft should hail what I can only describe as sharp needles onto cities. To this end, he got me to do some work on the penetrating power of such 'weapons' when fired from a crossbow, an instrument that we had to re-invent, since there were none to be bought off the shelf. Sometime later, he had an idea, which was dismissed by the Air Staff, that the German harvest could be disrupted by dropping small bombs, or steel spikes, among growing crops so as to interfere with the work of harvesting machines.

The Prof was naturally much concerned by the hostile reaction in official and unofficial quarters to our bomber offensive. On that Saturday night we discussed the possibilities of finding a more objective basis for the strategy of a bomber offensive than was implied by the simple belief that Germany could be bombed into submission. The idea that I put to him was that what was needed was a survey of the overall effects of bombing on some English cities. I suggested that we chose for study Hull and Birmingham, first because the Bomb Census had an almost complete tally of the bombs that had fallen on them, and second because they could be regarded as typical of manufacturing and port towns. The Prof agreed that the job was worth doing, and that it was something that Princes Risborough could carry out.

A few days after this talk, I wrote to Roy Harrod, who was then on the Prof's Whitehall staff, telling him about the conversation, and saying that certain information which was not available at Princes Risborough would be needed to answer the kind of question which the Prof suggested we should ask; for example, 'how many tons of bombs does it take to break a town', and 'how should the bombs be delivered—should it be in one sharp attack, or in what ratios should the total load be distributed and over how many nights'. I told Roy that the Prof was going to write to Stradling on the subject, and that 'in view of the fact that we would have to have authority to make enquiries over a much wider field than we are at present doing, he suggested that it might be as well to have a minute initialled by the P.M.'.

It was Sir John Anderson to whom the Prof finally sent the request. The instruction was passed to Stradling, who decided that Bernal and I should direct the enquiry, the responsibility for the casualty and social aspects of the investigation being mine, and the rest Bernal's. Apart from what we ourselves had learnt, R.E.8, one of the divisions of Stradling's Department, had carried out a number of general surveys of absenteeism resulting from German attacks. Helped by four young medical graduates whom I had recruited to my team, I had also carried out a general casualty survey of Birmingham during the attacks on that city towards the end of 1940. Bernal and I therefore had little difficulty in designing an enquiry that would cover such matters as physical damage, casualties, effects on production, absenteeism, evacuation, and even 'morale'.

But preparatory work, and the assembling of staff for the different investigations, took every bit of two months. The amount of paper that was generated when the work got under way, including psychiatric enquiries, was enormous. The results of some of the investigations, in particular those on mental stability, had not been analysed by the time our consolidated report had to be sent in. For example, I suggested that every school child in Hull between the ages of 10 and 14 should be asked to write an essay on 'what happened to me in an air raid'. The answers were roughly analysed, but I never had time to get down to the job of producing a picture of an air-raid as seen by children. I have often thought that it would be interesting to track down a sample of the writers of those essays to discover what, if anything, they remember of what they had written.

I kept feeding the Prof with information as it emerged, but even so, we were too slow for him. On 24 February 1942, I received a letter from D. M. Butt, a member of his staff, saying that the Prof had quoted some figures I had provided him, which related numbers of air-raid casualties to tonnages of bombs and to the density of housing, and that he had been asked to do 'certain calculations which involve them'. Butt had already prepared a report for the Prof[7]—it is referred to in most histories of the subject—in which he had revealed the inaccuracy of our bombing attacks on Germany. The letter went on to say that the Prof was not entirely clear about my 'definitions', and that they appeared to be unknown to the people at Princes Risborough to whom he had spoken on the telephone. What Butt was particularly anxious to know was the ratio of casualties per ton of bombs in areas with different housing densities. He concluded by saying, 'We do not want to anticipate any results of the Birmingham–Hull survey, but these figures are rather essential to an argument on quite different matters'.

The figures were presumably those referred to in the much-quoted Minute which the Prof sent Winston Churchill on 30 March 1942, and which is reproduced in full in Volume 1 of Webster and Frankland's official history of the *Strategic Air Offensive Against Germany*,[8] and in Lord Birkenhead's life of the Prof.[9] But even though the Prof did 'not want to anticipate any results of the Birmingham–Hull survey', which was issued little more than a week later, he certainly did—using one significant issue in a misguided fashion.

The Prof began his Minute by giving a figure for the number of dwellings demolished and people dispossessed, per ton of bombs falling on a city. By a simple calculation he then estimated that 4,000 to 8,000 Germans would be made homeless during the estimated lifetime of a British bomber. Taking into account the forecast output of our heavy bombers, and assuming that they focused their attacks on 58 German towns, each of which had more than 100,000 inhabitants (which on the basis of a 1938 census meant a total of 22 million people), he calculated that the great majority would become homeless. He went on to say: 'Investigation seems to show that having one's house demolished is most damaging to morale. People seem to mind it more than having their friends or even relatives killed. At Hull signs of strain were evident, though only one-tenth of the houses were demolished. On the above figures we should be able to do ten times as much harm to each of the 58 principal German towns. There seems little doubt that this would break the spirit of the people.' Damage to factories, services and communications he regarded as a bonus.

This Minute, which I did not see at the time it was issued, had a decisive influence on the outcome of the discussion about the policy of destroying German industrial cities by so-called 'area-bombing'. Our own summary report, which came out on 8 April 1942, was purely factual. But while the considerable controversy which the Prof's Minute stimulated has been referred to in various books, the Hull and Birmingham report, which was the basis of the Prof's Minute to the Prime Minister, has, to the best of my knowledge, never been reproduced before. Because it differs in a significant way from what the Prof stated, I have sometimes doubted if all that Bernal and I wrote was available to Webster and Frankland who, in their official history, nonetheless correctly observe that it was the source of the Prof's Minute. Their view is that the Prof's Minute settled nothing, despite its considerable impact at the time. As they say, 'It summarised the hopes and ideas of those who were working for the build up of the strategic bombing offensive. It did not convert those who were sceptical of the whole conception'.[10] This may be true as far as it goes. But it does not go far enough. In my view the outcome would have been very different if the Prof had not been there to put the weight of his authority, and his influence on Churchill, behind a bombing policy.

In the interests of history, the summary of our Report is reproduced as Appendix 2 at the end of the book. But what we said about morale needs to be quoted here because it was almost the reverse of what the Prof stated.

'In neither town was there any evidence of panic resulting either from a series of raids or from a single raid. The situation in Hull has been somewhat obscured, from this point of view, by the occurrence of trekking,* which was made possible by the availability of road transport and which was much publicized as a sign of breaking morale, but which in fact can be fairly regarded as a considered response to the situation. In both towns actual raids were, of course, associated with a degree of alarm and anxiety, which cannot in the circumstances be regarded as abnormal, and which in no instance was sufficient to provoke mass anti-social behaviour. There was no measurable effect on the health of either town.'[11]

The final preparation of our Report was a hectic business in which Bernal and I had to assemble as coherently as possible the mass of reports and summaries that had been produced. Some of us worked in the Beaumont Street offices of the O.E.M.U., some in the hut laboratory, and some in my house in Museum Road, pages being rushed from one place to another as they were re-typed. It was a period of strict blackout, of course, and a policeman became suspicious of the number of people coming to and leaving the Beaumont Street house. What he thought the place was I dared not think, but to allay his fears I allowed him to come in and see for himself two secretaries banging away at typewriters, while other people were sitting reading and correcting.

About a month after our Report appeared, the Air Ministry issued a commentary on it.[12] This began by quoting one of their 'blitz' reports, dated August 1941, in which it was claimed that the industrial activity

---

* The term used at the time for the nightly exodus of people from towns that were likely to be targets for bombs.

of a town would be seriously affected by a weight of attack of about seven tons of bombs per square mile. On the other hand, the commentary went on to say, the Hull and Birmingham enquiry now showed that an average intensity of bombing of the industrial, business and slum areas of Birmingham, which had been twice that figure, had not had more than a five per cent effect on production. But, so the wording implied, why waste time on such negative findings? Changes in operational factors, weapons and targets, which were in progress, or which were contemplated, made it unwise to assume that the analysis of the raids on Hull and Birmingham provided any reliable guide to the effects of the attacks we could mount against Germany. The commentary concluded with the observation that raids on Germany of five times the intensity which Hull and Birmingham had experienced would be a very different matter with respect to production, if not to morale. This prediction also turned out to be hopelessly wrong.

Cliff Emmens,* a fellow-physiologist who was then on my staff, continued studying the effects of bombing on 'morale' after the Hull and Birmingham enquiry had been completed. His further findings,[13] as well as the studies that the British Bombing Survey Unit (B.B.S.U.) carried out in Germany after the war,[14] corroborated the strange fact that however frightened people may have been during an air-raid, panic was almost unknown, and that morale never cracked. One early observation always stuck in my mind—when Coventry was bombed the country as a whole was shocked, but one heard people in neighbouring cities such as Birmingham saying, 'Hard luck on Coventry. Thank God it wasn't us.' The people of Coventry cleaned up the rubble and went on with their work, and the war-effort was hardly affected at all.

When the war ended, and I became Scientific Director of the B.B.S.U., I was responsible for the Unit's 'Overall Report' *The Strategic War Against Germany*, which appeared in 1946. What I then said about our Hull and Birmingham enquiry, is also relevant in the present context.

'The report of the Ministry [of Home Security]', I wrote, 'stated that there had been no breakdown in morale, nor fear of such a breakdown, with the intensity of raiding experienced by either town, and it also stated that loss of production was caused almost entirely by direct damage to factories. However correct these findings may have been, it is now possible to see that they provided relatively little basis for extrapolating to the effects of raids of much greater intensity than those which the Germans had delivered, or to the effects of attacks on Germany as opposed to England. Some indication of the prevailing ideas about intensities of bombing is given by the fact that a light raid was regarded as one which had achieved an intensity of 1 ton of bombs per square

* Now Professor of Veterinary Physiology in the University of Sydney.

mile of target area; medium attacks 5 tons per square mile, and heavy attacks 25 tons per square mile. Under favourable tactical conditions, in the spring of 1944 and onwards, densities from 30 to 50 times the figure suggested by the Ministry of Home Security as representative of a heavy raid were being achieved by R.A.F. Bomber Command whose technical performance, it may be noted here, was unequalled by any other Air Force operating in Europe.'[15]

The echoes of the dispute about bombing policy have not yet died down, partly because no clear view exists even now about what strategic bombing can achieve, and partly because of the dramatisation of the feud between the Prof on one hand, and Tizard[16] and Blackett (and those who sided with them), on the other. C. P. Snow's story of the argument, first presented in his 1960 Godkin Lectures, *Science and Government*,[17] and later amplified in the *Postscript*[18] which he published after the appearance of Webster and Frankland's history, seems to be based on no more than hearsay (he was certainly not involved in the argument), and his pictures of Cherwell and Tizard, with both of whom I worked closely, seem hardly real to me. I cannot see the Prof as some kind of Second World War Dr. Strangelove, oblivious of the critical comments of scientific colleagues, and exercising a great influence only because he was a member of Churchill's social circle. Nor can I see Tizard as the sound 'establishment man' of science, opposed to the bombing policy that was being proposed, and who, with Blackett, knew that the Prof's statistics had been deliberately designed to mislead. I am at one with the late Lord Birkenhead in believing that the picture of conflict in the corridors of power is altogether too simple and theatrical. Tizard did not, in fact, disagree with the principles behind the proposed bombing policy. Nor for that matter did Blackett. They simply doubted our ability to achieve it, taking into account the rate at which aircraft could be produced, the inaccuracy of our bombing at the time, the rate at which our aircraft were being lost, as well as other claims that were then being made on the R.A.F. It was the Prof's figures that they were questioning. In his biography of Tizard, Ronald Clark[19] quotes a letter which Tizard sent Cherwell on 20 April 1942, which begins with the sentence: 'I don't really disagree with you fundamentally, but only as a matter of timing . . .'. Blackett, who was then a chief scientist at the Admiralty, was much more forthright in his condemnation of the Prof's sums. He thought that 'Lord Cherwell's estimate of what can be achieved is at least 600% too high'.[20] Both Tizard and Blackett had our Hull and Birmingham report, and a note from Tizard to Air Vice-Marshal Charles Medhurst, an Assistant Chief of the Air Staff, which is quoted by Ronald Clark, says that Tizard had discussed our enquiry with Bernal.[21] He had also done so with me. What I find curious is that no-one who has ever written about the exchanges between Cherwell, Tizard and Blackett, not even Webster and Frankland, has noted that although the Prof used the results of our study to claim that bomber raids of the intensity that Hull and Birmingham had experienced were 'most damaging to morale', this was the very reverse of what we had stated.

The debatable effects of bombing on morale have been raised again in Tom Harrisson's posthumously published book, *Living through the Blitz*.[22] Most of what he wrote derives from the records of 'Mass Observation', the organisation of which he was head, and which for a time during the war was commissioned by the Ministry of Information and the Ministry of Home Security to provide what information it could about the way the British public was standing up to bombing. I do not know what value the Ministry of Information found in Tom's reports, but I do know that Stradling's department found all but none in the work which he carried out on its behalf. Since I was responsible for introducing Tom to Stradling, this was something of a disappointment to me, even though I was fully aware of Tom's propensity to generalise in a sweeping way from selected material. Tom's book indicates only indirectly that he had been brought into our work, and practically every reference to the Ministry of Home Security is so slanted that the book fails totally to reflect the atmosphere of the times and the environment of urgency within which the Ministry had to work.

Harrisson refers at length to the reports of the Hull and Birmingham enquiry, without apparently knowing who its authors were, and which he disapprovingly observes was characterised by 'war-conditioned undertones'. He also writes with approbation about an 'important paper' on morale by Cliff Emmens, without apparently realising that Cliff had also been concerned in the enquiry. And to confuse matters even further, he quotes a paragraph which he states came from the Report, whereas what he was quoting was lifted from the Air Ministry commentary on the Report, which was written by an air-intelligence liaison officer. So are myths born.

After the Hull and Birmingham Report was completed, the R.E.8 division of Stradling's department was formally asked to supplement the work of the relevant Intelligence bodies of the Air Ministry and to produce its own interpretations of the photocover of bombed German cities. Bernal and I were asked to direct this work, but other duties soon prevented me from giving it more than marginal attention.

In the course of the debate which the Prof's Minute opened up, Churchill decided to refer the question of bombing policy to Mr. Justice Singleton, with the following terms of reference:

'In the light of our experience of the German bombing of this country and of such information as is available of the results of our bombing of Germany, what results are we likely to achieve from continuing our air attacks on Germany at the greatest possible strength during the next 6, 12 and 18 months respectively?'[23]

Webster and Frankland make the same comment about Mr. Singleton's enquiry as they do about the Hull and Birmingham Report—it answered no questions and satisfied nobody. Here the comment is fully justified, even if they do not seem to have appreciated the significance of the fact that for the first time *a priori* opinion could now be tested against the scientific analysis of destruction. Both Bernal and I were summoned to Mr. Singleton's chambers. When I recall the questions he put about matters of which he knew nothing and which he did not have the technical competence to put, I am not surprised that his work was pointless. It would have been as appropriate for Bernal and me to have been asked to report on the desirability of some piece of legal reform as it was to ask a judge to provide a view about the possible effects of a bombing offensive.

There is just one postscript that needs to be added to this part of the story. In April 1961, *The Times* published a series of articles by R. V. Jones[24] to the title, 'Scientists at War—Lindemann v. Tizard'.[25] These pieces provoked a lively correspondence in which the dispute about area-bombing was again resurrected. Bernal got it into his head that it would be a good idea if we contributed to the exchanges, and to this end he sent me the draft of a letter which he suggested should be published over our two signatures. The letter told of the argument between Tizard and the Prof about bombing policy, and its drift was that Tizard had always been right, and the Prof always wrong. Des's letter included the sentence, 'I was never as deep as you in the 1942 controversy, and my files are so incomplete that I doubt if I looked them up they would provide anything you would not know or have access to. . . . Anything I write is just from memory.' That it certainly was. He appeared to have forgotten that the Prof's celebrated Minute had at least in theory been based on figures which he and I had provided. My own view was that it was inappropriate for us to participate in a public argument about two men whom we had both known, particularly as the draft letter was heavily slanted against the Prof. Having been reminded of the record, Bernal then agreed that no letter should be sent.

But I had another reason for not wanting to engage in the dispute. By his own admission Tizard believed as much as did the Prof in the policy of area-bombing. For that matter, as I have said, so did Blackett, at least implicitly. The difference between the three was a technical one— was the Prof using the basic figures we had given him accurately or not?

Blackett thought not. The truth is that neither he nor Tizard, nor indeed
the Prof himself, could have known what significance to attach to the
basic data. I suppose that Bernal and I knew more about the observations
from which they were derived than anyone else, but neither of us could
have said at the time whether the Prof was sixty per cent, six hundred per
cent, or six thousand per cent out. All the participants in the debate
were wrong. As we now know, bombing at about a hundred times the
intensity of anything ever suffered by European cities during the Second
World War at no moment broke the spirit of the people of Vietnam
against whom the American forces were fighting between 1964 and 1973.
In those nine years, seven million tons of bombs were dropped on South
Vietnam (which received about half of the total), North Vietnam, Laos
and Cambodia—three times the total tonnage of British, American and
German bombs dropped on European soil in the Second World War. [26,27]
And the seven million tons brought no victory—only death and destruc-
tion.

CHAPTER 8

COMBINED OPERATIONS

IT COULD have been little more than a week after Bernal and I had sent in our Report on Hull and Birmingham that I dined with an old friend who lived in the square next to the mews where Joan and I had our London flat. On my way, I recalled an earlier night when I had dined there, a night when incendiary and high explosive bombs were falling on London. We were all in high spirits, and my hostess dared me to go into the square and pick up an incendiary after it had been extinguished, because she wanted to send one to a friend in the States. I asked how it was going to get there. 'By diplomatic bag, of course,' she replied, looking at Harry Lucas, who presumably knew how this could be done. I had wined and dined well, and without thinking, left the others and went out to help the people who were putting out fire-bombs. I returned to the apartment with my prize, which in due course did arrive in America by diplomatic bag.

But on this later occasion, among the people who had been invited to dine was a new face, Group Captain Willetts. Our hostess had met him when flying back from the United States, where he had spent a few weeks on an official R.A.F. mission. Those were early days, but Willetts had already distinguished himself in a Commando raid on Norway, as he was also to do in the attack on St. Nazaire, and he sported the D.S.O. ribbon. Tongues were not as guarded then as they were to be later, and I soon discovered that Willetts was the 'number two' airman at Commando Headquarters (C.O.H.Q.), while he learnt about the surveys on the effects of air-raids that I had been carrying out. We got into a corner and I suggested that the information that we had been collecting to help our civil defence could readily be turned round and used in the planning of our own air attacks. We arranged that I should call on him next day in Richmond Terrace off Whitehall, to meet Air Vice-Marshal Robb, under whom he worked, and who was Deputy Chief in charge of the air element of C.O.H.Q.

Robb was not as impulsive as Willetts. I explained the work of Stradling's Department, and also told him about my particular contribution, emphasising the fact that through our experimental and field-studies we were able to assess the relative destructive and wounding power of bombs of different kinds and size. Robb did not commit himself that he thought this work could be useful in the kind of operations for which C.O.H.Q. was responsible, but it was left that he might get in touch with me.

Within a few days, Bernal asked me to meet him. He had received a letter from the Chief of Combined Operations, Lord Louis Mountbatten, as he was then styled, saying that Tizard had suggested that he, Bernal, should serve as scientific adviser to 'Combined Ops'. I told him of my talks with Willetts and Robb, and since we had worked as a team for Stradling, Bernal said that he would reply saying that he was ready to serve, but that I should also be invited. Almost immediately, I received a letter from Mountbatten asking me to join his staff. I replied very briefly saying that I should be pleased to serve, 'in association with Professor Bernal, as scientific liaison officer in the Experimental and Development Section of your Headquarters', adding, 'Would you let me know when you would like to see me?' Before a week had passed, Bernal and I were installed in Richmond Terrace.

The Commando organisation, several histories of which have been published, had been formally set up by Winston Churchill in June 1940. For a few weeks it was under the command of General A. G. B. Bourne, who was then replaced by Admiral of the Fleet Sir Roger Keyes, one of the great leaders of the First World War. The story of his stormy period of office is well told by Bernard Fergusson in *The Watery Maze*,[1] and in other books on the Commandos. The abrupt manner in which Mountbatten was informed in October 1941 that he was to succeed Keyes, is also described in various histories and biographies, and does not need retelling here, any more than I shall try at this stage to give my own picture of a man with whom my relations were in the end to become very close. But I soon became aware of the bewilderment of some professional officers on the C.O.H.Q. staff when they realised that Mountbatten, as Chief of Combined Operations (C.C.O.), proposed to bring in as advisers men who had had no background of military affairs. It was always part of Mountbatten's character to be wary of people who thought on conventional lines. However untrained independent scientific advisers might be in military matters, he firmly believed that their critical views would be bound to make the conventional planner sit up and take notice. I am not sure who stirred Mountbatten to get in touch with Tizard, and thus to write to Bernal and in turn to me. But when we arrived, he already had on his staff another civilian adviser, Geoffrey Pyke, not a scientist, but a man of a vivid and uncontrollable imagination, and a totally uninhibited tongue. It was Leo Amery, a Cabinet Minister, who had told Mountbatten about Pyke. Before this, Pyke, who was an old friend of Bernal, had already got in touch, uninvited, with Sir Roger Keyes, and had been rebuffed. Pyke once said to me, 'Mountbatten thinks he chose me. He's wrong. I chose him, because of the way he had devised new tactics for playing polo.'

Pyke has given his own picture of Mountbatten in an unpublished article which he prepared for a newspaper. It is reproduced in the biography that David Lampe wrote of Pyke.[2] 'Snobbery—by which in such a case is meant what the Americans call "snootiness"—is a violation of his [Mountbatten's] vitality. . . . To him an hour with an enthusiastic mechanic, or for that matter a stevedore, or scientist, or barrister, who will expand his personality by giving him an insight into their subject, their trade union or professional organisation, even their individual ambitions and fears, is more attractive than an hour of the laborious artificial laughter which constitutes so much of the social life of all of us . . .'. He also wrote that Mountbatten, while 'so quick in thought that few can get there before him . . . is almost, though not quite, inhibited from contemplation'. This to Pyke was one of Mountbatten's weaknesses. It was he who drew Mountbatten's attention to a sentence from one of G. K. Chesterton's Father Brown stories, in a note which he included in an enormous report that he had prepared on a project called *Habbakuk*, and which Mountbatten has ever since liked to quote. 'Father Brown', it goes, 'laid down his cigar and said carefully, "It isn't that they can't see the solution. It is that they can't see the problem" .' But as far as I was concerned in those first days, and I believe this was also true of Bernal, the first of Mountbatten's characteristics which appealed was his completely open mind, his dedication to his task, and his fabulous energy. I can remember seeing him in the evening, rocking on his feet with tiredness, but still as vigorous in his demands as he had been in the morning.

Pyke was already installed when Bernal and I were given an office in the Division of C.O.H.Q. which was responsible for new technical developments, and which was commanded by a naval captain, T. A. (Tom) Hussey. I was introduced for the first time to the world of initials, for which Mountbatten seemed to have a craze. Hussey was called C.X.D., an abbreviation for Coordinator of Experiments and Development. I do not know what Pyke was called, but Bernal and I were labelled X.S.A. 1 and X.S.A. 2. At first we shared an office, but Bernal, who became much busier than I, was soon given one of his own. I then shared an office for a short time with Douglas Fairbanks, a friend of Mountbatten who had joined the American Navy. Doug and I have been friends ever since. I was then put in with Pyke—that was not so easy. Unlike Bernal, I was not always privy to his problems, and I did not understand why he constantly moaned about the rest of the staff of Combined Ops, and about the world in general. A vivid memory of those days is of Pyke, on an occasion when he was condemning 'the machine', saying to me that he could see written in big letters on the walls of every Whitehall office, not 'mene, mene, tekel, upharsin', the words which Belshazzar failed to heed, but 'nothing should ever be done for the first time'.

In addition to meeting a number of officers who were concerned with the design of landing-craft, explosive devices, and a host of other military gadgets, I was also introduced to a glamorous mess (run by some very elegant ladies), of which I never really felt a member. More important, I was introduced to the planners: Colonel Antony Head,* Ian Collins, the publisher, and Robert Henriques, who was the only one I had met before. Robert, who had started life as a professional soldier, and then become a poet and a novelist, had rejoined the army just before the outbreak of hostilities. I had met him in Oxford about the time that France fell, when he was Brigade Major to General Carton de Wiart, a V.C. of the First World War who was reputed to have lost 'one of everything'. Robert had introduced himself to me, and had encouraged me and some of my friends to make 'molotov cocktails' to repel the expected invader. He would say, 'When we are driven out of Oxford, you are coming with us as our tame scientist, to hold out in the hills'. I forget exactly what mixture we put in our bottles, but I well remember our not very successful attempts to use fusee matches to ignite the contents. Robert was also much interested in my unsuccessful efforts to devise light-weight body-armour. The material which I used was two-inch-square packs made up of a hundred sheets of cellophane which we sewed into ordinary waistcoats. I gave up this venture when it became apparent that any material which was then available could stop a high-velocity fragment of metal, given that it had sufficient mass.

I first met the planners socially, as it were, and it was neither Bernal's nor my initiative that led Mountbatten to circulate a Minute to all his top staff which read as follows:

'I have decided that the two Scientific Liaison Officers, Professor Bernal and Professor Zuckerman, should be allowed to act as Scientific observers at the meetings of the planning syndicates, each taking a different operation in turn.

'2. This is an experiment to which I attach great importance as I am anxious to link up the scientists from the very beginning of operational planning so that when their scientific knowledge is required, they may be completely in the picture.

'3. For planning they will work directly under the R.M.A. just as for development they work directly under C.X.D.'

This instruction was issued little more than a month after we had

* In 1956 he became Minister of Defence in Anthony Eden's Government, and Viscount Head in 1960.

settled in Richmond Terrace. Settling down for me did not of course mean that I attended there every day. I still had the Oxford Extra-Mural Unit to look after, and from the record of the notes and papers that the Unit turned out, it is clear that its activities did not dwindle as a result of my new connection with Combined Ops. In fact, they multiplied. I spent the middle of the week in my London flat, the rest of my time being devoted to Oxford.

We were soon accepted as part of the 'establishment', and I have a feeling that the fact that we were a somewhat eccentric part was enjoyed not only by Mountbatten but in the end by many of our new colleagues. One day the whole staff was to be reviewed by King George VI on what some called 'the quarter-deck'. This was the terrace of Montagu House, the London home of the Dukes of Buccleuch, which at the time was part of the H.Q. of Combined Ops. It overlooked the Embankment and the Thames, and was demolished after the war to make room for the present Ministry of Defence. Bernal and I had been told to be on parade, but when I arrived, after most of the staff had already formed up, Des was not there. Mountbatten greeted me by saying that he was worried lest Bernal, who usually wore his hair very long, might have gone to have it cut. Fortunately, Des turned up in time, with his hair in its pristine state, and the King, who had been told what to expect, was not disappointed.

Bernal and I did not work on the same projects, and half the time I did not know where he was or what he was doing. The first specific job I was given by Mountbatten was to estimate the number of nights in a month in which the conditions would be suitable for small Commando raids across the Channel. I accepted the remit without question, and went off to the Air Ministry's 'Met. Office' to get as lengthy a series of records as I could about the direction and force of winds, on the assumption that these would give some indication of what was likely to occur in the future. There was no other way to get started. I then had to calculate the likelihood that winds of less than Force 5 would be associated with moonless nights and with the right height of tide on the enemy shore. The work of calculation was far more arduous than it was complicated, and was carried out mainly by Peter Krohn and Ben Burns in my Unit in Oxford. It took a month or so to do the sums with the help of a small manual calculator—there were no computers then—and at the end I proudly presented the results to Mountbatten with the words: 'Well, it turns out that there will never be a night suitable for a small raid'. This was not the only piece of useless work which I and others did in the war.

There were a number of other small jobs. I enquired into the possibility of using certain drugs to allay sea-sickness. I was called in to help in the training of a company of young marines who were commanded by Major 'Blondie' Hasler. What Hasler wanted from me were any tips which would make his men tougher than they already were, and in particular would improve their night vision. He also wanted to know how close he and his men could be, when swimming or diving, to an underwater explosion, a subject about which Admiralty information at the time was hardly accurate. I made a number of enquiries and also spent some days with his men at Southsea where they were being trained to handle canoes, and to slip in under cover of darkness in order to attach limpet mines to enemy ships. The one and only operation in which they engaged was both a success and a disaster, and has been recorded by Lucas Phillips in *Cockleshell Heroes*.[3]

Hasler and eleven men, with inflatable canoes, were transported by submarine to the mouth of the Gironde. One of the canoes was damaged when being launched, but the other five, with two men in each, set off up river to a point where several blockade-running cargo ships were at anchor. The seas were rough, however, and on their way in, first one boat with its crew of two disappeared, and then two others capsized. Two canoe crews managed to get through and set mines, but only Major Hasler and Marine Sparks returned home after a fantastic overland journey through occupied France into Spain. Those of the other eight who were not drowned were captured, and eventually shot by the Germans, the case being one of the war crimes that came up at the Nuremburg trials. When Hasler came to see me on his return, he remarked that he had failed to ask for something that would have made their task of escape much easier than it had been—'some smelly substance which would repel cattle'. When he and Sparks were lying up by day, they invariably found that cows gathered round them, so attracting the attention of the locals.

For some time I pursued the problem of night-vision as it affected Commando operations, but managed in the end to get this job taken over by others far better qualified to deal with the matter. Another problem that I was asked to investigate was the transporting of men who were wounded in small raids. The question of a ration pack for Commandos proved somewhat easier, and I tackled this, again with the help of Krohn and Burns. Until the middle of the war all troops were issued only with standard army rations, and the 'recipe' we devised, of compressed and dehydrated foods, had to be tried out in exercises in the Highlands, with Peter and Ben sharing in the endurance tests on limited calories which the troops had to undergo. A serious young major in the Commandos, Earl Jellicoe, was much interested in this work. He had just returned from the Middle East, where he had carried out some perilous operations which had earned him the D.S.O. He had several requirements, amongst them a device that would make it unnecessary for him and his men to carry the extra weight which the trimmings on their battledress entailed.

Every button, he explained to me, meant one bullet less. It pleases me to think that my long friendship with George Jellicoe, later to become a member of the Cabinet, and Eddie Shackleton's successor as Leader of the House of Lords, began in the austere framework of hard rations.

The first serious piece of planning I was given by C.C.O. was to devise a bombing programme for an operation called *Blazing*, the code name for a proposed assault on the island of Alderney. This was one of the Channel Islands whose defences had been considerably strengthened by the occupying German forces. The attacking force was to consist of a Commando and a Royal Marine Division, preliminary fire support being provided by a number of battleships and by some 250 aircraft of Bomber Command. I was instructed about the assault plan by Brigadier Copland-Griffiths, who had been deputed to lead the attack, and was told that the purpose of the aerial bombardment was to silence the batteries. I asked what this meant. His reply was 'to put the guns out of action'. 'How many guns are there to a battery?' I asked. 'That depends.' 'Is it necessary to destroy every gun? that is to say, to put a bomb down every barrel?' 'That also depends.' To my innocent mind the Brigadier seemed so imprecise about how bombs could silence a battery, and my questions must have seemed so stupid to him, that I decided to enquire in other quarters. I spoke to several officers whom I assumed had the necessary experience to answer my questions, and finally ended up with the Director of Artillery in the War Office. But my enquiries left me no wiser, and I was not surprised when no-one challenged my own arbitrary criterion for silencing a battery with bombs, which was to knock out, on average, one in every three guns. The idea at the back of my mind was that the density of bombing which this would demand would be bound to cause sufficient collateral damage to render the other two guns useless. Neither I nor anyone else knew anything about the 'vulnerable area' of a gun, much less that of a battery, but the concept of vulnerable areas was nonetheless valuable in assessing what any given weight of bombardment might achieve. Since it was clear that precision bombing could not be relied upon, and that on a most optimistic assumption the mean radial error of bombing would be a thousand yards, that is to say a thousand yards would be the average distance where bombs would fall from a designated aiming point, I made a series of laborious calculations for possible average errors of a thousand yards, fifteen hundred yards and even two thousand yards.

The idea was that there would be a single aiming point in the middle of the island, which measures $3\frac{1}{2}$ miles by 1. I therefore divided a map of Alderney into rectangles, and on the assumption that bombs fell in accordance with a normal probability distribution, I calculated the likely bombing density, in terms of tons per square mile, in each rectangle of

island, and particularly over the strong points which I was told had to
be damaged. I also tried to see what the effects might be if I superimposed
over a map of the island scale tracings of actual bomb plots as recorded
from German attacks on British towns. The results were not very encouraging, but nonetheless they did give some indication of the possible
damage that would result from the number of sorties which it was
assumed could be made in the space of an hour and a quarter before
the assault landings. It was also possible to show that significantly
different results would be achieved if the total bomb load was directed,
not at one, but at two targets. It was a striking indication of the in-
adequacy of our bombing techniques in those days that my calculations
showed that if one assumed a radial bombing area of a thousand yards,
one in five bombs aimed at the island would miss it, and that if the
average error were fifteen hundred yards, one in two. As well as making
estimates of the damage to strong-points, to big guns, and to the
proposed landing area, I also tried to assess the likely effect on the morale
of the defenders of what, in those days, was assumed to be a very heavy
aerial bombardment.

Since the island was within range of the big guns of Cherbourg, it had
never been intended to hold Alderney for more than some twenty-four
hours and, as I understood it, the purpose of the operation was to boost
British morale, and at the same time to show the Germans that we had
no intention of leaving them unmolested, either in the Channel Islands
or on the European mainland.

But the assault, planned for May 1942, had to be abandoned because,
as I understood at the time, the Germans had got wind of our intentions.
One historian, Michael Harrison, says that the real reason was that
Mountbatten had been ordered to transfer some of his forces to Montgomery in the Middle East.[4] Whatever the reason, the work provided me
with first-hand experience of what was in fact a new kind of planning.
At the time it did not occur to me to ask why the professionals were not
doing the kind of assessment that I had been asked to undertake. Only
later did I realise that I had been given the opportunity of opening up an
entirely new line of planning. The idea of carrying out an assault on the
island was resurrected later in the year under the new codename *Aimwell*,[5]
and I was asked to update my plan by assuming a different and larger
force of bombers, for what was intended to be a night raid on only the
eastern end of the island. Because of my earlier experience, this was not
difficult. But again the operation was called off. Little more than six
months later, however, I was called upon to apply the same variety of
planning analysis, but in a more sophisticated way, to the Italian island
of Pantelleria in the Mediterranean.

Neither Bernal nor I took part in the planning of the big raid on

Dieppe, but we knew what was in the wind, and had attended a rehearsal at which assault forces made a dawn landing at West Bay in Dorset. Mountbatten found me talking to some officers in the dark, and took me off to meet an American who had come to witness the operation. I had a fascinating talk sitting on an upturned fishing boat, and only as dawn broke did I discover that the man with whom I had been chatting was the famous cloak-and-dagger figure, 'Wild Bill Donovan'.*

Bernal and I asked to be allowed to go as observers in one of the naval support ships. This request was turned down by Mountbatten, who was unmoved by Bernal's comment that it was 'surprising that room could be found for war correspondents, but not for his two scientific advisers'. Whether we would have learnt anything had we gone, is another matter. Both of us, however, were deeply involved in various aspects of the subsequent post-mortem, Bernal reporting on the damage suffered by our naval and assault craft, and I on the casualties who returned. When I was discussing with the C.O.H.Q. planners what particular enquiries I should carry out, the door of their room opened, and an immaculately dressed officer entered. He paused a second, and then, addressing the 'desk warriors' with what seemed to me a slight note of contempt, asked 'Where are my wounded?' It was Lord Lovat, who had commanded the only fully successful part of the assault. I marvelled at the composure of a man who only a day or so before had been in an operation in which his small force on the right flank had completely wiped out the Germans defending the batteries and strong-points which it had been his responsibility to overrun.

The main enquiry that I carried out after Dieppe consisted of a survey of 500 of the 950 casualties who returned from the operation. They were not necessarily representative of all the forces that had been engaged, since some, like the Royal Regiment of Canada, had very few survivors. The survey was carried out with the help of a number of medically qualified members of my Extra-Mural Unit in Oxford, and once again I called on Peter Krohn and Ben Burns to help in the analysis. We were able to determine what weapons had caused most casualties, and the amount of protection given by different kinds of landing craft. It was also possible to show the extent to which the crew of landing craft were more vulnerable than the military personnel they carried—and in consequence, the considerable disorganisation which resulted when the crew were disabled. Mortar fire had been responsible for more injuries on shore than had been due to any other single weapon, and it was also apparent from the regional incidence of bullet wounds that the distribution of strikes on the body from rifle and machine-gun fire was almost a

* Major-General Donovan, the head of the United States Office of Strategic Services.

chance one. Soldiers took more than a little convincing in those days that the rifle was not a precision weapon under battle conditions. Whether or not our findings were of much use to those to whom they were submitted, I do not know. I myself did not gain much from the exercise. But years after, I remembered our sombre study when I stood under the Dieppe cliffs where so many had died.

The only other work in Combined Ops in which I was associated with Bernal, even if only for a short time, was project *Habbakuk*, the one which in the end drove Bernal and me along very different paths in the work we did during the war.

Habbakuk was the greatest and most monumental of Geoffrey Pyke's schemes. It was explained in a fat report sent to Mountbatten from Canada, where Pyke was trying to expedite work on a snow-vehicle called 'The Plough', another of his conceptions. I used to hear extraordinary stories about Pyke's eccentric behaviour in North America. One picture that sticks in my mind is of Pyke, in the company of a group of high-ranking officers, walking about in the snow in a shabby suit and a thin overcoat—and sockless. Another is of a meeting that had been arranged with Mackenzie King, the Canadian Prime Minister. For this Pyke had been encouraged to buy a new suit, the trousers of which were fitted with a zip, then a new-fangled contraption, instead of the usual fly-buttons. Before the interview, Pyke took the precaution of going to the lavatory, but unfortunately the zip stuck. Having failed to close his flies, Pyke decided not to waste any more time, and walking into King's office exclaimed, as he drew attention to his trousers, 'Prime Minister, I would not have to present myself to you in this state were it not for the fact that Canadian engineers are totally inefficient'.

The idea of *Habbakuk* was that a giant aircraft-carrier should be built out of a variety of reinforced ice, which in due course became known as Pykrete. The ship would have a hull thirty feet thick and be about half a mile long. It would contain workshops, living quarters, freezing plants, and would be able to launch any aircraft that was then either in service or on the drawing-board. No torpedo could sink it, and even though the ship cruised at only a few knots, it was virtually impregnable. The bound report was interleaved with pages on which Pyke had written personal and witty messages to Mountbatten who, having scanned it at home (when the report arrived he was away from the office with a feverish cold), passed it to Brigadier Wildman-Lushington, a marine officer who was his Chief of Staff, with a request that after he had read it it should be passed to Bernal. As Bernal was out of the office that day it was given to me. I returned it with the observation that my own experience was not wide enough to permit any comment except the general one that the idea of a vast ice-ship, if it ever could be achieved, was probably more suitable for times of peace than of war. Bernal then read it, and reported favourably. Mountbatten therefore felt justified in approaching Winston Churchill, whom he had no difficulty in infecting with his enthusiasm for the idea.

Instructions were given that *Habbakuk* should be pursued with all urgency and in the utmost secrecy. A *Habbakuk* Committee was set up with its own special registry, and I was told by C.C.O. that I was to be a member. I attended only the first meeting. Apart from regular serving officers, among the others who were there were the Prof, Bernal and Charles Goodeve,* a physical chemist who was Deputy Controller for research and development at the Admiralty. Pyke was still in America, becoming more and more frustrated with the slow progress being made with his 'Plough'. Neither the Prof nor Goodeve was enthusiastic about *Habbakuk*, and Goodeve's dampening comments angered Mountbatten considerably.

When the meeting broke up, I asked to be excused from the Committee, since there was nothing I could contribute. I was, however, invited to take part in one more meeting. In order to further the studies of the properties of fortified ice, Bernal had recruited Dr. Max Perutz, a brilliant young refugee glaciologist who had worked with him in the Cavendish Laboratory in Cambridge, and who, like Bernal, was interested in molecular structure. His achievements in this field were later to win him a Nobel prize. Perutz knew as much as anyone about the properties of ice, and had already been brought into the 'Plough' project. But by now he had been switched to work full-time on Pykrete. Consequently, by the time Pyke returned from North America, a considerable amount of work had been carried out to further his ideas. As usual, however, he was dissatisfied. At the time he was living in Cyril Ray's handsome flat in Albany, and being sick in bed with jaundice, he insisted that a meeting should be held in his room. I have memories of a most extraordinary conference with Mountbatten, Sir Harold Wernher, who was also on C.C.O.'s staff, Tom Hussey, Bernal and myself, all seated round the foot of a bed in which Pyke was sitting up, looking, with his strange beard, like some jaundiced Christ. Mountbatten tried to assure him that work was proceeding as fast as it possibly could. Pyke was not satisfied. 'Without faith', he kept protesting, 'nothing will come of this project.' 'But I have faith', replied Mountbatten. 'Yes,' said Pyke, 'but have the others got faith?', and turning to Harold Wernher he asked solemnly, 'Have you got faith, Brigadier?' Poor Wernher did not know what to say, but before he could utter a word, C.C.O. had chipped in with the remark 'Wernher's on my staff to see that I am not over-lavish with my own faith'.

* Goodeve later became Director of the British Iron and Steel Research Association.

That was the last direct contact I had with the project which, in spite of a considerable expenditure in resources, in the end came to nothing. *Habbakuk* was too big, it was too demanding in steel, and it was also too late in conception, to have any influence on the outcome of a war which was moving fast, and which was being waged by more conventional means.[6] It did however take up more and more of Bernal's time, and took him more than once to North America. He was in attendance at the Quebec Conference in the summer of 1943, at which Mountbatten gave a striking and now much reported demonstration of the properties of Pykrete. Having shown the Allied Chiefs of Staff who were present that a block of Pykrete, unlike one of ice, could not be shattered with an axe, he drew a pistol and fired first at a block of ice, which the bullet penetrated, and then at the Pykrete, off which the bullet merely bounced, fortunately not hitting any of the distinguished company. Bernal, at Winston Churchill's request, then had to demonstrate to President Roosevelt that Pykrete melted far more slowly than ice when put into hot water.

But if the President became convinced by all this, his Chiefs of Staff remained sceptical. They were accordingly instructed to prepare a paper setting out the precise nature of their objections. After his return to London from the Conference, Mountbatten told me that, realising that the American Chiefs were not as well informed as Bernal was about the 'pros and cons' of the project, the latter had offered them his help in drawing up their paper, and that his offer had been accepted. Bernal almost always—though certainly not always—knew both sides to a question. He had not been brought up by Jesuits for nothing. But his initiative on this occasion was brought to Winston Churchill's attention, who was not amused. 'Next time you come with me to a high-level conference', he told Mountbatten, 'you come without your scientific advisers.'

To the best of my knowledge, nothing practical has ever come out of the *Habbakuk* idea, whereas Pyke's snow-jeep, which never materialised in time to be used during the war, nonetheless was the prototype of a vehicle called 'The Weasel', which has played an important part in the exploration of polar regions. In his book on Pyke, David Lampe quotes Cyril Ray as saying that Pyke 'was the sort of man who would have invented the wheel'. My own view of Pyke is that if he had invented the wheel, he would have discovered, to his fury, that somebody else had developed a slightly different, possibly even a better, wheel, just before he had; or that the need which had generated the idea of a wheel had been satisfied in some other way. I always felt that the paradox of Pyke was that he usually combined an apparent precocity of view with being late on the scene. He was immensely imaginative, immensely courageous, and in a way a kind of genius. But practical genius demands both precocity and timeliness. Pyke seemed to be precocious because his ideas always appeared unnecessarily novel in relation to their defined purpose; and too late, because the environment which inspired him was always being transformed by other forces before he could catch up. Pyke was the kind of man who would never have rejected out of hand an idea, say, of freezing the clouds to make platforms for anti-aircraft guns. But he was never able to exercise the tolerance, which he would readily lavish on the new and improbable, on an idea that was accepted and proven. He was constantly being overwhelmed by the fantasies he created. He committed suicide in 1948.

I have said that *Habbakuk*, or rather Pyke, proved the beginning of a parting of the ways for Bernal and me. It happened like this. My overriding preoccupation in Combined Ops was with the question of the kind of fire-support that was necessary to assist assault forces, and also with the choice of bombs which could be used in operations in which the air cooperated with the army. The Battle of El Alamein had been fought during the last week of October and the beginning of November 1942, and in spite of Montgomery's victory, and of the bombing and strafing by the Desert Air Force, those of Rommel's men who had not become casualties or prisoners, had managed to retreat fairly successfully. As seen by some in London the simple question was: 'How did they get away in spite of continued attacks by our air forces?' I do not know whose suggestion it was, but it was proposed that Bernal and I should go out to the Middle East to see whether any lessons which could be useful to Combined Ops could be derived from a survey of the ground. At that time Sir Henry Tizard used to chair an informal committee of the 'independent scientific advisers' to the Service departments, and our proposed visit was discussed at a meeting early in December 1942. Various suggestions were made about matters into which we could enquire—Army/Air cooperation, and the relative effectiveness of fragmentation weapons being high on the list of priorities. The Staff of Combined Ops and the Staff of the Air Ministry also had their suggestions.

We did not manage to get away until 15 January 1943, flying tightly packed with two other passengers in a small Catalina flying-boat, which took off from Bournemouth. We came down first at Foynes on the west coast of Ireland, close to what is now Shannon Airport, and landed in a slight sea-fog. Bernal, who had been born in Ireland, was all but overcome with sentiment. After looking around, he turned to me and said, 'I feel like taking off my shoes, tying the laces together, slinging them around my neck, and just walking off into the mist'. At Foynes we and a growing number of other becalmed passengers were held up for nearly a week because of bad flying weather. The wait was very pleasant. We were out of the blackout for the first time in nearly two and a half years, and there was no scarcity of food or drink. We went for long walks across the countryside, where Bernal was at his very best, discoursing on the differences between the various ruined abbeys that we visited, and much else about the history of Ireland. Among the stranded company was Bob Robertson, who had been a member of the party of American scientists which had come to England in 1941. He was on his way back to England. Bob and I kept in touch from then on—he moved to the California Institute of Technology after the war—until his death in 1961 as a result of a car accident.

As soon as the weather improved, we flew on by way of Lisbon to Lagos. After two days there, we managed to get onto another aircraft which took us across Africa, stopping at Kano, where we spent a night, and then at Khartoum, where we stayed for three days. We reached Cairo, on 30 January, a fortnight after we had set out.

Headquarters of R.A.F. Middle East had been told by the Air Ministry that our task was to study at first hand the effects of British bombs on different types of target. Both Air Chief Marshal Sholto Douglas, who had recently taken over the Middle East Command from Air Chief Marshal Tedder, and Air Vice-Marshal Hugh Pughe Lloyd, then Senior Air Staff Officer, were interested in our remit, but wanted us first to go to Tripoli, which the 8th Army had just entered. Before we left London I had been given several letters of introduction, and those which I had the opportunity to present proved helpful, particularly one to General Tomlinson, the top medical man of the 8th Army, who had been asked by the War Office to help as much as he could in a casualty survey I was to carry out. We spent four very full days in Cairo talking to R.A.F. and Army officers about armaments, plans and policies, sorties, air photocover, and all manner of other subjects. The members of the small Army and R.A.F. Operational Research teams which had been set up in Cairo were much interested in our mission, and I gained the impression that they rather envied us our freedom. It had been arranged that while we had travelled out as civilians, we were to be treated as R.A.F. officers if anything went wrong, for example, if we were killed, and also that we should move around in quasi-military clothes, since if we got into trouble we would then be better treated than if we were dressed as civilians. Before our five days in Cairo were over, we were therefore not only loaded with masses of records, maps, photographs and rations, but also provided with the most makeshift uniform possible. Eccentric uniform was not unknown in the desert, with Montgomery setting the fashion, but I doubt whether two more awkwardly dressed men than ourselves existed in Africa. We must have looked less like airmen than like commissionaires of some seedy back-street hotel.

Montgomery had taken Tripoli on 23 January 1943, and it was there that about a week later Bernal and I were to start our enquiries. After spending a night at a camp called Marble Arch near Benghazi, we landed at the shattered Tripoli airfield of Castel Benito where we managed to get a lift into the town. Having first stopped at the R.A.F. Advanced Headquarters, we drove on to find accommodation. That done, we set out on foot to search for Brigadier Walker, the Deputy Director of Medical Services with the 8th Army. General Tomlinson had undertaken to warn him of our arrival.

More than a little lost, we decided to seek help in a small building which seemed to be some kind of H.Q., and where we asked a major in the outer office if he could put us in touch with the Brigadier. The major, whose name turned out to be Thomson, had every reason to be suspicious. We wore neither unit nor rank badges, and some wit in Cairo had thought it fun to fix a large brass crown to our fore-and-aft forage caps. Thomson had never seen anything like us before. We gave our names, and he then decided to help, but his efforts on a field-telephone failed to raise the Brigadier. Bernal then left in order to find an office where he could change some money. After a short silence, Thomson then asked, 'What did you say your name was?' I gave it to him again. 'Are you any relation to a man of that name who publishes in the *Journal of Physiology*?' he asked. I replied that I myself had published in that journal. Again a silence. And then, with his slight Scots accent, Thomson asked, 'Have you got a job for me?' I could only reply that he seemed to have a good job where he was. He then told me that he was medically qualified and officially attached to a unit concerned with chemical warfare, which was not going to happen, and that he had become tired of being pushed to and fro in the desert. He clearly had no strong belief that Rommel was not going to throw us back again. As he saw it, two scientists would not be in Tripoli if they were not going to do some interesting work. I said that of course we could use him, but how did we get him attached to us? 'Leave that to me, Sir,' was the reply. By then I thought he was fooling me, especially when he added—'and would you like me to report to you tomorrow with the Brigadier's car?'

By this time Bernal had returned, and I told him the gist of what had passed. For the next hour or so we walked around before going to our hotel, where we stayed up drinking and talking with two officers who had come into the town to buy wine for their unit which was camped on the outskirts.

I found Brigadier Walker the first thing next morning, but he was not much interested when I said we needed help. We then called on a Wing Commander White, the senior political officer in the military/political administration that had been set up in the captured town. He in turn

introduced us to the Prefect, the head of the Italian civil authority, who
offered to provide what help he could in the ground survey that we
wanted to undertake. Armed with these promises, we got a lift to R.A.F.
H.Q. at Castel Benito, where Major Thomson turned up with the message that Brigadier Walker had agreed that he could work with us. I
never did find out what tale he had invented for the Brigadier, on whom
we called after lunch. By this time he had received General Tomlinson's
letter, as a result of which he could not have been more affable. Above all,
he agreed with Thomson that we should be provided with a staff car.
The rest of the day, 'Sandy' Thomson came round with us as we explained to him the nature of our job. From nine o'clock the next morning
he was with us full-time. Neither of us could have guessed then that he
was to remain on my staff, first until the end of the war, and then as one
of my academic team in the University of Birmingham until my retirement from the Chair of Anatomy in 1968.

We spent a few days reconnoitring the town and harbour, deciding
what most needed to be done, and how to set about it. But just as we
were about to get started, Des said he had something to tell me. When
in Cairo he had been given a message which instructed him to make his
way as rapidly as possible to Canada for a meeting about *Habbakuk*. Des
had kept quiet about this for nearly a week. He had been just as nervous
about telling me as he always was when making a break with one of the
many women who used to fall in love with him. I was appalled at the
thought of being left alone, with the responsibility of carrying out not
only the enquiries for which I had become trained, but also those that
he would have done. I spent hours that evening, pleading with him by
candlelight—there was no electricity in the hotel—not to go, saying that
Habbakuk was nonsense, and rattling off a list of his many ideas and
projects about which he had got people excited in the past, and where
he had reversed his judgment at the last moment. I reminded him that he
had first urged that the bombs that we aimed at German cities should be
so fused that they would burst at roof height, and that after work had
accordingly been done on 'blast' bombs, he had then turned round and
said the idea was no good. He had been enthusiastic about the design of
more effective incendiary weapons, and then abandoned the idea. He
had formally proposed that when we dropped incendiary bombs on
German cities we should at the same time drop small anti-personnel
exploding bombs in order to deter the fire-fighters.[7] I gave a number of
other instances, most of them real, but a few no doubt imagined, where
his judgment had been at fault. Des became more and more silent as, in
desperation, I added accusation to accusation. But all to no avail. He had
already made arrangements to depart, and the next day I accompanied
him to the airport and sadly saw him fly away.

In retrospect, I used to think that if Bernal had not departed as he did, he, and not I, would have gone on to deal with strategic planning. In his book on Combined Operations, Bernard Fergusson refers to our parting, and writes that, 'The stratospherically high priority afforded him for the journey did not really do him much good: he was marooned thrice *en route,* once for a week on Ascension Island, again in Accra, and finally in the middle of a forest in Brazil (where Zuckerman would probably have been more at home) before he got to Ottawa.[1]

As it turned out, our parting effectively put an end to any further collaboration between us. That, however, belongs to a later story. But if I had lost Bernal, I certainly had a winner in Sandy Thomson.

CHAPTER 9

TRIPOLI

I COULD not afford to go on fretting about Bernal's departure; there was far too much to do and far too little time in which to do it. In any event, the few days we had had together had provided a really sound framework for the detailed enquiries that now had to be made. In addition to meeting Wing Commander White and the Italian Prefect, we had made ourselves known to Air Vice-Marshal Broadhurst,* who was just about to take over command of the Desert Air Force from Sir Arthur ('Maori' or 'Mary') Coningham. We had met his chief armaments officer, Wing Commander de Salis, who was much interested in what we were proposing to do, and who helped greatly in the enquiries on which I then embarked. The first time we lunched with de Salis in the R.A.F. H.Q. Mess (it had previously been Rommel's), Broadhurst came in late, noticed our presence, and said, 'Oh, you're the two fellows who've been sent out to see what's in a bomb hole'. He clearly was not much impressed by our mission.

I had again spoken to Brigadier Walker, and with Thomson had already visited a hospital full of wounded prisoners-of-war, and had arranged for a casualty survey to be carried out with the help of the Italian doctors. We had also made the acquaintance of some naval Intelligence officers who were anxious to follow the enquiries that had to be made of the damage to the quaysides and to the wrecks in the harbour, two or three of which we had boarded.

It was not exactly what I had come to the Middle East to do, but the chance of making a comprehensive study of an enemy town which the R.A.F. had bombed for more than two years was hardly to be missed. Such an enquiry had not been possible before. I would be able to study our operational orders, together with records of the numbers of sorties flown and of bombs dropped; there would be the debriefing reports of our own pilots who had carried out the attacks, and also Intelligence information from other sources, including assessments of damage made from the photocover taken after the raids. We had also been promised the enemy's own record of destruction and casualties, and of the extent to which the working of the town and its harbour had been dislocated.

* Now Air Chief Marshal Sir Harry Broadhurst.

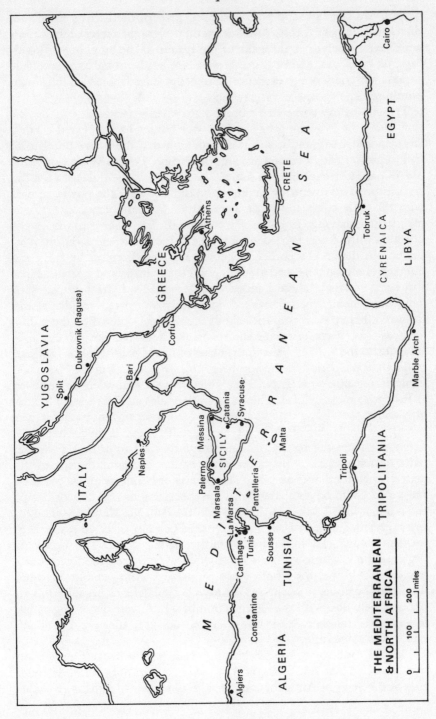

THE MEDITERRANEAN
& NORTH AFRICA

0   100   200 | miles

Tripoli had been a useful port of supply, first for the Italians alone, and then for Rommel's forces. And finally, there were the direct observations which we ourselves could make of the results of the bombing of buildings, of the docks, and of ships. It would at last be possible to reconcile a mass of converging evidence about the effectiveness of our own bombing. The prospect was exciting.

Tripoli was in a somewhat riotous state when we arrived. For the first time since the beginning of the war, our troops had captured a fairly large enemy town, and it was not surprising that the native population had to put up with a certain amount of jostling. But, as Wing Commander White sadly explained to me, although he was the link between the civilian population and the military, he did not have the power to deal with the daily complaints that were made about the way some of our men were behaving. In spite of the turmoil, the Italian authorities co-operated fully. I was provided with a list which gave the location of all the bombs they had recorded, together with the times of the raids, the number of aircraft that had attacked, and the damage and casualties that had been inflicted. These I indexed and marked on street maps. With Thomson's help I then embarked on a study of separate incidents, and followed this up with enquiries about the damage suffered by the public services: gas, water, sewerage and roads. As they were likely to be a useful index to the public's behaviour, I also obtained records of bus and rail traffic over the period of the bombing. Here again the Unione Nazionale Protezione Anti-Aerea (U.N.P.A.), which was the equivalent of our own A.R.P., was most helpful. The Italian authorities also gave me information about the claims that had been lodged for compensation for war damage. The identity of the bomb responsible for each incident had to be diagnosed from the nature of the damage that it had caused, from the pattern of strikes made by pieces of the casing, and from the size of the crater, when there was one. Such fragments of bomb casing as could be recovered could be compared with the specifications and dimensions of the bomb which I suspected had caused the damage. Naturally enough, my survey had to be a fairly general one. But I also selected some forty incidents which Thomson and I studied in fair detail. The U.N.P.A. organisation had thrown in its hand when we captured the town, but I encouraged White, for whom I had prepared a memorandum on what needed to be done, to reactivate the town's civil defence organisation, in order to help deal with the German bombs which were beginning to fall in increasing number. What was done was not very effective, but at any rate it was something.

The old Arab town, the Kasbah, filled me with sadness. One section was inhabited by a few thousand Jews who claimed to be lineal descendants of the Jews of Antioch, even though they seemed indistinguishable

from the Arabs amongst whom they lived. Both communities were fearful of the new invaders—their liberators—even more than they were of
the occasional German bomb. The densely-populated minute houses and
courtyards seemed to communicate with each other like the burrows of
a rabbit warren. When we were there a German bomb killed thirty people
in an area only 60 feet by 60 feet. Since such incidents could be investigated immediately, I took advantage of the opportunity of comparing
the relative effectiveness of our own weapons with their German and
American counterparts; for it turned out that American aircraft had also
raided the town during the weeks before its capture. Sandy and I
investigated the docks, which our own engineers were rapidly restoring
to working order, as we also did—to the extent it seemed useful—such
wrecks in the harbour, about six in all, as could be safely boarded. Here I
was closely shadowed by a naval Intelligence officer who seemed to
think that I was searching for something specific; he did not appear to
realise that I had never been on board a bombed and wrecked vessel
before, and that all I was doing was behaving like a naturalist, using my
eyes to take in what I saw, so that I could later draw whatever conclusions
were relevant. One day when we were in the dark on the lower deck of a
wrecked ship, he tripped badly, not having noticed a hole. I feared that
he had broken his ankle, and had some difficulty in helping him off the
wreck. He suspected that I had found out something which I was holding
secret, and that I wanted him out of the way.

Sandy was a quick learner, and was soon able to draw the required
plans, to take photographs of bombed buildings, and to make the necessary associated observations. In the end I had to leave much of this work
to him so that I could go off with de Salis into the countryside, on the
roads along which the retreating Germans and Italians had moved, in
order to study damage to guns, tanks and other vehicles. I was to see a
fair bit of destruction before the war came to an end, but the only
souvenirs which I came away with were two metal badges from the
charred remains of a soldier. One was the 'skull and crossbones' insignia
worn by members of the Waffen S.S., and the other a 'wound badge',
both of which I picked out of the ruins of a burnt-out troop carrier
close to the Tunisian border. Many months later I added to these the
tiny straw hats of a child's doll, which I found in the ruins of a house
near Cologne. My discussions with de Salis led us to arrange some crude
field-trials of the effectiveness of small bombs. I also took part in anti-
aircraft and strafing trials against abandoned tanks and guns, and was
impressed by neither. In addition to forays along the tracks of the
armies, I also had to continue my visits to the hospitals where I had
instituted the casualty survey, in order to find out how our prisoners-of-
war had been wounded, and in particular to see whether my previous

observations about the danger of small high-velocity fragments applied as much to the Middle East campaign as they had to the Dieppe operation. Sandy and I worked day and night, observing, recording, and bringing order to our notes; I kept a diary of each day's events. Only three or four times did I get away for a meal in the R.A.F. mess. Broadhurst had by now started to take an interest in my enquiries, and on one occasion I was pleasantly surprised to run into Patrick Kinross,* who was a Press Officer in Broadhurst's command. It was a change to talk to someone whom I had known before the war, to enquire about mutual friends, and to speculate about the way the post-war world would evolve.

It was soon clear that my work was going to be held up for lack of precise information about the attacks we had levelled against Tripoli, and about the weapons which had been used to strafe the retreating German and Italian forces. With only limited time at my disposal, but with Thomson well launched as a field worker, I therefore flew to Cairo towards the end of February, the aircraft in which I was flying coming down on an airstrip in the desert to pick up two captured German pilots. They had force-landed in our lines when strafing the day before, and were the first live Germans I had seen since the war began. One of them, an officer, was a good looking young man who spoke perfect English. His arrogant spirits were subdued only when he saw the new guard waiting for him when we landed at Cairo. He kept telling me that the tide would soon turn again in the Middle East, and that I was mad to believe that Hitler would be defeated.

I was extremely busy in Cairo, where I stayed for about two weeks, and where I was much helped by Hugh Pughe Lloyd, who, since our first meeting, had been given a new appointment as C.-in-C. of the Allied Coastal Air Forces in the Mediterranean. He was concerned to apply the lessons to which my findings already pointed—one of them being that we should stop fusing our bombs to explode on impact, which was then the prevailing practice in the Mediterranean, and instead fuse them to explode a fraction of a second after they had penetrated their targets. I also made the acquaintance of Air Commodore Traill, whose subsequent postings made it possible for us to go on being associated throughout the war. Sholto Douglas asked me to prepare an interim report of my findings. Bernal had, in fact, thought of committing to paper the general impressions which he had gained in the week he had been in the Middle East, but had abandoned the idea because, as he said in a letter he wrote before he flew off from Cairo, without the facts I was gathering he could only state 'generalities that got nowhere'. I felt much the same way when Sholto Douglas asked me for a report, but in spite of all the running

* Lord Kinross (Balfour before he succeeded to his title in 1939) an author and journalist, and a delightful host.

around that I had to do, I nonetheless managed to prepare a memorandum of about five thousand words[1] which, as it turned out, became the basis of the final report that I was to submit three months later.[2]

A Middle East R.A.F. Operational Research Section (O.R.S.) had been set up in Cairo towards the end of 1941. One of its members was John Kendrew,* a young chemist who had been put into the R.A.F., and whom Bernal and I met for the first time when we got to Cairo. He gave me a great deal of help, and undertook to be the 'post-office' through which Sandy would send me his field-work reports after I had left Tripoli. He also arranged for another O.R.S. officer to be detailed to collect such further information as I wanted. So as to get Sandy acquainted with the O.R.S. people in Cairo, I then arranged for him to join me there before I returned to Tripoli. I was also helped in Cairo by Patrick Johnson, the Director of an Army O.R.S., whom I had known as a science don in Oxford. Information was provided about the sorties that had been flown against Tripoli, including a number that had been carried out by the 9th U.S. Bomber Command, and about the casualties we had suffered. I also obtained aerial reconnaissance photographs of Tripoli and Tobruk and other targets, together with contemporary assessments of the damage we had caused. I had numerous discussions about the right fusing for our bombs, and successfully urged that trials of small fragmentation bombs, similar to those I had already laid on in Tripoli with de Salis, should be made in the Cairo region. Tank experts gave me their views about the most effective weapons to use in aerial attacks on tanks, and about the defects of our own armoured vehicles. Copies of interrogations of prisoners-of-war, and copies of reports which had been made of the effects of bombing during our pursuit of Rommel from El Alamein to Tobruk were also provided. In short, I was denied no information. A number of enquiries were launched at my request, and I was able to return to Tripoli confident that the data which we had already collected on the ground, and the further observations which were going to be made, could be fitted together.

On the other hand, by the time I had finished my various enquiries in Cairo, I had become fairly convinced that the records which were available about the land battle, or which were likely to be obtained about a battle, were of very varying quality. Usually they were too imprecise to provide information which could be analysed in the way that seemed

* After the war, Bernal encouraged John to take up the subject of which he became a leading exponent. He succeeded in unravelling the molecular structure of one of the most important proteins of the body, an achievement for which he was awarded a Nobel Prize. After I became Chief Scientific Adviser to the Ministry of Defence in 1960, John joined me for a time as my part-time Deputy. Today he is the Director of the European Molecular Biology Laboratory.

clear for air operations. It seemed pointless to enquire, as I had been asked to do before coming out, into the precise relation between numbers of casualties or yards of advance on the one hand, and different intensities of artillery bombardment or of aerial bombing and strafing on the other. A somewhat pessimistic note in my daily record reads:

'A battle is won in a certain way; it might very well have been lost. It might have been won or lost in a million ways. 80 tons of bombs . . . stopped the [German] tanks reforming for the attack on Kidney Ridge on the 27th Oct. A lucky shot from a rifleman the year before . . . killed the [German] C.O. on the spot, with the same result. In the first campaign revolvers . . . captured two divisions of German tanks; in this campaign the 90th L.D. German division were also taken in their shirts when bedding down.

'It seems that there is little that can be gleaned for scientific analysis in this sort of situation. One can hardly say that "this" is the best way to equip a battalion, and that "this way" will bring victory. One can merely say "this" is a better way than "that" way—on the slight assessment of weapons. Good weapons in the hands of poor troops are—within limits—much less effective than bad weapons in the hands of good troops. To assess which weapons are better requires in the first place experiment, and little else but that. Battle records don't seem to me to hold the answer.'

While in Cairo, Sandy and I flew to Tobruk, where we spent two days, the time permitting of little more than a general survey of the deserted, derelict town and harbour, a short report of which I subsequently appended to my more voluminous one on Tripoli. We managed to board one wreck and lunched on biscuits and sweets which we salvaged from a case that had been washed ashore from one of our own wrecked ships.

There was little time for any social life, but I was able to do some shopping in Cairo, buying presents for Joan. Through Combined Operations she had managed to send me a confidential telegram to say that I was about to be elected a Fellow of the Royal Society. That was very nice news which, however, I had to enjoy in secret until I got back.

I returned to Tripoli on 12 March and resumed my ground survey, this time helped by the sortie data, aerial photographs and photo-interpretations which I had brought from Cairo. The discrepancies between the photo-assessments of specific incidents and what had actually occurred were usually considerable. It had been arranged that Hugh Pughe Lloyd would pick me up in Tripoli on his way from Cairo to his new H.Q. in Algiers, where he wanted me to meet Air Chief Marshal Tedder, now Air C.-in-C. to Eisenhower in the North African

Theatre, before I returned to England. Sandy and I therefore agreed the lines of a precise programme for the house-to-house and casualty studies which he was to carry out while I was away, and of the further information which the Italians had to provide about damage to the public services. So anxious was I that there should be no delay in my getting the information he was to collect that we also arranged that he should send me daily a record of his work.

But not long after I left, and in spite of the continued support which he was given by Brigadier Walker, Sandy began to run into trouble with the Army authorities. It was one thing for me to have a staff car; as a major, he did not rate one. There was also trouble about his office accommodation. The next thing was that a senior R.A.M.C. officer who had learnt about the casualty survey that I had started, wanted to launch one himself and to have Sandy assigned to it. Then the Army O.R.S. in Cairo, which before had taken a keen interest in my work, decided that they should undertake a survey of the same kind. This, too, would have meant tripping Sandy up. And so it went on. Sandy kept me informed of his difficulties, and when back in London I tried to get him transferred from the chemical warfare branch of the 8th Army to an Operational Research group where he could be assigned to me. Fortunately, the Army authorities in London in the end took the view that the most economical way they could obtain the sort of information they wanted would be to use me as their agent. It was therefore possible to demolish one by one the obstacles that were being laid in Sandy's path by the Cairo authorities, so that in spite of much pin-pricking, he managed, in about two months, to complete the programme of work that I had given him. He even managed to complete rough and ready field-trials of two fragmenting missiles. These were about to be stopped because the armament officer who had undertaken to do them for me was posted to another job.

Hugh Pughe Lloyd's arrangement to pick me up in Tripoli worked perfectly. We arrived in Algiers on the afternoon of 15 March, and later that day I joined him at the Standard Oil Building, which was the H.Q. of the Northwest African Air Forces. Here I again met Robb, who had been sent out from Combined Operations to be Deputy to General 'Tooey' Spaatz, the Commanding General of the Northwest African Air Forces, to whom he introduced me. At dinner with them that night I met several of Spaatz's senior staff officers for the first time, including Brigadier General 'Pete' Quesada, and Colonel Lauris Norstad. They had only been in the war for a few months and were keen to hear about my enquiries. They were men who were learning, as I was learning, and unlike some professional military people whom I had already met, there was no assumption of superior knowledge, and no assurance that they knew how Germany was going to be defeated. We continued talking and speculating about bombing strategy and tactics until long after dinner.

Robb and Norstad wanted to involve me in their own affairs, and the next day was taken up with a continuous series of meetings about bombing objectives, tactics and accuracy, and about the fusing and size of bombs appropriate to different targets. At the time it was assumed that the Axis forces, which were being driven together from the east and west, would make a ferocious last stand in Tunisia, with our air forces heavily engaged in support of the Army. Again I found myself having to explain that biggest does not necessarily mean best, even in the world of bombs, and once more managed to organise some local field-trials to determine the relative effectiveness of such anti-personnel bombs as were available.

I also had several discussions about the way O.R. teams, which the Services were filling mainly with young academic scientists, should be used, and about the kind of enquiries they should undertake. An embryo O.R. organisation had already been set up in North Africa, but it was clearly remote from the real command. I had had similar talks in Cairo, particularly with Kendrew, who, until Hugh Pughe Lloyd left for Algiers, had been the latter's link with 'the scientists'. Hugh Pughe was particularly anxious that a good O.R. team should again be attached to his Command, but the question was: who? It seemed to be largely a matter of personalities. An unsuitable man or men might be way out on a limb, remote from the people who made the operational decisions. I had been surprised to find that several of the O.R. people I had met in Cairo had envied me the job I was doing. And at the start I could not understand why they had not, of their own initiative, followed in the wake of the army to study the effects of air operations. I soon realised that this was mainly because they were bureaucratically tied to the jobs to which they had been assigned, and because the men responsible for actual operations often failed to welcome their presence. Many of the O.R. people literally had nothing to do. They had simply been posted to the Middle East or North Africa, and that was that. Several who had been commissioned and selected for O.R. also lacked the imagination which the job demanded. It needed more than a young scientific 'hack' to open up what was to become a major field of interest, the natural history of war, and also to help operational research evolve into what today is the vast area of management studies, computerised systems analysis, and forecasting. Indeed, most of the scientists who were available for O.R. work were young men of average ability with no experience of research. I undertook to do all I could on my return to the U.K. to help improve the situation, and in particular to try to break down the isolation in which many O.R. people worked. What I wanted was to see them admitted to the innermost planning circles, and, where appropriate, to act as complementary 'brains' for the operational chiefs, in the way Mountbatten used his two scientists at C.O.H.Q. This did not seem to me too much to ask. After all, I did not regard myself as an O.R. man, yet my own observations about the fusing of bombs, made in the space of a few weeks, had modified the prevailing practice in the Middle East. Others should be able to do likewise. Kendrew and I exchanged several letters on the subject, but I doubt if the many protestations which I made on my return to London, to Tizard and others in positions of authority, achieved much.

During the course of the day's discussion, I met Major-General Jimmy Doolittle, who breezed in somewhat deafened after two days' flying, unperturbed by the fact that he had just crash-landed. I had heard of him as the man who had taken part in a small and audacious raid on Tokyo after the Pearl Harbour disaster, but was not prepared to find a two-star general who led his own bomber group in the air, and who was so open-minded and easy in his manner that it required no more than a few minutes talk with Norstad for him to agree to change the fusing of the bombs he was going to carry on an operation the next day.

It had originally been arranged that I was to remain only two nights in Algiers. But on the second day, in spite of my protests, Spaatz and Robb cancelled my flying orders, having decided that I was not to leave until they had got as much as they wanted from me. The next morning I arranged a set of small bomb trials with the Chief Ordnance Officer to the Northwest African Air Forces. The afternoon was spent with Tedder. We were alone for all but the first hour or so. He was very friendly and pleasant, and when we were left to ourselves our talk flowed smoothly, with questions and answers, comments and objections, coming without hesitation from either side. But during an interval when Brigadier General 'Pat' Timberlake, his Director of Operations, was with us, he sometimes adopted the sardonic manner for which I was to discover he was well known. 'What's the matter with you, Pat?' he said. 'You haven't asked a foolish question for quite ten minutes.' I was also struck by the fact that the telephone never interrupted us during the almost four hours I was with him.

There was hardly a topic on which we did not touch. We began with questions relating to armaments and tactics, for Tunis, Tedder told me, was going to be Germany's Dunkirk, and the Germans must not escape as we had done. We discussed personalities, the problems of bi-national command, and agreed that Norstad was outstanding among the young officers. We dealt with strategic matters. The air must win its own battle before it could help fight the army's or navy's, neither of which could help the air. Tedder then seemed to believe, even if not fervently, in the Trenchard policy of directing the bomber against the enemy's industrial

centres. He had been sent a copy of what I had written for Sholto Douglas, and was impressed by my preliminary report on Tripoli. He wanted
corresponding studies carried out on other enemy towns that had been
captured. But where were the men to do this work? Tedder gave me
more than a little to think about, and I marvelled that a man who had
such a load of immediate responsibility on his shoulders could give up
an entire afternoon for an exchange of views with me.

Next morning was again spent with Norstad, Robb, and Traill, who
by then had also been transferred to Algiers, and on that occasion I
managed to persuade them to arrange for my return to the U.K. the
following day. Acting on a suggestion made by Tedder, I was also sent
to see General Legentilhomme, of the Free French Army, and General
Bouscat, the head of the French Air Force, to encourage them to engage
French scientists in operational research. This was a fruitless task. As
professional military men they simply could not see what civilian scientists could contribute to their affairs.

I joined Spaatz for lunch, with talk of yet more jobs they all wanted
me to do. Throughout the afternoon I found myself being drawn into
their problems, with Doolittle offering to take me as an observer on his
next raid. Before dinner Robb called on me at my hotel for a final talk,
and after he left I barely had time to pack and get ready to go to Tedder,
who had decided that I should spend my last night under his roof. While
I was waiting on the hotel terrace for the officer who was to pick me up,
I heard my name being called. I looked up, and there on the pavement
was a young bearded seaman. It was Derek Mond, Henry Melchett's
elder son, and Joan's cousin. I had watched him grow up, and after he
had left Eton, a year before the war began, had encouraged him to try
for a Christ Church scholarship, which he had won. During the few
months that he had had to wait for the beginning of the University
term, he worked with me as a technician. In his next two years as an
undergraduate, he had become outstanding in student affairs, and had
married. He then enlisted in the navy as an ordinary seaman. When I
called to him to join me he was worried about coming into what was
obviously an officers' mess, but I assured him that since I did not know
the rules, he had to have a drink with me. He was killed about a year
later, shortly after he had received his commission.*

Tedder's other guests that evening were his four chief British and
American staff officers. From my point of view, Air Vice-Marshal
Wigglesworth, Tedder's Deputy, turned out to be the most significant,

* Derek's younger brother Julian joined the Fleet Air Arm as soon as he could,
and some time after the war became the first Chairman of the British Steel Corporation. On his death in 1973, his son Peter succeeded to the family title, and as the
present Lord Melchett is a Minister of State in Mr. Callaghan's Labour administration.

for I was to work very closely with him from then on. The four left fairly early, and Tedder and I stayed up talking until well after midnight. He seemed avid for conversation. At the time I did not know how lonely a man he was. His wife had been killed in an aircraft accident only two months before.

I left Algiers the next morning, having been warned by all my new friends that they were soon going to get me back, and flew to London by way of Marrakesh.

During the two months that I was at home, most of my energies went into the preparation of my main Tripoli report. For its period, the information that I had collected was unique, and its analysis necessitated the assistance not only of members of my Oxford Extra-Mural Unit, but also of some of Stradling's staff at Princes Risborough. With this help, I was able to complete a fairly full report of my enquiries,[2] which I submitted to the Air Staff and to Mountbatten in Combined Ops before returning to North Africa on 22 May 1943. Unfortunately, I could not discuss my findings with Bernal. For all except my last two days in England he was busy working on *Habbakuk*, for the better part of the time in Canada.

Most of my conclusions were pretty discouraging. In spite of the fact that the majority of the thousand or so R.A.F. aircraft which had attacked Tripoli at night during the preceding two years had claimed to have reached their primary target, fewer than twenty per cent of their bombs had fallen within the city limits, which comprised an area of approximately five square miles. Less than ten per cent had fallen within some two miles of the point at which they were aimed. The average bombing error of some 100 of 200 heavy and medium American bombers which had been sent to attack the town, and which had managed to reach their target, was only about half a mile. There was little relation between the claims made by pilots in their sortie records, the effects as they were experienced by the citizens of Tripoli, and the damage that Sandy and I had seen. The photo-assessments were also often wide of the mark. Compared with the air-raids on British towns, relatively little damage had been suffered by the public services. Casualties had also been relatively light, and analysis showed that the standardised casualty rates for our bombs were somewhat below those for German bombs that had fallen on English cities. Between 20 and 40 people had been dehoused for every ton of bombs dropped on Tripoli (as opposed to over 50 in Hull and Birmingham), but dehousing had not constituted a problem, since many Italians had already left for Italy, and as fast as people were bombed out, other houses became available. Morale in the town had nonetheless been poor, and the information that I collected indicated that during the period of the attacks, more than half the population had either evacuated to live on its outskirts, or 'trekked'—sleeping on the periphery and returning to their homes in the mornings.

It was particularly discouraging to discover that despite the many night sorties which the R.A.F. had directed at the harbour, only two ships had been put out of action completely, whereas four big enemy vessels had definitely been sunk by a relatively small number of American daylight sorties in the last week of November and the first weeks of December 1942. It also turned out that because of poor Intelligence, ships which had already been damaged had been designated as targets for further attack. The Tripoli docks had not been significantly touched, and daily unloading was little affected at any time. Tripoli had, however, never been absolutely vital, as had Tobruk, to the Axis armies in the Western Desert, and in any event Rommel had decided—probably at least a month before it was surrendered—that the town would not be defended. From that moment on, little shipping had entered the port. Tobruk had been bombed in a much more concentrated way, and from the point of view of damage to shipping, and to the timely destruction of one tanker in particular, our air operations there had been far more significant to the outcome of the war in the desert. The damage to Tobruk had also been far more extensive than in any comparable area of England. Every house showed some signs of damage, and about half had been damaged beyond repair.

From the point of view of possible immediate action, the most important of my findings was that, weight-for-weight, our own bombs were less destructive than their German or American counterparts. In addition, we had clearly not been using the best fusing techniques that were available to us. The observations I was able to make on the effects of our attacks on tanks, guns and motor vehicles were mostly negative, and of little practical value.

Apart from the preparation of the Tripoli report, I also had to bring myself up-to-date with the work of my Oxford Unit, and attend to my duties in Combined Operations. Without my realising it at the time, people were beginning to treat me as though I was an all-round expert on bombing operations. But I can see now that they had reason for doing so. An enormous amount of effort had been put into solving the technical and tactical problems of bombing, but at that time hardly any into the study of its effects. And that is where I came in. One accident after another had transformed me into a pioneer in this field of study. No sooner, therefore, was I back than several people wanted to see me. Mountbatten in particular wanted my up-to-date views about 'air support for assaults', and this meant preparing a special memorandum for him. I began by reflecting on Tedder's insistence that the primary function of air power was to achieve sufficient air superiority to allow our aircraft to operate freely. I went on to say that, given this superiority, the first targets that the air should take on should be those which were out of immediate reach of either land or sea power.

'This principle', I then added, 'may be said to underlie our policy of bombing industrial and other targets both in Germany and in enemy-occupied territories—a policy which further depends upon the assumption that our air strength is sufficiently great and our weapons sufficiently powerful to have a serious influence on the course of the war by this attack on central objectives. Other "secondary" activities of the R.A.F. include the provision of sorties against enemy shipping and submarines, and the provision of tactical groups to cooperate with land forces. The publicity given to our bombing obscures the fact that these other activities of the R.A.F. probably consume a far greater effort than is expended in air-attacks on Germany.

'The fact that there is controversy about the strategical disposal of the Air Force strength as between bomber, anti-shipping, anti-submarine and direct Army-support efforts shows that these issues are largely matters of opinion, and suggests that they are unlikely to be settled to everybody's satisfaction even when our air strength is double or treble what it is at present. Germany obviously does not dispose of its air strength in the same way that we do. In 1940 her major efforts were directed to bombing attacks on this country. Today they appear to be very largely given to direct support of Army operations (if one can judge from the slight reports there are on the use of the air on the Eastern Front, and from the absence of major air-raids on this country).'

Because heavy bombers could not at that time be relied upon to aim accurately, I went on to point out that it was useless to lay on 'a normal bomber attack to neutralize pin-point targets such as gun-positions. On the other hand, plastering an area target with a sufficient number of bombs may destroy fixed defences and will in any event seriously disturb enemy formations (a) directly, by causing casualties and damage to structures, and (b) indirectly, by its effect on morale.' I emphasised that bombing was not aerial artillery fire, and that bombing military targets with too little strength was wasted effort. The concentration which I advocated would have called for, on average, about seven 500 lb bomb strikes in every 100 yard square. I concluded with the question of bomb sizes, saying that: 'It should be noted that very large bombs such as our 4000 and 8000 lb varieties, in spite of the heavy advertisement which they continue to receive in the Press, are likely to do much less against fixed defences, per ton load and per sortie, than smaller bombs. It is known that they have very little effect against strong reinforced concrete fixed defences, and their lethal radius is not sufficiently great to encourage any belief that their use would wipe out an area from the point of view of personnel. The blast from an 8000 lb bomb will frequently not even kill a fully exposed rabbit at 100 ft. It certainly would not kill men at this distance.' I was, of course, referring only to the shock-wave set up by an explosion.

'Large bombs, as is believed by some, may pay handsomely by demoralising the enemy forces, but the best results against personnel in the open or slit trenches, against M.G. [machine gun] nests and against gun positions not heavily enclosed by, or covered over with, concrete would undoubtedly be achieved by the use of smaller bombs, including bombs even as small as the American 20 lb fragmentation bomb.'

This was only one of several memoranda which I had to prepare for Combined Ops, and my stay in England passed all too quickly. I wrote the finishing lines of the Tripoli Report before I had had time either to analyse all the material which I had brought back with me, or that which Thomson had sent.

On the 10 May a telegram arrived at Combined Ops from Robb asking me to return to North Africa as quickly as possible. I was not told precisely why I was wanted, but having learnt from my previous trip that I was not likely to be idle, I arranged that Ben Burns should come along from the O.E.M.U. to help in whatever I was asked to do. To expedite matters, it was also decided that I should be given the honorary rank of Group Captain in the R.A.F., and that Ben Burns should be made a Flight Lieutenant. Mountbatten gave me lunch shortly before I left, and had, in fact, advised me against accepting any rank. 'The most they would make you', he said, 'is an Air Vice-Marshal, and then you'd have to say "Yes, Sir", to an Air Marshal. And', he added, 'you don't even call me "Sir".' It nonetheless seemed prudent to do what the Air Ministry suggested.

Before I left London, there was one matter which had to be settled. I was asked to account for the £102 10s. 0d. which I had been given to cover my subsistence for the two months that I had been in Cairo and Tripoli. Since I could only account for £81 5s. 0d., I was asked to return the difference. My cheque was duly receipted.

PANTELLERIA

TEDDER'S OPENING words as I walked into his office in Algiers were, 'You're late'. He was in one of his facetious moods. A great deal had indeed happened during the two months I had been in England. After the failure of their counter-attack in the Kasserine battle, the Germans and Italians had been pushed further east into Tunisia, into which the remains of Rommel's command, defeated at the Mareth Line by the 8th Army, were being driven from the south. The Allied forces were now operating under a form of unified command, and the skilful deployment of our own forces prevented the Axis troops from consolidating any defensive position. Defeated on the ground, and with no means of escaping from Africa, they had wisely decided to surrender, rather than undertake any fight-to-the-death stand or expose themselves to an operational test of the efficacy of anti-personnel bombs. A quarter of a million prisoners were taken.

Tedder told me that Army–Air coordination had been far from perfect in the North-African Theatre, mainly because the campaign had not lasted long enough for the right lessons to be learnt—as they had been in the Western Desert. He was concerned lest the wrong conclusions would now be drawn about the role of air power in a land campaign. Too many generals seemed to regard aircraft as aerial artillery to be used in 'penny packets' when they wanted support, whereas in his view it was the concentrated air attack on shipping, as a result of which supplies had been denied to the enemy, that had mattered most in the North-African campaign—a view which, not surprisingly, I later found was contested by soldiers whom I met. After a while he beckoned me to a table on which were stacks of files, and invited me to go through the various operational orders and reports of the past two months, adding, 'tell me what we've done wrong since you've been away'.

Remembering my first meetings with him, I was not put off by his almost automatic bantering tone. But after about half an hour I had to say that apart from the attacks on shipping, the records could not be used as a basis for generalisation since they told little that was precise about the targets that had been bombed, or about the accuracy and results of the attacks. Our talk then turned to the forthcoming invasion of Sicily and Italy, and to the way the war was likely to develop. We were alone for nearly two hours, after which he suggested that I should visit the Chief Intelligence Officer to learn from him what I could. He, however, did not have the time to tell me very much, and I was relieved when Tedder collected me to take me to his house, where I was going to spend the night.

The other officers who were at dinner left fairly early, leaving me to talk with Tedder till after one in the morning. We discussed any number of matters, but he was not forthcoming when I asked why Robb had signalled for my return to the Mediterranean Theatre. The message I had received simply said that I was to study the enemy collapse in Tunisia and the effects of air-raids. The furthest Tedder would go was to say that I would learn the real reason for my recall on the following day, when he was having me flown to Constantine, where Tooey Spaatz now had his headquarters. Spaatz and Robb would explain exactly what it was that he, Tedder, wanted me to do. Having studied the matter carefully, I was then to telephone him as soon as possible, preferably not later than 48 hours after arriving, to say whether the operation could succeed—and for the sake of security, the shorter my message the better.

Next morning I visited the Army Medical Headquarters to introduce Ben Burns to Major-General Cowell of the Royal Army Medical Corps, so that Ben could start off yet another casualty survey. I also saw Hugh Pughe Lloyd, who was still commanding the Mediterranean Coastal Air Forces. Hugh Pughe (Tedder called him Huff Puff) was concerned that there had been no proper analysis of the effects of the earlier attacks on shipping, which in his view had hastened the German collapse, and none at all of the attacks which were still going on against Axis shipping in the Mediterranean. After lunching alone with Tedder, I was sent off to the airfield, where a plane was waiting for me. But after a short time in the air we had to return because of engine trouble. It was the middle of the afternoon before I reached Constantine.

Spaatz's staff were accommodated in a school, to which I was driven to see Norstad, who by this time had become Spaatz's Chief Operations Officer and a one-star general. We had a long talk about the part bombing might have played in the collapse of the Axis, and about the possibility that air attacks on the German land forces had deprived them of necessary supplies and so forced them to surrender. We then drove to General Spaatz's house, a somewhat unattractive small suburban villa overlooking the town, where I learnt that I was expected to provide a detailed plan to capture the island of Pantelleria by bombing. Robb was there, and I realised that the reason why he had called for me was that he saw in Pantelleria another Alderney, the island for whose capture I had planned when we were together in Combined Operations in London.

About eight of his most senior officers comprised Spaatz's mess, and talk was free and easy, both during and after dinner. A land assault on Pantelleria by the 1st British Infantry Division under Major-General Clutterbuck, whom Spaatz insisted on calling 'Clusterbottom', was planned for 11 June, only fifteen days away. Rear-Admiral Rhoderick McGrigor was in command of the naval forces that had been allocated for the operation, and Eisenhower himself was in overall command. There was no plan in the sense I understood the term, only a statement of intention, and I realised that I had to work hard in the next two days if I was to have an answer for Tedder who, as Air Commander-in-Chief under Eisenhower, was senior to Spaatz. I had, in effect, become adviser on planning to both.

Pantelleria is a small rugged volcanic island, some nine miles long and six miles wide, which lies between the Tunisian coast and Sicily. It had been a forbidden Italian defence zone since 1926, and was believed to be heavily fortified, being variously described as the Italian Gibraltar or Malta. Mussolini used to boast that it was impregnable. Together with its smaller sister island of Lampedusa, it was also an 'advanced listening post'. Obviously, therefore, the assault on Sicily, which was planned to take place in July, would be prejudiced if Pantelleria were not first reduced. Eisenhower regarded its capture as a vital strategic prerequisite to the invasion of Sicily. His plan, as it was set out later in his official Dispatch,[1] was to shatter the morale of the garrison—estimated to number about 12,000 men—by intense air and naval bombardment, and if possible, to induce it to surrender before the British Division went in.

Bombing operations, together with a certain amount of naval fire, had begun on 18 May, but when I arrived no-one seemed to know what effect they had had on the island's defences. The only obvious place for a landing was in the north of the island, the area of Porto di Pantelleria itself. The rest of the coastline was far too rocky, or too well defended wherever it seemed accessible from the sea. No-one knew whether any of the sixteen coastal batteries which protected the port had been silenced, nor whether the airfield with its underground hangar and workshops had suffered any significant damage. The targets for the air attacks that had been launched so far, and in the course of which some four hundred tons of bombs had been dropped, had been the port, the small town behind it, and the airfield—nothing more precise than that; and no-one seemed to have any clear ideas about the operational accuracy of the squadrons which had carried out the bombing. Tooey Spaatz was, as always, good humoured, but at the same time it was clear that he felt that a heavy load of responsibility rested on him in discharging the task, or indeed challenge, that had been assigned to him. It would be a major achievement if the air force, and particularly the American air force, could force an island fortress to surrender as a result of air bombardment alone.

I had been billeted in a small hotel that had been taken over as an officers' mess. I spent the next morning asking questions about the precise nature of the island's defences. I wanted to know how many batteries there were, how many and what kind of guns each comprised, the nature of the command posts, the construction of the underground hangar, the effectiveness of different categories of bomb, and so on. But the answers I was given only confirmed my impression of the night before—that little precise information was available. After lunch Spaatz, Norstad, George McDonald, their senior Intelligence Officer, and I had a meeting, and it was arranged that adequate photocover would immediately be obtained in order to supplement the detail shown on the available maps. My enquiries into the bombing accuracy of the squadrons which had attacked the island got nowhere. It transpired that since the photo-interpreters did not know the precise aiming points against which aircraft had released their bombs, there had been no reason for them to try to determine how close to their targets bombs had fallen.

At Spaatz's suggestion I therefore spent the rest of the afternoon with General Doolittle, who commanded the U.S. bomber forces which had been responsible for most of the attacks so far made against the island. He told me that his squadrons were trained to do 'pattern', not precision bombing, and that their targets had been given simply as the harbour, the town behind it, and the airfield, which in his view had been significantly damaged. Such photocover as I was shown, and which I then examined with the help of his photo-interpreters, revealed practically no damage to the batteries which covered the port.

It was clear that unless these were rendered ineffective, an assault by land forces on the harbour and its environs would be a risky business. Since no other area lent itself to a landing in force, the batteries simply had to be reduced. I then explained to General Doolittle the kind of probability calculations which I had made in drawing up the 1942 plan to capture Alderney, and why on that occasion I had devised my own criteria for the density of bomb strikes necessary to silence batteries. To do the same thing, but to do it better, for Pantelleria meant that we had to have some indication of the average bombing error of his squadrons when operating against small targets, assuming that they continued to enjoy all but total air superiority. Doolittle therefore had a search made for such photocover as could provide the necessary information. By the evening seven photographs which satisfied the necessary conditions were uncovered, making it possible for me to make a crude numerical estimate of the bomber effort that would be required to silence the batteries defending the port. My conclusion was that 'the job was on', given that from then on the bulk of our available bomber effort was directed against the coastal batteries in the northern half of the island, and provided that General Spaatz had allocated to him, and had under his command, the medium bombers commanded by Mary Coningham, now the Commander of the Northwest African Tactical Air Force. After dinner that night I returned to the school and continued with my sums. Before finishing for the night I telephoned Tedder in Algiers and, remembering his instruction, said only 'It's on, provided Mary is in'.

The next day I continued with my enquiries about the strength of the forces which could be assigned for the required air operations, and about the types of bomb and fuses that were available. Such help as I wanted was immediately made available. The local unit of photo-interpreters was put to work under my direction in order to estimate bombing accuracy, and a corporal in an administrative unit of the R.A.F. was assigned to me as secretary. Corporal, later Sergeant, 'Barney' Campion remained with me for the rest of the war, and then joined me again at its end, staying with me until his retirement from civilian work thirty years later.

Tooey Spaatz encouraged me to take a few hours off, and flew me to see the d'Erlanger Villa at La Marsa, close to Tunis, which was going to be his home when we left Constantine. And there, by some extraordinary chance, Sandy Thomson found me, and said that now that the work in Tripoli was finished, he was again at my disposal. Together with J. G. Angles, an R.A.F. Operational Research officer newly arrived in North Africa who had not yet been assigned to a job, and Ben Burns, whom I had called for from Algiers, that gave me a 'permanent' staff of three, to which a few others were assigned as the operation proceeded.

We all sat in a large schoolroom where fortunately we found log tables to help in the elementary calculations of probability which I wanted done. I had constant exchanges with Spaatz, Robb, Norstad, and McDonald. From the start they made it plain that they had every confidence in my ability to produce an effective and precise bombing plan of a kind that had not been designed before. Accordingly, I behaved as though I had done nothing else all my life except produce such plans, enjoying the feeling of being regarded as some kind of wizard.

On my third day in Constantine, I started to pull together my observations in a paper which carefully explained the steps that I had taken in making my estimates of the bomber effort that the operation would call for. That night was the last that I spent in the officers' mess. After dinner with Spaatz at his villa, I had returned to the school, and had gone on working until well after midnight. I was exhausted when I got back to my quarters, and was annoyed when the sergeant behind the desk told me that a major had been billeted with me, and was to share my bed. When I discovered that he was already fast asleep, I returned downstairs and was repeating my objections to the sergeant, when in walked Thornton Wilder. We had met the day before, and had chatted for a while in the street, without revealing to each other what we were doing in Constantine. All I had learnt was that he was 'in intelligence'. We went up to his room to have a drink, and he obviously thought that I was mad to make a fuss in the middle of a war about so small a matter as sharing a bed. It all ended with Thornton giving me his, while he moved to mine with the unknown major. Next day my belongings were picked up and taken to a tiny villa near General Spaatz's, which Larry Norstad and I shared from then on.

My bombing plans started to be implemented before they were finalised in writing. I had begun my report by pointing to the obvious fact that the scale of bomber attack necessary to reduce strong fixed defences was primarily determined by the degree of bombing accuracy which could be expected, in the face of ground and air opposition, against targets as small and as difficult to identify as gun positions and pill-boxes. 'The neutralization of strong prepared defence positions manned by determined troops', so I wrote, 'is usually regarded as a risky commit-ment for bomber forces. In so far as the task has never before been attempted on any large scale, Operation *Corkscrew* [the codename for the capture of the island] thus becomes a test of the tactical possibilities of this form of air attack, and an exercise in the most economical disposal of the available air strength.'

I then gave my appreciation of the defences of the island and, having referred to the possibility that the morale of the garrison might be broken by bombing, I urged that only the main batteries defending the port should be targets, and that they should be attacked only with five-hundred-pound or thousand-pound bombs fused to go off a split second after impact. The harbour and airfield, I advised, should be left in as serviceable a condition as possible for our own subsequent use. The next section of my plan discussed the limited nature of the information which could be used to estimate the vulnerable area of a gun; that is to say, the area around the gun within which the burst of a bomb could be expected to have a reasonable probability of making the weapon un-serviceable. My estimates of the bombing accuracy of the aircraft which would be employed in the operation indicated that it would require, on average, 15 to 60 bursts in a 100-yard square to silence a gun—a den-sity of strikes much higher than I had suggested to Mountbatten only a month or so before. From this it was possible to calculate the number of sorties which would be needed against each battery in order to achieve the required density of strikes. The answers were not very encouraging. The five hundred B.17 'Flying Fortresses', the most formidable day bomber then in operation in Spaatz's command, would, in the time available, be able to account for only five of the sixteen batteries whose reduction was essential, given that one was trying to achieve the direct destruction of only one in three guns. On the other hand, as I also pointed out, the density of strikes necessary to assure such a level of direct destruction would inevitably render all the guns of a battery unserviceable because of secondary effects such as the explosion of ammunition lockers, the disruption of communications, casualties among the gun crews, and so on. My final recommendations were:

'(a) Individual batteries should be taken as aiming points and the attack continued from day-to-day until it is reasonably certain that they have suffered 30 per cent to 50 per cent destruction.

Only batteries in the northern half of the island should be taken as targets, the highest priority being given to those around the harbour.

(b) Until D—3, the forces available should be concentrated on no more than four to six batteries a day.

(c) A strict analysis of the results of each day's effort should be made. This means that full details about the individual sorties despatched, about the bombs dropped and about the targets aimed at, should be available at H.Q.

Results should be estimated (i) from sortie claims, (ii) from strike photographs, and (iii) from daily P.R.W. [Photographic Reconnaissance Wing] cover.

Every burst should be plotted on a grid map and attention paid (a) to the relation of bombs identified in the photographic cover to total number dropped, (b) to the positions of the bursts in relation to the gun positions, and (c) to any damage caused.

Aiming points for each day's operations should be determined on the basis of the information thus provided. In order to achieve this, it will be necessary for P.R.W. interpeters to be available to analyse the daily photographs at Advanced H.Q.

If the operation is controlled in this way, it should be possible to determine, day-by-day, whether the effects achieved will be in accordance with the limited chance laws used in the present analysis, or whether chance will be "beaten" by even more accurate bombing than has been assumed.

(d) As soon as the island is taken, a ground survey should be made of the effects of the bombing.'[2]

Today this kind of planning would be regarded as elementary. At the time it was entirely novel.

The concentrated attacks on the batteries began on 30 May. It was Norstad's responsibility to channel the orders to the various Commands, and he was therefore in and out of my schoolroom throughout the day in order to learn from our analysis of aerial photocover and strike photographs which targets to assign next. Photo-reconnaissance sorties were flown daily, sometimes three times a day, the commander of the squadron, Elliot Roosevelt, the President's son, and his deputy, being instructed by me about the targets at which to direct their cameras. The cigar-smoking deputy would say, 'O.K., how'd you like a low-level oblique of batteries such and such'—and I could be confident that the photographs would be back in my room within a few hours. It was the interpreters' job not only to assess the damage which the batteries had suffered, but also to provide a running tally of the number of bombs which had fallen within a hundred yards of the individual guns.

Before the planned attacks began, the photographs had revealed only what was described as some 'probable' damage to a few guns in three of the batteries. My daily reports, addressed from then on to Norstad,[3] provided a picture of mounting destruction, and also a running check on my estimates of bombing errors and the vulnerable areas of the guns. The atmosphere of my room was almost that of a betting shop as I reported hits which, by my criteria, were close enough to have damaged the batteries. Norstad was only one of the members of Tooey's staff who were constantly in my room to learn the latest 'score'. Robert Lovett also kept coming in. He was then the Assistant Secretary of War for Air, and was on a visit from Washington. Every day he postponed his return because of the growing excitement engendered by the possibility that air forces alone might bring about the capitulation of the island. No-one in Constantine seemed to pay any attention to the occasional naval bombardments, and indeed the photo-interpreters failed to identify any damage which these may have caused. The naval attacks, like the photo-reconnaissance sorties, did, however, have the useful effect of revealing which batteries were still active after the island was bombed.

A joint naval and air bombardment had been planned for 8 June, and during the afternoon of the 7th I flew with Spaatz to Sousse, where Admiral McGrigor had his Headquarters, and from where part of General Clutterbuck's Infantry Division was going to sail on the 11th. The walk from the airstrip to the Admiral's office stands out in my memory for an odd reason. Tooey had taken along with him his personal W.A.C. officer, a charming girl called Sally Bagby, who was a family friend and whom he treated as a daughter. It was a hot day, and we had to pass through lines of soldiers in various stages of undress. The three of us were walking together, and Tooey, embarrassed that Sally had to be exposed to such sights, put his hand over her eyes as he steered her through the camp. When we got to the Admiral's office, I was called on to explain to the assembled soldiers and sailors the results of the bombing operations, to advise on the 'lay-on' of bombing targets for the following day, and then, in relation to the projected timing of the air attacks, to suggest aiming points for the naval guns. This meeting revealed the startling fact that the navy and air force had been using different code-numbers to designate the same batteries. Battery x which the air force had bombed was not battery x which the navy had shelled. So much for the planning of combined operations. In Sousse, as in Constantine, I seemed to be regarded as the oracle to be consulted about bombardments in general.

Spaatz, with two of his officers, and I were due to sail with the naval force before dawn the next morning. So after a meal and drinks with some naval officers, I decided to get a few hours sleep. Someone had suggested that I should bring my mosquito net from Constantine, and when I saw that a hard bench was all I had to sleep on, I wrapped myself in the net and tried to sleep. But mosquitoes and other insects made this impossible and, when I had been sufficiently bitten, I decided that I might as well walk round the block. Although I had been given the rank of Group Captain, I had felt that my wearing the uniform would be presumptuous when there were real Group Captains around. Neither Tedder nor Spaatz minded my dressing in khaki shorts and shirt, with my head covered by a brown felt hat, which Tooey called my 'brown derby', and which he pronounced 'durby'. As I was the only person in any of the military headquarters who was so dressed, my eccentric uniform served as a security pass. The sentries whom I met as I strolled in the dark of Sousse paid no attention, and I was back to join the others in time to embark at about four in the morning on H.M.S. *Whaddon*, the Hunt Class destroyer which Admiral McGrigor had taken over as his flag-ship for the occasion.

It was to be my only experience of any such operation, and on going aboard I was too excited to accept an invitation to turn in for a couple of hours. Instead, I spent most of the time on the bridge as we sailed north-eastwards across the Gulf of Hammamet towards Pantelleria. Dawn broke onto a lovely day, and the formation of seven widely-separated destroyers, with an occasional glimpse in the far distance behind us of one of the four cruisers which were taking part in the operation, looked like some beautiful stage-set. The island came into view at about ten o'clock. The attack was made well within range of the coastal batteries, and was carried out in two phases. The cruisers began by firing salvos at the town and towards the airfield. In an attempt to draw the fire of the coastal batteries, on which the destroyers had trained their guns, all vessels then turned away, only to return again, the destroyers closing to relatively short range, with three motor-torpedo boats dashing in to about a quarter of a mile of the shore.

The bridge of our destroyer was crowded. Forward of the rest was the ship's commander, with Admiral McGrigor, Tooey Spaatz and some other officers behind. Then came the ratings who manned the anti-aircraft Oerlikon guns, on a wheel of one of which I had hung my 'brown derby'. And finally, behind us stood the ship's surgeon-lieutenant, properly equipped to deal with minor emergencies. All the naval officers looked immaculate in their white shorts and shirts, making the rest of us look a bit scruffy—in my own case I did not realise just how scruffy until later. I was probably at least as familiar as anyone with the features of the coast which lay in front of us. During the previous week, I had hardly taken my eyes off photocover of the batteries. But I was probably far less familiar with the ensuing naval ritual. When we were within range, the ship's commander turned to Admiral McGrigor and asked, 'Permission to open fire, Sir?' The Admiral nodded his head. Soon afterwards, a signal came from *Aurora*, a fifth cruiser in which Eisenhower and Admiral Cunningham, the Commander-in-Chief of all the Mediterranean naval forces, had embarked to witness the operation, asking McGrigor's permission for them too to join in the engagement. Permission was granted. The moment the guns of the destroyer opened up, my hat was blown from its 'hook' and got caught under the circular base of the Oerlikon. Without a smile, and as if it happened every day, a rating picked it up, dusted it gently, and put it back on its perch. I felt I had never attended such a well-mannered party. Spaatz muttered to me, 'What the hell kind of damage do they think these small shells will do?'— a sentiment I was prepared to echo as a magnificent formation of B.17s slowly flew in to unleash their successive bomb loads at the two batteries which were their targets. The coastline became obscured in the dust of the explosions, but by watching closely I could see that only three batteries returned our fire. Spaatz and I were more than satisfied, since it followed that the previous air attacks had been more successful than the assessments, based on photocover, had suggested. This was no doubt at least because of the demoralisation of the gun crews. General Eisenhower's information, as recorded in his Dispatch on the operation, was that two batteries returned our fire throughout the operation, that one fired until it was silenced by a naval gun, and that three more fired 'a few desultory salvos'. I remember hearing at the time that one shell had crossed the stern of his cruiser.

After we had turned back for Sousse, I went to clean up before going to the wardroom for a meal. My admiration for the good manners of the navy was unbounded when I saw my face in a mirror, and wondered how they had tolerated a pock-marked, insect-bitten, unshaven and slovenly figure in the midst of all their calm elegance. I suppose that the fact that I was an easy member of a company of 'top brass' implied something to the ship's officers. Some of them may have known that I had designated the targets.

When we got back to Constantine, I returned to my schoolroom to prepare a report, comparing the observations that I had made during the operation with the most recent assessments of damage. I submitted this to Norstad during the course of the following day, and later that same day gave him an even more up-to-date report on the state of the batteries, taking into account the results of air attacks which had been delivered in the afternoon following the naval/air assault. My final progress report, two days later, concluded with the words: 'Of the 15 [*sic*] batteries so far attacked, about 10 were out of action by the evening of the 10th, and in only two was no significant damage caused.'[3]

The Governor of the island refused to surrender on the day of the combined bombardment. But he did so on the morning of the 11th after another day's concentrated bombing, and just as the 1st Infantry Division was about to land from assault and tank-landing craft. The following day, after a somewhat uncomfortable night-crossing in one of these craft, I arrived with my small team to launch a ground assessment of the damage the bombing had caused. The Germans had by then started to make sporadic attacks with fighter-bombers on our own very tight concentrations of ships in and around the port, and no sooner were we ashore and ready to move than some debris thrown up by a bomb exploding nearby struck an American officer who was in my team. The rest of us moved on to our work, while our not very badly injured colleague was removed to a field hospital, to be decorated in due course with the 'Purple Heart'.

There was practically no accommodation available on the island. Most people were sleeping rough, and General Clutterbuck suggested that we would do best to pitch some kind of camp in a field close to the coast at a point opposite to the port. After doing this, and with the one vehicle allotted to us, I set about organising the field-study of the damage caused by the bombing of the batteries, the town, airfield, roads, cable communications, and whatever else was relevant. Two Intelligence officers had been assigned to me to interrogate the commanders of the batteries about the morale of the garrisons.

It was warm and we slept in the open. On most nights there was a firework display as our anti-aircraft guns opened up against intruding German bombers. These did no significant damage, which was not, however, the case with the daylight raids on the harbour. On one occasion when my small team was busy measuring the craters within and around one of the bombed batteries just to the south of the port, we heard, and then saw, six German fighter-bombers, FW 190s, coming in on a fairly low-level attack. A big crane on the dock had survived our own bombardment, and I was bold enough to exclaim, as most of my party dived for cover, 'they certainly won't get that'—which, seconds later, is just what they did.

There was neither time nor opportunity for anything but work. Morning and evening, however, we were able to bathe off the rocks, although for the first two or three days we had to move some fifty yards away from our camp until the body of a drowned sailor, still in his cork life-jacket, was removed from a small inlet in the rocks. We never did discover his nationality. Occasionally I visited Brigadier General Strickland, who commanded the Air Service troops put in by General Spaatz when the island became one of our bases for the invasion of Sicily. He had taken over a charming house in the small port of Scauri on the western side of the island, and it was almost possible to forget the war as we lunched on the delicious lobsters which swarmed off the coast, ate the magnificent grapes and figs that the island provided, and drank the not-so-good, but very welcome, local wine. 'Big shots' from Constantine and even Algiers flew in every now and then to discuss with Strickland the repair of the airfield. A War Office general came from London to make his own survey of the effects of the air bombardment, but he soon disappeared. Stradling's Department also sent out a man whom I knew to do a survey. I immediately recruited him to my team.

Once the ground survey was properly under way, I returned to Constantine to prepare a comprehensive report of the operation. I flew back to the island for only the occasional day in order to discuss with Thomson and other members of my staff points in the reports they were sending me. On one occasion I returned in a two-seater fighter—it was an odd-looking machine. Because Focke-Wulf 190s were around, my pilot, a very experienced but slightly frustrated colonel, Pottinger by name, decided to fly about 100 feet above the surface of the sea. He put me in the gunner's seat behind him and told me to man the gun. When I protested that I did not know how to use it, he said: 'Do your best; they'll have to dive dangerously low if they're going to get us'. Skimming the surface of the sea for over fifty miles was yet another new experience.

On my return to Constantine, I had also been drawn into the planning of the bombing operations which were designed to pave the way for the invasion of Sicily. But there was also some time for relaxation. Robb and Norstad would occasionally pick me up to join them for a picnic lunch on 'K' rations—not the most wonderful fare—on the outskirts of Constantine. Professional zoologist though I was, I knew nothing about birds, but Robb was an amateur ornithologist, and I was fascinated by what he was able to teach me about the bird life around us.

On a few nights, I also went to the Constantine Casino. These gambling sorties came about by accident. The 'drill' at Spaatz's table was fairly predictable. As soon as dinner was finished, two or three airmen would, on occasion, be brought in to be decorated for bravery. Tooey's chief administrative officer would read the formal citations, the medals would be pinned on by Tooey, and the ceremony would end with us drinking the health of the recipients. Then there would be ten minutes or so for a game of darts, a diversion which I believe was introduced by Tommy Traill who, with Robb, represented the R.A.F. at Spaatz's H.Q. On one occasion, Tooey wagered a medium bomber against a heavy ack-ack gun in a game with an anti-aircraft officer who was a guest. Tooey lost, but the bomber which he delivered to the winner was promptly returned. As soon as darts were out of the way, poker, the serious business of the evening, began. I was tempted to join in, but soon realised that the stakes, as well as the level of play, were far beyond my reach. Some of Tooey's senior staff officers were rich men, and as an onlooker I used to feel that there was something wrong if in the first five minutes or so one of the players had not lost $1,000.

One day someone asked why I did not visit the local Casino, since I was obviously interested in the poker game. The military were barred from the Casino, but as was explained to me, all I would have to do would be to put on civilian clothes and present myself with my passport at the door. The first time I did this, I left, a modest winner, after an hour or so. Sandy Thomson had become the courier between my field team in Pantelleria and Constantine, and the next time I went to the Casino he accompanied me, wearing a borrowed suit of civilian clothes. As he had no passport, he was there as a non-playing observer. We must have done this two or three times, and each time I won a little, either at the roulette table or at chemin-de-fer. As there was so much else to do, we never stayed more than about an hour but at the end of it all, I had won enough to buy Joan two presumed antique rings which I later found in Palermo.

I sent my final report on Pantelleria to Tooey Spaatz about the middle of July.[4] In the introduction I reminded him that we had begun our attack 'on the defences in the full realization that the air was not undertaking to put a bomb on each gun. To attempt any such thing would have required a prolongation and magnification of effort which was out of all reason.' A reduction in fire power could be brought about by factors other than the direct destruction of guns; for example, 'such secondary factors as casualties and the disruption of communications, the destruction of rangefinders, predictors and searchlights, of control posts and ammunition stores, of communication trenches and roads, of barrack buildings and personnel shelters, of food and water supplies'. I went on to say that 'bombs not only damage the ground and the material units which make up a battery. They also demoralise, and demoralisation may play as big a part in the silencing of a battery as any other single factor. A hundred bombs falling within 100 yards of the guns of a six-gun battery might fail to score a single direct hit. Their secondary efforts might completely neutralize the position'.

I ended my introduction by emphasising that 'duration of effect is a vital factor where Combined Operations are concerned. . . . All primary and secondary effects of aerial bombardment could be made good if the opportunity were available; repair and replacement time thus represent the common measure by which gun damage can be estimated. Even if damage to guns is slight, it represents total unserviceability in a Combined Operation where the sea and land assault coincides with the period of temporary unserviceability. Continuity of air attack, by helping to remove the opportunity for repair and maintenance work, effectively prolongs a period of unserviceability into one of total unserviceability. In one sense, the general equation for air assaults of this kind, therefore, consists of two terms; namely, effort, and effects in terms of duration'.

In the report which I had submitted to Norstad on the evening before the 1st Infantry Division landed,[3] I had estimated that the fire-power of the 16 batteries which had been bombed had been reduced by amounts varying between 10 per cent and 75 per cent, with an average of about 40 per cent. The ground survey later showed that somewhat more than half of the total of eighty guns in the batteries were either completely destroyed or damaged, and that the control posts of seven batteries had also either been completely destroyed or rendered unserviceable. My assessments before the landing had not been far out. According to the captured Italian group and battery commanders, however, only two guns were still serviceable at the time of the landings.

Apart from the batteries, the most striking damage was to the town behind the port. For all practical purposes it had been wiped out, and all roads and communications leading from and to it had been seriously affected. Casualties were very light, the total number killed being between 100 and 200, and of wounded about 200. Most of the civilians in the northern half of the island had fled to the central hills, and few of the Italian battery crews had remained at their posts. 'The effects on morale were so striking', I wrote in my report to General Spaatz, 'that it has stimulated a fairly widespread view that the fall of the island was due almost entirely to the collapse of morale of a poor-spirited garrison, and little to the damage to fixed defences. This view is based on incomplete knowledge of the facts. There can be little question [but] that the coast defences in the northern half of the island had been so battered as to prevent them offering any serious opposition to an assault. So far as morale is concerned, it has been demanded of few people to stand up to bombing of the intensity experienced by the batteries (average of 1,000 tonnes per sq. mile). Perhaps only those who have experienced it are competent to judge whether any troops, of whatever nationality, would have succeeded where the Italians failed. The fact is that had the battery garrisons attempted to man their guns or service them during the period of attack, few would be alive to tell the tale today. Moral fibre', I added, 'is insufficient protection against the primary and secondary effects of explosions'; and I also pointed out that 'the Germans do not appear to have believed that a few determined men could have manned light defences and prevented our assault forces coming ashore, or alternatively that they could have made an assault very expensive for us; they withdrew all but 50 of the 600 men whom they had on the island at the start of the air offensive.'

There was, I fear, a tinge of unnecessary sarcasm in the reference to 'moral fibre'. When I had pressed the soldiers to say what was needed to silence a battery, the reply often included some remark suggesting that it all depended on the moral fibre of the gun crews. Anyhow, General Eisenhower did not mind. He included the passage in his Official Dispatch.[1] Nor did Tooey mind. By common consent, the capture of the island was essentially due to the bombing. Naval fire had had very little effect, and the soldiers had only to walk in. Tooey was delighted. He was one of the United States's top flying men of the First World War, and was also a disciple of Billy Mitchell, the man who was Trenchard's opposite number in the United States. Mitchell and Trenchard held that wars could be won by bombing alone. As Tooey and others explained to me, there was one 'A' too many in the designation of U.S.A.A.F.—the 'A' which stood for Army—and Pantelleria would help get rid of that. Tooey was immensely grateful and presented me with a 'citation'. Eisenhower was also very generous in his Dispatch. As he put it, if the operation had not gone the way it did, 'there would have been lacking essential data for the study of the tactical possibilities of scientifically directed air bombardment of strongpoints, and the most economic disposal of available air strength. Professor Zuckerman's exhaustive report on the subject may prove of as much value in the fight against the Axis as the capture of the island.'[1] I was bathed in praise.

But Tedder's assessment of the whole experience was much more sober. As he explains in his autobiography, the conclusion he drew was that an air operation of the type of Pantelleria was possible only 'when relative air superiority was gained and maintained, when careful estimates had been made in advance to show that the available bomber effort could cope with the task, when the defences were not so strong as to be invulnerable to the type of bomb available, and when the forces were allocated and controlled according to a precise plan'. And then, citing some further passages in my report he went on to say that his 'only concern was that false conclusions might be drawn from the Pantelleria operation'. On 14 June, he had written to tell Air Chief Marshal Sir Charles Portal, the Chief of the British Air Staff, that he had pointed out 'again and again right from the beginning that this operation is a most valuable laboratory experiment. The conditions are not such as we are likely to have again, e.g., no enemy air worthy of the name, an extremely limited objective and consequent ability to concentrate a terrific scale of effort on a very small area. Despite all I have said, however, even Eisenhower has now begun to say, can't we possibly do something like this for "Husky" [the Sicily operation]. In short, I can see Pantelleria becoming a perfect curse to us in this manner.'[5]

Tedder was no doubt wise to be less enthusiastic than the others. But I was far too absorbed in what I was doing to worry about the kind of lesson which might be drawn from the operation. The 'Professor of Anatomy', as they all knew me, had been offered an opportunity to show how he thought a bombing plan should be designed, and the plan had worked. From my point of view the operation had been an experiment, essentially because it had been possible to check daily whether certain arbitrary but necessary criteria to measure operational results had been achieved, and because it had then become possible to make a direct check of the whole operation. To that extent, Pantelleria was a scientific experiment. And I would have been less than human if I had not enjoyed the confidence that had been placed in me, and the many enduring friendships which resulted from the exercise.

CHAPTER II

SICILY

DURING THE month which passed between the fall of Pantelleria and
the invasion of Sicily, I commuted between Constantine and La Marsa,
where Eisenhower had now established an Advanced Command Post.
Tooey Spaatz, with whom I had become good friends, had included me
with those of his staff whom he accommodated in the palatial villa which
he had requisitioned as his home. Its main room was vast, and off it was
a dining-room which was furnished with a table that consisted of a single
slab of marble. The story was that it had been cut for a Roman senator,
but had failed to be delivered from the quarries of nearby Carthage. It
was only centuries later that it was put to the use for which it had
originally been intended. Most visitors to La Marsa seemed to end up in
Tooey's house, but I hardly ever saw Tedder there. At first he lived in a
caravan, but later he moved to a small and unpretentious house not far
from Tooey's villa. General Somervell, who in that period of the war
was in charge of all military supplies for the armed services of the
United States, was a guest on one occasion, and when those of us who
had not met him before were being presented, I was introduced as
Professor Zuckerman. 'Professor what?' asked Somervell, with a slight
note of disdain. 'Do we have any like that?'

The air attacks which preceded Montgomery's and Patton's landings
in Sicily were directed mainly against airfields, but in order to keep the
enemy guessing about our proposed landing areas, occasional raids were
made against towns on the west of the island, particularly Marsala. Ports
on the Italian mainland and some railway targets were also being bombed,
but as far as I could make out, these attacks were not designed to achieve
any clearly defined objective, other than that of forcing the enemy to
abandon his advanced airfields and to move his squadrons to the Italian
mainland. In his autobiography, Tedder notes that: 'By D-Day, 10 July,
the enemy did not have a single airfield in Sicily fully operational.'

When Tedder had first asked me to give him my ideas about what
bombing operations should precede the invasion of Sicily, I had suggested a plan to destroy the rail and road communications on which the
enemy depended. It departed from an earlier and official appreciation
that had been put forward on 4 June by the Intelligence Staff of the

Northwest African Tactical Air Force, and which proposed as 'targets of choice' the bombing of railway lines at points where they could not easily be repaired. This plan also advocated the creation of road blocks by the bombing of small towns through which 'strategic' roads ran. The plan that I suggested focused on the destruction of the nodal points which controlled the railway system of Sicily and Southern Italy.

On the Thursday before the actual invasion there was a meeting in Tedder's Command Post, in which I had an office, to agree final details for the operation. It was attended by most of the 'top brass', including Eisenhower and Harold Macmillan, then the Minister Resident at Allied H.Q. in North-West Africa. Macmillan arrived smartly dressed in a white summer suit. The last to turn up was Admiral Cunningham, also dressed in 'whites'. Air Commodore Whitney Straight, who was in charge of the R.A.F. Transport Command in the Mediterranean, and I were asked to wait outside. Only afterwards did I discover that this was because neither of us had yet been cleared to receive ULTRA Intelligence, the very secret intercepts of enemy messages, about which Group Captain Winterbotham has recently given an account.[1] It was sometime later that I was indoctrinated and allowed access to this inner compound of military Intelligence.

Among those who had flown in to witness the assault was Dickie Mountbatten, who spent a night under Tooey's roof. He did not contribute much to the talk at the dinner table, but when we broke up he asked me to go with him to his room where we sat talking for a long time about Anglo-American and inter-Service cooperation. He went on to Malta the next day, returning to London after our forces had landed in Sicily.

Part of the night before the invasion I spent with Tedder on the small terrace of his Command Post.[2] The sea was alive with shipping. Tedder was confident, but he seemed to enjoy talking about the Punic Wars, and he facetiously asked whether I thought our invasion would one day count as yet another in that series of operations. 'Fancy invading Italy from the South', he said. 'Even Hannibal had the sense to come in with his elephants over the Alps!' In spite of heavy losses in our airborne operations, we knew next day that a secure lodgement had been achieved both in the South-East and in the South.

The days which followed were immensely exciting. As news of our successes kept pouring in, I was again asked to suggest bombing targets whose attack would accelerate the enemy's defeat. One afternoon when I was busy with my maps and calculations Tedder walked in and suggested that we should go to his caravan to chat in peace. We were deep in conversation when Eisenhower walked in, followed by Mrs. Black, the Director of the R.A.F.'s Malcolm Clubs in North Africa, whom Tedder was soon to marry, and Kay Summersby, Eisenhower's driver and constant companion at the time. The two ladies sat near the door, while Eisenhower joined us at the other end of the caravan, saying that he hoped he was not interrupting. Tedder replied lightly that we were merely discussing the history of warfare in the Mediterranean. Eisenhower tried to keep the talk on an intellectual plane, but turned the conversation away from history by talking about the simple laws of probability which I had used in planning the Pantelleria operation. At one moment he offered the view that there was also something which could be called 'indeterminate probability'. He was not impressed by my suggestion that if we were dealing with statistical probability we were dealing with calculable probability. 'I would agree', he said, 'that if I were sitting in a poker game [for, as in Tooey's case, poker was one of his relaxations] I could calculate the chances of any one player drawing four Queens. On the other hand, if five of us are in the game, and one card only has been dealt and I turn mine over and see it is a Queen, it is impossible to calculate my chances of drawing the remaining three. That is what I mean by indeterminate probability.' Since he was far from convinced when I said that if the chances could be calculated before he turned over his first card they could also be after he had seen that he had already drawn one of the four Queens, I suggested that the best thing would be for me to send him a note giving a simple algebraic proof that he was wrong. This I did next day, but I never heard another word on the subject. Ike had a liking for simplifications and catch-phrases, but we were still more than ten years from his preoccupation with what became known as 'the domino theory' in diplomatic affairs, a preoccupation which was to commit the United States to its disastrous course of intervention in South-East Asia. While Ike had complete faith in Tedder, whom he was later to support powerfully in a major confrontation with Churchill over the use of the Allied Strategic Air Forces in Europe, I do not believe that he understood that Tedder's faith in me, like Mountbatten's, was not based just on trust and sentiment, but that it also had an empirical foundation. Tedder always wanted facts, not speculation.

It had been agreed that as soon as possible I should embark on a ground survey of the results of our bombing operations in Sicily, and since I did not have the necessary staff, Tedder, at my request, signalled the Air Ministry asking them to get Stradling to release four of his bomb-survey technical officers to work with me. At the same time I wrote to Stradling urging that this be done, pointing out that there was an enormous amount to be learnt in Sicily but that it was somewhat of a strain for one person both to help create debris and then to crawl over it.

The obvious place to set up shop in Sicily was Palermo. It was not only the island's biggest city, but its docks had been a target for attack

over the preceding three years. The town was captured by General
Patton on 22 July, less than two weeks after he had landed in the South.
A day or two later, an American general, one of those who had flown in
to be spectators of the invasion, took me with him on a day's visit to
see what was going on. We lunched on army rations in an olive grove,
and I felt that at last we were back in Europe. When we drove into
Palermo, I saw for the first time signs of the hard discipline which
Patton demanded of his troops. Military police on motor-cycles rode
slowly up and down the narrow streets, forcing civilians onto the pave-
ments and into doorways, where mothers sat picking lice from their
children's hair. No town looks gay when it has been captured; Palermo
looked particularly miserable.

Tedder had written to Major-General Lord Rennell, the Chief of the
Allied Military Government (A.M.G.O.T.) which had been set up to
administer the captured territories, asking him to arrange for accommodation, rations and transport for the team that I was assembling. In his
turn, Tooey had assigned to me as administrative officers a Colonel
Willis, in peacetime a Harvard historian, and a Wing Commander
Wheatley, a regular R.A.F. officer. Nothing was too good for me after
Pantelleria. Staff were rapidly collected, and a day after my visit to the
town, six officers and supporting N.C.O.s and men moved into Palermo,
among them Sandy Thomson and Campion, the only two who had any
idea of what was in store. Colonel Willis was a man of style, and instead
of finding quarters in war-torn Palermo, he went to the nearby coastal
resort of Mondello, and requisitioned three houses, which I understood
were owned by a wealthy Italian who was married to an American
woman. Both had been in Italy throughout the war. For my better comfort he had reserved for me a large room in the grand villa that had been
their home. I could walk through the garden on to a narrow wooden
pier from which I could dive straight into the sea. A few hundred yards
away on the beach was an abandoned Italian seaplane which had been
flown in, so I was told, by two military emissaries who had come to discuss terms of surrender.

After making what plans I could about surveying the results of our
air attacks, I returned to La Marsa. But I had not been back for more than
a day when a message arrived saying that General Patton was threatening
to remove my party from Mondello. Tooey undertook to pacify his
opposite number, but before he could get moving there was another
message saying that the team was under close arrest as they neither had
Eisenhower's authority nor Patton's consent to be in the area of operations of the 7th Army. The Head of A.M.G.O.T. clearly counted for as
little with Patton as did a survey of the results of bombing. I myself
received a friendly note from the Commanding General of the Northwest

African Air Forces Advanced Command Post asking me to find 10,000 lire for supplies for my party since, as he put it, 'they were now living with other aliens on bread and water'. The difficulty was temporarily resolved when Spaatz visited Patton—this was just before that colourful General had got into the news for striking a wounded soldier because he believed him to be a malingerer.

I then returned to Palermo and arranged the outline of the survey which I proposed to carry out into the effects of three years of bombing. I was particularly concerned to analyse the effects of the attacks on different kinds of railway target. Tripoli had revealed the value of contemporary records, and I was therefore pleased to find that the daily flow sheets which the Palermo railway staff had kept were excellent. The officials whom I saw were only too ready to start analysing them. Poor men—no trains were running, and they had nothing else to do. But it soon became clear that I did not have enough staff to supervise all the jobs which needed to be done. I therefore let Tedder and Norstad know that I would have to make a brief recruiting visit to the U.K. I also decided that before leaving it would be useful if I visited some of the bombed targets in the western foothills of Mount Etna, where the 8th Army was then being held up on its way to Messina, towards which Patton was racing along the north coast in order to prevent the retreat of the Axis forces to the Italian mainland. I also wanted to visit Marsala in the west to see the damage it had suffered from bombing.

Sandy Thomson and I set off in a jeep, frequently stopping to sight-see on the way, before ending up for the first night in Enna, a marvellous little hillside town where legend has it that Persephone disappeared into the earth. We arrived late in the afternoon, and Sandy, true to 8th Army form, asked the first soldier we saw, an American, where he could find the 'town major'. The American had never heard of such a functionary. After wandering around for a while, we stopped outside a building guarded by two sentries and put the same question. This time we were told that they were guarding the military governor's offices. 'Who's the Governor?' I asked. 'An English colonel called Rodd', the sentry thought. 'Colonel Peter Rodd?' I queried.[3] 'Perhaps that was the name.' We walked in, and up a staircase into a room which seemed to be full of American officers. A party was in progress. And then I spotted Peter Rodd—Prod to his friends. I went over to express my pleasure at seeing him, but before I could ask where we could spend the night, he drew me into a corner to say that he had immense secrets to tell me, but that he could not speak lest any of his guests overheard. He did, however, have enough time to say that in the fortnight that he had been Governor of Enna Province under A.M.G.O.T.—this seemed to me a piece of nepotism, since his brother was military Governor of the whole island—he had introduced more social reforms than Sicily had enjoyed in 2,000 years. Knowing Prod I did not press him further, but agreed to return to spend the night there. Even though we had to be on our way at dawn, Prod insisted on staying and talking in my bedroom until well after midnight. He explained all the measures which he was taking to improve conditions in the part of Sicily for which he was now responsible, but which he said was threatened by wicked Sicilians who crossed into Enna Province from the neighbouring and badly-governed Province of Catania. The sleep which he denied me was then further interrupted by the bells of a church tower which seemed to lean right into my room. At four-thirty I joined Sandy. To my surprise, Prod was up and handed me a sealed envelope which he wanted me to deliver to the Governor of Catania Province, Lord Gerald Wellesley, who became the 7th Duke of Wellington barely one month later, when his nephew was killed in the assault landings at Salerno. We then drove off to Syracuse.

One of the things which I had hoped to do during the course of my study of Tripoli was to examine on the ground the effects of one of the 4,000 lb 'block-buster' bombs, which were being increasingly used in our attacks on German cities. I had been told that a few had been dropped by bombers of the Western Desert Air Force, and that flash photographs were available to show their points of impact. What was necessary was to compare these photographs with local maps to see exactly where the bombs had exploded, and then to do the required ground survey. I had failed to find any 4,000 lb incident worth investigating in Tripoli or anywhere else in North Africa, but had in my hands an excellent flash photograph which could easily be related to a street map of Syracuse. We arrived at the scene sometime in the middle of the morning, only to be stopped by a sentry who told us that the place was 'off-limits'. 'What place?' we asked. 'The brothel, of course.' I explained that we had other reasons for being there and that I proposed examining the ground with the help, if possible, of such local inhabitants who might have been there when the bomb went off. He became interested and summoned the 'Madame', who emerged with all her girls. A noisy conference then ensued with everyone contributing. In spite of my very elementary Italian, enough was understood to form a background to a damage study which I later incorporated in what was the first published note that we had—the Germans may have had their own—of the destruction caused in actual operations by one of our block-busters.

After a brief drive around the town, we turned northwards to Catania where, in due course, I delivered the 'confidential' message from the Governor of Enna. The Governor of Catania read it, and then asked whether I was likely to see Peter Rodd again. If I did, would I please tell him that he had no intention of shutting his borders to those of Enna

Province. He seemed as amused as I was by the suggestion, and like me enjoyed Peter's never-failing imagination. Prod always had a lively mind, and behaved not a little like a modern Baron Munchausen.

We drove on to Etna, where we became entangled in military traffic that was moving on a very narrow lava road from the little town of Adrano to the south-west of the mountain, to Randazzo on its north. Montgomery's troops were held down at Bronte, some fifteen kilometres south of Randazzo. Tanks and trucks were nose to tail along the road, and Military Police were controlling them with difficulty. Here and there one could see guns deployed away from the road. Somewhat disturbed, I asked Sandy if he did not think our jeep was in the way. With all the confidence of an 8th Army man who had spent two years in the desert, he replied, 'No, it would all be different if we were in the battle zone. The men would all be wearing their tin hats. We're in nobody's way here.' At that very moment guns behind, to the side and in front of us, started firing. We were pushed to the side of the road and asked to turn back and to try not to hold up any vehicles going forward. That was my first sight of a land battle.

When we got back to Palermo, and before returning to La Marsa, I satisfied myself that the work I had set in hand was proceeding as well as circumstances allowed. Before leaving, however, I was flown by an American sergeant in a small artillery-spotter plane to Marsala. The flight was breath-taking, and I was not at all happy when, having landed on a road, my pilot jumped out and fired his revolver into the air several times as he shouted, 'Vino, vino'. All I could hope was that before we set out on our return journey he would not have more wine in him than he had when we started. Marsala was desolate, and I did not feel secure until we were back in Palermo, from where I flew the next day to Tunis.

So much happened in La Marsa during the next two weeks that in retrospect it appeared much longer. There was the immediate matter of proposing bombing targets to impede the enemy's movement in Southern Italy. This was not too difficult since at that time I did not have to contend with any rigid contrary doctrine on the subject. Fighters and fighter-bombers were engaged in the immediate battles, but my quick survey of the Sicilian railway records already pointed to the clear conclusion that the more we concentrated our bombing attacks on those nodal points in the system which regulated major traffic, and which were responsible for the maintenance of rolling-stock, the greater the return in terms of the dislocation of the movement of troops and military supplies. Having cross-examined me closely about the steps that had led to this view, Tedder agreed and acted accordingly. I also wanted to learn about the military value, if any, of trying to impede enemy movement by bombing small towns in order to create road-blocks. There were messages to pass to London about my forthcoming recruiting visit. Soon it was time to leave.

General Ira Eaker, who then commanded the U.S. 8th Air Force in England, had flown to La Marsa to greet the part of his bomber force which it was hoped would land at North African air bases after attacking the aircraft factories at Regensburg, some 100 km north of Munich. The other part, which was to bomb the ball-bearing plants at Schweinfurt, about the same distance east of Frankfurt, was due to return direct to England. The date was 17 August 1943, and the raid was to be the deepest daylight penetration into Germany that had so far been made by American bombers based in England. Everyone knew that the operation was going to be hazardous, and so it proved. In spite of long-range fighter support, sixty out of a force of 315 heavy bombers were shot down in an air battle which raged throughout the time the American bombers were over Germany. We did not know the extent of the losses until later, but during the afternoon, after lunch at Tooey's table, a game of poker was started in a side-room that was furnished in Moorish style and which led off from the main room of the villa. Tooey and Ira Eaker were playing, while I was looking on. So too was Pete Quesada, who had taken on the job of answering the telephone. I doubt if anyone had his mind on the game. Tooey was chain-smoking, while Eaker rolled his cigar from one corner of his mouth to the other, as they kept an ear open not only for the calls in the game, but also for the next ring of the telephone. Pete would leap to his feet to inform us, with his face aglow, that another two or three aircraft had landed successfully. It was a very moving afternoon.

Some weeks before there had been a very different party in that same Moorish den. After lunch on a day when Mary Coningham was with us, Tooey led us there to discuss an idea which had struck him. Mary, the successful Commander of the Desert Air Force, was now titularly under Tooey's command. But he had no great respect for his new superior. I doubt if he ever took the trouble to find out that however determined and obstinate he could be, Tooey was one of the kindest, most modest and most generous of men. Without a word, Mary suddenly got up and moved into the garden where we could see him picking blossoms from a hibiscus bush. He then returned and bent down on one knee in front of Tooey saying, as he proffered the flowers, 'Master, I bring you these'. Tooey was not amused. He knew well enough that the gesture was Mary's way of indicating that he had nothing to learn from an American general who had been in the war for less than a year. It was the first occasion on which I saw personal Anglo-American relations go wrong at that level.

Three days after the Regensburg attack, I flew from La Marsa with

General Eaker and Major-General Hodges (the Commander of one of Eaker's Divisions) in one of the B.17 bombers that had taken part in the raid. After about half-an-hour's flight, we stopped at an old R.A.F. base where we met Colonel Curtis LeMay. He had flown to Africa ahead of his Division, the one which had bombed Regensburg, for the intention then was that the raid would be the first of a continuous series of 'shuttle attacks', with the American heavy bombers taking off to attack German targets both from U.K. and North African bases. But, as emerged during the talk between him and Ira Eaker, LeMay had found that servicing and then re-assembling widely-dispersed aircraft was an almost impossible task. On this occasion, little more than half the force which had attacked Regensburg would be available to attack shipping in the Gironde on the way back to England. It was a strange experience to be a looker-on as the unshaven Colonel, the taciturn Ira Eaker, and General Hodges discussed the losses which they had sustained, and the number of days it would take to assemble a force for the return raid. The talk took place in a large mess-room whose walls were lavishly decorated with crude murals of well-endowed nudes.

We then flew on to Marrakesh in Morocco. The two American generals sat in a makeshift way in the belly of the bomber, silently playing gin rummy, with their minds seemingly on nothing else. I stretched myself out on the tail-gunner's perch, with its wide view of the desert below. I must have been there far too long, for it took me more than a day after we landed to get rid of the giddiness from which I suffered after leaving what had seemed a marvellous position for viewing the world. Tail-gunners who were able to lie on their stomachs impervious to the sinuous movements of their end of the aircraft clearly belonged to a separate race of men.

In Marrakesh we spent two nights in Mrs. Taylor's Villa, La Saadia, where Churchill and Roosevelt had stayed during the Casablanca Conference in January 1943. The two generals continued with their gin rummy, while I drifted round the town. Presumably they continued on to England in the same B.17 in which we had arrived. I took off in another just before dusk.

I realise now that during all those months in the Mediterranean, it never once occurred to me to ask who was looking after my flight arrangements. I would merely say where I needed to go, and somehow it happened. The captain of my B.17, which had arrived too late to form part of the main force that was heading for the Gironde, was very respectful to his 'professor' passenger. After we had taken off, he invited me to sit in the co-pilot's seat. We had been conversing amiably for some time when I noticed that we were flying over territory that was not blacked out. The pilot was clearly off course, and since neither he nor

the navigator knew exactly where we were, I suggested that perhaps we
had intruded into neutral Spanish air-space, and that the Spanish might
not like it. The captain immediately called his co-pilot back, at the same
time ordering his four gunners to their action stations. I had stepped
back on to the platform where the top-gunner stood behind the cockpit.
An enjoyable conversation with him went something like this. 'What
d'you know, apart from being a gunner, I'm the flight engineer. Say, are
you a real professor?' 'Yes, I think so', I replied. 'Jeez, I always wanted
an education.' 'But surely', I said, 'being a gunner and flight engineer is
an education?' 'This ain't no education', he answered, 'I wanted to be a
pilot, but they say they don't need no pilots—you can be an engineer.
And what do I get for it? Nothing. I've shot down five enemy planes
with this gun. And what do they say? One probable, one possible. Jeez,
I saw his eyes as he went spinning down, dead already. Nowadays when
I shoot them down, I don't say nothin', it ain't no use.'

The next morning in London I told this story to Portal, to whom I
was delivering a message from Tedder. He hardly smiled as he commented, 'I wish they were all so modest. We'd then be nearer the truth
about enemy losses.'

During the two months or so I was back I caught up with the work
of my Oxford Extra-Mural Unit, at the same time as I persuaded Stradling to release the men I wanted for what was now going to be called
the Bombing Survey Unit. Soon I was able to signal both Tedder and
Norstad that I had recruited sixteen men, that they had all been given
honorary ranks in the R.A.F., from wing commander to flight lieutenant, and that since they would be on their way immediately, could all
necessary arrangements be made for supporting-staff and housekeeping.
I also picked up the threads of some of the unfinished work which I had
started in Combined Operations H.Q., and soon became drawn into the
deliberations of the Graham Committee, an inter-Service body that had
been set up to consider how to neutralise the coastal defences which the
Germans were erecting in the North of France and Belgium. Here again,
because of Pantelleria, I found myself regarded as a kind of oracle. But
I had to warn my colleagues that what we would be up against on the
other side of the English Channel was likely to prove very much tougher
than anything we had faced in the Mediterranean. My own view was that
it was necessary to approach the problem of coastal defences from a
fairly broad point of view. Concrete bunkers fifteen-feet thick were not
going to be destroyed by bombs. But equally, they were not likely to
prove invulnerable. As Tedder had not stopped worrying about the likelihood of the wrong lessons being drawn from Pantelleria, I sent him a
reassuring message to the effect that the Whitehall planners were not
being unreasonable on the subject.

Ben Burns had returned to England by this time, and as I wanted Peter Krohn with me in Sicily, he had to work hard to get the War Office to approve and produce the compressed rations that we had devised. George Jellicoe particularly wanted a thousand of our ration packs before we left. Peter succeeded in the job, and I discovered later that our dehydrated concoctions became part of a standard army issue.

I also saw the Prof, who by now was completely committed to the view that Germany could be subjugated by night bombing. He was also convinced that the daylight raids of the American heavy bombers were both ineffectual and costly, and he urged me to persuade Spaatz to this effect on my return to the Mediterranean. I can still see the look on Tooey's face when I later transmitted the message. Air Marshal Sir Trafford Leigh-Mallory of Fighter Command, who, in August, had been designated Commander-in-Chief of the Allied Air Forces for the forthcoming cross-Channel invasion, got hold of me through Dickie Mountbatten, who was about to leave England to take over as Supreme Commander of the Allied Forces operating in South-East Asia. Over lunch Leigh-Mallory and his American deputy, a Brigadier General Hansell, asked me to join their prospective command as scientific adviser on planning as soon as I had finished my work in the Mediterranean, which they assumed would be by the end of the year. I agreed, but only in principle, knowing that I was already committed both to Tedder and to Mountbatten. Mountbatten wanted me to go with him to S. E. Asia, but at the same time I preferred the excitement of the work I had been doing in the Mediterranean. Designing operations with Tedder, Spaatz and Norstad was much more rewarding than designing ration packs or embarking on new casualty surveys. What I did not know at the time was that most of the senior military commanders in the Mediterranean were soon to be transferred to the U.K. to prepare for the invasion of France.

I returned to La Marsa and Sicily in the middle of October. The plane I was in had to make a stop at an airfield in Cornwall, and I was provided with a car to take me to St. Ives, where I spent a couple of hours with Ben Nicholson and Barbara Hepworth, with whom Joan and I had stayed a few days the year before. It was a relief to talk about matters which had nothing to do with the war, and to see the work that they had been doing.

Less than a week after my arrival in La Marsa, I was followed by the men whom I had persuaded to join me, among them Frank Yates, Peter Krohn and Cliff Emmens. Both Colonel Willis and Wing Commander Wheatley had been moved to other jobs, and in their place I had been allocated, as my administrative officer, a Squadron Leader Ford, an old R.A.F. man who had seen service as a soldier in the Boer War, and as a flying man in the First World War. While I had been in England, our headquarters had been moved to an old and delapidated house in Palermo, the Palazzo Spadaforo. The Palazzo must have been bigger than it seemed to me at the time. What with some twenty officers and about fifty supporting staff, the Bombing Survey Unit numbered about seventy, of whom, fortunately, many were always in the field. Squadron Leader Ford was a stickler for old-fashioned form, and he made a ritual of my coming into dinner last of all, allowing no-one to sit until I had taken my seat. I believe that he thought this drill to be one of the few ways open to him to impose some kind of military discipline on a company of pseudo-officers. His job was far from easy. There was plenty of wine, and no shortage of rations, but neither was very good. Sometimes there was too much of both, for not long after the main party arrived, our numbers were increased by two American officers, one of whom, Major Allan Palmer, had been one of my research students in Oxford before the war. Allan was medically qualified and had landed in England with the first contingent of American troops sent over after his country's entry into the war. The moment that he arrived he got in touch with me, and soon became determined to join my team. Instead, he had been posted to a military hospital where, as ill-luck would have it, his only work had been to look after soldiers with venereal disease. To while away the time he had organised a band—I helped get him some instruments—and whenever he could, he found his way to Oxford. On one of these visits he had learnt about my recruiting mission, and by pulling strings, between us we managed to have him transferred to my new Unit. Snowden Marshall, my other American officer, belonged to the same family as the great General Marshall, the top military man in the United States, and had had some training in economics.

Both Allan and Snowden treated life lightly, and they had not been with us for more than a couple of days before they disappeared on a reconnaissance. When they returned, they had arranged to draw rations from two American depots, in addition to what we drew from the R.A.F. depot to which we had been assigned. No-one seemed to mind the abundance of whisky which resulted, but eyebrows were raised when they later turned up with a mobile workshop, with the explanation that no respectable headquarters should be without one, whether needed or not, and when on Thanksgiving Day they arranged a ration of almost one turkey per man.

There was no time to lose if the information that could be collected was to be of use in the further planning in which I was already involved. First priority was the analysis of the results of air attacks on rail and road communications. Next on my list came the study of the effects of bombing on Palermo town and on the enemy's airfields. There was also the opportunity to carry out a study of the causes of casualties during the progress of an actual battle—we still knew very little either about the effectiveness in action of different kinds of anti-personnel weapon, or about the value of protective clothing. There were also a number of isolated incidents to be investigated. The purpose of every study I embarked upon was to get a measure of the effectiveness of air attacks in relation to their tactical or strategic purpose. I was not interested just in figures showing the extent of physical destruction; my main concern was whether we could achieve the objectives we were after better next time, either by choosing different targets or by using different methods of attack.

I divided my team as best I could, with the main body remaining with me in Palermo to help in the work that had to be done there, and to operate as a flying-squad in collecting data for the study of the breakdown of the enemy's communications. One group I sent to Messina to find out why constant bombing attacks on the ferry terminals and ferries which spanned the ten kilometres that separated Sicily from the Italian mainland had failed to prevent over half the Axis forces escaping from both Montgomery's and Patton's armies. We were hampered in our ground enquiries by lack of motor transport, but we did the best we could, and in little more than two months had collected a mass of data, some more valuable than the rest.

Peter Krohn's study of attacks on airfields,[4] the first scientific study of its kind, when combined with the results of the field trials which I had already organised into the relative effectiveness of different small fragmenting bombs, provided useful information about the type of weapon and the density of strikes needed to put airfields out of action. My report of what had happened to Palermo during three years of bombing[5] showed that apart from a limited amount of demoralisation of the civilian population, the only results of the attacks which might have helped the outcome of the war in the Mediterranean were the destruction of a few ships in the harbour, the interruption of repair work in the docks, and the dislocation of the railways at a critical period of the North African battle. Allan Palmer's first-hand survey of the casualties that Allied troops suffered during their attempts to cross the Rapido River south of Cassino was interesting,[6] but did not yield information that could be put to use.

The most important of the enquiries on which I had embarked was undoubtedly that of the effect of air attacks on the enemy's movement, and it entailed a considerable amount of work. The Sicilian authorities put at my disposal some twenty railway clerks to help in the analysis of all their war-time records. Bomb incidents had to be studied on the ground. Determining the vulnerability of rolling-stock, of lines and of other rail installations to different sizes of bomb, and to different fusings, meant not only field-surveys and statistical analysis, in which Yates's help was vital, but also an analysis of bomb craters to make certain that we could diagnose the exact weapon that had been responsible. Here I was helped by an expert from Princes Risborough who had been sent out to join my team. As the picture which the analyses unfolded became clearer, gaps in our knowledge became apparent, and these called for yet more field investigation; to fill in, to confirm, or to correct. The work became more and more exhilarating. And even though we were very short of clerks, Barney Campion was always ready to type and retype at any hour of the day or night. One could not have asked for a more willing assistant.

In the Report which I finally submitted about the bombing of the railway system, I stated that while there was little indication that air attacks had prevented 'the enemy from moving from place to place within the limits imposed by the capacity of the transport at his disposal', the offensive against rail targets in Sicily and Southern Italy had been 'an outstanding success'. The two factors which contributed most to the outcome of the offensive, I went on to say, 'were the destruction and damaging of rolling-stock and repair facilities'. Largely because of this, 'the Sicilian and Southern Italian rail systems had become practically paralysed by the end of July 1943—as a result of attacks on only six railway centres, Naples, Foggia, San Giovanni, Reggio, Messina, Palermo'. These particular attacks, I continued, had 'added at least as much to the enemy's supply difficulties in Tunisia as did the losses he incurred at sea'. This was an unexpected conclusion in the light of what I had been given to understand about the significance to our North African and Middle East campaigns of the enemy's shipping losses in the Mediterranean. So too was the finding that the most economic way to disrupt communications was not to cut lines, but to attack 'large railway centres which contain important repair facilities and large concentrations of locomotives and rolling-stock. . . . The efficiency of a railway system', I wrote, 'appears to fall very rapidly when bombing simultaneously leads to an increase in the calls upon, and a decrease in the capacity of the repair facilities.'

My enquiries had not only revealed the extent to which the dislocation of the Southern Italian and Sicilian railways had disrupted the movement of troops and supplies—civilian traffic had suffered sooner and even more severely. They had also taught me a great deal about railways in general and about the whole Italian system in particular. The Sicilian railway authorities were very willing teachers. I passed my lessons to La Marsa as fast as I learnt, in order that they could be taken into account in the day-to-day planning that was going on, and occasionally I flew over to spend a night with Tedder. But the final draft of my report was not ready until the last week of December 1943. In my cover note I remarked that the document was 'somewhat voluminous for a preliminary statement', but that I did not make apologies for this since 'so extensive and successful an air-effort could not be documented and analysed in a few pages'. 'My fear', I went on to say, 'is not that I have been too detailed but that, even for a preliminary statement, I have been able to consider too few of the facts—and then all too hurriedly.' My 'preliminary report' consisted of a general statement which, with its several appendices, amounted to a fairly lengthy book.[7] What with my reports on Palermo and other targets, my 'literary output' during my two and a half months in Palermo was pretty considerable.

There was another aspect of target selection in which I became concerned. Before I had returned to London to recruit staff, two Americans who, I believe, were attached to A.M.G.O.T., came to see me in the hope that I would tell Tedder about their concern that historic buildings and other treasures in Italy might be seriously damaged by bombing. Before they saw me, they had failed to get their message relayed to anyone in real authority, which they had been told I could do. In their view pilots were not being briefed to understand what it would mean if, for example, the leaning tower of Pisa were to collapse. They knew that there was an understanding that Rome would not be bombed, but clearly that was not enough. I told Tedder about their concern, and he took what action he could, at the same time as he asked me to enquire, when in London, whether Kenneth Clark, then the Director of the National Gallery, had any ideas about ways of preventing unnecessary destruction. Unfortunately he had none. When I got back from England, I found that a street map, copied from Baedeker and marked to show important buildings that were to be avoided, was now included in the briefing kits for each Italian town that was likely to be a target. I fear, however, that I did not have enough faith in the bombing accuracy of the aircrews to believe that this could be of real value. A booklet, *Italian Monuments Preservation*, was also produced. This helped. But Tedder continued to worry. Once when I was indicating on a town map a desired aiming point, taking into account the average bombing error of the squadrons which were going to attack, he said, 'No, let's move the aiming point. If we use yours, the maternity home is in danger'. There was no maternity home, but a church was within the possible danger zone. So the aiming point was moved. I was later approached by an American officer, who was also concerned with ancient monuments, who asked me to make representations about the Monastery of Monte Cassino. This time I failed.

Requests for information about what I was discovering also came in from the Air Ministry Bombing Committee in London, and from Stradling who, not surprisingly, wanted to know about the doings of the staff he had seconded to me. I responded as best I could. On one occasion

I took two days off to fly with Tooey and a few other officers to visit a number of our commanders on the Italian front. That trip stands out mainly because of the return journey. We had with us as extra passengers two German pilots who had been shot down, and the whole way back to La Marsa I talked with one of them as well as a mixture of poor German and poor English allowed. The contrast with the cocky Luftwaffe pilot I had met in similar circumstances in the Western Desert could not have been greater. The new prisoner was terrified; the war was horrible, civilisation was being destroyed, and the sooner Hitler was finished, the better the chance of anything surviving. Later I made another trip to the front with Wigglesworth, just before he moved to London, as Senior Air Staff Officer on Leigh-Mallory's staff, to prepare for the projected invasion of Europe. On this occasion we went as far forward as we could, and I was astonished to find how silent and peaceful a forward artillery observation post could be in the beautiful country in front of Monte Cassino. 'Wiggles', as he always signed himself to friends, was saying farewell to various people with whom he had had dealings in the Mediterranean. Amongst them was General Mark Clark, with whom we lunched at his H.Q. outside Naples, and who briefed us formally about the position of his army. We also called on Air Vice-Marshal Foster, who was commanding a scratch force of Italian airmen who had come over to our side, and who were operating from Bari on the Adriatic Coast. Wiggles was the officer who, in the Mediterranean, usually represented Tedder at meetings with Montgomery. But we did not call on Monty. On our way back from the strenuous up-and-down visit to the Italian front, Wiggles and I spent a night in Malta with Air Vice-Marshal Sir Keith Park, one of the outstanding fighter commanders of the Battle of Britain. I arrived with a splitting headache, which our host properly diagnosed as being due to dehydration, and which he cured with a quick succession of glasses of cold lager.

I had signalled to Tedder late in November to suggest that he should come and see for himself how the enquiry into the attacks on the railway system was proceeding. He made arrangements to fly over, but these had to be cancelled because, as I later discovered, he was called to the meeting which Churchill and Roosevelt had convened in Cairo with their respective military chiefs, before their meeting with Stalin in Teheran. Tedder then signalled to say that on his return from the Cairo Conference he wanted to bring Portal with him to Palermo. This however, proved impossible, so Tedder arrived accompanied by his new wife, 'Toppy' as she was generally known, dressed in her Malcolm Clubs uniform. I showed him round some of the areas of destruction that we had surveyed, introduced him to those of my staff who were in Palermo, and had them explain what they were doing. I also took him to the railway offices to see my volunteer Sicilian staff at work. He did not stop looking around until he had satisfied himself—as he records in his autobiography—that my recommendations about further targets were as soundly based as they could be.

I had arranged to take the Tedders to dine with the de Cruz's, the owners of the Mondello villa which Colonel Willis had taken over as my billet when we first arrived. Over an excellent meal with first-class French wine, Tedder appeared interested in what the conversation revealed about conditions in Sicily and Italy in the early years of the war, although he gave no indication that he believed much of what he was told. Without warning me, however, our hosts had invited to come in after dinner Colonel Poletti, an American of Italian descent who had formerly been Lieutenant Governor of New York State at the time when Fiorello La Guardia was the 'reform mayor' of New York City. He was now Lord Rennell's deputy. At the time there was a lot of talk in Palermo about vast amounts of American supplies which arrived at the docks, but which disappeared into the mists before reaching their proper destination. I knew nothing about the facts one way or another, but some time before I had told Tedder about these rumours, and that it was being said that A.M.G.O.T. was doing nothing effective to stop the leak. Tedder had wanted me to pass the story on to General Alexander, the Deputy Allied Commander-in-Chief, but I had not done so, feeling that it was none of my business. When Poletti walked into the de Cruz sitting room he was somewhat merry from drink, and had a pretty young Sicilian girl on each arm. 'Meet my Boticellis', he called out as he entered. We all rose, and Tedder, no doubt remembering what I had told him about the hijacking of supplies, greeted him with the words, 'I have long been wanting to meet one of the men who have taken so little time to undo what it took us so long, and cost us so much, to achieve'. Poletti did not know what to say, and I certainly did not know where to look.

Tedder's visit took place about the middle of December, and when he left he urged me, not that I needed much urging, to finish my reports as soon as possible. Soon after his departure, I received a message that he was sending an aircraft to fly me to La Marsa where Portal was making an overnight stop on his way back to England. In addition to Portal, Tedder had at dinner Air Commodore William Elliot,* the head of the Air Ministry's Planning Directorate, Robb, and Leslie Scarman, Tedder's Staff Officer. The talk focused mainly on the results of my enquiries, and on their applicability to the strategic air war against Germany, and in particular to the preparatory phase of the projected invasion of France.

* Air Chief Marshal Sir William Elliot became Chairman of the British Joint Services Commission in Washington and then Chairman of the Royal Institute of International Affairs. He died in 1971.

It was possibly on this occasion that Tedder, as he records in his auto-biography, suggested to Portal that he should get me back to London to 'put me in touch with the planners'. Portal seemed much impressed by what I had to relate, and said sadly, 'So we were laughed out of Hamm', referring back to those frustrating days in the early part of the war when our bombing and navigational accuracy was so poor that only rarely did a bomb explode anywhere near the railway centre at Hamm which was so often a target. At some moment during dinner we were interrupted by Flight Lieutenant Philip Wintle, Tedder's pilot and personal assistant, who came in and said in a lofty voice, 'There's a fellow on the 'phone from Algiers. Calls himself Anthony Eden. Says he needs a plane straight away to take him back to London. Damn cheek I call it.' In those days the younger R.A.F. officers affected a disdainful language of their own. Perhaps they still do.

I was told confidentially about Eisenhower's appointment as Supreme Allied Commander for the invasion of France, and of Tedder's as his Deputy. I was also asked to be ready to leave for the U.K. by the end of the month, and to arrange for the completion of all the enquiries I had in hand, the understanding being that Wing Commander E. C. Williams, the head of the R.A.F. Operational Research Section in the Mediter-ranean, would then take charge of my Unit. I worked flat out to keep to this timetable, and managed to issue my two bigger reports in time. Others were completed later, and the B.S.U. itself was not disbanded until the middle of 1944, although all the British personnel I had re-cruited were back in England not long after me. Six months after he took over, I received a letter from Williams in which he said, 'The policy for strategic bombing is not by any means constant and rather changes in accordance with the latest craze. It is extremely difficult to influence policy under the present set-up of the command.'* The Com-mand had indeed changed with the departure of Eisenhower and Tedder at the beginning of 1944.

On 30 December 1943, I left Palermo for La Marsa with my personal belongings and two heavy sealed mailbags full of secret papers. At La Marsa I said goodbye to my many friends and dined with Tedder. The next morning he sent me on to Casablanca in his own plane, which stopped at Algiers so that I could pay a last visit to friends in Eisen-hower's main headquarters. Having, as I thought, said my last goodbye, I was walking down a corridor when a door opened and a one-star American general whom I knew slightly, stuck his head out and said,

---

* E. C. Williams continued in public service after the war, first in the Ministry of Defence, then as Director of the S.H.A.P.E. Technical Centre and then as Chief Scientific Adviser in the Ministry of Transport and Department of Trade and Industry. He retired from the service as Chief Inspector of Nuclear Installations.

'Zuck, when we've finished with Germany, we'll still want you when we take on the Russians. Don't forget.' I never forgot the remark.

At Casablanca I was met by the American Station Commander who told me that there had been a hitch, and that my flight would not be taking off for the U.K. for an hour or so. A guard was mounted over my two secret bags, and I went with him while he sorted the matter out. It was cleared up after a brief call to Algiers, and I was then accompanied out to a DC.3 (a Dakota) which was already fully loaded with a group of British officers. As I got to the steps, an officer left the plane to make room for me and my bags. My fellow passengers turned out to be Montgomery's main staff returning to England to start planning for *Overlord*, the codename for the invasion of France. I was sorry about the displaced Brigadier, but an aircraft had its maximum load and nothing could be done about it. However, when my sealed bags were opened in England, I was much taken aback to discover that Allan Palmer had taken the opportunity of enclosing some very heavy souvenirs he had collected in Sicily, among them a handsome brass symbol of the fasces which, during Mussolini's regime, used to be mounted on the front of Italian locomotives. At the time I was not very pleased by what Allan had done. Years later, when it adorned one of the walls of his library in San Francisco, I could look at it with admiration.

CHAPTER 12

PREPARATIONS FOR OVERLORD

TEDDER HAD given me a sealed envelope which had to be delivered personally into Portal's hands, and I was therefore not surprised to find a car waiting to take me to the Air Ministry in London from the airfield where we landed. Having read the letter, Portal remarked that it was essential that Air Chief Marshal Sir Arthur Harris, the Commander-in-Chief of R.A.F. Bomber Command, known to his friends as Bert, to the public as 'Bomber Harris', and in his Command as 'Butch', should be informed immediately about such lessons of the Mediterranean campaign as might bear on the forthcoming allied invasion of France, and particularly about the desirability of launching a bomber offensive against the railway network of North-West Europe. Had I yet spoken to Harris, he asked? When I said no, he suggested that I should do so that very day. Instead I offered the following night, as I first wanted to see Joan and to be brought up to date with my affairs in Oxford. A tie-line connected Portal's desk with that of Harris at his headquarters near High Wycombe, and after the two had spoken, Portal said that the following night would do, but that before leaving London I ought at least to see Leigh-Mallory, who was now fully confirmed as Commander-in-Chief of the Allied Expeditionary Air Force (A.E.A.F.) for *Overlord*. Leigh-Mallory, Portal said, expected me to work with him.

Leigh-Mallory and Wigglesworth, now in his new post as Senior Air Staff Officer (S.A.S.O.) to A.E.A.F., received me without delay at their headquarters in Norfolk House in St. James's Square, and introduced me to Air Commodore Kingston-McCloughry, their Head of Operational Plans and Deputy Chief of Operations. I was to work very closely with him for several months. After the usual kind of welcoming talk, Leigh-Mallory suggested that I should read the plan for the preparatory phases of the invasion which had been produced by a joint planning staff consisting of representatives of the Army and of A.E.A.F. Kingston led me to his office and, as I read the few pages in which the air plan was set out, he sat gazing at me from his desk in the opposite corner of the room. He had still to study my Sicily Report,[1] but Portal had made the Air Staff aware of its broad conclusions, and Wiggles had no doubt also told what he knew. I suspect that before I began reading

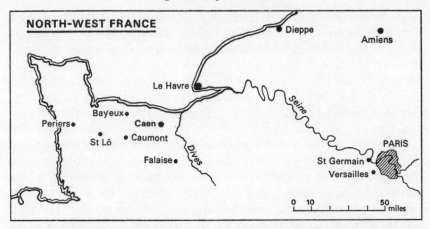

NORTH-WEST FRANCE

Dieppe • Amiens •

Le Havre •

Bayeux •
Periers •
Caen •
St Lô • • Caumont

Falaise •

Seine

Dives

PARIS

St Germain •
Versailles •

0 10   50 miles

Kingston must have known that I was going to judge the plan inadequate. In effect, all that it said was that enemy reinforcements had to be delayed by bombing some twenty points on the railway system in an arc about fifty to sixty miles from the area of our landings. Because of the obvious need for tight security, these attacks had to be carried out close to D-Day. Coastal defences were to be subdued by bombing and naval fire, while air supremacy was to be assured over the beaches by fighter attacks on that part of the German Air Force which had not already been crippled by the strategic offensive against the factories by which it was sustained.[2] This plan accorded with the general directive which General Sir Frederick Morgan, who was responsible for the initial planning of *Overlord*, had sent Leigh-Mallory when he became C.-in-C. of A.E.A.F., but it seemed to me no more than an expression of hope.

Kingston accepted my immediate comment that it would be hazardous in the extreme to rely on good flying weather in the two to three weeks before the proposed date of the assault, and on the very precise bombing operations which the plan demanded. I also expressed doubts about the ability of our fighter-bombers to cut railway lines and destroy tunnels and bridges in order to force the enemy to detrain some hundred miles from the assault area. Kingston was also ready to believe, what Italian experience had revealed, that the desired disruption of communications could be more securely achieved by a 'strategic' attack on the railway network than by any attempt to cut it at specific points. We therefore agreed that the moment I got back to London I would prepare an alternative plan which he would then submit to Leigh-Mallory.

It was New Year's Day, and it was a joy to get back to Oxford. Towards the end of the afternoon of the following day, during which I caught up with the work that my Extra-Mural Unit had been doing while I was away, a car from Bomber Command turned up to take me to

High Wycombe. I arrived at Harris's house just as he was returning from
his headquarters nearby, and apart from his wife, we were alone at
dinner. I had never met him before, and was much taken by his quiet
sense of power and determination. No two of the many air marshals
whom I already knew were alike, but he seemed more remote, more self-
contained, than any I had met before. He changed into a mulberry-
coloured velvet smoking jacket and disappeared into the kitchen to prepare Eggs Benedictine with his own hands, so revealing to me that the
culinary arts were one of the joys of his life. At the end of the meal he
also surprised me by the ceremonial way he prepared what I took to be
snuff. But after his wife left us, there was no question of my telling him
anything about air operations in the Mediterranean. Nor did he put any
questions to me. He began by expressing his bitter dismay that Ira Eaker
was about to be transferred to the Mediterranean Theatre in place of
Tooey Spaatz, who was returning to the United Kingdom to become
commanding general of all the American Air Forces in Europe. This
transfer he described as a disaster, and the sacrifice of a man whose heavy
bombers had become more and more effective over the course of the
preceding year, and who understood about the vital importance of the
strategic bombing of Germany, which he thought Spaatz appreciated
not at all.

The famous secret 'Blue Book', about which Harris has written in his
autobiography,[3] was produced, and I was invited to admire aerial photographs of destroyed German cities. Gossip had it that there were three
such books into which were pasted copies of the latest aircover photographs of the cities which Bomber Command had attacked. Harris had
one, one was with Winston Churchill, and a third was said to be kept
up-to-date in Moscow by a Wing Commander whose job it was to try
to persuade the Russian authorities about the value of Bomber Command's operations. Many of the photographs in the book had passed
through R.E.8 at Princes Risborough, and I had learnt not to be over-
impressed by pictures of physical destruction. What had concerned
Bernal, Frank Yates and me in Princes Risborough were the functional
inferences about the disruption of German industry that one could draw
from aerial photographs of devastated towns. I also knew full well that
Intelligence sources at the time indicated that war production in Hitler's
Reich was still mounting, in spite of the vast physical damage that had
been wreaked by Bomber Command.

By the time Harris suggested that we should go to bed, he had still
not asked a single question about the Mediterranean war. That came
next morning when we were alone at breakfast. He had only one question to put, he said, and he wanted a straight answer, 'yes or no—
nothing more'. 'Could heavy bombers be used to bomb coastal defences?'

I paused a second, and then said, 'yes'. It was clearly not the answer he wanted, and no further word was spoken. When we rose from the table he invited me to his headquarters, where I listened to briefings about weather, aircraft in readiness, the choice of targets, and so on. The decisiveness with which Harris gave his orders for the coming night was highly impressive. I returned to Oxford and then to London for the start of five months intensive work.

Apart from achieving and maintaining air superiority over the Luft-waffe, the major tasks which it was recognised the air forces would have to undertake, in order to ensure a successful landing by our assault troops, were the destruction or neutralisation of coastal defences; the clearing of the air over our shipping lanes and the assault beaches; and the delaying of enemy reinforcements. Every Intelligence appreciation which had been put to C.O.S.S.A.C., the codename by which General Morgan was known, to Leigh-Mallory, and later to Eisenhower and Tedder, implied that unless we did something to prevent it, the Germans could build up their forces against our lodgement area in Normandy—given that we achieved one—much faster than we could possibly rein-force. They had the necessary troops and the free use of a rich network of railways and roads. The plans which I had seen on my arrival at Norfolk House assumed, as I have said, that the air could do what was wanted by attacks on a few targets just before, or at the time of the landings. Indeed, it was then held that it would be unnecessary to make a direct call on the strategic air forces for a period longer than a fortnight before D-Day. Leigh-Mallory seemed to have accepted this general view, but I do not believe that he had as yet given much thought to the problem. L-M (as most called him) was an inspired commander of fighter forces, and had distinguished himself in the Battle of Britain. He had also learnt a lesson about the need for fire support from the disastrous raid on Dieppe in 1942, a raid which had cost us some four thousand casualties and pri-soners-of-war out of an assault force of about six thousand, and in which he had commanded the fighter forces. He was convinced that the main fight for air supremacy would take place over the Normandy beaches. Air supremacy was his preoccupation. As Commander-in-Chief of A.E.A.F., he was to have under his command only the British and a part of the American fighters and fighter-bombers which were based in the United Kingdom, but to my mind these were clearly not enough for what I saw needed to be done. The heavy bombers—the Lancasters and Stirlings of Bomber Command, and the Flying Fortresses (B.17s) and Liberators (B.24s) of the American 8th Air Force—which it was assumed were to remain under the British and American strategic bomber com-mands, had to be brought in. The U.S. 8th and 15th Air Forces together made up the U.S. Strategic Air Forces in Europe (U.S.S.T.A.F.).

The day after I returned to London I was introduced to a Captain Sherrington and his colleague Mr. Brant, who were known as 'the railway experts'. Sherrington was the head of the Research Service of the Railway Executive Committee, which was responsible for the organisation of British railways during the war, and when I discovered that he was the son of *the* Sir Charles Sherrington, I was more than ready to accept him as an expert. At a meeting on 6 January, he had approved the list of seventeen targets that appeared in the Joint Planning Staff's document which was entitled 'The Delay of Enemy Reserves during the Initial Stages of Operation *Neptune*'.[4] But while he and Brant knew a great deal about the layout and normal workings of the continental railway system, they knew absolutely nothing about bombing or about the relative vulnerability of different parts of a railway system to bombs. Correspondingly, the military planners whom they were helping were merely working from a map, on which they had arbitrarily drawn a line where they hoped the Germans would be forced to detrain. They had little or no idea how long it would take a determined enemy to repair broken railway lines or viaducts, or to find river crossings other than bridges that had been destroyed or damaged by bombs. What also amazed me was that the Air Force planners who had accepted the Joint Staff plan did not at that time appear to have been seriously concerned by the possibility that the weather might be unfavourable for flying operations during the two or three weeks preceding the likely date of the invasion, and also that conditions for visual bombing, which was the prevailing technique in those days, might prevent any precise bombing attacks. If the lessons of Sicily and Italy were to be put to use in devising a better plan, my first job therefore was to learn from the railway experts about the layout of the systems of North-West Europe, at the same time as I persuaded them to study the reports that I had brought back, the empirical basis of which they soon accepted. On the following two days, Kingston invited the 21 Army Group transportation experts to join in our talks.

Leigh-Mallory then agreed to convene a small 'Allied Air Force Bombing Committee' consisting of representatives of A.E.A.F., R.A.F. Bomber Command, the American Air Forces, and the Air Ministry. I set about drafting a comprehensive plan as a basis for discussion, and Sherrington was made responsible for drawing up a list of railway centres of different categories which should be bombed in the implementation of the 'strategic plan' that I was preparing. The Committee met first on 10 January 1944, and then several more times during the month, with Leigh-Mallory occasionally, but Kingston usually, taking the chair. After each meeting I agreed with Kingston what amendments in the list of targets seemed desirable, but without ever altering the basis or intent of what was to become the outline air plan for the invasion.

The first few meetings of the A.E.A.F. Bombing Committee were peaceful, even though, as the minutes of the first meeting record, I unhesitatingly urged that 'a strategic policy should be adopted against the railways forthwith' (*sic*).[5] Our friendly start was at least partly due to Air Marshal Sir Richard Peck, an Assistant Chief of the Air Staff, in whose domain of planning the matter lay. He had been authorised to circulate a statement to the effect that the Air Staff concurred in the conclusions and recommendations of my Sicily Report, 'based as they are on the result of much operational experience'. This he did in a letter which he addressed to Leigh-Mallory on 2 February, and which was couched in the formal language that characterised, and I suppose still characterises, such messages. The letter set out the main conclusions and recommendations of my report, and ended with the words: 'I am accordingly to request that they may be brought to the notice of all concerned in your Command, and action taken upon them as necessary'.[6] Not surprisingly, Air Marshal Peck's representative on the A.E.A.F. Bombing Committee was therefore enthusiastic about the new plan. So was Colonel Hughes,* his opposite number from the American Air Forces. The date of Peck's letter is significant to the story.

In my innocence, I did not realise that it was all too good to last. Those first three or four weeks of January were passed in a state of euphoria, working to all hours in Norfolk House, occasionally rushing out to some friend's house for a drink or meal, or escaping with Kingston to one of two nearby restaurants which provided better food than did the Norfolk House Mess. Kingston has left a record of our times in St. James's Square in his book *The Direction of War*.[7] So that there was always someone to take dictation and type, three W.A.A.F. officers had been assigned to me as secretaries. But I had all but no professional staff to help in, for example, calculations about the likely size of force that would be required to achieve a given density of strikes in an area of such and such a size. When I needed help in calculating the effort needed against a particular target, I usually disguised the problem and had the sums done by one of my staff in Oxford. My time was taken up in studying intelligence appreciations and maps, learning about the communication network of the continent, its coastal defences and airfields, seeing people, putting and answering questions, dictating and writing, and attending meetings. There were never enough hours in the twenty-four.

Shortly after I had returned from the Mediterranean, and before the first meeting of the A.E.A.F. Committee, Portal, as Chief of the Air

---

* Hughes was a one-time professional English soldier who had become an American citizen.

Staff had, however, circulated a memorandum that I had not seen, and which began:

> 'On the one hand there is a school of thought which says that a bomb on Germany is worth x times as many as anywhere else. At the other end of the scale there are those who think that every bomb we can drop should be directed at communications in order to hinder the German build up. As with most controversies of this kind, I expect that the truth lies somewhere between these two extremes, and of course timing will enter vitally into the answer. . . . It behoves us to try to find the right answer for ourselves and then to argue the case in such a way as to bring the resulting compromise as nearly as possible to the optimum in which we ourselves believe.'[8]

It was therefore only five days after this note was issued that I had publicly urged, at the first meeting of the A.E.A.F. Committee, that the destruction of the railway network of Western Europe should become a prime strategic objective, *sui generis*, and not just a series of targets related to *Overlord*. I was therefore unwittingly marking myself as being opposed to the prevailing policy of the strategic air forces. While no objections were ever raised against any of the other and less significant parts of the new plan, the section which dealt with what is variously referred to in books as the 'Railway', 'Transportation', 'Communications', or 'Zuckerman' Plan, started to come under fire. However, after about five successive amendments, the plan received Leigh-Mallory's full authority, and by the end of January was in some form of final shape. The vigour of the controversy which ensued is anything but exaggerated in the various American and British official histories and biographies in which it is recorded.

The issue was simple. If the new plan were to be implemented, it would mean a diversion of effort from the existing commitment of the heavy bomber forces. According to the U.S./U.K. *Pointblank* directive of June 1943, their priority commitment was to destroy the fighter forces of the German Air Force and the industry sustaining them. In implementing this directive, the American Air Forces were to make precision day attacks on specified German plants and airfields, at the same time as R.A.F. Bomber Command made 'area-attacks' by night on German towns which were immediately concerned in aircraft production. The new *Overlord* plan was clearly generating a new strategic objective. It was proclaiming without qualification that the deeper attacks on the railway system were pressed into Germany, the sooner would *all* German industry be brought to a halt. The plan was therefore seen as a threat to the independence of the American and British strategic air commands, for if it were accepted, they would necessarily come under Eisenhower's command, and through him under that of Tedder and Leigh-Mallory. It was also being advanced at the very moment that Harris was claiming that Germany was about to collapse under the weight of his Command's attacks—a view which had been supported by an appreciation made by the Air Ministry in November 1943.[9]

The autobiography which he published shortly after the end of the war implies that Harris supported the A.E.A.F. plan from the start.[10] The truth is that it was he who started what was to become an argument which could well have wrecked *Overlord*. The British and American official histories, as well as Tedder's autobiography, provide a decidedly clearer and also a fuller picture of what really happened.

Harris's opening broadside was a long and articulate letter which he addressed to Portal on 13 January. This was sent to Leigh-Mallory who passed it to Kingston and me for comment. It began with the somewhat grudging sentence: 'Overlord must now presumably be regarded as an inescapable commitment'. It then went on to state unequivocally that Bomber Command's role was to destroy the centres of German industry. It was for this purpose that Harris's force had been designed and it was not suited for the type of task now being considered. The obvious conclusion, therefore, was that the only effective support that Bomber Command could give to *Overlord* was to intensify its offensive against German industrial cities. 'If', Harris's letter ended, 'we attempt to substitute for this process attacks on gun emplacements, beach defences, communications or dumps in occupied territory we shall commit the irremedial error of diverting our best weapon from the military function for which it has been equipped and trained, to tasks which it cannot effectively carry out. Though this might give a specious appearance of "supporting" the Army, in reality it would lead directly to disaster.'

There were twenty-two paragraphs, each supposedly embodying a different proposition, in the letter of 13 January. Most turned out to be merely a restatement of Bomber Command's prevailing commitments and capacities, and an indication that the idea of attacking railways in France, the Low Countries and Western Germany, implied a more difficult operational task than did attacks on industrial cities deep inside Germany.[11] Kingston agreed that we should arrange Harris's assertions in a column, and add our own comments against each of them. Leigh-Mallory sent the result as it stood to Portal. The Air Ministry then added a third column of comment. The final document was given a fairly wide circulation in planning circles,[12] the idea being that after *Overlord* had been launched, a fourth column of comment would be added by the Air Staff as a judgment on the correctness or otherwise of our observations on Harris's contentions, and of the views to which they themselves were ready to subscribe.

Portal had already lent the weight of his authority to the principles which underlay the plan to which Tedder and now Leigh-Mallory were committed. On his return from La Marsa he had certainly persuaded some of the senior members of the Air Staff to the same view. It was not surprising, therefore, that on this occasion the Air Ministry's comments on Harris's assertions supported the A.E.A.F. contentions far more than they did those of Bomber Command. As Harris himself makes only too plain in his autobiography, his relations with the Ministry were anything but easy at the time. An enormous burden and a terrifying responsibility of decision rested on his shoulders. Night after night he was launching hundreds of bombers into the air, and night after night scores of young men under his command were either killed or shot down to become prisoners of war. It was only natural that he should be hostile to any comment that could be construed as an attack on his judgment and authority. When the Air Ministry intervened in his affairs he saw it as a body trying to 'run a force without', as he put it, 'direct responsibility for the results which must, of course, remain with the Commander'.[13] Some senior staff officers tried to bring Harris to heel when on occasion he departed, in what seemed a deliberate and high-handed way, from the instructions that he had received from Portal, who was responsible to the Chiefs of Staff Committee, and so to the War Cabinet, for all air operations. For example, shortly after the middle of January 1944, Harris had been told to concentrate his effort on the 'remaining' most vital targets concerned with German fighter production. A few days later, however, he ordered a major attack by some 650 bombers on Magdeburg, a city which did not even figure in the Air Ministry list of industrial areas associated with aircraft production. All that Portal's staff in the Air Ministry could do was draw attention to the fact that Harris had picked Magdeburg as his 'target for tonight' even though he could have attacked nearby Leipzig which, as the Air Ministry pointed out, was on their list, and also had a bigger population (*sic*).[14]

The Ministry, it seemed, simply did not know how to check Harris when he stepped out of line, and when he carried out an area attack of lesser priority than one endorsed by the Chiefs of Staff. Under Churchill's protection, Harris had become almost a law unto himself. Indeed, it was not until a year later, after Bomber Command's tragic attack on Dresden, that the Prime Minister withdrew the umbrella of his protection. This he did in a Minute which was issued on 1 April 1945, about six weeks after the Dresden raid, and which bluntly said that any further attacks on German cities would hinder the Allies more than they would hurt the Germans. An earlier draft of the same Minute had in fact been circulated four days before, but had been withdrawn after the Air Staff, and Harris, had protested because it also stated that German cities were being bombed 'simply for the sake of increasing the terror, though under

other pretexts'. The absence of these offending words in the final
Minute did not, however, restore the situation for Harris, and from that
moment on he found himself deprived of the support which for so long
had made him an unassailable war leader.[15] The extraordinary tone of his
protestations against the wording of Churchill's first Minute is recounted
on p. 352.

At the time the A.E.A.F. plan was unveiled, however, Harris's
authority was to all intents and purposes supreme, and it was only a
matter of a week or two before the bulk of opinion in the Air Ministry
was behind him. He was, after all, on firm ground. As seen from Britain,
the joint bombing offensive against the German homeland by the R.A.F.
and the U.S. Strategic Air Forces, was the mainstay of the Allied fight.
Furthermore, at a meeting called by Portal as late as 19 January, Harris,
Spaatz *and* Leigh-Mallory had jointly put their names to a signal, which
was sent next day to the Combined Chiefs of Staff in Washington, affirm-
ing their faith in the *Pointblank* directive of 10 June 1943. This in
effect could have been taken to mean that even the C.-in-C. of A.E.A.F.
was not in favour of the new plan his staff had by then formulated for the
use of heavy bombers. I myself was far too busy discussing minor
amendments to the Outline Plan we were preparing, and with other
matters, to pay attention to all the pieces of paper that were passed
around the headquarters, and I was not as disturbed as was Kingston
at this piece of backsliding, as he saw it, by the C.-in-C. Leigh-Mallory
himself chaired a meeting of his Bombing Committee four days after the
joint signal was sent, and on this occasion when I pressed for an immediate start in the implementation of our plan, he made it plain that I was
too precipitate. In retrospect I am sure he was wrong, even if he was
far more realistic than I about the possibilities of gaining even indirect
control of the heavy bombers.

Kingston always mistrusted commanders-in-chief. An Australian by
birth, he had joined the Royal Flying Corps in the First World War,
and by the age of 22 had already been awarded the D.S.O. and the D.F.C.
In effect, he was a contemporary of the men who were now running
the Royal Air Force. He had already all but ruined his career by using
unconventional means in a fruitless attempt to unseat Air Chief Marshal
Sir Cyril Newall, Portal's predecessor as Chief of the Air Staff, because,
in Kingston's view, Newall had misled the Cabinet about Britain's air
strength. But Kingston failed to get me excited about the telegram of
20 January, and in any event, I knew that Eisenhower and Tedder had
the final word, and that Tedder, who was on no more than nodding terms
with Kingston, was not going to be diverted from what he believed to
be right by any number of commanders-in-chief sending affirmations to
the Combined Chiefs of Staff.

It was then that the opposition parties really started to organise, even if at the beginning their left hand hardly knew what the right was doing. Two days after the Air Ministry, through Air Marshal Peck, had directed planners to accept the principles which underlay the new plan, A.E.A.F. received a communication from the Air Ministry saying that it was going to delay issuing a factual summary of my Mediterranean Report because 'certain differences of opinion' about it had started to emerge among members of the Air Staff. This message arrived *after* the Initial Joint Plan for the whole of *Overlord*, a plan that incorporated the new A.E.A.F. proposals,[16] had been sent by the three Commanders-in-Chief of the *Overlord* forces to Eisenhower who, as Supreme Commander, had in turn endorsed it. No-one seemed to think it odd that a factual report was being suppressed. And not even I had the time to be disturbed by so ridiculous a piece of censorship, which to the best of my knowledge was never lifted.

Encouraged by both Kingston and Wigglesworth who, apart from being S.A.S.O. to Leigh-Mallory was also, of course, one of Tedder's trusted lieutenants, I kept urging Leigh-Mallory, whenever possible, to protest about the delays in implementing the plan, and about the imposition of any limitations on its scope. The planning staff of 21 Army Group had by now started to keep clear of the debate; they had stated their 'requirement': that the air execute such operations as would make it difficult for the Germans to reinforce the Normandy area. Tedder and Eisenhower were also keeping themselves aloof from the immediate controversy. But I knew that Tedder, with whom I was in daily contact after his return from the Mediterranean, was merely biding his time, as he worried about the problem of coordinating the various objectives of the air forces, a matter which he was discussing constantly with Portal. So too at this stage were Winston Churchill and the Prof, both of whom powerfully supported the 'bomber barons' against A.E.A.F.

The Air Ministry's Directorate of Bomber Operations, and in particular its Chief, Air Commodore Sidney Bufton, were soon at one with Bomber Command in opposing the new plan. The Intelligence wing of the Ministry had also swung round. The Enemy Objectives Unit of the U.S. Economic Warfare Department was against us. Its Director, C. P. Kindleberger,* worked hand-in-glove not only with Bufton, but also with O. L. Lawrence, the Head of the Objectives Department of the British Ministry of Economic Warfare, which was yet another source of opposition. Kindleberger's Unit was manned by a group of young and enthusiastic economists. Among them were Walt Rostow, later to gain fame as a kingpin of President Johnson's National Security Council

---

* After the war, Kindleberger was one of the team which prepared the Marshall Plan. He then settled at M.I.T. as Professor of Economics.

in the period of the Vietnam War, and Carl Kaysen, who between 1966 and 1976 was President of the Institute for Advanced Study at Princeton. After the war, and during his White House days, Rostow and I occasionally had official dealings, but I always had the feeling that he regarded me as some kind of devil who had been determined to prejudice the future of the United States Air Forces. Carl Kaysen, Lieutenant Kaysen as he was then, became a close and good friend. Later, when he was on President Kennedy's staff, he and I collaborated during the negotiations which led up to the Partial Test Ban Treaty of 1963.

There were other 'authorities' who sniped from the sidelines. Even Air Chief Marshal Sir John Slessor, who had succeeded Tedder in the Mediterranean after leaving R.A.F. Coastal Command, of which he had been so inspired a leader, weighed in against the plan. This, however, was towards the end of the 'debate'. But, as he added at the end of a memorandum attacking the plan which he sent to Portal from Italy, he did not 'really know enough about it' [the thinking behind the plan] and felt that what he had written was 'all very amateur and half-baked'.[17] So it was. But after the war Slessor was to write that 'the Overlord people were unquestionably right in attaching the importance they did to dislocating the enemy communication system in Northern France; indeed, it was probably the most decisive factor in the success of the invasion'.[18]

Before the dispute was at its height, I was visited by emissaries of the three main centres of opposition, each of whom tried to persuade me that I was misguided in relying on the results of my analysis of the Mediterranean bomber offensive against enemy communications rather than accepting the fruits of their abstract reasoning. The first to come was Harry Weldon, whom I had known in Oxford. During the war he was a Wing Commander on Harris's staff, and at the time rumour had it that the clarity and force of Harris's minutes to the Prime Minister, to whom Harris had direct access, owed not a little to Weldon, and that their style markedly deteriorated when Weldon returned to Oxford after *Overlord* had been launched. Harry did not try very hard. We met in my house in Oxford. He told me about Bomber Command's current objectives, and the success with which they were being achieved, and then asked a few questions. But he abandoned his mission when he realised from my answers that the plans I was advancing had a sound empirical basis. Then came John Strachey, who was now a Squadron Leader in the Air Ministry's Directorate of Bomber Operations. He brought with him to Norfolk House a Wing Commander Morley, whom I understood to be Bufton's deputy. I had a feeling that John had told his colleagues that he knew me well enough to make me bend to sweet reason. It was all very friendly and polite, but in the end he too realised that I was not going to advise that the new A.E.A.F. plan, based as it was on a scientific analysis of the results of actual operations, should be set aside in favour of unproven assertions.

Sometime later Kindleberger tried to show me the error of my ways. I had arranged for him to wait in an unoccupied room close to mine in Norfolk House because my own was full of highly secret papers, and while I knew that he was in a powerful position from which he could affect the thinking of the American air chiefs, I did not know the extent to which he was privy to *Overlord* planning. I suspected afterwards that he had resented being made to wait in an empty office. My memory of him then was of an intensely serious and hostile young man, totally different from the amiable and friendly person whom I met after his retirement from M.I.T.

Kindleberger wasted no time in indicating that I was hopelessly misguided, and that whatever the lessons I had learnt from actual operations in the Mediterranean, they had no relevance to North-West Europe. He seemed pretty discouraged by my reaction to his comments, and I made no secret of my view that I did not believe he knew much about the matter, or about the potentialities of bombing. In response to a remark that he could not understand how a man like Eisenhower had committed himself to so ridiculous a plan, my sarcastic reply was: 'It's obvious. Trains run faster the more you bomb the railway system, and anyhow, Eisenhower is in my pay.' It was a silly thing to say. There was no need to intensify the enmity by which we were now surrounded. Even Tooey Spaatz, who at first had no feelings either way about the plan, got at me, inviting me over a drink in a suite in the Dorchester Hotel, together with two other American air generals recently arrived from Washington, to give up working 'with that man Leigh-Mallory and join us'. Strangely enough, the only personal support I was offered from outside the inner circle came from John Winant, the American Ambassador, who telephoned asking me to call on him. One of his sons who had been serving with the U.S. Air Forces had just been reported missing, and our talk over a drink before dinner was pretty gloomy. He had summoned me to say that he knew that I was being personally assailed because of the A.E.A.F. plan, which he himself believed to be soundly based, and that if I felt there was anything he could do to help, all I had to do was call on him. It was not arrogance on my part that made this talk about Allied air plans the only one I had with Winant. I simply did not realise that the U.S. Ambassador would necessarily be informed about, or could if he wished become privy to most, if not all, secret matters. I stupidly wondered, too, if he had been cleared for ULTRA information. Furthermore, I did not see how he could help. The fact is that at the time I was exhilarated, not cast down, by the opposition and the continuing debate.

I was totally unconscious of the fact that my central position in the dispute was resented by many who felt that a civilian who was not even a government official had no right to advise on high-level and controversial strategic matters, even though he had been designated 'scientific adviser on planning' to A.E.A.F. and to S.H.A.E.F. (Supreme Headquarters Allied Expeditionary Force). Anyhow, the knowledge that Tedder was not shaken was more than I needed to sustain my own confidence.

The documents fired in the counter-offensive to the A.E.A.F. plan were passed to me as they arrived and, encouraged by Kingston, Wigglesworth and Leigh-Mallory, who became firmer as the dispute became hotter, I worked all hours of the day and night answering the criticisms. The meetings of the Bombing Committee which Leigh-Mallory himself chaired achieved little. When they attended, it was plain that the representatives of Bomber Command—usually led either by Air Marshal Saundby or by Harris's S.A.S.O., Air Vice-Marshal Oxland—and those of the U.S. Strategic Air Forces, treated Leigh-Mallory respectfully only because of his higher rank. They saw him as a tactical air commander who simply did not understand the significance of the air war against the enemy's homeland, and their suspicions multiplied as the weeks passed.

In May the A.E.A.F. headquarters top staff moved to Bentley Priory, the main fighter control centre near Stanmore on the outskirts of London. The War Room was underground in a nearby building which one entered through a narrow enclosed sloping walkway. Connected to it was the Communications Centre, and also the big operations room with its vast map table on which quiet W.A.A.F.s wearing headphones used croupiers' sticks to move symbolic aircraft and ships around as instructed by their controllers, who were linked to our radar network. Bentley Priory itself was shabby and poorly furnished—quite unlike what it must have been in the days when it was the home of Queen Adelaide, who died there in 1849. Today the house is modernised and serves as the headquarters of No. 11 Group Strike Command.

As a headquarters, the Priory was anything but happy. Its large staff of British and American officers was supposed to constitute an 'integrated H.Q.'. In fact, in the first two or three months of 1944, when we were in Norfolk House, the A.E.A.F. staff was not integrated at all. This generated not a little resentment in U.S. circles. I was probably the only British member of A.E.A.F. who then enjoyed the confidence of Spaatz, and of those of his officers who had been with him in the Mediterranean—in particular General Vandenberg* who, in the interval before

* Vandenberg later became Commander-in-Chief of the U.S. 9th Air Force and, after the war, the Chief of Staff of the U.S. Air Forces. When he gave up the post, he became the first Director of the unified C.I.A. He died of cancer in 1954.

coming to England as Leigh-Mallory's Deputy, had spent six months in Washington. The close friendships I had made in the Mediterranean were proof against any dismay my American friends may have felt about my apparent loss of reason in the advice I was now giving A.E.A.F.

The upper echelons of the A.E.A.F. staff included not only Vandenberg but also Brigadier General 'Freddie' Smith who, because he was a son-in-law of Admiral King, the American naval chief of staff in Washington, was understood to exercise greater power than his rank implied. He had been posted to Bentley Priory as Deputy S.A.S.O. and Chief of Operations, and in effect had been placed above Kingston. But these two top American appointments in the hierarchy in no way satisfied the American High Command. Whatever problems Leigh-Mallory had in relation to Tedder and Bomber Command, to the Americans he was simply an unfortunate burden they had to bear or bypass; they regarded his appointment as unnecessary, as indeed some of them regarded A.E.A.F. itself. In order to make the A.E.A.F. H.Q. staff more allied than British, the Americans therefore introduced a 'points system' of appointments. An American colonel by the name of McKinnon was posted to cover Kingston's activities, but Kingston generated even more resentment than he had before, by refusing to allow the man to share his office. No doubt with a twinkle in his eye, Tooey sent an elderly ordnance colonel to cover what I was doing. Colonel Huff was a dear old thing, and we got along well. But while I was on occasion concerned with armaments, my opposite number did not have the slightest interest in the other matters that took up most of my time. I asked Tooey to let Bob Robertson pair off with me, but this, alas, could not be arranged, because Bob was then deeply involved, with R. V. Jones the Oxford physicist, in the assessment of secret technical intelligence and in particular in the elucidation of the V.1 and V.2 threats.

It was unfortunate that Leigh-Mallory did not seem to understand the easy personal relationships that senior American officers enjoyed. One strange incident still stands out in my memory. About a fortnight before D-Day, Leigh-Mallory had presided over a meeting which was attended by all the air barons, including Tedder, Harris, Spaatz, Doolittle and Brereton.[19] Leigh-Mallory unfortunately opened the proceedings by asking two one-star generals to leave the room, one of them being Brigadier General Cabell,* to whom he referred as 'a planning officer whose attendance was unnecessary'. After the meeting, Tooey asked me to lunch, and in the long drive back to his house we reviewed the matters that had been discussed, and considered the plans which he had in mind for the U.S. Strategic Air Forces after D-Day. When we arrived at his

* Brigadier General Charles P. Cabell was, in fact, a very influential and ambitious officer who, after the war, became Deputy Director of the C.I.A.

house, we found that the main topic of conversation between Tooey's generals was Cabell's ejection from the meeting. Sympathy was not entirely with him, and I got the feeling that one or two were not displeased that he had been humbled in public. To calm his feelings, however, General Fred Anderson, a friendly man who earlier had been one of Ira Eaker's Commanders in the build-up of the 8th Bomber Command, and who was now Deputy Commander for Operations, U.S.S.T.A.F., under Spaatz, put it to Cabell that Leigh-Mallory had merely given a hint that he wanted at his meeting only Commanders-in-Chief, their Deputies, and their immediate advisers, and that Cabell was the only one who had had the good sense to respond correctly. Tooey then chipped in, saying, 'Now Cabell, that's not burning you up, is it? You start worrying when *I* throw you out.' To most of the company at lunch the incident was just another example of what they regarded as Leigh-Mallory's obtuseness.

At one of Leigh-Mallory's early meetings, when we were still in Norfolk House, he must have realised from the expression on my face that I had been taken aback by his failure to assert the authority which I assumed to be his. When the meeting ended, he beckoned to me to stay behind. The moment we were alone, the colour faded from his face. 'Zuck,' he said, 'I know you are thinking that I am hopelessly weak. But you must realise that there would have been no point in my pressing them further than I was doing. They were all under instructions. Nobody is supporting me. If only Tedder would indicate openly that he is behind this plan, and if only Eisenhower were to speak out, all would be different. I believe in the plan, I am committed to it, but without their open support I cannot direct people whom I do not command, but whose forces we will need well before D-Day.'

The basic trouble was that the Combined Chiefs of Staff had not yet agreed to rescind or amend the *Pointblank* directive of June 1943, to which Leigh-Mallory was still under orders to lend maximum support with the forces which he commanded. But neither Eisenhower nor Tedder, both of whom were every bit as committed to the A.E.A.F. plan as Leigh-Mallory had become, was as morally bound to support *Pointblank* as he was. On 15 February, Leigh-Mallory accordingly called a meeting which was attended by, among others, Tedder, Harris, Spaatz and Anderson, with the object of considering the latest draft of our plan. This began with the general statement that:

'An essential preliminary to enable Operation "OVERLORD" to take place is the accomplishment of certain vital tasks by the Strategical and Tactical Air Forces. Unless these are completed by D Day, the success of the Operation will be jeopardised, not only because our Naval and ground forces would then have to contend with a highly unfavourable situation, but also because the air would not be in any position to lend full support to the actual assault, or to deal with the subsequent activities of the enemy. Subject to a satisfactory air situation the main object of the preliminary air operations is to paralyse the railways from Western Germany to the assault area to such an extent that major reinforcement by rail would be virtually impossible. If this is achieved the whole weight of the air offensive could then be concentrated on other targets which could affect the tactical situation during the opening phases of the land assault.'

The paper then went on to state, unequivocally, that if the Air was to play its proper part, a large proportion of *all* the available bomber forces would have to be employed for three months preceding D-Day on tasks directly related to *Overlord*. The achievement of air superiority, which was a prerequisite to everything else, was not discussed in detail. The need to continue with the bomber offensive against the Luftwaffe and the German fighter factories was underlined, and a plan suggested for the neutralisation of enemy airfields which would otherwise be used to cover the assault area. This was to be done in two phases of attack beginning three weeks before D-Day, care again being taken not to jeopardise security.

After dismissing the so-called 'tactical plan' for cutting railway lines just before D-Day, the paper instead proposed that the railway network of North-West Europe should be crippled by attacks on its 76 most important nodal points. Upon them depended the regulation of all rail traffic. They also included the main servicing and repair facilities. 'The result of successful attacks', I wrote,

'should be virtually the devastation of the larger servicing and traffic centres in North-West Europe. The free functioning of these centres is an essential condition for the necessary flow of rail traffic. Elimination of a number of adjacent railway centres would paralyse movement in the whole region they serve. . . . What is primarily aimed at is not the cutting of communcations in the sense that an artery is cut, but the widespread destruction of the means of communication, and the means of maintaining the railway system in operation. . . . In any event, the effect will be such that the subsequent movement by rail of major reserves into France should almost be impossible.'

And I went on to say that 'This effect may be achieved even before the full plan is completed'.

Having then referred to the strain that would be imposed on the enemy by being forced, through the denial of rail transport, to the roads, this section of the plan ended with the categorical statement that:

'the supply difficulties which the enemy's military machine will experience are merely an indication of the even more severe difficulties to which the German civilian supply system will be subjected as a result of attacks on German rail targets. The more servicing repair centres are destroyed in Germany, the more difficult will it become for the enemy to maintain his home front. Even now, before attacks have begun, the enemy is operating his railways under a considerable strain. . . . The sooner Western Germany is attacked, the sooner will difficulties of movement impose a considerable strain on such industry as remains to the enemy in the Rhineland. The proposed attacks on German rail centres may, in fact, contribute at least as much to the sterilisation of this area so far as its influence on the enemy's war potential is concerned, as attacks on the war industries they serve. The further, therefore, the attack on railway communications or railway centres is pushed Eastwards into Germany, the greater will be the effect on Germany's war production.'

In addition to the strategic attacks on rail centres, the plan also called for the destruction of specific bridges affecting the assault area, it being understood that for security reasons these operations would have to take place nearer the time of the invasion. Finally, having considered how the coastal defences which would threaten the approach to the landing areas should be dealt with, the paper ended with an estimate of the total bomber effort that would be required for all the tasks that had to be discharged. This was based on the most reliable figures which I could then get of the accuracy of the American heavy bombers in precision attacks by day, and of Bomber Command's by night, in which the radio and radar aids then available were used. I estimated that the preparatory bombing requirement amounted to less than half of Bomber Command's potential effort before D-Day, and well over half of that of the U.S. forces.[20]

Two days after this Outline Plan was issued, Harris sent a memorandum to A.E.A.F. and to Bomber Command which attacked almost every technical point that we had made, and in which he asserted that if his Command were to play the part envisaged for it, the bomber offensive, meaning his programme of so-called area-attacks, would have to be entirely given up. But he reserved his strongest comment for his last paragraph. 'I have given my reasons', he wrote, 'for my conviction that the commitments assigned in this Paper to Bomber Command cannot be fulfilled, and I am compelled to disavow any responsibility for the consequences which their non-fulfilment will entail.'[21]

At the meeting,[22] he both amplified the arguments that he had set out in writing, and also attacked the calculations that I had made about the bomber effort for which the A.E.A.F. plan called, declaring that I had taken as the basis for my sums optimum rather than average figures for the accuracy of his crews. This I flatly denied, and I made it quite plain that I did not accept Harris's usual contention that the average error of his forces in night operations was about a thousand yards. From other sources I knew that many of his squadrons could do better, particularly with the new bombing aids which were coming into use. I had gone up to Huntingdon, to the H.Q. of Bomber Command's 'Pathfinder' Group, and had discussed the matter closely with Air Vice-Marshal Bennett, the Group's Commander who, in effect, told me not to believe a word about potential bombing accuracy that was emanating from High Wycombe. I also knew at first-hand that other Bomber Groups had begun to feel affronted by the current argument of their Commander-in-Chief that they were inherently inaccurate in their operations.

Because he was going to make a major issue of my views about accuracy, Harris had brought to the meeting Dr. B. G. Dickens, the Head of his Command's central Operational Research Section. It turned out that Dickens had been told that 400 aircraft would be expected simultaneously to bomb each of the railway targets named in the A.E.A.F. plan, and that he had therefore assumed that the attacks would be bound to degenerate into inaccurate area-bombing even if the targets were well-marked by flares which had been dropped at the start to serve as aiming points. When I pointed out that not a single target on the list would need a force of more than a hundred bombers, and that there was no need to assume that a railway centre would necessarily become obscured in the dust from hundreds, or thousands of explosions, Dickens had to concede that Bomber Command could destroy a large proportion of the targets that we had listed. This was the first, but unfortunately not the last time that it became apparent to me that not all scientists who during the war had been drawn into Service posts were as questioning and independent in their judgments as they could have been. On occasion, they were constrained by assumptions which uncannily fitted their masters' preconceived ideas. There was also a tendency to defer more to the rank than the intellectual competence of the officers they served.

Spaatz's line at the meeting was simply that the *Overlord* plan conflicted with his existing *Pointblank* directive, and that unlike Leigh-Mallory, he did not believe that the decisive battles for air supremacy would be fought over the beaches. When Tedder interrupted to indicate his disbelief that anyone could predict in advance which targets, whether close to U.K. bases or deep in Germany, would bring the German Air Force into action, Tooey admitted that he would have no argument with the choice of railway targets if they stimulated the Luftwaffe to fight.

He then turned to Leigh-Mallory and asked for the date when he proposed to take control of the Strategic Air Forces in the implementation of the *Overlord* air plan. Without the slightest hesitation Leigh-Mallory replied, 'March the 1st'. Spaatz's comment was: 'That's all I want to know; I've nothing further to say'. That he left the meeting determined to do everything in his power to prevent his Strategic Air Forces coming under Leigh-Mallory became quickly apparent. Tedder states in his autobiography that Spaatz would 'not accept orders, or even coordination, from Leigh-Mallory'.[23]

In a way Tooey was in a more powerful position than was Harris. Harris commanded only the heavy bombers, but Tooey was Commander-in-Chief of all the U.S. Air Forces in Europe, fighters and bombers alike, and although on paper he took his orders from Portal, as the responsible representative of the Combined Chiefs of Staff, Tooey also had a direct line to General 'Hap' Arnold in Washington, that very powerful figure who, as American Chief of Staff, was in overall command of all the U.S. Air Forces.

At the time of this meeting, Spaatz hardly knew Leigh-Mallory, and he was only beginning to get to know Harris, with neither of whom do I believe he ever felt on easy personal terms. I do not recall that their photographs figured among those which all but covered one wall of his small study in the house in which he died in 1974. Both were somewhat too humourless and austere, too 'English', for his liking. One Saturday during the early phase of the controversy, Tooey came up to Oxford to dine with me at Christ Church. There was a large turn-out, both at the High Table and in the Common Room, and Tooey proved a great success. The Prof was there, but I do not believe that the two had much opportunity to discuss either *Overlord* or the United States policy of daylight bombing, about both of which the Prof was worried. After the port had circulated a couple of times, I heard Tooey, who was then commanding a great deal of attention, declaring that Bach sounded better when played on a guitar than on a church organ. This he claimed to know from experience, and if he only had his guitar with him he would show them. Someone then suggested that we could at least go into the Cathedral, which was all but next door to the Common Room, where we could hear Bach played on the organ. With the exception of myself and an elderly don who had never heard of Spaatz, and who neither understood nor cared about what was going on, the whole Common Room then trooped out, including Dr. Armstrong,* the Christ Church Cathedral organist. I stayed behind, terrified at the thought that my guest was getting out of hand. I wondered what was coming next. It was all too much like the opening scene in Evelyn Waugh's *Decline and Fall*,[24] when the members

* Now Sir Thomas Armstrong.

of the Bollinger Club, dressed in their finery, were rampaging in the garden quad of Scone College. As one of Evelyn Waugh's dons reminded another, the more the damage, the more the fines, and that would mean 'a week of Founder's port. Please God, make them attack the Chapel.' After a time, the party returned to the Common Room, with Tooey exclaiming, 'There, didn't I tell you? Bach would surely sound better on a guitar'. We then turned again to the decanters.

Only when I helped him to bed later that night did Tooey pull himself together and become serious. He muttered that he knew that the A.E.A.F. plan had Tedder's support. 'I'm not against the plan,' said Tooey, 'I believe you are right. But what worries me is that Harris is being allowed to get off scot-free. He'll go on bombing Germany and will be given a chance of defeating her before the invasion, while I am put under Leigh-Mallory's command.' I assured him that Harris was not, to the best of my knowledge, going to be allowed to divorce himself from *Overlord*, and then waited until he was safely tucked up before putting out the light. As I have said, one thing about which all professional United States airmen agreed was the need to be as independent a service, in name as well as in fact, as was the Royal Air Force. They had to wait until after the war before they succeeded.

On another occasion, not long after Tooey's visit, Tedder also came up to dine. I had told the Prof of the visit, knowing that he, the Prof, regarded himself as the author of Bomber Command's policy of hitting at Germany's industrial cities. He therefore suggested that we went to his rooms before going into Hall. After a glass of the sweet sherry which he was inclined to dispense to his guests (he himself never touched alcohol), the conversation began with him saying: 'Well, Tedder, you surely don't believe in this nonsense of Solly's about bombing railways?' To which Tedder replied, 'What nonsense? I never believe in nonsense'. 'This plan', went on the Prof, 'to divert a major effort of the strategic air forces from the bombing of Germany in order to prepare for *Overlord*.' Tedder made some evasive reply, and that was about all the discussion amounted to. He was not going to be drawn into an argument. As was being borne in on me more and more, Tedder still had no intention of becoming openly involved in any controversy. Battle lines were still being drawn, and the battle still had to be fought.

After a thirty-year gap, I am utterly amazed by the nonsensical arguments about the plan to which one had to listen, and which are on record in contemporary documents and minutes of meetings. I had incorrectly assumed that planners were concerned to extract, as quickly as they could and for use in further planning, such facts as experimental enquiry and analysis of past operations could provide. This, however, was clearly not general practice. Most of the people with whom I was now dealing seemed to prefer *a priori* belief to disciplined observation. And Leigh-Mallory's meeting of 15 February had been a turning point. From now on rational discussion of what was being proposed was at an end. All the opposing parties joined to defeat the apparent threat which the A.E.A.F. plan implied to the independence of the strategic air forces. It did not matter what considerations were advanced to upturn it.

The counter-arguments were marshalled and formalised mainly by what became known as 'the Committee of Four', and by an influential inter-Service body, which was set up as a sub-committee of the Joint Technical Warfare Committee under the chairmanship of Professor Charles Ellis, a high-energy physicist who was Scientific Adviser to the Army Council. I was appointed one of this sub-committee's five members. The other four represented the War Office, the Air Ministry, and the *Overlord* planning staff. Members of the Army's Directorate of Transportation, of the Air Staff, and of appropriate Intelligence organisations, attended as required. The terms of reference of the sub-committee were to 'carry out an investigation of the dislocation and disorganisation of the fighting potential of enemy formations engaged in, or about to engage in, battle, produced by attacks of various kinds upon the enemy's fighting formation and his lines of communication. This investigation should be based on a study of past campaigns and related as closely as possible to future plans. To deduce general principles as a guide for the future in the form of a relationship between a given effort and the resulting fall in the fighting efficiency of enemy troops at the front.'[25]

I was unable to attend the first meeting of Ellis's Committee, but at the second, on 4 February, I strongly challenged his remit, because I could not see how general principles could be deduced from an *a priori* study of so complex a problem. The Director of Air Tactics at the Air Ministry supported me, as did C.O.S.S.A.C., who soon took steps to see that the sub-committee's deliberations were properly divorced from the planning of *Overlord*.[26] From the very start, therefore, I found myself at odds with Ellis's Committee, which seemed to grow in number with each meeting, and not one of whose members other than myself had studied the actual effects of a sustained air attack on a rail system. In the end, I was unable to subscribe to the report which it produced,[27] and was therefore invited to write my own minority statement.[28]

Having studied the two submissions, the parent Committee sent both back to Ellis with the instruction that his committee try to meet my objections. But once again I was unable to agree an attempted compromise, and in my second minority report, which was sent in on 5 June, the day before the invasion was launched, I warned that

'Any report which is intended to be of use in strategic, and still more in tactical operations, should aim at giving those responsible for the actual execution of these operations as clear a picture as possible of what is definitely known and of the limits of this knowledge. It should not lay down rigid or apparently rigid rules for operations where in fact the fluctuating situation of battle demands a flexible procedure. This must be the case even when we have a full knowledge of the effects of different types of operation. It is even more important when our knowledge of these effects is fragmentary and uncertain. It is equally important, when making an investigation the results of which are to be put to practical use, that the actual problem to be dealt with should not be oversimplified. Conclusions which would be correct if a certain set of assumptions were fulfilled are of no value—indeed they can be actively misleading—if in fact there is a good chance that these assumptions will not be fulfilled.'

I ended my note by saying that

'In view of the points which I have discussed, it is my view that our present report gives far too little heed to the two cardinal principles to which I have referred in my opening paragraphs. As a result the report suffers . . . from excessive rigidity. Thus the alternative types of railway target which are considered by no means exhaust the possibilities of attack on railways. Again, they are considered only from the limited aspect of interrupting through communications. Rigid quantitative estimates are given of the weights of attack required to produce a cut and of the delay caused, which have no adequate basis of fact, and which are liable to be particularly misleading at the present time, when new methods of attack are constantly being developed.'[29]

As a result of my second minority statement, the Joint Technical Warfare Committee decided to defer their consideration of the argument until '*Overlord* experience' became available. But from the point of view of the opposition, Ellis had done what was needed. The drafts of his report which were circulated to a number of prominent individuals gave no indication that the arguments that it advanced were very much in question. The many people who attended from time to time also fed their respective staffs with what the future was shortly to show to be groundless speculation.

The Committee of Four was a different and more formidable opposition, mainly because it had closer links with the staffs which were bent on blocking the A.E.A.F. plan. One of its members was an officer who in civilian life was a barrister, but who was then on the Intelligence Staff of the Air Ministry. He had served amicably on the A.E.A.F. Bombing Committee at its first meetings, but he switched when his Chief joined Bufton in opposing the A.E.A.F. plan. Kindleberger and Lawrence, to whom I have already referred, were members. The fourth was a colonel on the staff of the Director of Army Transportation, the man whose nose Kingston and I thought had been put out of joint because we had not consulted him before the A.E.A.F. plan was formulated. These four, not one of whom again had had the slightest practical experience of the issues that were involved, worked in concert, and provided the intellectual back-up for all the 'authorities' who were opposing the plan. Essentially their main arguments were those which Kindleberger's group of economists had already advanced on the basis of a presumed logical analysis. It was a simple 'one and one make two' stand, based on the assumption that the dislocation of a vast interlocking functional system such as a railway network could be assessed in terms of capacity. The argument was that the destruction of railway centres in North-West Europe, with the consequent 'local' crippling of motive power and the damaging of rolling-stock, was of no significance because the enemy had vast reserves of locomotives and wagons on which to draw within Axis Europe. As Kindleberger's Unit saw it, the A.E.A.F. plan was therefore useless from a tactical point of view while, from the strategic point of view, rail transportation had been 'adequately analysed as a strategic target system', and had 'usually received low ratings on the grounds that damage to rail transport can under most circumstances be absorbed in the general economic system without producing effects on the fighting capabilities of the enemy.'[30] Moreover, so it was argued, military traffic formed so small a proportion of total rail movement, it could not be significantly affected 'in any relevant period of time' by attacks limited to North-West Europe—or indeed by even an extensive attack on the railway system of the whole of Axis Europe. 'The average depth of the whole rail transport system', so the paper continued, 'is certainly as great as the average depth of the whole production cycle; this is at least nine months, and may be as much as a year.'[31]

What this last observation had to do with the possible effects of an attack on a railway system I never did learn, any more than I ever heard anyone criticizing the factual analysis which I had made of the breakdown of railway communications in Southern Italy and Sicily.

In effect, the Committee of Four did no more than make an estimate of all the locomotives in use in Germany at any one time, and then subtract the figure from the total number that were available, so proving that there was 'spare capacity'. In the report which they submitted they concluded that the A.E.A.F. plan of attack on railway centres would have 'to be continued for 12 months before the German war effort could be adversely affected'.[32] They could never have written this if only they had considered how vulnerable a railway system is to breakdown; even to the kind of breakdown which can result from bad weather, leave

alone bombing. For example, in the freeze-up of February 1947, hardly
any trains ran for a month in the United Kingdom. Industry was all but
at a standstill, and all of us were on even shorter rations than the post-war
rationing system had bargained for.

The dispute came fully into the open at a meeting of 'railway experts'
which Leigh-Mallory convened on 25 February,[33] little more than a
week after the one at which Tooey had thrown down the gauntlet. This
meeting pre-empted one which Bufton had intended to call, and he
accordingly took it upon himself to bring with him a number of what a
record of the meeting called 'uninvited guests', including Lawrence and
Kindleberger. The main participants at this extraordinary meeting, the
minutes of which run to 43 pages of typescript, were the six leading members
of the British Railway Executive Committee and Research Service, who
were there to tell about the damage the U.K. railways had suffered during
the blitz. It was very much a case of the blind leading the blind. A number of the 'experts' who were there were not even privy to the A.E.A.F.
plan.

By now I was completely inured to the kind of attack which our plan
had to face and, as its initiator, it was always left to me at meetings other
than those of the air barons themselves, to rebut the theoretical assertions of our opponents. It was also my task to explain the empirical
foundation of the plan. The counter-arguments at the technical level
were inevitably theoretical and based on the same assumptions as underlay the arguments advanced by Ellis's Committee, namely, that it would
take only so many hours to repair a break in a railway line, and so many
to repair a water-tower, and so on. In trying to persuade our opponents
that the aim of the A.E.A.F. plan was to disrupt a system, to create 'a
railway desert', as I put it, and not just to make a series of cuts at isolated
points, I constantly resorted to biological analogies. In one record I find
myself saying that in order to incapacitate a man it is not necessary to
wound him everywhere; in the head, body and all four limbs. The fact
that one part of the body could continue to have a circulation did not
materially help another, whose main arteries had been critically damaged.
And when dealing with the argument about the number of locomotives
the Germans had at their disposal, I argued that a railway system can
still possess an enormous number of serviceable locomotives and yet be
in a state of paralysis, in the same way as the number of red blood cor-
puscles in a man who has just been killed need not necessarily be fewer
than the number circulating in his blood vessels at the moment immediately before his death. I also kept on pointing to the many inconsist-
encies in the opposition arguments: for example, the assertion that while
the Germans could quickly repair damage to lines and other railway
installations after a sustained 'strategic' offensive against the communica-

tions network of North-West Europe, they would be incapable of doing so if we rested content with the tactical plan which predicated attacks on the French railways at only a small number of specific points about the time of D-Day.

In spite of the wrangling, this particular meeting provided us with the powerful and open support of General Napier, who was in charge of Movement and Transportation at Supreme Headquarters. On the following day he sent A.E.A.F. a statement which ended with the following lines:

'We must neither underestimate nor overestimate the results of this bombing policy. One thing is certain—any half policy would have virtually no effect; results are achieved only after the elastic limit of the Transportation system has been passed. At the highest the effects of a whole-policy would prevent any massive prolongation of the struggle in N.W. France. After say D + 6 weeks, he might have to go back to the Siegfried Line because of the weakness of his whole communication zone. At the lowest we will have hampered his conduct of the campaign and war effort in N. France, while the weakening of his locomotive power position may affect other fronts (East, South or the industrial front in Germany). These effects have to be weighed against alternative uses of air power in support of the campaign.[34]

This judgment echoed a corresponding view that had already been stated at a meeting of the A.E.A.F. Bombing Committee on 24 January by General Whitefoord, another senior officer on Eisenhower's staff.[35] History was to show that they were not far out in their estimate of the time the Germans could hold out before retreating.

Although Leigh-Mallory was in command of the fighter and medium bombers, and in spite of the fact that the plan had been endorsed by the Supreme Commander, none of the railway targets we had listed could be attacked until the whole plan had been cleared through higher authority, namely the Combined British and American Chiefs of Staff. The A.E.A.F. staff were becoming desperately impatient, and Leigh-Mallory increasingly bitter. Kingston and I were the most outspoken, with Wigglesworth maintaining his customary calm. In the first week of March, however, we were allowed to launch a few medium bomber attacks on French railway centres. Then, encouraged by the Air Ministry, Harris himself decided to try an experiment. On 6 March he ordered a night attack on the railway centre at Trappes by Nos. 4 and 6 Groups of his Command. The raid was an outstanding success. Photocover revealed that the target had been devastated, and from the density of strikes it was then possible to prove that Bomber Command's C.-in-C. had been exaggerating the average bombing error of his forces. In the following week,

the Command made equally successful attacks on the railway centres at
Le Mans and Amiens-Longueau.

But whatever elation might have been felt by a few of us at this vindica-
tion of one of our points, it made no difference at all to the main dispute.
Regardless of successive demonstrations that at least some Groups of
Bomber Command were more accurate than the C.-in-C. claimed, Harris's
representatives at the A.E.A.F. meetings remained loyal to their master
in asserting that R.A.F. Bomber Command had not been designed to
carry out the precise kind of attacks which the A.E.A.F. plan called for,
attacks which I posited had to try to achieve an average density of four
500 lb bomb strikes to the acre over the area of a railway centre, which
sometimes covered as much as three hundred acres. Harris was so certain
of his case that shortly after the fateful meeting of 15 February, it
became necessary to deal critically with one of his earlier submissions,
in which he had contended that on the basis of past performance,
Germany would be brought to her knees before the invasion could be
launched.

This was right up my street. Contrary to what Harris implies in his
autobiography, it was not Bomber Command's Operational Research
Section, nor the Targets Section of the Economic Warfare Department,
nor the Directorate of Bomber Operations in the Air Ministry, which
had devised a method—and however crude it was, it was the only one
we had at the time—for translating areas of physical destruction into a
functional assessment of what was happening to German war production.
This had started in Princes Risborough with the study that Bernal and I
made of Hull and Birmingham. I was therefore in a position to check that
part of Harris's claim which related to destruction. Equally, and again
contrary to what Harris implies in his book, it was not the Operational
Research Section of Bomber Command which had pioneered attempts to
estimate numerically the size of force necessary to achieve a given distribution of bombs over a target.[36] That, too, came out of Princes Risborough, and had been applied first in the abortive Combined Operations' plan to capture the island of Alderney, and then in the actual
operations against Pantelleria. R.E.8, which Stradling established with
the responsibility of assessing the functional implications of physical
destruction, and which had been set up at the instigation of Bernal and
myself, was in due course to be taken over by the Air Ministry as its
own assessment staff. But this was only after Eisenhower became
responsible for *Overlord*.

I got Frank Yates to do the necessary calculations to check the assertion that, in view of the success being achieved by bombing German
industrial cities, it would be disastrous to divert Bomber Command to
help with *Overlord*. Frank had recently returned from Sicily and had gone

straight into an R.A.F. hospital to have his gall-bladder removed. The matter was so urgent, however, that without worrying him about the background of the problem, I visited him two or three days after his operation in order to get him to go over Bomber Command's figures. I was then able to tell Tedder that whoever it was who had done Harris's sums did not understand what he was doing. Yates's authority as a statistician and as an objective scientist was unassailable, and we could rely on him.

Tedder refers in his autobiography to the memorandum that I sent him and which I based on Yates's criticisms.[37] In it I said that if Bomber Harris were to continue with his existing plans, his Command could not in the available time achieve more than a 7 per cent reduction in Germany's overall output. I also wrote that on the basis of past experience, I myself did not believe that German morale would break as a result of three more months of bombing. My memorandum concluded with the remark that: 'I suppose the argument therefore is between a long chance of a clean "air victory", given that the Air applies its major effort during the next couple of months to the targets it is at present attacking, and a high chance of the failure of Overlord—unless the Air puts a certain amount of its effort into preparatory Overlord tasks in addition to the winning of air supremacy.'

As I have said, when compromise did not affect the underlying policy, the A.E.A.F. plan was revised with one suggested railway target in our list being changed for another. But something had to break with only about three months left before the projected landings. Talk of resignation was in the air, and Eisenhower decided to appeal to the British Chiefs of Staff Committee to bring the heavy bombers into action against railway centres. The Chiefs of Staff in turn asked that Portal, who as C.A.S. was one of their number, should re-examine the whole issue on their behalf. By this time, too, the U.S. Air Forces had formally proposed that instead of the railway network of North-West Europe, Germany's synthetic oil plants should become their first-priority targets, with the 'remains' of the German fighter industry, the rubber industry and then the German bomber plants next in the list. Transportation targets were to be only 'targets of last resort'. This plan, which became known as 'Spaatz's Oil Plan', repeated all the old arguments against the A.E.A.F. plan, and had been endorsed both by the Intelligence and the Bomber Operations Directorates of the British Air Ministry.[31]

On 25 March, Portal therefore summoned a meeting of all the military and air commanders, as well as of the Intelligence staffs concerned.[38] Eisenhower attended, but in order to keep the general temperature down, Tedder decided that I was not to come. I had, however, helped draft the paper which he tabled for the meeting, and needless to say it firmly

upheld the A.E.A.F. plan. 'Since attacks on railway centres have repercussions far beyond the immediate targets,' one section read, 'attacks on
such centres within the Reich will certainly assist in creating the general
dislocation required for Overlord. Moreover, since the railway system is
the one common denominator of the whole enemy war effort, it may well
be that systematic attack on it will prove to be the final straw.'[39]

The counter-comment by Bufton to this proposition was that 'Attacks
on railway centres in the Reich will represent effort dissipated in some
measure against one (in view of its fragmentation and dispersal) of the
most invulnerable targets of the German economic system. The fact that
the railway system is the one common denominator of the whole enemy
war effort is a clear indication of its unsuitability as a vital target system
in strategic attack.'[40] Bufton was merely repeating the view that had
been stated by Lawrence of M.E.W. and by Kindleberger of the parallel
American unit. For the rest, the arguments were the same as always:
R.A.F. Bomber Command could and would smash Germany through its
night raids on German cities, while the American Strategic Forces would
do so by precise attacks on the arsenals of German air-power—aircraft
and aircraft component factories, and on Germany's synthetic oil plants.
The inconsistency between the assumption that bombing conditions
would always be good enough to permit of the 'taking out'—to use the
jargon current at the time—of such targets deep in Germany, and the
contention that bombing accuracy was not adequate for the easier task of
destroying railway centres in France, the Low Countries, and Western
Germany, was neither here nor there. The only issue on which there
was no argument was the need to assure air supremacy in the period
before D-Day.

At the end of a long meeting, Portal summed up by stating his firm
view that there was no suitable alternative to the 'railway plan', at the
same time as he accepted that attacks on the German Air Force had overriding priority over all other targets. He was also ready to agree that the
German synthetic oil industry represented a potentially profitable target
system, although from the point of view of the initial *Overlord* assault,
not as profitable as the railway network of Western Europe.

Not one member of the Intelligence staffs, nor any of the 'experts'
of the Ministry of Economic Warfare who were present at this meeting,
nor even Tooey Spaatz suggested that an offensive against oil plants
would yield immediate results in the military field. That was to come
later. Portal, together with Eisenhower as Supreme Commander, therefore proposed that the A.E.A.F. plan had to be given top priority, but
that Spaatz's 'Oil Plan' should be seriously considered after the first
'crisis' of *Overlord* was past, and once the Allied forces were firmly established on the continent. What mattered to Eisenhower was, as he put

it, the 'first thirty days', and for this period only the railway plan was relevant.

The decision taken at Portal's meeting was transmitted to the American and British Combined Chiefs of Staff who, on 27 March 1944, directed that the control of all the Air Forces, including the strategic bombers, should in consequence pass to Eisenhower.[41] He in turn delegated Tedder as his Deputy to coordinate the employment of all the bomber forces.

It looked as though the A.E.A.F., although not Leigh-Mallory, had won. But neither Harris nor Spaatz was yet ready to accept defeat at the hands of the A.E.A.F. and S.H.A.E.F. planners. They continued to make representations to still higher authority, so that it took three more weeks before Eisenhower could send a directive to the two bomber forces (17 April 1944).[42] This simply stated that from then on the mission of the heavy bomber forces was (a) to deplete the German air forces, particularly the German fighter forces, and to destroy and disorganise the facilities supporting them, and (b) to disrupt the enemy's rail communications, particularly those affecting the enemy's movement towards the *Overlord* lodgement area. But even this directive, issued by the Supreme Commander with the full authority of the joint U.S. and British Chiefs of Staff, failed to bring the necessary action. Indeed, in practice *Pointblank* enjoyed effective superiority over *Overlord* right to the time of the invasion. What is extraordinary, too, is that immediately after Portal's meeting, Tooey Spaatz had sent a message to Hap Arnold in Washington[43]—Tooey showed me a copy about a month later—in which he expressed his full agreement with what had been decided.

CHAPTER 13

DISPUTES ABOUT CASUALTIES

Up to the time of Portal's meeting, I had been only vaguely conscious of the fact that concern was being expressed in many quarters because attacks on targets in occupied France would cause casualties among the very French civilians whom we were committed to liberate from the Germans. General Morgan, who as C.O.S.S.A.C. was fully aware of the plans we were hatching, had written to Leigh-Mallory early in January to say that this was something that should be borne in mind.[1] I cannot find any paper which suggests that I myself had given the issue much, if any, thought when the plan was first conceived. By that stage of the war, I had become inured to the idea of casualties, whether our own or the enemy's. That was what war was about. But the way Portal had referred to the matter at his meeting made it clear that someone had been sufficiently concerned to have estimates made of the numbers of civilians who might become casualties, and that the War Cabinet had been alerted to the matter.

The next intimation that I, or for that matter anyone else in A.E.A.F., was given that this had happened, was when I was summoned to Portal's office on the afternoon of 5 April, a few hours before the War Cabinet's Defence Committee was due to consider the A.E.A.F. plan for the first time. With Portal were Tedder, Air Marshal Bottomley (Deputy Chief of the Air Staff), and Bufton, and the four were studying a paper which purported to give the cost of the A.E.A.F. plan in terms of French civilian casualties. I was asked to examine the estimates, the derivation of which it was obvious Bufton did not understand. It turned out that he had got in touch with Stradling, who had assigned two of his staff to help the Operational Research Section of Bomber Command to do what sums they thought necessary. It was also clear that the formulae that had been used to estimate the numbers of people who would, on average, be expected to be killed or wounded for every ton of bombs aimed at the railway centres named in the A.E.A.F. plan were those which I had derived from studies of German attacks on England. It was also apparent that the operational assumptions which the Princes Risborough people had been told to accept meant that the use of my formulae had led to a gross exaggeration of the likely scale of French casualties. Tedder and I did not believe that any humanitarian considerations had stirred the people who were concerned in this mathematical exercise. It seemed more like a deliberate effort to find an additional argument against the A.E.A.F. plan.

I was told to return to Portal's office later that evening to accompany him and Tedder to the Defence Committee meeting—to one of what some called Winston Churchill's 'midnight follies'. The Committee met in the Defence Map Room, a small sub-basement bomb-proof room at the Storey's Gate corner of what today is the main Treasury Building. The room is now preserved in its wartime state as an historical monument.

Portal's quarters were in the same building, but at the opposite corner on the second floor, where most of the senior members of the Air Ministry had their offices. Tedder was already there when I arrived, and after I had been given some idea of what the meeting was going to be like, the three of us made our way to the basement, being among the last to arrive for the ten-thirty start. The Prof was there, and from the look on his face I realised that he had not been warned that Portal was going to bring me along. Apart from the Prof and Sir Archibald Sinclair, I did not know any of the others who were waiting. But I recognised Attlee, the Deputy Prime Minister; Anthony Eden, the Foreign Secretary; Oliver Lyttelton, the Minister of Production, whom I had met once before; and Portal's two colleagues on the Chiefs-of-Staff Committee: Cunningham, the 'old man of the seas', and Field Marshal Sir Alan Brooke, the Chief of the Imperial General Staff. With them were the Ministers who headed their Departments: A. V. Alexander, the First Lord of the Admiralty, and Sir James Grigg, the Secretary for War. General Ismay, the military chief of Churchill's Defence Ministry, and the two members of his staff who constituted the secretariat, were also there, as were Bottomley and Bufton.

While the Prof and Portal were still exchanging quips about my presence, Churchill came in from his near-by bedroom wearing his celebrated siren-suit, with a large tumbler of what looked like whisky and soda in one hand, and a big cigar in the other. Neither had been fully consumed before we broke up in the early hours of the next morning. Churchill went to his seat, patted the chair to his right, and said, 'Where's the Prof?' Attlee sat on Winston's left, and then came Eden. The Service Ministers and the Chiefs of Staff were crowded on the opposite side of the table. Portal, with Tedder at his side, almost faced the P.M., and I sat between Tedder and Archie Sinclair, with Bottomley and Bufton, the only two who could not be accommodated at the table, behind us. I felt just as excited as I would have been before the curtain went up at a theatre, although I was certainly not ready for the high drama that followed.

It started quietly enough, and in good humour, with the P.M. reading from what looked like a narrow sheet of script, which it soon transpired was a brief written by the Prof. It began something like this. The meeting had been called to discuss the A.E.A.F. proposals for the use of strategic bombers in the preparation for *Overlord*, and everyone was aware that Leigh-Mallory knew nothing about bombing or about the merits of the plan. The whole thing was 'the brain child of a biologist who happened to be passing through the Mediterranean'. These words were pleasurably imprinted into my brain. Portal then interrupted to say that that particular observation was grossly unfair, and that the biologist in question had done more than anyone else to analyse the effects of air operations. At this point the Prof moved his hand as though to pull the brief from the P.M. There were smiles on some faces as Churchill looked up, seemingly aware for the first time that the said biologist was in the room. He continued to read, and finished by asking Tedder whether the plan had his backing. Tedder replied that it had. 'You don't know a better plan?' asked the P.M. 'There is no better plan', replied Tedder. 'I'll show you a better plan', said the P.M., and I saw Tedder's knuckles whiten as he grasped the edge of the table. He knew better than I what the next few hours were going to bring.[2]

Two papers had been tabled for the meeting. I had seen the one that had been prepared for Leigh-Mallory, and which sought authority to attack a number of the railway centres on the A.E.A.F. list of targets. The other was new to me. It was a document which had been prepared for the Chiefs of Staff by the Joint Intelligence Committee (J.I.C.) in which they assessed the probable reaction of the French and Belgians to the bombing of targets within their territories, and to which they had appended the fallacious casualty estimates. The P.M. remarked that the 'experts' differed considerably about the merits of the plan, and, furthermore, that if casualties were going to be as numerous as the J.I.C. suggested, an unhealable breach would very likely be caused between France on the one hand, and Great Britain and the United States on the other. He therefore felt it was first necessary to discuss the military merits of the plan and then, if it were approved, to approach President Roosevelt to get his views about the likelihood of an adverse reaction from the French. This, he said, would mean informing General de Gaulle about the plan, which he clearly implied would be a bad thing. He was not disposed to consult de Gaulle because if he did, he would then have to reveal to him details of the whole *Overlord* plan—which he had not yet done—and which he did not propose doing.

The P.M. spoke in his characteristic forceful way. There was, as he put it, a big difference between people losing their lives in the heat of battle, and a policy which was bound to result in the 'cold-blooded butchering' of large numbers of helpless French people well before the invasion had started.

Portal was then asked for his views. He began by saying that while he had been opposed to the plan at the start, he now felt that it was absolutely essential to carry it out if the air was going to play its part in preparing the way for *Overlord*. He also felt that it was vital to the success of the whole invasion that the plan be properly executed. The ease with which he spoke was in sharp contrast with that of Tedder, by whom he was followed. Tedder was tense, but he did not waver and declared that nothing which he had heard since his return from the Mediterranean had shaken his confidence in the plan. He ended by repeating that there was no satisfactory alternative to what was being proposed.

The Prof was then asked for his opinion, and it came as no surprise that what he said was in line with the criticisms put forward by all our opponents. The views of the economists had been swallowed, 'hook, line and sinker'. According to the Prof, the Germans were not likely to call upon more than a sixth of the capacity of the French railways to support the forces which they would be likely to use to counter our invasion. His information, too, was that it took only a few hours to carry out the repairs necessary to provide through lines in centres which had been bombed. He ended by saying that there must be a far better plan than the one Leigh-Mallory had put forward.

The P.M. then invited me to speak. While I did not feel in any way overawed by the occasion, nor surprised by the Prof's remarks, I had been somewhat taken aback by their tone. Almost as a reaction, I began rather pompously by saying that while I did not claim to be a railway expert, at least I would speak as a scientist—my intention being to imply that the Prof had certainly not done so. I then explained that the A.E.A.F. plan was based neither on theory nor speculation, but on an analysis of real events, and continued to argue in its favour until I could see from his expression that Winston was becoming bored. When I had finished, Bufton was called upon to give his views, Portal introducing him by saying that regardless of the policy to which he, as Chief of the Air Staff, was committed, and which Bufton, as his subordinate, would have to support in public, he wanted him to speak his mind freely that evening, since he represented the R.A.F. opposition to the A.E.A.F. plan. Bufton certainly did speak freely.

Although presumably he had been party to the view that the twenty specific points in the railway network feeding the invasion area could be dealt with successfully immediately before the date of the landings, what Bufton now said boiled down to the firm opinion that the 76 railway targets which the A.E.A.F. plan named could not be attacked successfully during the course of three months. In any event, Bufton felt that the

Overlord targets should be 'tactical in nature', for example, airparks, factory aerodromes, repair facilities, and the night-fighter aerodromes on which the German Air Force depended. He also believed that training centres and ammunition dumps should be attacked.

Portal then put the cat among the pigeons by saying that the figures of probable civilian casualties which had been presented by the Chiefs of Staff to the Prime Minister were incorrect, first because they had been based on a number of false premises, and second, because of certain misunderstandings on the part of the Ministry of Home Security. Quoting what I had told him, he pointed out that no allowance had been made in the calculations for any move of population from the target areas; that it had been assumed that every bomb carried on an unsuccessful mission against a railway target would nonetheless cause civilian casualties; and further, that Bomber Command, so as to be on the safe side, had multiplied the original estimates of the bomber effort required by what was called an 'operational factor' of three. Portal also explained that the casualty formulae, for which I had been responsible, had been incorrectly used.

By this time, the temperature of the discussion had risen markedly. The P.M. turned to me and angrily asked how it was that incorrect estimates of casualties could be presented to the Chiefs of Staff. I could only reply that I had not been involved in the calculations, but that I proposed reviewing them with the people concerned. Of the Ministers present, only Archie Sinclair supported the plan. Both Attlee and Eden held that it was militarily unsound, and that great hostility would be caused among the French if the offensive were to proceed on the lines proposed. Oliver Lyttelton, on the other hand, said that he was ready to believe that the bombing would have a considerable effect on the French railway system, but that nonetheless the problem of casualties did seem an over-riding consideration. Alan Brooke did not like the plan, whereas Cunningham was confident that there was no worthwhile alternative. He was therefore in favour of the programme of attacks going ahead, but he wanted the civilian population to be warned.

And so it went on. At one moment, when the P.M. was waxing eloquent about the horror of causing casualties among a friendly population, I scribbled a hasty note to Portal saying that the A.E.A.F. would in due course be putting forward a further plan, based on a request from General Montgomery, who was going to 'insist' that villages should be bombed at the time of the invasion in order to create road blocks which would hinder the movement of enemy forces. And I added that this would be bound to cause civilian casualties. I passed this note across Tedder to Portal who, having glanced at it, interrupted Winston to read what I had written, almost without paraphrase. I can still hear the fury in Winston's voice as he barked 'Who is Montgomery that he can *insist* that this, that or the other should be done?'

As the night wore on, Portal provided the main vocal opposition to the P.M. who, in the end (it was well after midnight), said that he did not propose that the meeting should reach a firm decision that night, but that Tedder should discuss the matter further with Eisenhower to see whether he could exclude from the suggested programme of attacks those targets where the risk of civilian casualties was greatest.

On his way back to his house in Kingston upon Thames, Tedder dropped me off at my flat. He had clearly been shaken by the evening's proceedings, and particularly by the personal hostility which Winston had directed at him as the night wore on. As I got out of the car, he said in his usual sardonic manner, 'I suppose that this might be the end, Zuck. I wonder how much it will cost to set up as a tomato grower?' I knew at the time that he was so committed that he would have asked to be relieved of his post as Deputy Supreme Commander if the decision had gone against the plan.

In the diary which Dick (R. H. S.) Crossman wrote of his life as a member of Harold Wilson's Government in the 1960s,[3] he tells how he learnt that official minutes do not necessarily provide a full record of the various views that might have been expressed at a Cabinet meeting. I made the same discovery on the morning after my first Defence Committee meeting. What I read set me back so much that in my innocence I telephoned Portal to draw his attention to what seemed to be clear errors in the record. He listened without interrupting, and then said that while it was up to me to protest if I wished, he would not do so if he were in my place. I took his advice. What had annoyed me was, first, that while I was recorded as saying that I could not speak as a railway expert— words which I had used sarcastically—there was no reference to my next remark, that I could speak as a scientist on the basis of fact, with the intended implication that the Prof had not been speaking objectively or indeed honestly. It was of course childish of me to want to see this put right. Second, there was no reference to the fact that it was not the A.E.A.F.'s fault that the casualty estimates were wrong; this point had been clearly made in the discussion.

Instead of questioning the record of the Defence Committee meeting,[4] I therefore prepared a note for Tedder and Leigh-Mallory to show that contrary to the impression conveyed at the meeting, there were many 'experts' not connected with A.E.A.F. and S.H.A.E.F. who were favourably disposed to the plan. I also set about the revision of the casualty estimates which Bufton had submitted to the Chiefs of Staff, inviting to Norfolk House the Princes Risborough scientists who had done the original sums, but who, in all innocence, had used Bufton's misleading assumptions about the weight of bomber effort that would be necessary. These turned out to be not the only misleading factors in the first set of calculations. Frank Yates helped with the new sums. There was nothing complicated about them, but to show that all was fair and above board, I saw to it that the actual computations were supervised by an R.A.F. Intelligence officer who was attached to R.E.8. By the end of the day I therefore had ready for Tedder a detailed paper giving the revised figures and showing how they were computed. I also made quite sure that it was signed not only by me, but also by the man who had calculated the earlier figures, *and* by R.E.8's R.A.F. Intelligence officer. The new estimates suggested that some 12,000 civilians might be killed and 6,000 seriously wounded if 69 targets on the present A.E.A.F. list were bombed. The previous figures had been 40,000 killed and 120,000 wounded. The paper also pointed out that if, as was almost certain to happen once it became known that railway centres were prime targets, people left their homes at night, or left them altogether, the number of casualties would be much lower. The document also emphasised that the standardised casualty rates used in the calculations, which were those that I had derived from German bombs, were likely to be on the high side. These commonsense provisos turned out to be fully justified. The best estimates of what actually did happen were about ten thousand killed and wounded.[5] In some of the raids, the number of German casualties exceeded that of the French and Belgian.[6]

I was continually worried about the so-called 'operational factor' which Bomber Command introduced into their sums when making their own calculations of the bomb-lift necessary for a particular task. In calculating the standardised figures which I used for the areas which were vulnerable to bombs of different size, account had been taken of all factors which past experience had shown influenced the measurable results of actual bomber operations; for example, the observed destructiveness of each type of bomb we dropped, errors in navigation and average bombing errors. Allowance had also been made for abortive sorties. Yet for some reason which was never defined, the Bomber Command chiefs kept multiplying the estimates they were given by their 'experts' of the amount of effort required to deal with a particular target, by a mystical number which they called the 'operational factor', in order to make allowances for undefinable variables which they assumed had not been considered. It was useless pointing out to them that the standardised values of casualties or physical damage, as provided by Stradling's Department, were based on actual experience. It was also impossible to get across the fact that any analysis of Bomber Command's sums showed that the so-called 'operational factor' varied in a completely unpredictable way. Sometimes the calculated force that was required for a given task was multiplied by two, occasionally it was halved, and sometimes it was left as it was. It all seemed to depend on how Bomber Harris and his staff felt on the day. And it certainly showed that the men who planned and laid on actual operations either did not understand what their Operational Research people were doing, or that the latter were not doing enough.

I emphasised all this to Tedder and Leigh-Mallory and explained that the net effect of the use of 'operational factors' was not only to magnify the casualty figures, but also to make the A.E.A.F. plan less politically acceptable than it otherwise was, because the exaggerated figures of effort required would bite too hard into the prevailing programmes of the R.A.F. and American bomber commands. I also made it quite plain that there was nothing magical about the criterion which I had chosen; that is to say the need to achieve an average of four strikes to every acre of railway centre in order to damage it significantly. In computing our own figures for the bomber effort which the A.E.A.F. plan called for, I had worked to this particular criterion only for the most critical parts of the railway centres. In fact, the actual density of strikes in the first three targets which had been destroyed by Bomber Command were 1·9, 1·8 and 1·0 to the acre (Le Mans, Trappes, Amiens). If on the basis of this experience we now accepted as our criterion a density of 1·5 rather than of 4 strikes, our revised casualty estimates, as I pointed out, could be correspondingly divided by nearly three.

Sometime after D-Day, when the A.E.A.F. H.Q. was in Bentley Priory, I witnessed a very cool illustration of the 'operational factor' at work. Starting on 23 May, the British and American Air Commanders, under the chairmanship of Leigh-Mallory, met regularly at what were sometimes called 'the morning prayers of the air barons'. Tedder usually attended, as did Eisenhower on at least one occasion. Each meeting was usually preceded by a small briefing meeting in Leigh-Mallory's office, attended by some six of us, including only Vandenberg and Smith from the American contingent. The more lengthy 'morning prayers' always opened with the senior meteorological officer telling us what weather conditions to expect that day and night. He would be followed by the senior Army and Navy liaison officers who had been assigned to Leigh-Mallory's H.Q. It was their job to tell us about the enemy's dispositions and to give such indications as could be derived from Intelligence reports about his intentions. They then had to explain what their Commanders proposed doing. On the morning in question, the senior naval liaison officer, when giving his report of enemy naval activities, referred to the fact that Le Havre harbour was inexplicably alive with small craft. The Board of Admiralty, he said, therefore hoped that Bomber Command would very quickly take on the harbour as a target. He then suggested the size of the heavy bomber force which would be necessary to do the job, the figure he mentioned no doubt having been calculated by the O.R.S. scientists in the Admiralty. Harris listened impassively to all this, with his long cigarette holder in his mouth. When the naval officer had finished, he and Leigh-Mallory exchanged glances, and Harris nodded. He then turned to his S.A.S.O., Air Vice-Marshal Oxland, who was standing behind him, and told him to give the necessary orders to attack Le Havre the following day,* employing—and here he multiplied the naval estimate of the number of bombers by three. The Air Force cry was always: tell us what you want done, but don't tell us how to do it.

But to return to April 1944—I was able to let Tedder have the revised casualty estimates the night after the Defence Committee meeting. On the following day, I handed him another Minute which our main 'railway expert', Brant, signed with me. In this we had arranged the proposed targets in accordance with the scale of casualties which might occur, and we discussed the consequences to the success of the whole plan of eliminating those targets which were associated with the greatest risk of civilian casualties. Tedder used this Minute as a basis for the submission he had been told to prepare for the next meeting of the Defence Committee. The covering letter to his note ended with the following paragraph:

> I must emphasize that the systematic execution of this plan and the progressive dislocation of the enemy-controlled railway system which is its object, are essential preliminaries to the actual assault. Only if the railway system feeding the 'NEPTUNE' area† has already been gravely disorganized can we hope, at the time of the assault, effectively to interfere with the enemy's movement and concentration and so gain time which will be a vital factor in the opening phase of the campaign.[7]

Tedder was not going to be cowed by the almost universal opposition to the plan. And Eisenhower was firmly behind him.

The next meeting took place on the night of 13 April.[8] Neither Anthony Eden nor Bufton was there, but the cast was otherwise the same as at the first meeting, except that Leigh-Mallory had been asked to attend. The P.M. seemed in high spirits, and began lightheartedly by saying to Portal that he hoped 'his Air Commodore', meaning Bufton, had not been exiled because of his opposing views. But as the night wore on Churchill became increasingly overbearing. Portal began by explaining the new casualty estimates, and Winston lashed out at me once again

---

* This attack took place on 14 June 1944.

† The *Neptune* area was that part of the Normandy coast where the landings were going to take place.

because the original figures had been different.* He then went on to say that while he was prepared to accept the new estimates—adding that he had always thought the first too high—he still questioned the strategic merits of the plan. These were once again defended by Portal, Archie Sinclair and Tedder, with Leigh-Mallory indicating his full support but, judging by the look on Winston's face, to no real effect. The Prof again voiced his firm opposition, saying that when the plan was first mooted he believed that 'nearly everybody' was against it. Portal then suggested and the P.M. agreed, that in order to encourage the evacuation of target areas, a general warning should be broadcast to enemy-occupied Europe that from now on railway centres were going to become bomber targets. The meeting ended with authority being granted to carry on with the plan for yet another week, when the Defence Committee would meet once again to consider both the results and the reaction of the French people.

I was not at the next meeting on 19 April, which was attended by both Leigh-Mallory and Tedder.[9] The P.M. continued with his opposition, even though Intelligence reports indicated that the number of civilian casualties was far lower than had been anticipated, mainly because those who lived in the vicinity of railway centres had fled, as was only to be expected.

Robb, who had returned from the Mediterranean to become Tedder's Deputy at S.H.A.E.F., substituted for Tedder at the meeting which followed,[10] and I was asked to go along with him. By now I was used to the atmosphere of the meetings, with Winston seemingly amiable at the start, but becoming increasingly hostile and domineering, with tension rising in the room as the meeting continued into the early hours. On this occasion, all the Service Ministers and Chiefs, apart from Mr. Alexander, who always seemed to fawn on the Prime Minister, urged that the plan, having proceeded as far as it had, should be agreed fully. But at the end Winston was not prepared to allow more than another limited go-ahead. Robb was new to it all, and when after the meeting we stepped into the dark night at Storey's Gate, he said that he felt physically sick, and I really thought he was going to be. Winston's menacing power could be overwhelming.

After this meeting, and one of the War Cabinet on the next day, 27 April, the P.M. decided to convey to Eisenhower the Cabinet's grave misgivings about the whole plan, and his own doubts about its military value, which he therefore wanted Eisenhower to reconsider. The long letter which he sent embodied the whole of Bufton's alternative tactical

---

* Portal announced that it was clear from Intelligence sources that the number of civilian casualties resulting from the attacks that had taken place so far was even fewer than the revised estimates had indicated. But this did nothing to mollify Churchill.

plan, and I suspected that it was drafted, at least in part, by the Prof, helped by Bufton. Eisenhower replied saying that he was totally committed to the A.E.A.F. plan, and that the alternative proposals had been carefully considered and rejected.[11]

The Defence Committee was then reconvened, and on this occasion (3 May),[12] the A.E.A.F. plan was considered for the last time, and endorsed, subject to the condition that casualties should not exceed 10,000—as though this could be guaranteed, or as though, if the figure were exceeded, one could explain the cutting short of an operation as though its military value could be judged in terms of a fixed number of innocent lives sacrificed. In the light of the Vietnam war, and of the never-ending debate about the possible use of nuclear weapons, the condition about numbers does, however, reveal how callous we have all become in comparison with what in those distant days troubled even so martial a political leader as Churchill. Still dissatisfied, on 7 May, the P.M. sent a long message to President Roosevelt[13]—a message in which he quoted, not the revised and lower estimate of French civilian casualties, but the original figure which had already been shown to be totally fallacious—asking him to intervene. This Roosevelt refused to do, saying in his reply of 11 May that he was unprepared 'to impose from this distance any restriction on military action by the responsible Commanders that in their opinion might militate against the success of Overlord'.[14] On 16 May Churchill circulated a short minute which gave the gist of Roosevelt's message, and in which he said, 'I believe the Cabinet will be content not to press this matter further than the lines now agreed'.[15] And so the open debate, but not the dispute, ended.

In spite of Bomber Harris's negative attitude to the plan, the attention he paid to its execution during the two months or so after Portal's meeting of 25 March, was all that could have been asked for. Spaatz, who commanded not only Doolittle's 8th Air Force based in the U.K., but also Ira Eaker's 15th, based in the Mediterranean, as well as the medium bombers under Brereton, was far less enthusiastic. Nevertheless, by D-Day on 6 June, the whole programme of attacks on railway centres had been effectively completed. Seventy-nine designated targets in Northern France and the Low Countries, to which fourteen others in South-East France were added during the early stages of the planning, making ninety-three in all, had been bombed.[16] The 15th U.S. Air Force dealt with their fourteen targets just before D-Day. In addition, attacks on bridges, which were laid on for the ostensible purpose of imposing more durable interruptions of through traffic than it was thought could be achieved by the bombing of rail centres, were officially authorised on 6 May.[17] A few experimental attacks had been carried out in the preceding two weeks, all more or less within the Normandy area. These were then stopped for reasons of security. It was all too easy to provide the enemy with a clue to the area that we wanted to seal off. Moreover, Tooey Spaatz had just returned from a visit to Italy with information which confirmed the views that I had stated from the start—that attacks on bridges of the kind that heavy bombers were then able to undertake, were a pretty expensive proposition. Only a direct hit counted on a bridge, whereas any bomb on a railway centre caused damage. It is interesting that the only exchanges which I had after the war with members of the American Enemy Objectives Unit revealed that with the passage of time the objections which they had advanced against the A.E.A.F. plan had been rationalised to a difference of view about the ability of aircraft to destroy bridges by bombing. This, which had always been a trivial part of the argument, had now become in their minds its central feature. They had totally forgotten their assertions that a railway network had so much spare capacity that it was one of the most invulnerable targets of the German economic system. Time can be more than a great healer.

In the fortnight or so before D-Day, wide-ranging attacks on bridges were authorised, and by the time of our invasion all the Seine rail and road bridges, and some ten others as far east as Liège in Belgium (which were among a number that were attacked as part of the cover plan), had been bombed by fighter- and medium-bombers and were reported either destroyed or seriously damaged for what, in retrospect, seems a trivial effort.[16]

The arguments about the plan had generated much bitterness, and, as I have said, opposition did not die down even after the final political decision had been reached. Apart from the small group who supported the plan from the start, most people believed that nothing significantly useful was being achieved, and *ipso facto* that valuable bombing effort was being wasted. Even after D-Day the Intelligence Section (G-2) of Eisenhower's own headquarters continued to press the view that the A.E.A.F. plan had not by then seriously impaired (and never would) the enemy's ability to move his troops by rail—this in spite of the fact that Eisenhower and Tedder, to whom the Section was subordinate, were publicly declaring the opposite view. Less than two weeks before D-Day, G-2 S.H.A.E.F. had in fact issued a detailed report[18] to this effect, under a cover note which stated that the Intelligence staff was sensitive to the imputation that they were 'being accused of wilfully belittling the effects of the recent attacks' on railway centres.[19] The day *after* D-Day they issued another paper, under a covering letter, which was to bedevil discussion of the matter for the rest of the war, and which was to confuse military thinking for years afterwards. In this memorandum, the Intelligence people justified their stand by differentiating what they called 'interdiction attacks' against a communications network, from 'attrition attacks'.[20] By the latter term, the Intelligence experts implied 'wearing down the [railway] system' so that it could no longer function. By the former, they meant interrupting rail routes 'at a sufficient number of points' so that it was no longer 'a practical proposition' for the enemy to move by rail. In the view of the Intelligence chiefs, rail centre attacks in North-West Europe had 'failed to so reduce the railway operating facilities as to impair the enemy's ability to move up reinforcements and maintain his forces in the West'. And in this view, the S.H.A.E.F. Intelligence people had the support of their opposite numbers in 21 Army Group, the Air Ministry, the American Commands, and even those in A.E.A.F. They were all wrong.

I had never heard the word 'interdiction' used before in a military context. According to the *Oxford English Dictionary*, it had mainly a legal or ecclesiastical connotation, implying the forbidding of a given action. Out of interest I wrote in guarded language to Dr. Onions of Magdalen College, one of the *Dictionary*'s editors, to ask whether the word could be used in this new sense. To my astonishment, his reaction to my letter was one of delight since, as far as he was concerned, it meant that he now had a new entry.

Gradually, however, the term 'interdiction' caught on. At first I understood that it was being used to signify the destruction of bridges. But its meaning soon became more and more diffuse until it applied to almost anything. Long after the war had ended, there were 'interdiction plans' in the Korean war. I was once told, but I hope it was meant ironically, that there was a plan which called for 'the total interdiction of Korea'.

CHAPTER 14

GLIMPSES OF NORMANDY

WHILE THE plan to disrupt the railway system of North-West Europe was my over-riding concern, a great deal more came my way in the months before D-Day. Leigh-Mallory was not only Commander-in-Chief of A.E.A.F. but, as the man responsible for the fighter defence of Great Britain, he also had under him the force called Air Defence of Great Britain. This was commanded by Air Marshal Sir Roderic Hill, who after the war became the Rector of Imperial College. Leigh-Mallory was therefore responsible for coordinating the *Crossbow* air offensive against the flying-bomb launching pads which the Germans were building on the Belgian and French coasts, and indeed for almost all air operations other than those of Coastal and Transport Commands, and those which Bomber Command and the American Strategic Air Forces were carrying out in the implementation of their *Pointblank* directive. However little the heavy bomber forces expected—or hoped—to be called on in the preparatory phases of *Overlord*, it was generally accepted that the planning of attacks on the enemy's coastal defences was Leigh-Mallory's responsibility. Inevitably I became involved in this part of A.E.A.F.'s work.

After Pantelleria I had started to feel that coastal batteries would always look more menacing than they were likely to prove in action. But since I was not going to risk my life in putting this opinion to the test, while others were, I did not press my view, to which I held despite the fact that aerial photographs showed that the batteries and other defences which the Germans had built to deter a cross-Channel invasion were structurally far more formidable than anything I had ever seen in the Mediterranean. A programme of air attacks had to be undertaken, and in order to keep the Germans guessing, it was accepted that as a cover plan we were to bomb two batteries outside the projected assault area, in the area known as *Fortitude*, for every one inside it (the *Neptune* area). The pre-D-Day raids extended from as far as Le Havre in the west, to the Pas-de-Calais in the east.

Using the best information that I could get about bombing accuracy, including that provided by photocover of the precision attacks on the V.1 sites,[1] I calculated that, on average, as many as fifteen hundred bombs would have to be aimed at a single coastal battery to give a reasonable chance of it being significantly damaged. Since the maximum number of bombs which could be dropped by the heavy bombers in any one raid would not be much more than fourteen thousand,[2] and since bombing in the *Fortitude* area was as essential as in *Neptune*, it followed that the number of batteries that could effectively be attacked from the air would be little more than ten. I was emphatic that visual daylight bombing would not be adequate, and that if the attacks on the critical batteries were to succeed, the bombing aid called *Oboe* would have to be used at night, and then only by the specially trained 617 Squadron of Bomber Command. This was the squadron known as The Dam Busters, in recognition of their famous attack on the Möhne and Eder dams in May 1943. Leigh-Mallory was far from convinced when I first advanced these views at a meeting towards the end of January,[3] at least partly because he thought that what I was suggesting would compromise security. Later, however, at a meeting on 21 March, he swung round, even though the case I was arguing meant that in the time available only a few batteries could be effectively attacked. I find it extraordinary when I am reminded today that on the night before D-Day each of ten batteries in the assault area was bombed by more than a hundred aircraft of R.A.F. Bomber Command, and that this single operation involved the whole of the Command's effort for the night, at an expenditure of some six thousand tons of bombs.[4] Security alone would have precluded any such operation before that date.

At the same March meeting, we discussed the beach bombing that was scheduled to take place at the time of the landings. The Army wanted to be assured that the German troops manning the defences would 'keep their heads down' right to the moment that our landing-craft beached. It had therefore been agreed that the batteries which covered the assault area were to be both bombed and attacked by naval fire in the critical minutes before the landings, and that these attacks would be preceded by waves of bomber attacks on, and just behind, the five landing beaches. I tried to impart to this particular discussion some statistical flavour, pointing out, unsuccessfully, that the effort against particular areas in the landing zones could be reduced by as much as twenty-five per cent without seriously reducing the likely effectiveness of the attacks. To the airmen and soldiers, more meant better. If a small hammer was all that was needed to crack a nut, but a sledgehammer was also available, then use the sledgehammer.

I then became worried lest the armament which was available to R.A.F. Bomber Command was unsuitable for the bombing of the beaches. Most of the Command's weapons had been developed in relation to its directive to destroy the industrial cities of Germany. I wanted to be assured that enough short-delay fuses and medium-charge bombs were available to prevent undue cratering of the beaches—which would impede the advance of our tanks when they rolled off the landing-craft, and which would certainly happen if our bombs were so fused that they exploded only after they had fully penetrated the sand.

Kingston and I went to the Air Ministry to see Bottomley, in whose area of responsibility the matter lay. Together the three of us went through an inventory of the bombs and fuses available to the R.A.F. Still dissatisfied, I suggested to Leigh-Mallory that we ought to have a demonstration of the amount of cratering which would result from the bombing of the beaches. This test was laid on at Thornham on the north coast of Norfolk, not ten miles from where I am now writing.

I flew from Northolt with Group Captain Dru Drury, a most affable, good-looking man, who was the Chief Armaments Officer of the A.E.A.F. Dru had arranged that we would fly as 'tail-end Charlie', the last of the last squadron of bombers, so that we could observe the operation from the air before landing at a near-by airfield, to which a most impressive staff-car had been sent to take us back to the beach. We must have looked an odd pair emerging from so grand a car in order to plod along the edge of the sea inspecting craters. The whole show was very impressive, but I cannot remember whether we were satisfied with the results. This flight was the first of many I had with Dru.

One thing which puzzled me after the war, was whether the beach which we bombed was the same as the one that is said by Bernard Fergusson in *The Watery Maze*[5] to have been investigated by Bernal in order to determine whether the Normandy beaches would be firm enough to take the weight of our tanks. The story goes that when Combined Operations let Bernal into the secret of the general area of the proposed landings, he remembered that the structure of the Normandy beaches, where he had once spent some time with a girl-friend, consisted of a mixture of peat and mud, which he believed was the same as could be found at Brancaster, only three miles to the east of Thornham. Here he is reported to have carried out some tests, on the basis of which it was decided that we had no reason to be worried about the weight of our tanks. Bernal was not, however, with us when we tried to find out what cratering would do.

There was endless variety in the day-to-day business of Leigh-Mallory's headquarters, and it would have been easy for me to become distracted from what was clearly the main task; that of getting the railway network of the continent accepted as a strategic target. But one important matter which came my way at an early stage, that of confusing the enemy's radar defences, had a tragic end.

Billy Moy-Thomas had become one of my close friends in Oxford.

He was usually full of fun, but as Europe had moved towards war he had become increasingly, and surprisingly, very jumpy. As soon as war was declared, when some of us had started doing jobs like filling sandbags, Billy came round to say that it would not be long before we regretted what we were doing since Hitler was bound to win in a matter of weeks. This phase of depression did not last long. He then decided to become a Special Constable, but this palled after only a few months. Finally he joined the R.A.F., and was given a commission as a navigator in a squadron based at Swanton Morley in Norfolk, close to the headquarters of the famed 100 Group. When Billy discovered that I was on Leigh-Mallory's staff, and also Tedder's scientific adviser, he telephoned suggesting that I should meet him and one of his brother officers to discuss an important idea on which they were working. Without having the slightest notion where or when the invasion was going to take place, it turned out that they were quite sure that it would be doomed to failure unless we first destroyed some of the Würzburg radar installations which the Germans had erected on the cliffs overlooking the Channel. Billy was not alone in believing that the Würzburgs were a menace, and his idea was to home in on the radar installations and shoot them up.[6] He realised that the operation would be hazardous, but he felt sure that it was not suicidal. The trouble was that he could not get his colleagues to agree to the idea. Would I therefore get Leigh-Mallory to issue the necessary instruction?

I must have told either Leigh-Mallory or Wigglesworth about the scheme, for Billy then arranged to discuss details with me. The only time which was convenient was one night after eight o'clock. That evening Kingston left early, and there were only a few of us working late at Norfolk House. My W.A.A.F. officer who was on duty, a girl who at the time was constantly in tears because her fiancé, a Polish pilot, had just been killed, came in to tell me that the Swanton Morley duty officer was on the line. His message was that Billy had left for London, but that his car had crashed into a tank in a narrow country lane. He was now lying critically injured in the big Norwich hospital. Did I know who was his next of kin? Billy had a brother, Edward, whom I had met before the war, and who was now in a Guards regiment. Norfolk House managed to find him without too much difficulty, and over the telephone I told him that he should go immediately to Norwich to see Billy. With his slight stammer, Edward asked, 'This is a damned nuisance. Are you sure it's serious? We've got guests in the mess and it's jolly inconvenient to leave now.' I told him to get moving as fast as he could, but Billy was dead when he arrived. Edward spoke to me from the hospital, but I never heard from him after that. He had survived the paratroop landings in Sicily, but was killed dropping into Normandy on D-Day. War had to do with death, and in terms of numbers I was used to it. But Billy's death shook me. There I was at the centre of things, helping to plan operations in which men would be killed, and I was running none of the risks. It used to be said that the cream of British science was destroyed in the First World War. There can have been few scientists of Billy's quality killed in the second. Had he lived, I have little doubt that he would have become one of the world's leading palaeontologists.

Another matter with which I became accidentally involved for a brief moment concerned the Free French in London. One day when I had stepped into Wiggles's office for a general chat, he began to express indignation at an extraordinary request he had just had from an emissary of the Free French Forces, who had asked us to lay on a bomber attack to breach a prison at Amiens, in order to allow some important members of the Resistance to escape. In his usual bluff way Wiggles asked, 'Who the devil do they think we are? Have you ever heard of anyone making holes in walls with bombs to let people escape?' 'How do you know it can't be done?' I asked. He looked at me in amazement as I continued, 'Supposing some Mosquitos were to fly in low and launch bombs against the wall? Surely it would all depend on the pilot and the wall?' 'Do you really mean that?' asked Wiggles, and when I said that I did, he called for his P.A. and told him to bring back the diagrams which the Frenchman had left. We laid them out on the table and, after measuring the thickness of the walls as shown on the plans, I said that I was sure the job could be done provided that really skilled pilots were prepared to risk their lives, and that the overall gain to the Resistance was worth the risk. 'In that case', said Wiggles, 'we'll have to look at it again.'

In due course an attack was laid on. On 18 February nineteen Mosquitos approached the prison along the Amiens–Albert road. Everything went according to plan, except for one thing. Squadron Leader Charles Pickard, who led the attack, was killed. I could only hope that the importance to the Allied cause of the prisoners who escaped compensated for the death of so brave and successful an R.A.F. officer.

Conferences and meetings multiplied apace as D-Day approached. A week before the landings, at the second of the regular meetings at which all the Allied Air Commanders gathered in the War Room at Bentley Priory,[7] I was asked to provide an appreciation of the results that had been achieved so far by air attacks on the coastal defences. My estimate, which was based on an analysis of photocover, was that only eighteen of some fifty guns in the batteries that had been attacked in the *Neptune* area had been damaged, and then only partially; the corresponding number in the *Fortitude* area was twenty-five out of a hundred. On the other hand, eight batteries under construction had all but been destroyed. On the basis of this analysis, I told the assembled air barons that a formidable, almost impossible, bomber effort would be necessary in the following week if significantly more was to be achieved. My view that this could neither be attempted nor justified, was accepted, and the bomber assault on the coastal defences was therefore not stepped up before D-Day. Clearly the halo I had gained as an 'expert' on bomber operations in the Mediterranean was still intact when it came to coastal batteries, however much it may have been tarnished by the controversy over bombing the railways.

It was shortly after this meeting that I became conscious of the fact that while general warnings had been issued to the French and Belgians about attacks on railway centres, no arrangements had been made to warn villagers who lived in the *Neptune* area that bombs might be falling on them in the hours preceding our landings. Casualties among the civilian population were also certain to be an inevitable consequence of the so-called beach-drenching, and of the bombing of small villages in order to create the road-blocks which 21 Army Group insisted had to be made. It was Portal's reference to these plans which had provoked Churchill's anger at the first of the Defence Committee meetings at which the A.E.A.F. plan was discussed.

I drove over to Eisenhower's H.Q. at Bushy Park to ask Tedder what arrangements had been made to alert French civilians to the danger. He knew of none, and asked me to find out if it would be possible to issue such a warning without, at the same time, alerting the Germans. The obvious organisation to ask was the Political Warfare Executive, whose H.Q. was in Bush House in the Strand. Ritchie Calder was its Director of Plans and Operations, and Harry Lucas, another member of the Tots and Quots, was his Deputy. It is a good indication of the pace at which we were all working that the first moment all of us could get together was at three in the morning.

When I arrived I was introduced to Ritchie's American opposite number, George Backer. I explained the problem, and Ritchie decided that something could certainly be done, but that since a major question of security was involved he felt that it was necessary to talk the matter over with Tedder himself. I arranged the meeting for later that day.

Tedder was with Eisenhower when Ritchie and Harry met me at Bushy Park, and while we waited, chatting with Leslie Scarman, I noticed that Harry was coughing and occasionally putting his handkerchief to his mouth. I knew that he had once had T.B., and when he saw the worried look on my face, he asked if I could take him to the nearest lavatory. When we got there I discovered that he was spitting blood. He protested that it was nothing, that it frequently happened, and that he wanted to wait until Tedder returned. This I refused to allow, and it ended with us leaving Ritchie on his own, while I took Harry to his flat in the centre of London. Poor Harry, that was the beginning of a fatal illness. After a spell at his flat, he moved to his country house near Newbury, before being taken to a hospital south of London, where he died. We were in touch almost to the end, but unfortunately circumstances made it impossible for me to see him after he had been taken to hospital. There must have been many like him in those days who though fatally ill drove themselves to the grave.[8]

Ritchie made himself responsible for the preparation of the warning pamphlets, which were dropped just before the landings. No-one knows how many, if indeed any, French civilians were saved because of this precautionary move, or indeed whether the beach bombing itself—which because of the bad weather was carried out 'blind'—helped save the lives of any significant number of our assault troops.

As D-Day drew closer, the Commanders-in-Chief and the other air barons at Leigh-Mallory's morning meetings started to behave as though they had never quarrelled about pre-D-Day air strategy. On occasion, however, personal antipathies did reassert themselves, and at times the situation became electric. At a meeting only three days before D-Day a sharp difference of view about the use of heavy bombers in the battle zone revealed itself between Leigh-Mallory on the one hand, and Tedder and Spaatz on the other. Leigh-Mallory emphasised that the responsibility for the air plan was his, and that he was prepared to accept it.[9] He was not, however, going to do so if the plan were changed. And when later the same day Montgomery telephoned to find out if any modifications had been made to the plan, Leigh-Mallory assured him that he stood by it absolutely and would resign rather than abandon it.[10]

There were also some pre-D-Day meetings at Stanmore with the army, even down to divisional commander level. These were strange meetings since our sense of security had been so sharpened that even though we were discussing fire-support, some of us from A.E.A.F. kept our mouths shut lest anything that was said indicated an awareness of information that had been derived from ULTRA sources, or of information that gave away the entire scale of our projected landings.

With the approach of D-Day, I also visited Southwick House near Portsmouth—where Eisenhower and the Army and Navy Commanders-in-Chief had set up their headquarters—in order to take part in meetings at which the A.E.A.F. staff had to agree final arrangements with the Army and Navy chiefs. The Navy representatives at these discussions seemed to me to be far more realistic in their appreciation of what the Air could and could not do in the way of support than were those from the Army. Some of the latter, as Tedder never stopped pointing out, seemed to treat the heavy bombers as an alternative form of precise artillery. On one occasion, when I stayed over for a night, I had a long

talk with Major-General de Guingand, Montgomery's Chief of Staff, and
Brigadier R. F. K. (David) Belchem, Montgomery's Chief Operations
Officer, about the unhappy relationships that prevailed in A.E.A.F. headquarters between senior British and American officers. It turned out that
Monty's staff were not without their own Anglo-American problems.
On the same occasion, I was sad to learn that civilian advisers were out
of favour. Blackett, who had helped enormously at the start of the war
in showing how anti-aircraft fire should be used, and who was now the
best-known scientist in the Admiralty, was in evidence in Portsmouth,
but somehow or other he was no longer in good odour with his naval
colleagues. He never attended any of our meetings, and when I asked
why, Kingston told me that he was, in fact, being denied access to the
War Room. It seemed incredible that this could have happened to the
man who, if anyone deserved the description, was the father of Operational Research. Whatever the trouble was, I presumed that professional
jealousy had played its part. In a note I made of the visit, I said, 'It is all
very unfortunate. Blackett explained to me that Bernal was unpopular
since he had raised unnecessary hares about the difficulties of the beaches.
This is not surprising since J. D. B. as often as not raises hares.' I myself
had been warned not to discuss with either of them the planning problems in which I was involved.

Leigh-Mallory had posted Kingston as his liaison officer at Portsmouth, and I spent the night before D-Day at Stanmore, mostly in the
War Room, where I followed the positions of our ships and aircraft as
they were plotted on the operations table and on wall charts. The big
question was when, and if, the Germans would react. As is now well-
known, they did not do so until the last moment. There was some final
discussion about the fusing of the bombs for the beach-drenching operation, for by then it had become clear that conditions were too bad for
visual bombing. In spite of this, Leigh-Mallory decided that the entire
heavy bomber force, not just the squadrons equipped with the new
radar bombing aids, should be sent in.

During the course of the day following the landings, 7 June, it became
clear that quite a lot had not gone according to plan; in particular,
that the bulk of our forces on the left flank were being held north of
Caen, instead of driving straight through the town and on to Falaise,
as had been hoped. At the Air Commanders' meeting on the following
morning,[11] Leigh-Mallory also reported that the original plan to hinder
the first moves of the enemy's reserve divisions by bombing small towns
in order to create 'choke points' had failed because of bad weather. The
Germans had therefore been able to deploy their immediate reserves in
the tactical area. Since the weather now precluded all air-support operations, Leigh-Mallory thought that the right policy was for the air forces

to interrupt communications as far afield as the Seine, the Loire and the Paris–Orleans Gap. The record shows me as arguing at the time that instead of doing this, we should apply the weight of our air attack on to forward areas rather than as far away as the Paris region. This view did not appeal. I therefore prepared a paper in which I set out my case, copies of which I gave to Leigh-Mallory, Vandenberg, Wigglesworth and Tedder.[12] My contention was that it would be far better to find targets close to our forces, than to plan deeper raids, for example, into Germany. If, as I put it, 'the aim of such a bombardment is to interfere with the enemy's movement, clearly we will be getting much more effect with a given weight of bombs on a narrow front close to the battle than we would on a wide front further away.' But I kept on being told that there were no aiming points close to the battle zone which were suitable for attacks by heavy bombers. To this my answer was that if there were no specific aiming points near our lodgement area, whose neutralisation might help the immediate land battle, identifying such points further afield would be equally difficult. Vandenberg in particular urged that what I was proposing would be a misuse of the strategical air forces. On the morning of 14 June, however, Leigh-Mallory was less opposed, and so, to some extent was Tedder, whose view was that the situation on our eastern flank, where 21 Army Group was held up north of Caen, only twelve miles from the Channel, might at any moment become critical. He therefore felt that all the air forces should be held in readiness to help the armies in the emergency he foresaw.[13] This was the reason Tedder gave for withholding his sanction for a daylight attack on Berlin which the U.S. 8th Air Force had planned for the following day.

By the time of this meeting I was well ahead with a study, based on photocover, in which I tried to identify possible aiming points in the battle area. This took into account what we knew about the enemy's and our own dispositions, as well as what we had learnt about bombing accuracy. With Kingston's encouragement and help, a plan was being prepared for the eventuality which was in Tedder's mind.

It was at this period that the flying bombs became a major diversion. The Germans had launched their first salvos at London during the night of 12/13 June, and as a result, most of the business at the Commanders' meeting on the 16th[14] was devoted to an appreciation of the threat they constituted, and of the way by which the 'doodle-bugs' could be countered. The V.1s were coming over continuously during the course of the meeting, and at its end most of us trooped into the operations room where their flight-paths were being plotted. As the officer who had the responsibility for seeing that these new weapons were destroyed in the air, it was Roderic Hill's duty to tell the Commanders at their morning meetings how well, or badly, we were doing. There was one day when he gave his five-minute talk in a very distracted way, a fact on which I commented to one of our colleagues as we left the meeting. 'Didn't you hear?', he said, 'Roderic was told, just before we started, that one of his sons had been lost in last night's operations.'

By the end of the following week, it became plain that unless the mobile launching ramps were put out of action, or the supply lines to the sites dislocated, mainly by intensifying our attacks on the railway system (for the earlier attacks on the sites had succeeded in making the first generation of concrete ramps inoperable), the threat was going to become much more serious than we had at first supposed. The air barons were reluctant, however, to reduce the scale of their offensive against targets in Germany in favour of making the V.1 installations a prime target. So it was that our first big reaction to the flying-bomb offensive was a reprisal day-raid by American heavy bombers on Berlin on 21 June.[15] I was taken aback by the decision to allow this attack, and immediately after the meeting[16] went to my room where I penned a Minute to Tedder which I entitled 'The Logic of Desire, or Why We should Bomb Berlin'. I wrote it in a sarcastic vein, pointing out that the only logic behind the decision was simply 'if you want to do a thing hard enough, you can always find an argument to support your case'. The U.S. 8th Air Force was simply determined to show that they could bomb Berlin in force, and having been held back the week before, felt that here was their chance. Tedder thought that my Minute was both unfair and silly.

On the afternoon of 14 June,[17] Leigh-Mallory flew to France, taking Kingston with him. On his return that evening we were told that he had found Montgomery fairly confident, but ready to admit that the original plan to encircle Caen from the east and west had broken down. Leigh-Mallory had not agreed to Montgomery's suggestion that airborne troops should be used to loosen up the static situation behind Caen, and instead had proposed the plan which Kingston and I had already discussed with him at Stanmore: namely, that the stalemate could be ended by bringing in the heavy and medium bombers to break down enemy opposition in the battle area, in preparation for an advance by our forces. To this Monty agreed.

Kingston was accordingly instructed to arrange that a party went over to France to discuss details with General Dempsey, Commander of the British 2nd Army, and General Crocker, Commander of 1 Corps of the 2nd Army. Next morning,[18] Kingston, Brigadier General Smith and I from A.E.A.F., Brigadier C. L. Richardson,* A.E.A.F.'s military liaison officer, Oxland from Bomber Command, and Brigadier General Schlatter from U.S.S.T.A.F., flew to Normandy in a Dakota. I took with

* Retired from the Army as General Sir Charles Richardson, Master-General of the Ordnance.

me the map on which I had marked my suggested aiming points, round which I had drawn circles within which the bulk of the bomb loads would fall. The aircraft was not equipped for passengers, and it was more than obvious from the silence and the expressions on their faces that Kingston and I were thoroughly out of favour with our colleagues. I started fiddling with a parachute pack, and I can still see the look of pleasure on Oxland's face when the parachute started unfolding in the belly of the aircraft, with me, a stupid civilian, obviously incapable of doing anything about it.

An angry Broadhurst, who commanded the R.A.F. fighter-bombers (83 Group) which had been moved to Normandy, was at the airstrip where we landed, but he did not accompany us to what I took to be a village school outside Bayeux, where Generals Dempsey and Crocker, together with a bevy of Major-Generals and Brigadiers, were waiting. It was all a little theatrical. A depressed Dempsey wearing riding breeches walked up and down in front of the row of desks at which we sat, tapping his boots with a riding crop while he explained the disposition of our forces and that of the Germans. He told us that his troops were weary, and that if the combined operation we had in mind was too hazardous, he dared not take the risk of his men being killed by our own bombs. When, looking at my map, I interrupted to say that the average aiming errors of Bomber Command would allow of certain targets being tackled without any undue risk to our troops, Oxland glowered at me and said that he, not I, would speak for Bomber Command whose accuracy—repeating the old parrot-cry—was far worse than I was making out.

At that moment the door opened and in stalked Tedder, closely followed by Coningham and Broadhurst. Together with Dempsey and Crocker they moved to a side room where they remained for some ten minutes, after which our party was called in—the two generals having withdrawn—and firmly told that the matter was none of our business. Any air support Monty needed would be dealt with by the tactical air forces under Coningham. Taking advantage of my special relationship with Tedder, I argued back, pointing out that while we were no doubt dealing with a land battle, a new factor had to be considered; namely, the weight of bombs that could be accurately put down by the strategic as well as the tactical air forces. Kingston also wanted to know why the army was stuck if the Tactical Air Command could give adequate air-support. This remark was also brushed aside and the class, as it were, dismissed.

We drove into Bayeux where most of us bought what cheese there was, mainly Camembert, which I had not tasted for three years. It and the Pont l'Evêque had the right smell, even though their chalk content far outweighed that of their fat—'30 pourcent matière gras'. Having done that, we set off for the airstrip, all but losing ourselves on the way. This became obvious when, at a small crossroads, we spotted some soldiers crawling on their stomachs along a ditch at the side of the road. I took it that if we had not turned off at that point we would have driven straight into the German lines. When we landed in the U.K., I had myself driven to Oxford where the abortive trip was turned into a major success by the welcome Joan gave me and my cheese.

At the time I did not understand exactly why Tedder, who knew full well about the plan I had been devising, had broken up the meeting. It turned out that part of the explanation was that the formal chain of command had not been used. As the story is told by Kingston, he, Kingston, following instructions, had tried to get hold of Mary Coningham the night before, but Mary had been dining in London at an address unknown to his Normandy H.Q. Since Mary was the C.-in-C. of the Advanced A.E.A.F., it had been technically wrong of Leigh-Mallory to have bypassed him when arranging with Montgomery for a planning team to confer with 21 Army Group's Corps Commanders. Kingston also writes that he realised that we were not going to get far as soon as he saw that Montgomery had left the meeting to Dempsey. Another point he makes is that Leigh-Mallory was so infuriated when he heard what had happened, that once again he had to be dissuaded from asking to be relieved of his command.[19] In my view, however, the outcome would have been the same whatever the mistakes in dealing with the service hierarchy. Apart from Kingston and myself, the rest of the team was concerned only to sabotage the plan Leigh-Mallory had put to Monty, and about which they had not been consulted. The failure to consult was neither due to stupidity nor to bad manners on my part. The representatives of the strategic air forces would have then been automatically opposed to the use of their commands in the battle zone. They had their own war to fight.

Tedder's own account of the incident fails to tell how he himself had broken up our meeting, and is wrong in saying that our party did not include any representatives of Spaatz—it included two, Smith and Schlatter. But Tedder relates that later in the day he 'confirmed to Montgomery that his [Monty's] opposite number was Coningham, and Dempsey's was Air Vice-Marshal Harry Broadhurst', information which Tedder says seemed to relieve Montgomery.[20] I can hardly see why it should have done. Kingston, who was soon to spend some days in Normandy as Leigh-Mallory's liaison officer with Monty, for whom he had the greatest admiration, told me that Monty disliked Mary Coningham and insisted on keeping in direct contact with Broadhurst. Moreover, according to Tedder, not many days after our visit Monty started

demanding that Mary should be relieved of his Command. Monty made
his attitude to Mary plain in his *Memoirs*, where he writes that Coningham 'could scarcely appreciate' what his—Monty's—strategy was.[21]

Whether or not Mary did, and this depends on what one understands
Monty's strategy to have been, it was nonetheless ironical that at the Air
Commanders' meeting the day after we were sent home by Tedder,
Mary, who had been partly instrumental in having us thrown out, said
that it was time that Montgomery admitted that his plans had failed, and
that the Second Army was now on the defensive.[22] Whatever the respective antipathies of the various Commanders, the fact is that on 18
June Montgomery issued an order for an all-out offensive towards Caen,
and that on 25 June, a thrust by our ground forces was preceded by an
attack by medium bombers on some of the strong points that were holding up our troops. This operation failed to make any significant headway,
but at least it kept the Germans pinned down in force in and to the south
of Caen.

During the next three weeks, the U.S. 8th Air Force, and on occasion
Bomber Command, continued to focus their attention on targets inside
Germany, including Berlin. One of these raids particularly maddened
Leigh-Mallory. On 29 June, with our armies still precariously bogged
down in the lodgement area, particularly in the British sector, the whole
of the 8th Air Force, bombers and fighters alike, attacked aircraft factories and oil plants in southern Germany, all to little effect. This operation, like an earlier one on 9 June, had been laid on without Leigh-
Mallory's knowledge, and without Tedder's authority. Not surprisingly,
neither Kingston nor I knew it was to take place. But I have no doubt
that American staff officers in A.E.A.F., and indeed in S.H.A.E.F., knew
that the operation was being planned.

Flying bombs continued to provide their own peculiar excitement to
my life as I shuttled between London, Stanmore, and Bushy Park. One
day in particular stands out in my memory when, after a Commanders'
meeting at Bentley Priory, Robb and I had accepted an invitation to
lunch with Tooey Spaatz. Flying bombs were already coming over in
the morning as I was being driven to Stanmore from London. One
exploded behind me in the Finchley Road about half a minute after I had
passed. A second landed slightly to the right of the road just when my
driver turned on to the bypass to Stanmore. That was not the end. After
the usual morning meeting, Robb took off for Tooey's house a few
minutes before me. When I arrived, I remarked that a flying bomb had
made rather a mess of a roundabout on the way there. 'There was no
mess there when I passed,' said Robb. It was clearly my lucky day, having
been missed by flying bombs by little more than seconds on three
separate occasions. Another time, when Bob Robertson, Marc Peter—an

American architect who worked at Princes Risborough—Joan and I had
dined together in London and were back in our mews flat, a fusillade
of bombs started coming over. Neither of the two Americans wanted to
leave while the noise continued. In spite of what he had learnt at
Princes Risborough, Marc was still sufficiently superstitious to believe
that any shelter was better than none, and took cover under a table. Bob,
who smoked cigars incessantly, used up my very limited supply in the
three hours that the attack lasted. But I certainly had no cause to complain. For many years after the end of the war he kept me supplied with
cigars to make up for those which he had smoked that evening.

July came, the weather continued to be against us, and we were still
confined to our lodgement area. In his unpublished record, Kingston
writes that with the prospects as they were, and in spite of Tedder's
objections, Leigh-Mallory had not quite given up the idea of using the
heavy bombers to break the stalemate. To strengthen his case, he and
Wiggles went over to see Monty to ask him specifically whether or not
he wanted the support of the heavy bombers. 'Monty', he writes, 'could
not have given a more emphatic "yes".' Kingston also says—in his
Direction of War—that a 'day came when Churchill informed Montgomery that he had to break through at Caen or someone else would be
found to do the job. Montgomery's immediate reply was he could
capture Caen over the week-end if he was given heavy bomber support.
Immediately, the Prime Minister overruled the objections of the bomber
barons: Bomber Command was ordered to the task and the support
plan, pigeon-holed for so long, was put in hand.'[23]

The operation may have been laid on speedily, but Kingston is wrong
in implying that the air plan for the operation, which became known by
the codeword *Charnwood*, was exactly the same as the plan we had proposed during the first week after our landings, that is when our forces
were tied down less than twelve miles from the sea, and before the
Germans had consolidated their defensive positions. The bomber plan of
7 July had only two main aiming points; the earlier one I had proposed
had seven.

The news about the operation, which began with heavy bombing on
the night of 7 July and continued with fighting on the ground for three
days, was very encouraging. Accordingly, Kingston and I decided that
it would be useful to see at first hand whether we could derive any lessons
which could be put into effect for further operations of the same kind.
Oxland decided to accompany us, and we went over as a party of six,
including an officer on Coningham's staff, a colonel from 21 Army
Group H.Q., and an Intelligence officer from S.H.A.E.F. As agreed by
Monty, the plan had been for R.A.F. Bomber Command to make a heavy
attack on the northern outskirts of Caen on the first night, and that a

three-divisional advance from our lines would start at four-thirty the following dawn, with the object of capturing Caen itself. Some five hundred heavy bombers of R.A.F. Bomber Command took part. The first aircraft was over the target at about ten in the evening, and the entire air operation was completed in about an hour. Six thousand bombs, mostly thousand-pounders, were aimed at two target points, eighty-five per cent of them so fused as to explode six hours after they landed, and at about the time when it was planned that our troops would begin their advance.

When we reached the outskirts of Caen after the operation, our party split up. Kingston and I decided to inspect the aiming points and to see for ourselves what kind of destruction had been wreaked. The report which we prepared on our return states that 'a brief survey of parts of the bombed areas failed to reveal signs of enemy gun positions, tanks or of enemy dead. This negative finding agrees with that of the troops who first crossed the bombed areas.'[24] There was so little to be seen, that one official report of the operation even bothered to note the trivial fact that six smoke-generators were picked up in the northern outskirts of the area which was pockmarked with bomb-craters.

I decided that it would be useful to meet various officers who had been directly concerned in the attack. Accordingly, Kingston and I started by talking to a young Lieutenant-Colonel, Harris by name, who had commanded the 2nd Battalion of the Royal Ulsters, which had led the advance into the city. We then spoke to the Commanding Officer and several staff officers of the 9th British Brigade, to which the 2nd Royal Ulsters was attached. We saw officers of the 3rd British Division, of which the 9th Brigade was part, and of the 2nd Army. For good measure I suggested that we should also see Alan Moorehead, a war correspondent whom I knew, and who had been with the Royal Ulsters when they entered Caen. There was also a Squadron Leader Sprawson of Bomber Command, who had been sheltered by French civilians in and around Caen since he had been shot down on the night of D-Day.

21 Army Group's intention was that Bomber Command should ease the advance of our troops by destroying strong defences to the north of Caen, including concrete positions, of which Kingston and I could find no sign. It was because of their presumed existence that the 21 Army Group representatives, at the only meeting that Leigh-Mallory himself called to discuss the joint Army/Air plan, had said that they were prepared to accept cratering, and that they wanted some of the bombs to be fitted with the six-hour delay fuses. Whatever else our talks with the forces involved revealed, it became quite plain that someone had failed to get across to them the reasons why the heavy bombers had been brought in.

The explanation for the bombing as given by 2nd Army staff officers was the same as that stated by 21 Army Group, but they did not refer to the existence of concrete positions. They had a map which showed that Bomber Command had been given six German batteries as targets. 2nd Army believed that a secondary aim of the attack had been to prevent the Germans bringing up reinforcements through Caen in order to check the advance of our infantry. In particular, the bombing was supposed to deny the enemy the opportunity of forming up a counter-attack with tanks *north* of the city. We were told that 2nd Corps had stressed this latter aim as being the most important result that could be achieved. Similar views were stated at Divisional level, but the people with whom we talked wondered why, in fact, the particular targets which had been bombed had been chosen. They had known of better ones. When we got to the 9th British Brigade, the Commanding Officer and many of his staff had no idea at all why the bombers had been in action. The same bewilderment was expressed by Lieutenant-Colonel Harris, who had not seen any concrete defences either. So far as Broadhurst was concerned, all the aiming points had been selected by the 2nd Army, and none by the Air Force. It had been none of his concern, even though he was now the air officer in most immediate touch with Monty.

On the basis of Intelligence reports, it had been believed that the bombed area had contained the headquarters of the 31st German Air Force Regiment. Neither the officers of the 9th British Brigade, nor Lieutenant-Colonel Harris, was able to give us any hard information as to the whereabouts of this headquarters. They thought, however, that if it had existed at all, we would find it in a house on a road in the northern part of the city. When Kingston and I got there, all we found was a German helmet (which we assumed had belonged to a dispatch rider), some clothing, and a small number of bullets and grenades. All these were in the garage of the house, and I began to have my doubts about that H.Q.

We also tried to discover, but without much success, how many French civilians had lost their lives or been wounded in the attack. What we did find out was that between two and three thousand had been killed during the whole of the month in which the town had been bombed and shelled. Our report then noted that 'civilians were met who had been in the area of the bombing at the time it took place. One who was closely questioned failed to give any information about the enemy positions.'

From what we ourselves saw on the ground, and from what photo-cover of the bombed area later revealed, it was clear that the bombing had nonetheless been concentrated and accurate. The total area in which all the bombs fell was little more than about 2·5 to 3 square miles, which meant an average density of about four bomb strikes to the acre. Every officer to whom we spoke assured us that no bombs had fallen into our own lines. Those parts of the city that were within the bomb pattern were totally devastated. Where bombs had fallen on open ground to the north and north-west of the city, we found that crater debris had formed a practically uniform carpet of clods of hard clay earth.

We also learnt that quite apart from the bombing, and in spite of a creeping artillery barrage which had preceded the advance of our leading troops and during which *a quarter of a million rounds* of shells were fired, our advance was held up, particularly in two areas, by enemy troops who had clearly not been demoralised by the bombing, and who had held out until practically every one of them had been killed. It took some ten hours to overrun a position held by only some two hundred and fifty men of the 16th German Air Force Regiment. Not surprisingly, our people paid the highest possible tributes to the valour of the defenders. Officers of the 9th British Brigade referred to the enemy who held dug-outs round the small villages of La Bijude and Galmanche as 'suicide squads'.

Subsequent views about the value of the bombing varied every bit as much as did the supposedly eye-witness accounts of what had happened. Monty's own report of the operation, issued on 10 July, went so far as to declare that Caen had been captured.[25] In fact, some of its suburbs were still in German hands, and we were certainly not the city's occu-piers. Indeed, after the Royal Ulsters had withdrawn, enemy patrols had returned during the night to the furthest limits of the city's bombed area. According to the account issued by 21 Army Group, the bombing had been a decisive element in the military success of the operation; the enemy had been driven back across the River Orne, which divided the city. The staff officers of the 2nd Army were not so positive. As they saw it, 'the outstanding effect of the bombing was its inspiring example. Everyone who viewed it, and nearly everybody in the British sector was in a position to view its progress, was immensely impressed by the way the R.A.F. Bombers came in without deviating in the face of flak, and by the way they put their bombs down right in front of Caen.' The officer in charge of 3rd Division's artillery was somewhat less impressed. His view was that the bombing had blocked the direct route into town, and so had definitely slowed down the ultimate phase of the advance— an opinion which accorded with the fact that the Royal Ulsters found the going extremely difficult because of craters and wreckage. Only four of their tanks in fact managed to penetrate into Caen, and then along a side road. They therefore withdrew on the evening of 8 July, re-entering the next morning when an attempt was made to clear the rubble so as to ease the way for the tanks.

Nor did the 3rd Division's artillery commander or his brother officers believe that the bombs had destroyed any enemy positions or batteries, as we had been told by the 2nd Army staff officers. Equally, they did not know whether any of the men of their Division had come across destroyed equipment or enemy dead during their advance into the city. 'They did not think that the enemy had intended either to resist in front of the town', or to defend it by street fighting. 'They had seen no indication of road blocks being erected or of any strong points being built.' The same view was independently stated by staff officers of the 9th Brigade of the 3rd Division. Apart from the enormous lift to their morale which the appearance of the heavy bombers had given, their view was that the bombing had made no material difference to the whole operation. They could not even understand why heavy bombing had been called for and, like the men of the Royal Ulsters, they said that not a single dead German or any enemy equipment had been found in the area that had been bombed.

Alan Moorehead was amazed when I led a team of high-ranking officers into his room at the *Lion d'Or* in Bayeux, and after the war we used to laugh about the incident. According to him, the feeling amongst the French civilians in and around Caen was that the bombing had had no military value at all since there were no Germans or German defences in the areas we had destroyed. All we had achieved was the destruction of French life and property. Squadron Leader Sprawson also gave as his view that there had been no enemy guns in the target areas, and that many batteries a little south of the badly cratered area were still firing on the morning after Bomber Command's attack.

When Kingston and I returned from reconnoitring the damage, we joined up with the rest of the party. While we were strolling along a narrow road lined by poplars, we heard a continuous rattle of anti-aircraft fire, and then the sound of an approaching aircraft. I looked up, and there was the last low-flying German plane I was to see—I could even see the pilot's face—in the whole war. Presumably he had been sent on a reconnaissance, and had managed to fly unscathed through the flak. The rest of the party had taken cover on the opposite side of the road and were shouting incomprehensibly at me. When the aircraft had disappeared, Kingston walked over and quietly asked why I had not taken cover. He looked astonished when I asked him why I should have done so. 'But he was firing,' said Kingston. 'How do you know?' I asked, 'I didn't hear anything.' 'Didn't you notice the leaves of the trees showering down?' he replied. I had noticed nothing. I was mesmerised by the pilot's face, not a hundred feet above me.

Kingston and I ended the report of our observations with a section headed 'Lessons of the operation and some statements of the obvious'. It was idle, we pointed out, to expect the best from the Air by calling in heavy bombers as a frill to a ground plan that was already made; the whole fire plan had to be integrated at the start of the planning, as was done in the case of the air and naval bombardment which preceded our landings on D-Day. The report then went on to discuss the timing, duration and intensity of the air bombardment, and pointed out that the shorter the interval between the cessation of air bombardment and the advance of ground forces, the better the results. In the case of the Caen operation, our forward elements did not reach the bombed areas until some twenty-four hours after the bombing had ended. During this interval small numbers of the enemy had been able to infiltrate the area north of the town. I then went on to make certain generalisations about 'bomb lines'. Here I said that the optimal condition would be one in which our own troops were dug in to the very edge of the area that was to be bombed, so that they could advance the moment the bombing stopped. Bombing, however, as I pointed out, is subject to errors, and it was a matter of opinion as to what constitutes a reasonable risk for our own troops. My own view was that in the case of Bomber Command it would be reasonable to assume that no more than 1·5 per cent of all bombs dropped would fall more than 2,500 yards from an assigned aiming point, and that in the case of the U.S. 8th Air Force, 90 per cent of the bombs would be expected to fall within a circle of radius 700 yards.

The report was ready two days after we returned from Caen, but Tedder decided that it was not to be widely circulated. When I protested, he gave as his reason that he had never read a more demoralising document. And that is where the matter rested.[26]

On 18 July, ten days after the first combined operation against Caen, a second was mounted in which both R.A.F. Bomber Command and the U.S. 8th Air Force took part. In this operation, which was laid on under the codename *Goodwood*, both strategic air forces bombed at first light. About 6,500 tons of bombs were aimed at six relatively small areas which were presumed to contain enemy strongpoints, while General Brereton's U.S. 9th Air Force, which was accustomed to army support operations, 'swept' the intervening ground with another six hundred tons. The bombing, which was associated with considerable artillery preparation and support was, in most cases, very accurate. Nevertheless, the advance of the ground forces was again more limited than had been planned. Our troops succeeded in capturing the part of Caen that was still held by the enemy, but strenuous opposition stopped their advance after a few miles.

In the report which I prepared of this operation, I again emphasised the fact that the bombing had not been well timed in relation to the ground advance. I had gone over for the operation as a highly interested onlooker, and was in the town not long after the air bombardment

ceased and as our troops advanced. It was all very impressive and noisy.
Before we started to move Kingston and I had placed ourselves next to
one of our batteries of heavy guns. I was acutely interested in what was
going on because again I knew from photocover almost every inch of the
ground. But none of the questions I asked about targets made sense to
the gunners. When we got into the town, I was again totally incapable of
making sense of anything that was happening, nor was Kingston much
help with my questions. At one moment when the gunfire was pretty
intense, a Canadian major threw himself to the ground near me. When
he rose to his feet again, I asked him, 'why?' He looked at me strangely
and said, 'Didn't you know that the shells were likely to fall short?'
When, in the interests of knowledge, I asked him how he knew the
difference between German shells and our own, he simply moved away
from me. At that moment I was sure that no-one could have told from
which direction fire was coming. A little later in the day we were at an
airstrip where fighter-bombers were landing and taking off again as soon
as they had reloaded. I idly asked a young pilot who was waiting to get
back into the air what his target was. 'Haven't a clue, Sir', was the reply.
'When Bill, there, peels off and goes down I follow and then let my
bombs go'. In the real world, targets were turning out to be somewhat
different from those on a planner's map.

The experience of these two operations was not encouraging, and
with rumours starting to fly around about Montgomery's leadership, I
jumped at an invitation from Pete Quesada to confer with him at his
forward H.Q. on our western flank. Pete then stood in the same relationship to General Bradley as C.-in-C. of the U.S. Advanced Tactical Air
Forces as Mary Coningham did to Montgomery. Kingston had never
met him and was keen to come along.

The car which met us at an airstrip took us straight to an H.Q. under
canvas, and to a tent where Pete was studying an operations map with
General Bradley, and Major-General Collins, the Commander of the U.S.
7th Corps. In Bradley's *A Soldier's Story* I appear as a 'tweedy civilian',
and as 'bomb expert for the R.A.F.', who had 'clashed' with Spaatz
'in the showdown on priority of strategic targets that previous spring'.[27]
The 'tweedy' was no doubt a reference to the fact that when Bradley and
I first met in the early part of the year, I was in the habit of wearing tweeds
to counter the cold of unheated headquarters. Pete greeted me with,
'You've come just at the right time. Tell us where to set the bomb-line.'
I introduced Kingston and we were then told about the disposition of
the American troops and the German forces facing them, and about
Bradley's determination to break loose into France, with General Patton
ready to move with his 3rd Army as soon as a hole had been punched in
the German lines. Even if they expressed little interest in Monty's opera-

tions, the Americans knew that the support provided him by the air had not helped to get him through Caen. They were determined to do better. 'I know you helped plan those air attacks, Zuck. We want something better. What do you think?'

The American 1st Army was then poised along a 25-km line, which was well defended by a mixed group of German forces,[28] between St. Lô to the south-east and Périers to the north-west. If, as I suggested, the U.S. Commanders were to live up to their tough intentions, the bomb-line had to be close in. I suggested a figure which on probability calculations was justified by the average accuracy that was then being achieved by the heavy bombers of the U.S. 8th Air Force. But, I also pointed out, Bradley and Collins had to realise that some bombs were bound to fall short and probably kill or wound some of their own men. This condition was accepted, as was also the suggestion that anti-personnel fragmentation, as well as H.E. bombs, should be dropped. The rest was therefore up to Pete, who had to transmit both his own and the Army Commanders' views to the 8th Air Force. Given we could get leave from A.E.A.F., the three generals were only too ready to agree that Kingston and I could be there when the operation was launched and, further, that we could line up with the forward troops in order to show that we had faith in the figures I had given about bombing accuracy and bomb-lines.

Our visit had taken place about a couple of days after *Goodwood*, and I had a suspicion that in spite of Tedder's embargo on our first Caen report, it had been seen by Pete Quesada and possibly also by Bradley. The Americans were anxious to get on with the attack, and after returning to Stanmore for a night or two, Kingston and I rejoined Pete at his H.Q. By then, however, the weather had turned sour. It rained and rained, and there was no possibility of a combined operation being launched. Kingston, with whom I shared a tent, has written that the Americans 'had few clues about making themselves comfortable under canvas in the rain', and that he found the 'ablutions' more uncomfortable than he could remember in any camp. He then goes on to say that during our first night we had a rather unpleasant experience. 'The alert signal for a gas attack was a rifle shot, and as a result of a false alarm distant shots were taken up by nearer and nearer shots until finally they reached a crescendo from all the local rifles while sentries came round to every tent in our compound checking that gas-masks were being worn.'[29] Needless to say, neither of us possessed a gas-mask. I remember turning over and telling the American soldier who had stuck his head into our tent, 'to get the hell out of it'. Not for one second did I believe that the Germans would attempt a gas attack. The risks were too great.

Kingston was not exaggerating when he said that the camp was uncomfortable. Bradley, Collins, Quesada and their top staff shared one big mess tent where we all had our meals. I discovered that the three top officers had their private covered latrine—all the rest were in the open. One day as I walked in, General Bradley was coming out. He was even more serious than usual as we stood in the rain to talk. 'I can't afford to stay here,' he said. 'I lose all my best boys. They're the ones who stick their heads through hedges and then have them blown off.'

Before operation *Cobra*, as it was called, could be launched, a message was received from Stanmore demanding our return. We were therefore not present when the big attack was launched on 25 July, nor had either of us been involved in the detailed planning of the operation, which was both the prelude to our breakout into France, and the occasion of a tragic misunderstanding between the heavy Air Forces on the one hand, and Bradley, Collins and Pete Quesada on the other. Quite apart from the fact that the bombers approached from a totally unexpected direction (they were supposed to come in from the north, but instead came in along the line of troops as they stood ready to advance), there were other mishaps, as a result of which several bombs fell short. Among the many American casualties from our own bombs was a three-star general, General McNair. Probability estimates were all very well, but they did not reveal who was going to be killed. When I heard about General McNair, I could not help wondering what might have happened to Kingston and me if we had not been called back.

The American push from the St. Lô–Périers line was the first combined operation in which a significant proportion of the bombs dropped by heavy bombers were fragmenting as opposed to cratering weapons. But once again, an examination of the ground after Bradley's troops had advanced failed to reveal that the sixty thousand or so bombs that were dropped in the operation caused many casualties among the German defenders, or destroyed any significant number of guns and armour. The casualties among our own forces made a greater impression.

I remember hearing a rumour that in his subsequent drive eastwards to the Seine, Patton had light-heartedly sent a message to Bradley asking whether instead of continuing on his way, he, Patton, should turn north and sweep Monty into the sea. Be this as it may, the rapid advance of the American 1st Army under General Hodges and the 3rd under General Patton, the two components of Bradley's 12th Army Group, made it necessary on 31 July for the British forces to launch an assault in the centre of the Allied line to the south of Caumont. R.A.F. Bomber Command provided fire support for this operation, which, however, again did not result in any major advance. Attention then shifted once more to the region of Caen, and on 7 August operation *Totalize* was carried out with the aim of effecting a break-through of the British forces on the left. In its opening phases R.A.F. Bomber Command, together with the U.S. 9th Air Force, dropped some five thousand tons of bombs on eight target areas in the battle zone. The ground attack, which was carried out by the Canadians, again came to a stop before a break-through was effected. Accordingly, yet another and similar operation, *Tractable*, was mounted a week later on 14 August. The resultant ground advance into Falaise on 17 August more or less completed the encirclement of the enemy in what became known as the Falaise–Argentan Pocket. But this did not prevent the Germans from making a successful and massive retreat eastwards across the Seine.

This series of 'combined operations' in Normandy did not lead to any clear rules for coordinating artillery fire with air bombardment, or for timing a ground advance in relation to heavy bomber attacks. As the enemy withdrew from France, heavy bombers were nevertheless called upon to assist in clearing them from a number of coastal strong points, extending all the way from the Bay of Biscay as far as Holland. In some of these operations, notably that against Le Havre, the results were very striking, in so far as the German garrisons surrendered after heavy pre-paratory air bombardments without offering much resistance. In others, for example those against such more westerly strong points at St. Malo, Brest and the Ile de Cezembre off St. Malo, the enemy held out for long periods in spite of very heavy shelling and air bombardment. The garri-son of the 30-acre Ile de Cezembre, numbering some four hundred Germans and Italians, was shelled from the land and sea and bombed for almost the whole of August 1944 before giving in. And then their surrender was due more to lack of ammunition, food and water than to the destruction caused by the fire to which they had been subjected—in the course of which some four thousand tons of H.E. bombs were dropped which, as a ground survey by one of my teams later showed, resulted in an average density of forty-five bomb strikes per acre over the whole of the small island.

Having been a staunch advocate of all these combined operations, which Tedder was not, I later searched the military records but found that they did not lend themselves to any clear and objective conclusion about the contribution which the heavy bomber forces might have made to the success of the armies. It was not even possible to decide whether or not our ground forces would have been greatly handicapped if heavy air support had not been forthcoming. All that the facts established with certainty was that, in general, no matter how high a density of bomb strikes was achieved, the direct effect on enemy vehicles, guns and per-sonnel remained small. As Tedder had forecast, it also became clear that the British and American armies increasingly came to consider this type of air support as a necessary part of any heavily opposed ground opera-tion. The case of Dieppe stands out in my memory. The Canadians had

been given the honour of forcing its German garrison to surrender—as
I understood it at the time, partly to redress the balance of the disastrous
Dieppe Commando raid of 1942, in which they had suffered so grievously.
Bomber Command had been laid on to provide the usual kind of support
in the expectation of serious resistance. I was with Tedder just after the
news came in that the town had been surrendered. Some of the bombers
were already airborne but, 'Thank God', said Tedder, 'we've been able
to recall them'.

Some four months after the German collapse in Normandy, by which
time I had set up a Bombing Analysis Unit in France (the B.A.U.), I put
Cliff Emmens in charge of a team of four men, one of whom represented
the United States Air Forces, and another R.A.F. Bomber Command,
to determine the extent to which the destruction of the Seine bridges had
impeded the enemy's escape from Normandy. The field-work this entailed was laborious, and was then supplemented by all the Intelligence
information that was available. Because the study was not completed
until after fighting had stopped in Europe, and at a time when the B.A.U.
was being disbanded, the report which was submitted to me, while it had
been printed, was never circulated. Its conclusions did, however, provide
an answer to that part of the dispute about the bombing of communications which concerned 'bridge interdiction', as opposed to the destruction
of railway centres. After a lapse of so many years they make interesting
reading. Here is what one reads in the summary:

'By 19 August, 1944, the Falaise "pocket" was closing on the
remnants of 19 German divisions, and 11 other divisions were in
retreat from the battle area to the Seine. These 30 divisions originally
comprised about 270,000 men. A further 50,000 army troops are
believed to have been present in the area between the front line and
the Seine, making a grand total of approximately 320,000.

'These German forces possessed about 28,000 motor vehicles, 5,400
motor cycles and 800 tanks, and may have impressed about 10,000 other
vehicles during the retreat. Thus, between 40,000 and 45,000 motor
vehicles, including motor cycles, were initially involved in the battles.

'It appears that while the enemy in all lost about one third of his
motor vehicles, other than tanks, about 90 percent of those that
reached the Seine succeeded in crossing. The corresponding figures
for tanks are 80 percent and 70 percent. Probably at least 95 percent of
the men reaching the Seine also crossed. Thus, while the presence of
the Seine no doubt contributed to losses in material, by helping to
cause congestion on the roads to its west, once reached it was not a
serious obstacle, in spite of the fact that almost all its permanent
bridges were out of commission.'[30]

As at El Alamein, the Germans retreated successfully in spite of being harried by air attacks, and in spite of the fact that they themselves were without effective air cover. It is obvious that they were extremely disciplined and highly ingenious in their retreat. But equally, the results of the Seine study provided ample justification, were any needed, for Tedder's confidence in supporting, and then urging, a strategical as opposed to a tactical answer to the question of dislocating German movement.

In his autobiography[31] and elsewhere Monty has insisted that, as ground force commander, his plan for the Normandy battle had always been to draw the main enemy strength to oppose the 2nd British Army on his left (eastern) flank, thus making it easier for the American 1st Army under Bradley to break through on the west. If this was *always* the 'master plan', it is not difficult to see why there was confusion. It was certainly not what was believed by Eisenhower and Tedder. On 14 April, Monty had in fact written to the Commanders of the 1st U.S. Army and the 2nd British Army who were to lead the invasion force telling them that 'the best way to interfere with the enemy concentrations and counter-measures will be to push forward fairly powerful armoured force thrusts on the afternoon of D-Day'. 'To wait till D plus 1 would be to lose the opportunity, and also to lose the initiative . . . speed and boldness are then required, and the armoured thrusts must force their way inland. The result of such tactics will be the establishment of firm bases well in advance of our own main bodies.'[32] Later, however, Monty was to write that the 'false conception [that it was his intention to break out on the eastern flank towards the Seine] existed only at Supreme Headquarters', and that it was fostered almost as a conspiracy by General Morgan—C.O.S.S.A.C.—aided and abetted by 'the airmen', who 'wanted the airfields on the eastern flank beyond Caen'.[33]

In fact, the 'false conception' was held to be 'the plan', not only at Supreme Headquarters, but also in A.E.A.F., where it had been expected that Monty would be through Caen and on to Falaise on the day of the landings. I do not recall any piece of paper which set out what Monty later declared to be his basic strategy, the essentials of which seem so obvious and simple that it seems incredible that they could have been misunderstood either by Eisenhower or Tedder, and by a host of lesser mortals. It was because of the belief that Monty had failed to do what he intended, i.e. to get beyond Caen straightaway, that I was encouraged by Leigh-Mallory—and, at the start, contrary to what Tedder believed should be done—to devise a plan for the heavy bombers to be used as they actually were in the end. Moreover, I can hardly imagine that Monty would have welcomed the proposal for a combined offensive to take Caen, put to him by Leigh-Mallory only eight days after the landings, if at the time it was not his hope that he could break through on his left flank. He admits that after the deferred operation of 7 July, he was 'too exultant' when he met the Press,[34] and so had given the false impression that Caen had been captured, and that it had been his intention to break through. But whatever Monty might have come to believe in retrospect, whether it had always been his firm, even if secret, intention to hold his left flank as the 'hinge' round which the Americans on the right swung southwards towards Paris and then to the east, there can be no question but that he meant the 'hinge' to be south, and not north, of Caen.

My own view is that Monty wisely changed the 'original plan' when it transpired that it could not be carried out 'without suffering unjustified casualties'. In fact, he admits as much when he writes that:

'It had been my original intention to secure the high ground between Caen and Falaise as early as possible, as being a suitable area for the construction of airfields; but this was not vital, and when I found it could not be done in accordance with the original plan without suffering unjustified casualties, I did not proceed with that venture. This was not popular with the Air Command.'[35]

The trouble was that Monty did not make his change of plan clear to anyone except, apparently, Bradley, who, nonetheless, notes that Monty had taken '33 days to capture the city he had once hoped to grab on D day'. Bradley also writes that Eisenhower had agreed Monty's new plan,[36] but I have failed to find anything written anywhere to show that this was so, nor can I believe that, if Eisenhower had agreed, he would not have told Tedder and got him to fall in line. Tedder may not have liked Monty, but he was too wise and good a man deliberately to misrepresent Monty's intentions, and by so doing not only endanger the lives of thousands, but put in jeopardy the whole war.

No-one will ever know how to apportion what blame there is for all the misunderstandings about this matter. Part must certainly lie with Monty because of the way he isolated himself both from Eisenhower and Tedder, and indeed from many with whom one would have expected a Commander-in-Chief to keep in close touch. But Monty was not a usual general. As Bradley describes him,

'Whereas I preferred to live, work, and eat in the field with my staff, Monty sought the solitude of a lonely camp, removed and isolated from his main 21st Group CP. There he lived with his personal staff: one American and two British aides, a Canadian P.A.—or personal assistant, a British M.A.—or military assistant. A signal detachment and a security guard equipped with black American jeeps rounded out the tiny caravan camp.'[37]

Monty was disdainful of authority, and did not disguise the contempt he felt for some people with whom he had to work—for example, General Morgan. Many learnt, and particularly Eisenhower, that he was intolerant of opinion which opposed his own. He was outspoken, brash and wounding in comment, almost to the point where the American Government and Eisenhower at least once seemed insistent that he should be removed. It was all in the character of the man. As Kingston puts it, in the 'first few critical weeks of Normandy he had become something of a dictator, something of a mystic; it was difficult to track him down and to get an audience with him. Save for the privileged few, none of his own staff or commanders had much opportunity of seeing him except when he was visiting his troops. . . . It is said that even the Supreme Commander had difficulty in contacting Montgomery . . .'.[38]

Monty usually sent de Guingand to discuss matters with the Supreme Commander, and if a difference of opinion could not be cleared up, it was Eisenhower who went to see Montgomery—not the other way round. Monty knew who was Mahomed and who the mountain.

Although I came across and had dealings with many of the leading Allied commanders of the war, it would never have occurred to me at that time to try to meet Monty. When we did meet years later, in the early 1960s, after he had left his post as Deputy to the Supreme Commander of N.A.T.O., I realised at first hand, and for the first time, why he could write in the Foreword to his *Memoirs*: 'Throughout my life and conduct my criterion has been not the approval of others nor of the world; it has been my inward convictions, my duty and my conscience'.[39]

Monty had style. I learnt to know, and to admire, sometimes to be amused by, the grandness of the man.

CHAPTER 15

PARIS IN A RAILWAY DESERT

Seldom have intelligence estimates been so wrong. They were wrong primarily because the method of statistical evaluation took no account of either cumulative or critical damage. A machine only 10 per cent worn out may still be incapable of functioning. Similarly, destruction of a single cotter pin, an infinitesimal portion of a machine by weight, nevertheless may precipitate the shattering of the whole mechanism. By D Day the Allied air forces, ably assisted by saboteurs of the French Resistance, had knocked cotter pins out of the railroads all over France, and the transportation system was on the point of total collapse. (Harrison, G. A., 1951, *Cross-Channel Attack*, Washington, D.C., U.S. Government Printing Office, p. 224.)

PARIS WAS liberated on 25 August 1944, and I joined Tedder there a few days later. My nagging to get the Air Ministry's authority for the setting-up of a group of operational researchers to work under my direction in France had succeeded, and a Bombing Analysis Unit was ready to go to France before the U.S. Army had broken through the St. Lô–Périers line, and well before the retreat of the German army across the Seine. Mr. Rowe, a production engineer who had joined Eisenhower's staff as technical adviser, did not give Tedder and me much help in setting up the Unit. He seemed to be totally inexperienced about military matters, and seemingly innocent about what was going on around him. It was not surprising that he did not understand what it was that we wanted to see done.

Dru Drury was appointed executive officer to the Unit, and we drove into Paris together, his first job being to find offices and living quarters for the staff we were assembling. My own first task was to make arrangements with the French Railway authorities for an immediate analysis of train movements in France over the preceding months.

As we made our way to the Hotel *Vendôme,* where Tedder had taken rooms and where he expected me to live, we passed the Avenue d'Iena, and I remembered that an old aunt of Joan's, whom I had never met, lived there. I asked Dru to stop the jeep, and dressed in my Group Captain's uniform—I had been told that the eccentric uniform I was allowed to wear in the Mediterranean would not be appropriate for France—I asked the concierge if Madame was in. I was told that she lived on the fourth floor, and that I would have to use the stairs, since there was no electricity to work the lifts. I followed a maid into a large drawing room where two old ladies, one in ordinary clothes, the other—Joan's aunt—in jade-green silk pyjamas, were drinking pink champagne. I was given a warm welcome when I introduced myself—'c'est vrai que vous êtes le mari de Joan?' I declined the glass of wine that was offered to me, saying that I had a friend down below who was waiting for me, and that I had only dropped in by chance. 'Bring him up', the old lady insisted, and accordingly I stepped out onto a small balcony and yelled to Dru to join me. His face was a study when he saw the company I was in, but we happily drank another bottle of pink champagne before going on our way. On the occasional Sunday in the months that followed I would lunch with Aunt May and marvel at her belief that she had suffered hardships while the Germans had been in charge. Her food and wine were always exquisite, and the company I met at her table was as remote from the real world as she was. 'They talk to me of the black-market where you can buy anything', she would say. 'Where is this black-market? Nobody tells me where it is. I'd starve if it weren't for the arrangement that I have with friends in Normandy who every week send me three kilos of butter, six chickens, and cheese and meat'.

For many years, I used to be amazed that some of those who had argued against the A.E.A.F. plan, both before and after D-Day, were still able to persuade themselves, even long after the war had ended, that the plan had utterly failed to achieve its declared purpose. At the time of the dispute I accepted that people in the planning and Intelligence circles with whom I had to deal were not used to judging the quality of different kinds of evidence in the way a practising and empirical scientist has to every day of his life. But there were other reasons for their attitude, on which I shall touch later, for I think I now have a slightly better understanding of some of the deep issues that lay behind the opposition we had met. Since, however, the Intelligence chiefs in the Air Ministry, in S.H.A.E.F., in 21 Army Group, and even in A.E.A.F. were united in their gloomy interpretations of what was happening, and because I was certain that their almost ritual and concerted opposition to the plan coloured their seemingly dispassionate assessments—a view which Tedder fully shared—I had decided, long before D-Day, to prepare my own appreciation of the secret Intelligence that was coming in about the effects of the attacks on the railway system.

When Eisenhower, at Portal's meeting on 25 March, had insisted that the A.E.A.F. plan had to be given top priority, he had also said that what mattered to him was the situation as it would develop in the first thirty days. I therefore embarked on my own analysis of the evidence, set against the background of my personal experience of what a sustained bomber offensive against a railway system could achieve.

D plus 30 would have been 7 July. My study was finished on 25 July, at a time when we were still hemmed into our lodgement area, between the Cotentin Peninsula to the west and the river Dives to the east.

My raw material consisted, first, of the hard evidence of destruction provided by an analysis of the daily aerial photographs of bombed railway centres and bridges. Then there were the collated assessments provided by the Intelligence departments of the various Commands, starting with A.E.A.F. These were based on ULTRA intercepts of enemy messages, on agents' reports, and even on interpretations of enemy broadcasts. The most important source was obviously ULTRA, Winston's 'secret weapon' as we were told he called it. In those days, security about its very existence was so tight that even in our own headquarters only a limited number of people who had been specially cleared knew that this source existed, and what it provided. Since my main purpose was to determine the extent to which enemy movement was being dislocated, ULTRA was much more useful than agents' reports, which usually arrived a few days after the information was first passed on 'through channels'. I used to doubt whether it ever arrived in time for the Air to take effective action. ULTRA, too, usually came to its small list of recipients in the form of a general interpretation of one or a series of intercepted messages. Before Tedder, Leigh-Mallory or I saw the material, it had already passed through the interpretation sieve of the Intelligence community. The Intelligence run-down at the Commanders' morning meetings was always like some predigested meal. I did not add to my popularity when, backed by both Tedder and Leigh-Mallory, I demanded that all the relevant basic and undigested ULTRA material that came to Stanmore was to be passed to me. Air Commodore Claude Pelly, whom I had met briefly during the course of my short tour in the Western Desert, when he was Chief Intelligence Officer to the Desert Air Force, had been posted in the same capacity to Leigh-Mallory's Command. He did not like my request one little bit.

The outcome of my work was a fairly lengthy report which I drafted more in the form of a scientific monograph than the kind of Intelligence appreciation to which the military were accustomed. It began with the general proviso that we did not yet have enough information to draw more than a broad picture of the transport difficulties under which the enemy had been labouring, nor an indication of the particular factors that had contributed to whatever success had been achieved in fulfilling the purpose of the whole operation, which I explicitly stated to be that of crippling the railway system to 'as great an extent as the air effort available for the task' made possible. I also referred to the information that we were receiving about sabotage action carried out both by the French Resistance groups and by those of our own people who had been dropped behind the enemy lines. Here I had to point out that the returns from their very valiant efforts were significantly less important to us than those resulting from bombing. I analysed the air effort of the different Commands, both against railway centres and bridges, and then drew what conclusions were possible about the time taken to repair bridges and to reopen lines through bombed rail centres and junctions. This done, I turned to the central question of the effect the attacks had had on the build-up of German forces, and on their movement to the invasion area from other parts of France and Germany.

The picture may have had to be drawn in outline, but the indications were clear. Far from the Germans reinforcing at a rate which would exceed that at which we could ferry troops across the channel, the reverse had happened, and the reason was the near-total disorganisation and disruption of rail travel. For example, one S.S. Panzer Division was delayed for almost a week at its entraining station, partly because of the difficulty of assembling transport, and partly, it was assumed, because *Fortitude* was still holding, which meant that the Germans were still wondering whether we were also going to land in the Pas-de-Calais. Once this Division started to move, it had to do so in the most roundabout way, because 'incidents' had occurred on almost every route which it tried. The 9th and 10th S.S. Panzer Divisions from Poland, which had been posted to Normandy, were in large part forced to detrain as far east of our lodgement area as Nancy and Bar-le-Duc. The S.S. Panzer Grenadier Regiment 20, belonging to the 9th S.S., detrained even further east, near Mulhouse. The devastated state of the railways in the North and North-East was further illustrated by a report that part of another regiment had been routed from Belgium to Normandy via Alsace. The implication was not that it was physically impossible to move trains from the East, but that the capacity of the railways was so reduced and their state of disorganisation so grave that even the highest priority military traffic could not be handled properly.

I ended my report with a section which I called 'Lessons of Transportation Plan'. This began with a criticism of the quasi-economic approach to the problem which had been adopted by the opponents of the A.E.A.F. plan. Once again I resorted to the biological analogies which I had used in the arguments before D-Day, pointing out that the comparison 'might seem strange to such idealistic planners as are able to fit railways into conceptual and conjectural worlds which are divorced from the real world. The parallel is not likely to be remote to those who have had to do with, or who have studied social phenomena at first hand. Vast organisations, such as a railway system, which depend for their efficient running on the handling, by thousands of human beings, of almost innumerable component parts, in a well-knit time schedule are immensely susceptible to delay, disorganisation and dislocation if the normal set-up is disturbed. When it is seriously disturbed, as was the case with the French railway network, it is not surprising that the dislocation becomes such that it merits the term "paralysis". It is pertinent to point these facts out here, since similar pseudo-economic arguments about the effects of attacks on railway systems which, it should be remembered, were not accepted by railway men with operating experience who were consulted during the Planning phase of Overlord, might otherwise influence future plans—as well as distort the views of the young historian of tomorrow who attempts to retrace recent history.'

In conclusion, I once again urged that the offensive against communications should be carried into Germany, since its economic and industrial life, as well as the freedom of military movement, depended on the untrammelled use of a railway system.[1]

After all the work which it had entailed, I was very disappointed when Tedder decided not to give the Report, to which he refers in his autobiography,[2] a wide circulation. No doubt it was a wise decision. We still had enough troubles, and there was no point in adding unnecessary fuel to a fire which was still blazing vigorously. But equally, I thought that once in Paris, the hard evidence which could be provided by the French Railway authorities could not be regarded with suspicion by anyone. I felt it would have to be accepted, by both sides to the dispute, whatever it revealed. Little did I know.

Getting the necessary authority and help for what in the end was to prove an arduous and lengthy task, was no problem. The French authorities were only too willing to open their books, and all I had to do was recruit assistants, preferably French, to assemble the data and then to help in their analysis. In my first few days in liberated Paris I had rushed round to see how my old French friends had fared during the German occupation. The obvious person to whom to turn was Joliot-Curie, the man who had done some of the most basic work which had led to the splitting of the atom, and who some of us had hoped would leave France in 1940 with the party brought out by Lord Suffolk. Joliot, however, had decided to stay, partly at least in order to stiffen the morale of the French scientific community. He was almost certainly one of the most, if not the most, outstanding name in French science at the time, and was the hero of the younger generation of French savants.

It was natural that he should have taken charge of the Centre National de la Recherche Scientifique when Longchambon and Laugier escaped to England.

The offices of the C.N.R.S. were on the Quai Voltaire, all but overlooking the Pont d'Iena. It was a miserable, drizzling day when I walked into his office, and after we had exchanged a general greeting, and spoken about mutual friends—I in my elementary French, and he in his equally poor English—I told him that I urgently wanted him to suggest the names of a few young French scientists who could work with me on the French railway records. I explained that the information we sought could affect future operations, and that there was therefore no time to lose. He agreed to help, but before letting me leave, he drew me to a window and said bitterly, 'I was acceptable to you while the Germans were here, but now that the Americans and de Gaulle are here, I have suddenly become a dangerous communist plotting revolution. Look at the revolution!' pointing at the well-nigh empty bridge. I said that I would try to arrange for him to meet Eisenhower and Tedder. In spite of his great prestige, however, it was not many years after the war before the French authorities removed him from his post in the C.N.R.S., although not from his professorship at the Collège de France. This was no doubt due to the fact that he strongly opposed the direction that French nuclear policy was taking.

The following day I was again in his office. This time he had with him Boris Ephrussi, a geneticist and molecular biologist whom I already knew, and who had somehow or other managed to get back to Paris. Boris, who was Russian by birth, spoke perfect English so there was going to be no difficulty on that score in working with him. Within a few days the two had assembled a young team, some of them still wearing clothes stained by the explosives they had fashioned for the fighting which marked the days before the Allied troops had entered Paris. In the meantime, Dru had managed to get some members of the B.A.U. team to Paris and had arranged a temporary H.Q. for the Unit in St. Germain to the west of Paris, in the same building as the corresponding American unit, under a General Fickel, with which we worked closely until December 1944. The B.A.U. then moved into two hideous new apartment buildings in Butte Rouge, a few kilometres away. So far as I was concerned, what mattered was that Frank Yates was there. It did not take long before the team that I had assembled to sift the railway records was hard at work in the Gare du Nord.

From then until the end of the war, Paris was my main base. I had a sitting-room and bedroom in the *Vendôme*, where I would occasionally have meals with some of the others who had made the hotel their home. Among them were General Vanier, the Canadian representative to de Gaulle's new Government, and Charles Peake, the senior British political adviser to Supreme Headquarters, which in September moved to Versailles. Tedder and Toppy, who had her Malcolm Clubs to look after, had taken a house near Versailles, where he and Eisenhower had offices in the Petit Trianon. But they also kept a room at the *Vendôme*, for those nights which they wished to spend in Paris. I was often in Tedder's

office at Versailles, but my main base was the B.A.U. H.Q. where I had
my W.A.A.F. secretariat, and where I could keep in touch with the
progress of the work which I was organising.

My field staff built up rapidly, and in due course was responsible for
a variety of reports on many matters with which the air forces were
concerned. As the Germans retreated across the Seine, they had tried to
hold a few of the French channel ports, and made their final and main
stand in Calais, which was encircled first by two, and then by a single,
Canadian Brigade. The Commanding Officer of the investing forces
agreed to my having an Anglo-American team of six officers and men
with his troops. The Germans surrendered after six days of siege,[3] but
the B.A.U. party took several weeks to finish the work that I had set
them. What I had wanted was to check the belief, which still prevailed
in some quarters, that the success or otherwise of an operation could be
measured in terms of the fire power that was used. To this end, we made
a record of every shot which the German garrison fired, and of the
damage which it caused, and correlated this with the damage done by
our own fire. In the end, we were unable to draw any generalisations of
value from the exercise.

Sandy Thomson, who was in charge of the Calais team, had run into
trouble before I managed to get him from the Mediterranean. I had left
him in Sicily to put the finishing touches to various jobs which I had not
had the time to clear up myself. From there he had written to say that the
8th Army, to which he still belonged, had notified him that he was
regarded as being 'absent without leave'. His wife, who lived in Glasgow,
had also written to say that it had been months since she had received
any of his army pay. Sandy's view was that the only way the matter
could be cleared up would be for me to get Tedder to intercede with
Montgomery. This Tedder did, and the result was that Sandy was
gazetted as a substantive Major and awarded the M.B.E., while his wife
received all his back pay. Another member of my Calais team was Michael
Noble, on whose land I had tested the wounding power of high-velocity
bullets. Michael was now dressed as a squadron leader. At the beginning
of the war I had persuaded him to transfer to the Princes Risborough
Bomb Census team from the post that he had on the staff of the Regional
Commissioner for South-East England.*

I flew back to England as often as I could, not only to keep in touch
with the main A.E.A.F. H.Q., but also to get back to Oxford. I was
becoming less and less interested in the work of my Extra-Mural Unit.
The programme of work on which I had embarked had been relevant

---

* After the war Michael became a member, first of Harold Macmillan's and then of
Ted Heath's Cabinet. Today he hides under the name of Glenkinglas in the House of
Lords.

earlier on, but it now seemed remote from the real problems of the war. Le Gros Clark had also begun to regard the Unit as a nuisance, and as an obstacle to the plans he was laying for the Anatomy Department when the war came to an end. And Stanmore was also closing down. Kingston had been posted from A.E.A.F. as the Air member of a three-man party which was to visit India to consider the problems that would be involved in withdrawing British troops after the war. The Army member was Brigadier Enoch Powell, a name better known today than it was then. Dickie Mountbatten had arranged for Leigh-Mallory to be transferred to South-East Asia as Air Commander-in-Chief. I saw him a few times after this news became known, and had dinner alone with him and his wife shortly before he left for Ceylon. He was in a happy frame of mind, and particularly delighted at the prospect of no longer having to try to discharge the duties of a Commander-in-Chief in a hostile environment. He was like a schoolboy with the end of term in sight, and although I knew nothing about fly-fishing, he made me try the weight of a new rod which he was looking forward to using in Ceylon. He was very generous in his tributes to me, and I was sad to say goodbye. A day or two later I learnt that his aircraft had crashed in the Alps on its way to Ceylon.

When I was not working with Tedder or on the various enquiries on which I had set my B.A.U. teams, I discovered a new and very enticing Paris. First of all there were my old French scientific friends, such as Professor Courrier, who was still at the Collège de France, and who later became Secrétaire Perpétuel of the Académie des Sciences. The first night I dined at his house, it was obvious that he and his wife had gone to considerable trouble to find the wines and the ingredients of the dishes they laid before me. But the evening was a sad one. Both were in mourning for their only daughter who had been killed a few months earlier during an R.A.F. raid on the Renault factory. And there I was at their table in R.A.F. uniform. Some of the young Frenchmen who had been recruited for my team in the Gare du Nord were fascinating company, imbued with high hopes of a new world to come. My name was well-known to them because of my *La Vie Sexuelle et Sociale des Singes*. A stream of interesting people started to visit Paris, and I would often find myself being called upon by people I had known before, and by some who were new. There was George Orwell, of whom I knew only because of his book, *Down and Out in Paris and London* (*Nineteen Eighty-Four* was still to come). He was always immensely serious. There were Constant Lambert and Margot Fonteyn, who put on a show in the small Théâtre Marigny. I had arranged to pick them up after a performance one evening, and while I forget where we had supper, I do remember that it was only with great difficulty that I got them out of my small sitting-room at the *Vendôme* at about three in the morning, with Constant much the worse for drink. Gerald Barry, who was then editor of the now-defunct *News Chronicle*, was in Paris from time to time in connection with his work for our Ministry of Information. One day I picked him up for lunch on my way from the Institut Pasteur, where I had been given a large tome which had been published during the war by a friend of mine, Albert Raynaud. One of the chapters, entitled 'L'Hypothèse Zuckerman', critically discussed and upheld the views which I had put forward before the war about the inter-relationship of the tissues which react to the female oestrogenic hormone. Gerald was much amused, and for years afterwards, whenever we met, he would mutter the words, 'l'Hypothèse Zuckerman'. One day he gave a dinner party in what I took to be the basement of the *Vendôme*, which in those days did not have a proper dining room. It was bitterly cold, but the company included Paul Valéry, and the Duff Coopers, who had recently arrived in Paris to take over the British Embassy. Paul Valéry, whom up to then I had only known by name, seemed to be far more interested in hearing my views about the social behaviour of animals than he was in discovering what I thought of his poetry and philosophy. Ever since I have liked to quote that phrase of his: 'we move into the future backwards'—'Nous entrons dans l'avenir à reculons'.[4]

There were two occasions of which I have special memories. The first was a ceremony which took place in the winter of 1944 in the big amphitheatre of the Sorbonne, at which honour was paid to Paul Langevin, the doyen of French science, on his return to Paris from a concentration camp. I had been charged to deliver a public message from the Royal Society, expressing its pleasure at Langevin's safe return from the captivity which at his age should have meant certain death. The Council left it to me to compose the necessary words, which Boris Ephrussi then translated into French. He made me read through the text again and again so as to improve my accent for the occasion. The hall was full, and the proceedings solemn. Langevin looked magnificent sitting in the centre of the platform, flanked by other great figures of academic France. Duff Cooper was there in his official capacity as British Ambassador. And it was extremely cold. The moment came, and I stepped on to the platform to deliver my message, wearing an R.A.F. greatcoat over my shabby battle-dress. When I had finished, I was given the nearest thing to an ovation that I have ever received, and was embraced by Langevin. Even though the war was not yet won, and R.A.F. uniform notwithstanding, there was a great sentimental feeling that this ceremony marked the re-opening of at least part of the universe of science.

The second occasion that stands out in my memory is of a luncheon given in my honour by Laugier, who had now become a Minister in de Gaulle's first Government. He had decided to do this as a form of public recognition of the small part I had played in helping French scientists when they had escaped from France, and also for the efforts I had made to get his party released from house arrest when they had arrived in London in 1940. This luncheon was given in a club called Le Cercle Interallié, which occupied an old Rothschild mansion in the Faubourg St. Honoré. Not knowing beforehand how the occasion was going to develop, I had not prepared anything in advance, but in response to Laugier I somehow or other improvised an after-luncheon speech in my execrable French, to the theme that there was no chance of either France or the United Kingdom regenerating after the sacrifices of the war unless they combined forces in, for example, the formulation and then execution of common policies in fields such as energy. In so far as they had understood the point I was making, this testimony to Anglo-French solidarity was very well greeted by the company. I then forgot all that I had tried to say. Next morning I was awakened by a knock at my door in the *Vendôme*. Still in pyjamas, I opened it, and in came a young man whom I had not seen before but who apparently had been at the luncheon. When I asked why he had come, he told me that Laugier had sent him to discuss with me 'Le Projet Zuckerman'. So there I was, associated not only with an 'hypothèse' but also with a·'projet'. Jean Gottman, that young man, is now Professor of Geography at Oxford University, and has been a treasured friend from that day.

There was also the occasion, several months later, and after our troops had entered Germany, when Douglas Cooper, the art critic and friend of Picasso and Braque, turned up in the uniform of a Wing Commander, but eccentrically wearing brown suede shoes. While drinking together on the terrace of a restaurant, he explained that he was hot on the trail of two senior Air Force officers whom he suspected were guilty of looting works of art. I tried to persuade him that it was no moment for a scandal which might implicate highly-placed officers, and which would be bound to affect discipline throughout the R.A.F. But nothing I said could dull the glint in Cooper's eye as he explained how useful a lesson it would be to all officers not to go in for high-grade looting. The moment we parted, I got my driver to take me to Tedder to whom I explained the matter. He in turn took action so that when Cooper caught up with his quarty, the loot, if there ever had been any, had been returned.

There was another contact with the art world, but of a totally different kind. Hearing that I was in Paris, Barbara Hepworth and Ben Nicholson wrote to me through Joan, to say that Gabo, a sculptor whom we knew well, and who was living in St. Ives in the artists' colony of which Barbara and Ben were part, had a brother called Pevsner who had survived the German occupation of Paris without falling into the hands of the Gestapo. I was given an address, and found Pevsner recovering from

pneumonia in the two rooms he and his wife shared in a shabby block of
flats on the outskirts of Paris. They were well-nigh starving, and it was
not difficult to provide them with most of what they needed. I became
much impressed by his work, and enjoyed hearing him talk about the
directions that abstract art was taking. Sometimes I would take a friend
along to see his sculpture. It was from him that I learnt that, depending
on their orientation, the most beautiful curved surfaces could be derived
from straight lines. I ran into Sartre and Camus, neither of whom, I
confess, I understood, and into Louise Vilmorin, whom I did. It was
British Intelligence which asked me whether I knew Arthur Koestler
and if so whether I would call on Madame Koestler who was in need of
help. She had gone underground during the war, after Koestler had
escaped to Spain, and she, too, had succeeded in evading the German
secret police. There was Martha Gellhorn, now a war correspondent,
who would flit through Paris. And there was even her former husband,
Ernest Hemingway, staying at the Ritz with Mary Welsh, his wife-to-be.

I kept my promise to Joliot, and took him to lunch with Tedder. The
understanding was that Eisenhower would also be there, but at the last
moment he was called away. It was curious hearing Joliot very quietly
explaining to Tedder, Bedell Smith (Eisenhower's Chief of Staff), Robb,
and a number of other generals, how inefficient they were, given that
killing was the measure of military success. His argument was that almost
any cemetery in France could show that simple epidemics carried off more
people than war had ever done. At that time, however, we did not know
what the Germans had managed to achieve in the concentration camps.
What was extraordinary about the luncheon was that no-one round the
table knew as much as Joliot did about the atom bomb. One of the
reasons why the British and Americans had wanted him to leave France
when Paris fell in 1940 was simply that locked in his brain at the time
were more potential military secrets than were at the command of any
other scientist on the Continent.

The Bombing Analysis Unit had its own mess, but it was only rarely
that I went there. There always seemed to be a somewhat noisy party in
progress in the evenings, and I took the view that I would be better
assured, in command circles, of what today is called 'credibility' the less
I had to do with what some described as 'the B.A.U. Nightclub'. In so
far as I had any regular social base when I was not at work in the evenings, it was with Tedder, sometimes with Spaatz, and occasionally with
the Duff Coopers at the Embassy.

Until the end of September, my main attention was focused on the
work that was being done at the Gare du Nord and then at the Gare de
l'Est. Tedder had obviously not felt confident that my earlier analysis
of the data which I had collated from Intelligence sources would carry

conviction with the air barons or their staffs. I therefore kept him fully informed about what was emerging from the new analyses, knowing that he would return to the attack when he believed that he had enough ammunition. As his autobiography makes plain, he was under great stress at the time, and sometimes I thought that he was literally becoming greyer. He writes that he was increasingly concerned because of the bad relations which were developing in several sectors of Eisenhower's Command. But there was more to it than just the quarrels between Generals Bradley and Patton, and Montgomery. The directives concerning the control of the air forces that Eisenhower had been given by the Combined Chiefs of Staff had not been cancelled, but his efforts to have them implemented were constantly being challenged. The Supreme Commander's 'command' of the U.S.S.T.A.F. and of R.A.F. Bomber Command had, in fact, become more of a pretence than a reality. In spite of Eisenhower's support, Tedder simply did not know how far to press the strategic air forces in pursuing the policy of disrupting the communications network of Germany. In my frequent visits to the American Air headquarters, various officers whom I knew seemed to take a malicious pleasure in making me aware that while transportation targets might be 'number one priority' for Eisenhower, they were certainly not that for them. My reception from those of Tooey's staff who had not been with him in the Mediterranean, as from members of the Intelligence organisations, continued to be cool, if not openly hostile.

One day I told Tedder that I was sure that I had exhausted my usefulness, and that my presence had become more of an embarrassment to him than a help. It was not, I told him, Spaatz about whom I was worried, but the staff officers who directed the daily operations of his strategic air forces. As long as I was around, they knew that I would go on urging the Supreme Command to continue with the railway offensive, and so long as I did so, they would oppose. When I got to the point and suggested that our ways should part, Tedder rose to his feet and said, 'Zuck, I've got to stick this out. *You* are going to as long as I have to'. I apologised, and shortly afterwards left his office.

At that time Tooey had begun to follow the erstwhile habit of some of the Mediterranean commanders, and had equipped himself with a caravan, as Tedder did later when Supreme Headquarters moved to Reims. I got my driver to take me straight from the Petit Trianon to Tooey's caravan. Whatever my differences with his staff, my relations with him had remained as cordial as ever. He continued to invite me to meals and expected me to drop in on him in the way I always had. On this occasion he was not alone, but we were soon left to ourselves. Over a drink I told him about the exchanges I had just had with Tedder. Tooey's comment was that he was surprised that I had become worried by the hostility I was experiencing. He thought I was tougher than that. Then with a serious look he surprised me by saying that he was certain that history would show that the right decision had been made when the railway communications network had been declared the main priority for the air forces before *Overlord*, and that it was right that it should remain at the top of the target list now. When I asked him how he reconciled this view with the current programme of operations of the U.S. heavy bombers, he said that there was enough effort available to deal with railways as well as with oil installations. But his air forces had to learn to penetrate deep into German territory, and for this oil was the best target. I left him with the feeling that I had made more fuss than was necessary.

At the Quebec meeting in September, Churchill and Roosevelt had agreed that the command of the strategic air forces, which had been vested in Eisenhower from 14 April, should revert to the Joint Chiefs.[5] This decision was the inevitable result of the unceasing pressure which Spaatz and Harris were bringing to bear in order to regain their independence as Commanders-in-Chief, both of them being still convinced that they could bring about Germany's surrender on their own. To some extent, it was also a consequence of the fact that once Eisenhower and Tedder had made their headquarters on the Continent, they were cut off from the Air Staffs on whom they would have to depend in managing the strategic air forces. In effect, the change of control meant that Portal became responsible for R.A.F. Bomber Command, and Arnold, his opposite number in the United States, for the U.S. Strategic Air Forces, their authority being delegated to Portal's deputy, Bottomley, on the one hand, and to Spaatz on the other. Tedder had consulted with Bottomley before the decision was taken in Quebec, and had agreed that once control passed, the synthetic oil plants should become first priority targets, with the German transportation system and tank and military vehicle production plants and ordnance depots equal in second priority.[6]

It was not long after this that the situation changed dramatically. One morning I received a telephone call from Major Derek Ezra.* He was then a member of G-2 S.H.A.E.F., that is to say, of the team of Intelligence officers who had consistently denigrated the results of the bomber offensive against the railways, and some of whom had been heard to say that the offensive had been a diversion which had prolonged the war. Ezra had found some German documents which he thought might interest me. His unit was quartered in the Ecuries of the main Palace at Versailles, and here he handed me what appeared to be two rolls of wallpaper which, when spread out, proved to be graph-paper charts showing the daily flow of all rail traffic in the German-controlled railway region

* Today, Sir Derek Ezra, Head of the National Coal Board.

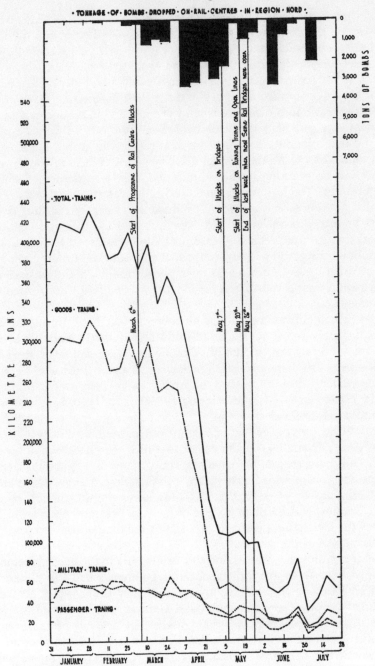

· TONNAGE · OF · BOMBS · DROPPED · ON · RAIL · CENTRES · IN · REGION · NORD ·

*Decline in railway movement, in the region of France affecting the
Normandy area, as a result of bombing in the first half of 1944
(Taken from B.A.U. Report No. 8.)*
D-Day was 6 June

which had Brussels as its centre (H.V.D. Brussels). The records started in 1940, on the day that the Germans had occupied France and the Low Countries, and ended in the last week of May 1944. One glance showed that the enemy had themselves provided us with the evidence which was going to carry conviction, given that anything could. Full of excitement, I got my driver to take me quickly to the Petit Trianon.

Tedder was not in his office when I arrived, and in his account of the incident says that he was with Eisenhower. Without waiting, I spread out the two rolls on the floor of his ante-room with Robb, Leslie Scarman, and Colonel Milne, Tedder's military aide, watching me closely. There was no question in their minds about the significance of what I had brought. Tedder then arrived, and as he describes in his autobiography, got down on his knees to examine the charts.[7] According to his story, he turned to me and asked, 'Zuck, is your German good enough to serve as an interpreter?' I remember the occasion all too well. The captions on the graph were in German, and what in fact I thought he had meant when he said, 'Is your German good enough', was that since the information was so valuable, someone might think that I had forged the documents.

The French railway records had already revealed that a precipitous fall in traffic had begun about the middle of March that year, and that by the beginning of July the volume of all traffic in France had fallen to about 20 per cent of its January level. The fall began about three weeks before corresponding declines started occurring in military traffic originating in France, and in traffic entering France from abroad. It was well advanced before the destruction of the Seine bridges in the last week of May. Railway movement had of course been affected differently in different regions, depending on the extent to which they had been attacked. In the northern region, for example, the volume of originating traffic, expressed in wagon loadings, started to fall seriously about the middle of March, and by 26 May, that is to say *before* the destruction of the Seine bridges, had fallen to 20 per cent of its previous peak level. By D-Day the level was 13 per cent. It was this region that had received the heaviest share of the attacks.

It was not only the volume of traffic originating in the bombed regions that had been so dramatically reduced. The attacks had had almost as great an effect on the military and non-military traffic which was circulating between France, Belgium and Germany, and between the five parts of the French railway system itself. The analysis of the French records, which we published as a B.A.U. paper early in November under the general title 'The Effects of the Overlord Air Plan to Disrupt Enemy Rail Communications',[8] made it perfectly plain that the disorganisation caused by the attacks had made it impossible for the railways of any region to accept and deal with much of even the highest priority traffic from outside. In general, all the main communications between French cities, and between French industries, were crippled. The transport of coal had dwindled for want of locomotives, wagons, marshalling facilities and lines. Two or three months of bombing had in fact paralysed the economic life of France.

While the bomber offensive did not affect German troop movements as dramatically as it did French economic and German non-military traffic, highly significant declines had nonetheless occurred before D-Day in the overall volume of military traffic, including building materials for the north coast anti-invasion defences and for German V-weapon installations between Amiens and the Pas-de-Calais. The dislocation of the railway system had thus become indirectly responsible for reducing the scale of the flying-bomb attacks, since the functioning of the mobile ramps depended on an uninterrupted daily supply of goods and materials. Slowly and surely almost all military trains other than those concerned in the movement of troops and their supplies had been squeezed out. During the first fortnight after the landings on the Normandy coast, even troop movements had dwindled to a trickle in the North and West Regions.

By the time Ezra gave me the German charts, the analysis of the French railway records had left no doubt about the conclusions to which they pointed. In effect, the German graphs thus told us nothing of a general nature that we did not know before. Their value lay in the fact that they constituted evidence which could not be regarded as having been coloured by any preconceived ideas. But, in addition, they told us something else, and a very important something. The records dealt with Belgium and parts of the North-East and East of France. This Region was responsible for moving the iron ore mined in Eastern France and Luxembourg to the steel mills of the Saar, and upon them also depended the smooth running of industry in the area, which at the time was receiving its coal from the Ruhr and working mostly in the German interest. What the records showed was that from the start of the attacks on the railway network of the region, the volume of traffic began to decline, and that by the end of May the number of trains moving daily had fallen to about a third of their normal level. All coke, coal and oil traffic, general goods trains and passenger trains, had declined catastrophically, with the overall result that industry in the region had more or less come to a standstill before the Normandy landings. The cessation of the Minette-ore traffic was the first major shock suffered during the war by the German steel industry, representing as it did a 20 per cent drop in its normal level of supply.

The time relations of the attacks both in France and Belgium made it plain, too, that the railway paralysis was in the main due to the destruction of the centres which regulated traffic. What was particularly important was the destruction of the depots in which locomotives were housed, serviced and repaired. Both the French and German records testified to the extreme and immediate sensitivity of traffic flow to such attacks. In this respect, the complex rail network of France and Belgium had behaved in precisely the same way as had the much simpler railway system of Sicily and Southern Italy.

On 26 October, within a few days of my showing him the German charts, Tedder convened a meeting at Versailles of all the bomber chiefs and their aides. The meeting was a large one, but once again I was not amongst those around the table. Tedder had good reason to regard me as a red rag to a bull, and he therefore asked me to stand by, ready to be called in with the German charts and the digest of the French railway records. Spaatz was there, Bottomley was there, so were Bufton and a number of the other 'experts' who had advised against the A.E.A.F. plan. Tedder had a fine time telling them, as he says, 'not for the first time, that they had been wrong about the communications offensive'.[9] But according to what I was told afterwards, he probably went too far in rubbing Bufton's nose in the facts. The outcome of the meeting[10] was an agreement to have the prevailing directives of the Combined Chiefs of Staff amended, in so far as was necessary, with oil installations still accorded first priority, but with transportation, particularly rail centres, on its own as second. I was not called in to show the German charts or to discuss the results of the analysis of the French railway records. But at the end of the meeting Bottomley and one or two others asked to see my exhibits. As he left the room, Tooey spotted that I was wearing the uniform and stripes of a group captain, and with a kind of wink, said: 'Hi, what's wrong, Zuck? Have they run out of G.I. uniforms?'

As the weeks passed I did not disguise my disappointment at the upshot of the meeting. In May, before the Normandy landings, Tedder had agreed both with Spaatz and Harris that German synthetic oil plants should be bombed as targets which were second priority to railway centres.[11] In general this meant that it was left to Harris on one hand, and Spaatz on the other, to decide when circumstances dictated one target as opposed to another. Harris was far less enthusiastic about the oil targets than was Spaatz. In his mind they fell into the category of what he disdainfully described as 'panacea targets'. He was contemptuously outspoken about the advice given by so-called 'economic experts' who pretended to know how German industry could be brought to a halt by bombing its critical elements, advice he was not averse to describing as 'mendacious'. He did not believe, for example, that if ball-bearing plants were successfully attacked Germany would be incapable of continuing the war. He was absolutely convinced that the safer policy was to bring German industry to a halt through the general destruction of her industrial cities. And he was certainly right in pointing out that the official views about the value of bombing Germany's synthetic oil plants had varied considerably.[12]

On the other hand, I remained convinced that the faster and further the attacks on the railway network were pressed into Germany, the sooner she would collapse totally. I knew that Tedder shared this view, and that the agreement which he had now reached with Bottomley and Portal, and no doubt with Spaatz as well, was the best he could expect to achieve, given the facts of the situation and the personalities with whom he was dealing. And at the time it did not seem strange to me, although it does now, that neither Bufton nor his opposite numbers in Bomber Command and in the American forces ever wanted to examine the German or French records. So far as they were concerned, the hard evidence which now lay even more strongly behind our plan could not match the *a priori* assumptions and wishful thinking that lay behind their alternative strategies. It is also astonishing that in none of the many published accounts of the controversy other than Tedder's or my own,[13,14] is there any reference to the German charts or the French records. The British official History does not mention them.

To my way of thinking, the meeting which he called on 26 October, was only a pyrrhic victory for Tedder. Early that month a committee called the Combined Strategic Targets Committee had been set up to coordinate the bombing programme of the British and American strategic air forces. Bufton and his opposite number in the American Air Forces, Colonel Maxwell, were the joint Chairmen. It was this Committee which advised Bottomley and Spaatz about the targets the heavy bombers should take on. As Tedder writes in his autobiography, it was no secret that most members of this Committee, and especially the Chairmen, not only favoured oil as a prime target, but were also opposed to attacking the railway network. At a meeting held on 24 October, they were still contending that 'the enemy's rail facilities were so vastly in excess of his military requirements that no appreciable effect could possibly be achieved within the envisaged time period, the ninety days in which, so it was hoped, the war would be won.'[15] Tedder had vainly hoped that their views would be changed at the meeting which he convened two days later, when he had in his hands cast-iron evidence to prove that they were talking nonsense. But he was wrong. Whatever was agreed at the meeting, and whatever was put down on paper, under the guidance of the Combined Strategic Targets Committee the two heavy bomber forces continued to pay only lip-service to the directive to attack communication targets. The Americans preferred the more difficult and

hazardous deeper penetration that was needed to attack oil plants, while
Harris went on with his area bombing of German cities, of which he
claimed that forty-five of the leading ones had by now been 'virtually
destroyed'.[16]

In an earlier chapter I referred to the first memorandum which Bomber
Harris levelled against the plan that A.E.A.F. was preparing,[17] and in
which he argued that the only way his command could contribute to the
success of the projected invasion was by having nothing to do with it.
I have also described how we set out in a column the various propositions
which were embodied in his broadside, and how we wrote against each
the counter-arguments, and also how the Air Ministry then added a
third column of its own comment.[18] I said that I had always understood
that the intention was that a fourth column would be added by the Air
Ministry as soon as *Overlord* had been launched. I had imagined that this
had not been done, for certainly no additional observations by the Air
Ministry ever came to A.E.A.F. before it was disbanded, and to the best
of my knowledge, none to S.H.A.E.F. I was therefore very surprised
when the missing column came to light as a historical document in the
Public Record Office when I was checking some of my references. The
document is dated 28 June 1944—three weeks after D-Day—and
what it does is merely reinforce the criticisms we made when Harris's
memorandum was forwarded to A.E.A.F. The final paragraph of the
paper reads:

> 'Generally, the conclusions of the Bomber Command memorandum
> have proved entirely incorrect. The support which Bomber Command
> has, in fact, been capable of affording has played an outstanding part in
> the successful establishment of the bridgehead. The statement that "the
> only effective support Bomber Command could give to operation
> OVERLORD was the intensification of attacks against industrial targets
> in Germany" has proved to be very far indeed from the truth.'*[19]

Apart from discovering that there had after all been a fourth column,
I can hardly say that I found any cause for surprise in its content, for
which, no doubt, some conscientious young officers in the Air Ministry,
whose task it was to monitor Bomber Command's activities, were
responsible. But, in the light of what had gone before, and what was
still to come, I was amused to see that the memorandum had been
circulated to only a very few people under a cover note signed by Air
Commodore Bufton, the focal point of the opposition which Leigh-
Mallory and Tedder had to face. It is a pity that the latter did not have
it in his hands at the gathering at which he revealed the existence of the
German charts.

* See Appendix 4 for the full text of all four columns.

At the time of this meeting, we were less than two months from the German counter-attack in the Ardennes. And, as the evidence was to show, Germany was already tottering on the verge of a transportation collapse. Only a slight push, even a modest intensification of bomber attacks on rail centres, might have prevented her build-up for the Ardennes offensive. But this was not to be.

CHAPTER 16

THE ARDENNES AND BEYOND

FROM THE field of view open to me, all seemed quiet, very quiet, at the beginning of December 1944. Tedder had made his point, and there was nothing further he could do in urging that the heavy bomber forces should press on with the job of crippling the German railway network. Rail and oil were complementary strategic objectives, in the sense that both the German economy and military machine depended on them for their motive power. We simply had to shut our eyes to the fact that the Combined Strategic Targets Committee as well as the Staffs of the heavy bomber commands just did not like railway targets.

With the Combined Chiefs of Staff urging Eisenhower to bring the war in Europe to a close by the end of the year, the British and American armies were ready to carry on with their advance to the Rhine. But Montgomery was already arguing with Eisenhower and Bradley about which of the Allied armies was going to make the most forceful thrust.

The forward part of the American line was then the Eschweiler salient, with its apex at the small town of that name. Eschweiler lies a few kilometres east of Aachen, which I had visited after its capture by the Americans on 21 October. Talk at Versailles was that it was possibly here that we could make our break-out. The troops holding the salient were the American 1st Army, and the zone was covered by the 19th Tactical Air Command under Pete Quesada. Because I knew Pete well, Tedder therefore thought that it would be a good idea if I joined a party of air chiefs whom Pete had invited to his H.Q. about the middle of December to discuss the possibilities of a combined operation in which the heavy bombers would help end the stalemate on the ground. I could not have been better pleased, and arranged to stay with Pete at his house in Spa, a few kilometres from his H.Q. at Verviers. Spa itself was the H.Q. town for the U.S. 1st Army under General Hodges. As it happened, I timed my visit to coincide almost to the hour with the opening of von Rundstedt's counter-thrust in the Ardennes. As I knew that Tedder would want a full report of what I saw, and as I needed a note of action to be followed up, I kept a daily record of events as I saw them during the ensuing week.

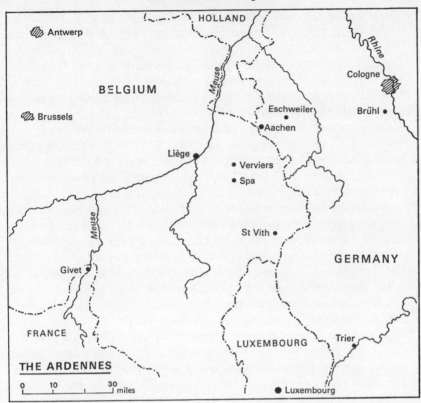

Antwerp

HOLLAND

BELGIUM

Brussels

Meuse

Rhine

Cologne

Eschweiler

Brühl

Aachen

Liège

Verviers

Spa

Meuse

St Vith

GERMANY

Givet

FRANCE

LUXEMBOURG

Trier

THE ARDENNES

0   10   30 miles

Luxembourg

Saturday, December 16, 1944

I left Paris at 8.30 a.m. for Spa, via Reims, Rethel, Sedan, and
Marche. Lunched at a small village to the west of Sedan in the
westerly part of the Ardennes. The inn-keeper had seen only two other
members of the British forces before, and told me that he had very
rarely seen Germans during the period of their occupation. He said
the village was too small to be any cause for worry. I had an excellent
meal and was invited to stay behind to join in a wild goat hunt. While
lunching, I got an impression of the position of our line from a French
newspaper. I decided to make for Spa either by the Marche–Hotton
road or by way of Malmédy. Sergeant Thomson, my driver, decided
on the Marche road.

The roads through the Ardennes were practically free of traffic, and
we rarely saw more than a few M.P.s in the villages through which we
passed. Arrived at Spa at 4.30 p.m. A telephone call to General
Quesada's Personal Assistant in Verviers directed me to his house.
About an hour after my arrival, Pete turned up, together with a party

consisting of General Fred Anderson, General Orvil A. Anderson, of the 8th Air Force, General Vandenberg (Van), now C-in-C of the 9th Air Force, Colonel Hughes, Chief Intelligence Officer of the US Strategic Air Forces, Air Commodore Dickens of Bomber Command, and two other US colonels whose names I did not get. They arrived with the news that the Germans were being a little more adventurous than usual, and that on the previous day they had revealed a new 'secret weapon' in the shape of a small calibre shell whose range was estimated to be not less than 30 miles. A few casualties had been caused, both in Verviers and Spa. From the moment I got there, V.1s were flying over Spa, presumably from mobile ramps to our east, with Antwerp as their target.

A meeting had been arranged to take place next day with the Army, to agree a 'lay-on' for our own push through the Aachen (Eschweiler) salient. While we were having cocktails, there was a certain amount of talk about the proposed operation. Dinner was sumptuous, with the chef coming in to prepare the final course, crêpes suzettes, at the table. We drank an excellent claret—Cantenac Brown 1938. At dinner and later, the discussion focused on the desirability of throwing all air forces into Germany in small parties, even singly, rather than in the tight and big formations now in practice. Fred Anderson was all for doing this, and so was Van. Orvil Anderson was strongly opposed and argued against almost everyone else except Dickens, who sided with him. One bone of contention was the question of losses due to enemy fighters and flak. Another issue was accuracy, which unfortunately I could not get Orvil Anderson to discuss. Upon it depended all estimates of the amount of effort required to deal with a vast number of targets, as opposed to a major effort against a smaller number. The discussion was particularly interesting because of Fred Anderson's championship of the new tactics. I recall a discussion after dinner at Spaatz's house before *Overlord* when Tooey tried to force this issue on Anderson and his other staff officers, but against a wall of almost inarticulate resistance. At that time Fred was totally opposed to such tactics, or to operating the 8th Air Force under the conditions which they later accepted.

During the whole of our after-dinner discussion there was no reference to the fact that the Germans were nibbling at our lines. During the night there appeared to be slightly greater flying bomb activity, but there were no other noises of note.

Sunday morning, December 17

The staircase from the first floor led into a hall/dining room. I was last down to breakfast to find the others sitting sombrely round the table. As I was about to step into the room, Pete asked: 'Zuck, who do you think are our nearest front line troops?' 'I suppose two damn good US armoured divisions', I replied. 'No, we are', was the answer. At least two of his guests had loaded revolvers on the table beside them. It appeared that a detachment of German paratroopers had dropped close to Spa during the night and that the whole of the front was in motion, with the Germans advancing in force. There was no further talk either about the general problem of bombing tactics or of the immediate problem of planning which had brought us all together. After breakfast Pete and the other Generals went off to a meeting with Hodges of the 1st, and Simpson of the 9th US Army, while I went on to Verviers with Pete's P.A. to proceed with the arrangements I had made the day before to visit Aachen and points east of it. When I got to Verviers, a Lt. Col. on Pete's staff was told to accompany me. Before setting out we spent some time in the Operations Room and what was called 'the sweep-stake room', gathering what news we could of the fluid land situation, and of the air battle which was in progress. It seemed that the most northerly point of activity was just south of Spa, and that the situation on the roads to Malmédy, and at points east, west and south of it, was very obscure. Flying bombs were coming over fast, the V.1s looking very beautiful as they roared by to some distant target. Owing to trouble with my car, we did not set out for Aachen until lunchtime. Watered petrol had been put into the tank at an army gas station (I was told there was a lot of this going on at the time), and poor Thomson had to siphon it out by mouth with a rubber tube he carried for the purpose. The road through Eupen was relatively free of traffic, and we made good time. We lingered in Aachen looking at the devastation, which was greater in extent than anything I had ever seen. Very few of our troops seemed to be in the town itself, and I was struck by the relatively large numbers of German civilians and of men of military age. In spite of the utter squalor in which they must have been living, none appeared to be ill-dressed, and every German had obviously made an effort to turn himself out well. I had a feeling that both the civilians in Aachen and those one saw outside the town, and probably even people on the Belgian side of the frontier, had remarkably good opportunities for watching our movements. I hoped they had fewer for passing information back to the Germans.

After an hour we took what we thought was the Eschweiler road, and stopped at a control point about four miles from the town to enquire our way. We were told that we were on the wrong road, and that we were in a small town north of Aachen instead of due east. A guide took us through this little town, which was severely battered—

mainly by shell fire—and put us on a cross-roads about two miles along, on which we passed no Allied vehicles. We ended up on the main Aachen–Eschweiler autobahn, and then moved into Eschweiler, which was full of troops. The small town had been very badly damaged, again mainly by shell fire. After looking around, we took the autobahn back to Aachen, stopping *en route* to look at some German strong-points that we had taken. There was no indication that bombing had materially assisted in the capture of these beautifully camouflaged concrete pill-boxes. On the other hand, there was every indication of the very great destructive power of the American artillery, which in several cases had scored direct hits on the pill-boxes, doing consider-able damage. The weight of shell-fire was best seen not only in the numerous craters in the fields, but also in the 'decapitation' of about every second tree in a small wood. While shell-fire had undoubtedly damaged some of the pill-boxes, it was interesting that it had failed to cause any serious damage to the massive four-storey concrete air-raid shelters in Aachen itself.

On our way back to Verviers, we ran into the first American units pulling out to deal with the German break-through. These were the 7th Armoured Division and what I took to be a unit of 'tank-busters' from another Corps. The M.P.s were doing a marvellous job, and the road was practically never blocked to on-coming traffic. There was no nonsense either about the men. The tanks were moving fast, with only the tank commanders' heads appearing through the turret-hatches—dirty, unfrightened, unsmiling, just determined and on the job. The crews of the tank-busters looked as though they were on a routine manoeuvre.

We got back to the Verviers H.Q. at about five o'clock. First Pete and then Van arrived, and much later Orvil Anderson and Dick Hughes. Fred Anderson, Dickens and one of the American colonels had departed. It was apparent that from now on the only issue was the German break-through, and Pete was wonderfully excited and en-thusiastic about the remarkably fine job his boys had done that day. He dictated telegrams of congratulations, to his subordinate comman-ders, as did Van to Mary Coningham, thanking him for the participa-tion of the RAF 2nd Tactical Air Force in the day's fight. (Next morning Pete and Van were more than a little cross when they read in the Operations reports that the 2nd T.A.F. had put up only six sorties—I hope this was a mistake in the records.) We stayed in Verviers till about six-thirty in the evening discussing the day's developments and the need for an even greater air effort next day. The weather had been excellent on the Sunday and everyone hoped it would continue fine for Monday. It did not.

At about seven o'clock that evening we left for Spa, Pete directing my driver, and with everyone making somewhat unfunny jokes about the possibility of meeting parachutists *en route*. When we got to the outskirts of Spa we were stopped and told to put out our headlights. There was no doubt about Spa being on the alert. We sat down to what at first I thought might prove only a single sombre and slightly nervous cocktail. It was followed by a second, and the conversation then became somewhat light-hearted. In the meantime scraps of news about the extent of the enemy's break-through that day were coming in on the telephone. Dinner was again a magnificent meal, with a fine claret followed by a vintage port. The previous owner of the house (a German) had good taste. The talk at the table was mainly about the day's events, and the possibility of the Germans over-running Spa, and the need to bring every available aircraft, heavy or light, to bear on the battle. All talk of air operations over the Aachen salient was forgotten. Orvil Anderson had arranged that the 8th's heavy bombers would make a deep penetration raid into Germany the following day, and he was being urged, but apparently without success, to bring them into the battle area instead. On the other hand, he was quite funny about the personal situation in which we had found ourselves. After dinner Pete and Van went off to another meeting with Hodges, while Orvil Anderson, Dick Hughes and I continued to talk over whisky. I got into a corner with Dick Hughes and we disinterred the bones of the pre-D-Day arguments about transportation targets. There is not the slightest doubt that Hughes knows extraordinarily little about the actual effects of the transportation plan, and that he also has a personal and special view about what were its aims. He insisted that it had been claimed in black and white that we would (1) interrupt *all* essential supplies to the potential bridgehead, (2) interrupt *all* local movement from the Pas-de-Calais to the potential bridgehead area, and (3) interrupt *all* strategic reinforcements from areas further east. He was categorical that this was what was written in the AEAF plans. I have not yet had an opportunity of checking, but since I was responsible for writing most of the transportation plan, I am certain that no such absolute claims were ever made for it.

At about 10.30 Van and Pete returned looking grim. The news which they had been given by General Hodges showed that the position was very grave, and that every ounce of effort was necessary to halt the German push. Pete threw a piece of paper to me, saying: 'Zuck, read that, and then you'll know what this war is about'. I replied that I already knew. The paper, which he had got at his meeting with Hodges, gave a brief account of a massacre at Malmédy, a few kilometres from us. Scores of US prisoners were mown down by the

Germans after they had been herded into a field. A few had feigned
death and later escaped to tell the tale.

Four divisions were taking up new positions, one of which I had
seen on the move just before dinner. Two air-borne divisions were
being rushed up from Reims, and it was already apparent that the
whole front, right from Patton's sector in the south to Montgomery's
in the north, was affected. There was no suggestion of any immediate
evacuation of Spa, but Pete, Van and the others were going around
armed. The doors of the house were locked and some of the staff were
up most of the night.

Orvil was shaken by the news and immediately got on the line and
ordered a new lay-on of the 8th's heavy bombers for the following
day. At the same time, a succession of telephone calls was made as it
was appreciated that nobody outside the area probably realised how
bad things were. The gist of the calls to Tooey Spaatz and others was
that the local situation was developing into the biggest thing since
D-Day. Pete and Van, who had already spoken to Spaatz, did not at
first fall in with my suggestion that, since they were telephoning all and
sundry, it was only fair that they also spoke to Tedder. After another
in-coming call, however, Pete agreed and I put through a call. Tedder
was not at his house at Versailles and Van spoke to Freddie Morgan
(COSSAC). I was not satisfied with this, however, and tracked Tedder
down to the *Vendôme* just after midnight and, having got him out of
bed, and joked about his having sent his tame scientist into battle,
had Van speak to him. The next afternoon I learnt that Tedder was
grateful that he had been rung up.

After this round of telephone calls, everybody except Pete, his staff
colonel and I, went to bed. I sat up for about an hour with Pete,
discussing the inadequacies of Army Intelligence (G-2) and the fact
that here again was an illustration of the Air being committed without
warning to a situation for which G-2 more than anybody was responsible. In my view this was not the first time that the dependence of the
Air on Army G-2 and G-3 had proved dangerous. Pete was in complete agreement. Suddenly, at about one in the morning the air-raid
sirens started wailing. I asked Pete whether air-raid sirens were as a
rule used so close to the front, and he replied 'no'. I asked what he
thought it meant, and he suggested that perhaps the Germans were in
the town. I said that in that case I had better go and burn some papers.
I went upstairs to collect such confidential papers as I had with me,
and returned to find Pete on the telephone. He was trying to get
information about the alert, and when he put down the telephone he
suggested that if it was unnecessary to keep them, my papers had
better be on the fire. He helped destroy them and we then went to bed.

Monday, December 18

I woke very early and my first concern was to see what transport it was that was passing along the road outside the house. The first lorry that I was able to distinguish properly was full of Belgian civilians, presumably pushed back by the German advance and by our own troops. Breakfast was again marked by a display of revolvers, and we had a certain amount of anxious talk about the weather. After breakfast Pete and Van went to meet Hodges, while I went to the H.Q. at Verviers with their two P.A.s. It was apparent that every civilian in Spa knew what was afoot, and it was equally clear that 1st Army H.Q. was packed and ready to move—which it did, together with Pete, later in the day. At Verviers everybody was absorbed in the battle and thirsty for information about the ground situation. I listened in on a fighter attack—in which one of Pete's squadrons downed eight German planes. There was still a great deal of flying-bomb activity and some military movement through the town. At about 11.30 Pete and Van returned from their meeting, very serious about the weather which closed in that afternoon, and about the general situation. Van was about to take off for Versailles.

I left at mid-day, on the road for Liège. Troops were on the alert, but as yet there were no check patrols. Thomson got pretty thoroughly lost in Liège, but finally found the road to Dinant, as at first I thought we should take the straight road—Dinant, Givet, Laon, Paris. Some miles before Dinant, however, I decided to take a more westerly road through Ciney and Celles. There was practically nothing in the way of military traffic on this road—in fact over a stretch of about twelve miles we passed only one vehicle. We drove through a beautiful valley, but when we got to within a few miles of the French frontier we had to turn back because two bridges which the Germans had blown up a few months earlier in their retreat from France had not been repaired. (A week later Ciney and Celles were the most westerly points which the Germans reached, and it is interesting that they were then stopped by their own demolitions.) We turned back, and after about a further eight miles' driving, got to Givet, a very sombre and ill-kept small mining town. The troops here were not on the alert, and hardly looked like fighting soldiers. We managed to get something to eat in a humble bistro—not very elegant, but charming—the French family would not accept any payment.

From Givet we took the road for Laon down the west bank of the Meuse, but were stopped after we had gone about eight miles by M.P.s on motor-cycles. They told us that we were on a very bad road (which it certainly was). They also wanted my help in dealing with three RAF Lancaster bombers which had crashed early that morning within a mile or two of where we were. There was nothing to do about this, because the only surviving member of the three crews was being thoroughly well looked after. We were then put on the road to Rethel, from where we took the Reims road to Paris, which we reached at 9 p.m. I telephoned Tedder and arranged to see him next morning.

Tuesday, December 19

Tedder was anxious to talk, and much interested in the fact that I had learnt from the 9th Tactical Air Command Control that so far as they could determine, all the movements of the German army to the region of its break-through had been by rail, and that fighter-bomber attempts to interrupt rail movement in the past weeks had been ineffective. Occasionally they managed to hit a train or cut a line, but according to Pete's staff they had achieved very little. Bridges had also been on their list of targets—bridges which, after numerous attempts, had not been destroyed.

Tedder had been informed by SHAEF Intelligence about the situation, and seemed a bit grey about the whole affair. I asked him whether he knew how much heavy bomber effort had been put on to German rail centres since November 1st when they were made second priority to oil. He did not know, and so I went along to G-2 and A-2 (the Army and Air Force Intelligence sections). Ezra, in G-2, told me that he himself had been aware of the extent of German rail movement, and that he also knew the names of the detraining stations which I had been shown on the 9th Tactical Command Control map. I asked whether he did not think that the Strategic Air Forces should have been called in to stop the build-up, and received the correct reply that that was not his business. I then asked for a map showing the rail centres which had been designated as targets for the heavy bombers, after which I had a talk with Bailey-King, a Lieutenant Colonel on the staff of Major-General Strong, Eisenhower's Chief Intelligence Officer. Bailey-King told me that they had had an Intelligence appreciation from G-2 US 1st Army about the imminence of a German attack, but that since it implied an unimaginable effort on the part of the Germans, this paper had been received with a certain amount of scepticism. I was shown the memo, and where it enumerated the strength of the force which the Germans were going to throw into the counter-thrust, someone—I wondered if it was Bailey-King—had written in the margin—'and the kitchen sink too'. He did not seem to think it the least bit odd that the highest echelon of Allied Intelligence had been so distrustful of the views of the forward Intelligence officers. It is probable that the G-2 SHAEF attitude to the 1st Army Intelligence explains why at least Tedder had no inkling of the German preparations.

I then went off and prepared a map showing the centres which had been attacked in France and Belgium before and after D-Day, and that evening returned to Tedder to show him that the projected rail-centre targets for Germany were relatively less dense and in too thin a belt to achieve the same effect as had the bombing of the rail centres west of the Rhine. I also showed him some preliminary figures I had extracted about the post D-Day attacks that had already been made on rail centres, and since what they revealed was far from encouraging, he asked me to arrange with G-2 to 'thicken up' the list of targets.

Wednesday, December 20

I saw Tedder again in the morning, before he went off to join Eisenhower in a talk with Bradley. I spent the rest of the day assembling exact figures for the attacks that had been made on rail centres, and in encouraging Ezra to prepare a more extensive list of rail targets for the Combined Strategic Targets Committee in London. At about six o'clock I was back in Tedder's office working at his desk, when he unexpectedly returned. The new figures of the strategic bomber effort that had been expended showed that in spite of the fact that they were second priority to oil installations, only about six of all the attacks on rail centres had been carried out under visual conditions. Moreover, a fairly considerable tonnage of bombs had been dropped, to no effect, on, or rather around, three railway viaducts which the Combined Strategic Targets Committee had accorded a higher priority than rail centres. I was also able to tell Tedder that G-2—in the person of Ezra —was now fully cooperating in 'thickening up' the rail centre belt.

By this time, as indeed the day before, there were control posts everywhere; guards examining identity cards, in the search for German 'thugs' who had been sent back, or dropped, for the specific purpose of doing prime bits of sabotage, including the murder of higher-ranking Allied officers. There was talk of Skorzeny being around.[1] I went off to Tooey Spaatz's and had a drink with him, and then stayed to dine. Tooey did not appear to view the situation gravely, although according to Tedder he had been in a slight flap. When he and Van had seen Tedder, they had suggested that all the Strategic Air Forces should for the moment be placed under the command of the tactical commanders. I stayed and watched Spaatz play poker till about ten o'clock and then returned to Paris.

Thursday, December 21

This day, like Wednesday, was spent between Tedder's office and G-2 and A-2, seeking agreement about new railway-centre targets. I also searched the map for possible 'choke-points' in small towns such as St. Vith. It did not appear that the heavy bombers could at that moment be called in to try to impede German road movement. Their ground forces and ours were far too intermingled. A curfew was declared that night, and I therefore stayed in the *Vendôme*.

Friday, December 22

I was able to take Tedder a complete map of suggested rail centre targets. He suggested that the belt ought to be moved forward. I said that G-2 did not feel that they were in a position to suggest to the Committee in London that the forward targets he was suggesting should be bombed; G-2's view was that they had gone as far as they could. Tedder however suggested that I should get them to agree to mark centres west of the Ruhr on the same target map. It did not matter whether medium or heavy bombers were called in to attack; the important thing was to show on a single map all the rail centres which should be targets. I was due to take off for the U.K. from Villacoublay with Fred Anderson at two o'clock and, after leaving the Petit Trianon, I failed to find Ezra in his office in the Ecuries. I was therefore rushed to my own office at Butte Rouge, picked up some papers, left a note for Ezra, and made off for the airfield. It was very foggy when we arrived.

Instead of trying to find the control tower, Thomson idiotically drove around in the fog in search of any aircraft in readiness to take off. Suddenly we heard the noise of engines starting. I told Thomson to drive in the direction of the sound, but we arrived to see the B.17 rolling down the runway. I returned sadly to Paris and telephoned Tedder to say that I had missed my plane. He suggested that I should spend the evening with him and Toppy. I went first in search of Ezra to discuss targets. When I arrived at the Tedders' house he remarked that he was glad I was enjoying my evening, because he was not quite certain that I would have enjoyed it in England. When I asked him why, he replied: 'The aircraft in which you were going to fly crashed while landing. No-one has been seriously hurt, but there were some minor injuries.'

Saturday, December 23

Having missed Fred Anderson's B.17, I arranged to go back to London in Tedder's plane. We went out to Villacoublay at nine in the morning, but by mid-day we had given up the attempt to leave as the machine was unserviceable. I returned to Tedder's office and lunched at his house, and then went off to Le Bourget with Lt. Colonel Milne, Tedder's military aide, hoping to get a lift in any plane, but with no success. The rest of Saturday was again spent on B.A.U. papers, and again I dined with Tedder.

Sunday, December 24

This time we managed to get off and arrived back in England at mid-day. . . .

And this is where my diary ended.

It was believed that some of the divisions which had been committed to the Ardennes offensive had originally been formed in eastern Germany for the Russian front. In the week before I left for the U.K., I had heard of discussions about the need to coordinate our own operations with the drive that we now hoped the Russians would launch on the Eastern front. But because the Russians always seemed to keep their strategic intentions to themselves, Churchill and Roosevelt decided to make a joint approach to Stalin, and asked him to receive 'a very high-ranking officer' from S.H.A.E.F. Stalin agreed, and Tedder was sent. Before he set out, I had indicated my eagerness to be included in his small party, but to no avail. Tedder left for Moscow on 1 January 1945, but it was not until the 14th, after a somewhat chequered journey, that he finally arrived. He was given an account of the offensive which the Russians had launched on 12 January, and a clear picture of their intentions. At the same time he was able to inform Stalin about our own intention to cross the Rhine sometime between early March and mid-April. He was back in Versailles by 26 January, by when the Russians were already in Upper Silesia. While he was away, von Rundstedt's counter-attack had been halted, and the salient which he had driven into Belgium had been obliterated.

When I returned to Paris in the first week of the new year, after a happy break in Oxford, Tedder was still away. I spent much of my time on the affairs of the Bombing Analysis Unit. But there were two other matters with which I was concerned. The first was that in spite of von Rundstedt's counter-thrust in the Ardennes, the strategic air forces were still reluctant to put any weight behind the offensive against the nodal points of the German railway network. The second was that I had to decide whether there was any point at all in attempting a scientific analysis of field warfare in the way one could of the air war. After our breakthrough in Normandy, the armies had moved too swiftly for me to get any better idea of the answer to this question than the discouraging one which I had learnt from the Normandy battles. It was some weeks before I was able to get back to the Ardennes.

What I learnt about the railway offensive was very depressing. Tooey Spaatz, with whom I lunched soon after my return, told me that because of special circumstances, which he did not define, he had decided to reduce the weight of his heavy bomber attacks on railway centres in favour of attacks on synthetic oil plants and aircraft factories, particularly those turning out the new jet fighter, the Me.262. On the other hand, members of the S.H.A.E.F. Intelligence staff to whom I spoke seemed pleased with themselves for having persuaded the Strategic Targets Committee in London—so they assured me—to order attacks on rail installations. But I was dismayed to discover that they had not yet realised that the whole network, not just nodal points west of the Rhine, needed to be attacked.

Tedder's small staff had by then been reinforced by Group Captain Morley, the very man who, when a Wing Commander, had been deputy to Bufton, and who I had always suspected was the latter's 'brains'. When I first heard that Tedder had arranged with Portal for his transfer to our staff, I had expressed astonishment, but Tedder had replied that Morley was less dangerous in our sight than out of it. While Tedder was away in Russia, Morley had started to behave as though he, and not Robb, was Tedder's deputy, and had taken it as his responsibility to press Tedder's views with the Strategic Targets Committee in London.

When Tedder returned, we had a long talk about the situation. His somewhat cynical view was that our 'amateurs' had to be prevented from leading us completely astray. He fully agreed that with the whole of Germany now disorganised as a result of the Russian advance, there could be no better target for any aircraft than the communications network. One of our difficulties was that after the transfer of control of the strategic air forces from the Supreme Commander to the Combined Chiefs of Staff, no-one in S.H.A.E.F. had been charged with the responsibility of keeping a daily record of such attacks as were being levelled at the system. What was worse, most of our Intelligence people still shared the view of the Combined Strategic Targets Committee that the rail network was a useless target. There was no doubt a lesson to be learnt from the fact that such views were being strongly and effectively urged by top Intelligence people well after, as we were subsequently to learn, Speer had informed Bormann that the bombing attacks against the Ruhr and against communication centres were having a serious effect on Germany's entire armament and war production. 'In addition to the bombing of production plants in the Ruhr', Speer wrote, 'the systematic attacks carried out on railway installations are largely responsible for the critical situation. While the former can result in an appreciable drop in our total war output, the disruption of our communications may well lead to a production crisis which will gravely jeopardise our capacity to continue the war.'[2]

But whatever there was to be learnt from ULTRA and from other sources, this was not the message that our Intelligence people were prepared to accept. Their minds were made up, as were those of the members of the Strategic Targets Committee. The only rail-centre targets that they were prepared to designate for R.A.F. Bomber Command and the U.S. Strategic Air Forces were in a narrow band west of the Rhine. It all seemed very odd to me. We knew that such attacks as had been carried out on the railways after the start of the Ardennes offensive had seriously affected von Rundstedt's ability to move ammunition and reinforcements to his front, and that these attacks were therefore at least partly responsible for his subsequent withdrawal. It was equally odd that Morley was only half convinced by the evidence, and that while he spoke about the need to urge the use of heavy bombers in a 'tactical role' for dislocating communications if the Germans again tried to counter-attack, he nonetheless felt it was up to me to impress on the Intelligence people the need to have a background strategic plan of attacks on communications.

With the German defences crumbling on all sides, it was ridiculous to try to differentiate between a strategic and a tactical air war. 'It could', as I put it in a note at the time, 'well be argued that at this stage it would make little difference if the level of synthetic oil production were raised from an assumed level of twenty per cent, or whatever, to forty per cent.' The attacks on communications were disrupting industrial production completely—whether synthetic oil, or explosives, or tanks and guns. The people in London who were designating targets did not seem to appreciate that in modern industry, component parts have got to be moved from factory to factory, from region to region, and that practically nothing is self-contained. I found myself agreeing more and more at this point with Bomber Harris's dislike of 'panacea targets', even though I still did not understand why, having accepted industrial cities as generalised targets, the communications network did not appeal to him in the same way, especially now that he knew full well how successful Bomber Command's offensive against the railway centres of France and Belgium had been. Tedder moreover had told me that he had found that the Russians were not much impressed by the overall results of our strategic bombing offensive, and that they did not believe that the Germans were going to be seriously crippled if at that stage of the war synthetic oil production were to be reduced to below the level at which the plants were able to operate when under attack—they had enough in storage.

Tedder also told me that on his railway journey from the Crimea to Moscow, he had passed through no town, other than Sevastopol, which was as badly damaged as were most of those of our own bombing targets which we had already over-run. He had also been interested to find that, however badly hit, damaged plants were soon put back into production.

The enormous strength of the Russian Air Force, mainly a fighter-bomber force, had impressed him, but his view was that the Russians had no understanding, in the sense that we had, of the proper use of an air force. To them it had been perfected as another form of artillery. In the note that I made of this conversation, I asked myself who was right—the Russians or us?

When the tide turned in the Ardennes, I decided to have a break from the frustrating business of helping to persuade the Combined Strategic Targets Committee about what Tedder saw as necessary, and to go forward and see what the situation was like on the ground. Accordingly I drove towards Spa, stopping for a night *en route* with Pete Quesada, who had moved his headquarters. I then drove around the wastes where battles had been raging until just a few days before. The snow was lying thick on the ground, and was weighing down the branches of the bare trees. It seemed incredible to me that men had been tough enough to fight in such circumstances. All around was the usual debris of battle, including some shot-up Tiger IIs, the new and powerful tanks which the Germans had thrown into the battle. One looked grotesque, with the legs of one of its crew sticking from its turret. I could not imagine how the man had been killed in so strange a position, with his head in the belly of the tank and his feet sticking through the turret-hatch. Feeling that no-one should be left in so undignified a position, I got on to the tank, but Sergeant Thomson, a taciturn man who was thoroughly used to my strange comings and goings, was reluctant to help get the man out. He reminded me about booby-traps, and said that we did not even know whether the verges of the road had been mined. The Ardennes that day was a lonely, cold and terrifying place. There were only the dead where I was scavenging, and it was not long before I had had enough.

By 27 January, the Russians were in parts of what is now East Germany, and on 11 March we were on the Rhine. Eisenhower and Tedder had in the meantime made Reims their Advanced Headquarters, and we were still at odds with the strategic air planners in London. Towards the end of February, the American plan for a widespread attack on a multitude of targets in Germany, a plan which I had heard discussed more than once in the previous year, materialised in an operation called *Clarion*. It was a massive demonstration of air-power, against little or no opposition, with some nine thousand aircraft of all kinds attacking rail targets, canals, motor-vehicles, and whatever else took a pilot's fancy. I was among the few who were more than dubious about the value, or indeed the purpose of such dispersed operations, unless it was to intensify the terror of a civilian population which was staring defeat in the face, and which already knew that Allied bombers could come and go more or less as they pleased. In his autobiography, Tedder is more generous in his comment on the operation than I recall him being at the time. I could not see the point of the operation when, with a little thought, the elimination of a few remaining central nodal points would have totally disrupted the German railway system, which we already knew was struggling to operate even on a minimal scale. The plan called *Bugle*, on which I had been working with Tedder, was designed specifically to isolate the Ruhr from the rest of Germany. It had to wait. As Tedder wrote in a signal he drafted to send to Bottomley in the first week of March (he later substituted what he called a more temperate version) 'the fact that the operations of the immense Strategic Air Forces are supposed to be directed by a Committee advised by a series of Committees and Sub-Committees, is so remarkable and constitutes such a unique method of conducting military operations, that there is no risk of its being forgotten.'[3]

Desmond Bernal wanted to visit my Bombing Analysis Unit, and to see as much as he could of the targets that we had bombed since D-Day. Early in April, therefore, I arranged a splendid tour of which the first four days were spent in Paris, where Des had some business of his own to conduct. In addition to talks at the B.A.U. H.Q., we got together with some of our old French scientific colleagues, and I arranged a token dinner of the Anglo-French Society of Sciences which the Tots and Quots had inaugurated in Paris just before it fell in 1940. Joliot-Curie and his wife, with whom he had shared a Nobel prize, were there. So were Boris Ephrussi, Wurmser, the biochemist, and Francis Perrin, who was to succeed Joliot as head of the French Atomic Energy Commission. Freddie Ayer, who was on an Intelligence job at the time, joined us. I also took Des to dine with the Duff Coopers at the Embassy. We visited the B.A.U. team at Calais—it had not yet completed its field study of the investing operation—where Michael Noble and Sandy insisted that Des, now dressed in a naval lieutenant's uniform (his Combined Operations disguise), be given a haircut before proceeding further. After a couple of days in the Calais area, I took him to Reims to dine with Tedder, who enjoyed meeting him as much as did most of the people to whom I introduced him on that trip. On the following day we made our way south of Cologne where I had arranged we would spend the night with Pete Quesada, whose headquarters had again been moved as the armies advanced. The next morning we inspected Cologne, of which the part to the west of the Rhine was in our hands. Des had never seen a town so devastated. The area round the cathedral had been 'bombed flat', and to this day I incorrectly visualise that great church as standing in some vast square. Needless to say, Des's encyclopaedic knowledge demanded that he check some of its architectural features, but as we started to walk across the open space we were stopped by a platoon of American

rangers who politely told us that the structure of the cathedral was un-
safe and that German guns were trained on the area from the other side
of the river.

Some months before, soon after I had seen Aachen, I had dined in
London with Cyril Connolly. He was then editing *Horizon*, the only
highbrow monthly of any significance which was still being published
in England. I had been so moved by the devastation I had seen in
Aachen, which I described to him, that he eagerly agreed to my suggestion
that I should write for him a piece to the title, 'The Natural History of
Destruction'. It was never finished. My first view of Cologne, and particularly of the cathedral, cried out for a more eloquent piece than I could ever
have written. After sneaking our way to the big bridge which had been
wrecked when its demolition charges had accidently gone off in one of our
earlier raids, and whose collapse, with the consequent interruption of Rhine
traffic, I was later to learn had seriously disrupted production in industrial
centres as far south as Karlsruhe, we returned to Brühl. After a second
night with Pete I drove Des to Brussels and got him a seat on a plane
back to London.

I then turned back to the Ardennes, where I wanted to see how the
B.A.U. field team which we had sent there was faring, but I failed to find
them. The roads around Spa and Malmédy were so bad that my car was
soon in trouble. Knowing that Vandenberg had set up his 9th U.S. Air
Force H.Q. in Luxembourg, I thought that we might as well go back
that way. By the time we reached Trier, about thirty miles north-east of
Luxembourg, we were crawling, and I asked for help from an American
maintenance depot. The men to whom I spoke could not have been less
interested. When I asked whether they could let me have another car to
take me on, they looked at me as if I were mad. There was nothing to do
but to carry on. We drove at less than ten miles an hour until we got
into Luxembourg, where we were directed to Van's headquarters. I was
taken to his room, where I found him with his feet on the desk dictating
his daily diary to his P.A., a charming English girl who was wearing an
American W.A.C. uniform. Van welcomed me warmly, and when I
explained the situation, said that he would get me to Paris the next day.
Until then, there was a lot, he said, to talk about.

The three of us had a quick drink, and it then being about six o'clock,
Van asked me to join him at his evening briefing meeting. When we
entered his war-room, his top staff were already standing to attention by
their chairs, and Van and I took the two central seats. I recognised
several people—among them Kindleberger—whose expressions showed
plainly that they thought their C.-in-C. was in bad company. After the
usual briefing followed by the G-3 suggesting and getting approval for
the lay-on of aircraft for the next day's operations, Van and I rejoined his

P.A. The three of us then went off to an excellent dinner, and continued talking till nearly midnight. But I still did not know how I was going to get to Paris. This, Van said, he would decide in the morning. Perhaps he might even fly me back himself—which, in the end, is what he did.

Unlike the weather in the Ardennes, it was a beautiful cold and clear day in Paris. We had a quick lunch in Van's house in the Avenue Foch, and then, instead of my going to see Tedder, we went off to sit in the sun in the Bois de Boulogne drinking beer. Van had taken French leave from his lofty position of command, while I left it until late in the afternoon before I reported that I had returned.

I spent most of the following month in Paris, with an occasional trip to Reims to see Tedder, with whom I had for some time been discussing the future of the B.A.U., and the setting up of a more ambitious enquiry on German territory. Occasionally I had a meal with Tooey at St. Germain, and now that Germany was on the point of collapse we spoke mainly about the war in the Pacific, in which he was soon to become engaged.

The end came in a rush. We crossed the Rhine on the night of 23/24 March. The Russians reached the outskirts of Berlin on 20 April. Hitler committed suicide on 30 April, and on 4 May the German armies facing the British and Americans surrendered. Early on 7 May, I went to Reims, only to find that most of Tedder's staff were suffering from hangovers. The formal instrument of surrender had been signed in the early hours of that morning. Robb and I lunched with the Tedders, Robb being on the point of returning to England to take over as Commander-in-Chief of Fighter Command. In the afternoon, Tedder and I had a long talk about the post-war enquiries that we wanted to launch. We had a quiet dinner, since Tedder had to take off for Berlin early the next morning to sign, as Eisenhower's representative, with the Russians and Field Marshal Keitel, the formal ratification of Germany's surrender. I was the last down to breakfast the next morning, to find that he had already left. Somehow or other I felt that it was a let-down.

I reached Paris late that afternoon, dined with a friend who was in the Free French forces, and then returned to the *Vendôme*, where I found about a dozen members of the B.A.U. waiting for me to celebrate with them. They left well after midnight. After all, it was V.E. night.

CHAPTER 17

FIELD STUDIES AND HISTORIES

ONCE THE noise of exploding bombs had died away, and the sense of fear that went with it, I always wanted to get as quickly as possible to the place that had suffered. It was more than just being a voyeur of destruction. In the *terra incognita* of war, there was always something for me to learn; and in so far as there were any professional students of destruction in the field, I had without doubt become one.

But I was certainly not alone in wishing to see what bombing had done to Germany. Almost everyone who had played any part in the arguments about the air-war wanted to see the rubble of Germany with their own eyes; some to gape, some to gloat, some with serious, and some even with sinister, intent. I had known for some time that the B.A.U. had very insecure foundations. Its official life had started only at the end of August 1944, but within two months, when the A.E.A.F. had ceased to exist as an entity, its future had already become uncertain. Who was now going to pay the salaries and costs of the non-regular R.A.F. staff? Tedder and I regarded the B.A.U. as an instrument of planning, not just an outfit that had been set up to carry out academic post-mortems. So long as it could be of use, Tedder was determined that the Unit should be kept going, and in the end he won. After several exchanges with the Air Ministry, the B.A.U. was allowed to become, first, the 'S.H.A.E.F. B.A.U.', and then, in January 1945, the 'R.A.F. B.A.U.'. But by the time the war ended, nothing had been decided about the completion of the many investigations on which I had embarked, or the new ones that needed to be started, in spite of the fact that the Air Ministry had been badgered on the subject for months.

Dru Drury, with whom all of us had got on famously, had been posted to a different R.A.F. job in January 1945, and had been succeeded as executive commander of the unit by another regular R.A.F. Group Captain, with whom few of us were in sympathy. Combe was a devout member of the evangelistic 'Oxford Group', but his manifest goodness was matched by a corresponding austerity and by an odd lack of imagination. He simply could not understand that however crude our enquiries, we were doing research, that the scientists whom I had recruited were not there to do a series of routine exercises, and that they

would vanish overnight if he were to give them 'orders' about what problems to investigate and how to investigate them. Nor did he seem to get on with, or understand, the Americans with whom we had to work. I therefore made quite sure that if the B.A.U. were wound up and absorbed in some successor body, he was not to remain part of it. In his serious businesslike way, Combe insisted that I put all this down in writing, which I did, making it plain what the alternatives were. He had to see that what work I wanted done was done, or resign, or appreciate that I would withdraw, together with my scientific colleagues.

Dru knew about these manoeuvrings, and also of my hope that he would be included in whatever arrangements were made for the continuation of our field-work. I therefore arranged for him to join me, in the week after Germany's surrender, in a rapid reconnaissance of some German towns. After a night in Spa with B.A.U. people, we drove through the Ruhr, stopping to exchange an occasional word with civilians in towns that had been destroyed. Public transport was nonexistent, but there was no lack of the familiar sight of dejected people on the move to their homes in other parts of Germany, either in carts, or on foot pushing hand-carts loaded with bundles. Inhabitants of the towns through which we passed were inevitably neat and cleanly turned out. We even visited the famous marshalling yards at Hamm, some kilometres from which we came across our first liberated Russian slave-labour camp. We travelled as far south as Heidelberg. I made notes of the trip as we went along, of which the following entry was typical of the rest.

'Frankenthal, a small town to the north-west of Mannheim had also been destroyed by H.E. and fire. Practically nothing of it appeared to have been left. But still amidst the ruins one saw the young German civilians, neither awed nor bomb happy nor dazed. How the German civilians stuck the bombardments, or rather how the German propaganda machine persuaded them to stick them, is a mystery. Kaiserslautern was another picture of the same type of damage, most of it old. The railway yards to its west were full of immobilized useless locomotives and broken-up rolling stock. There must have been at least fifty locomotives present. The rolling stock, also immobilized, in larger part contained various types of industrial material—lathes, gas drums, etc. The looters had been at work here too. One of the coaches which had been looted contained the trappings of some German theatrical group, and it was very odd to see bits of music, advertising sheets, photographs of actors, wigs, costumes, etc. lying around. All had previously been gone over.'

Shortly afterwards, I made another quick trip through Germany, this time with Kingston-McCloughry, who had just returned from India. Eisenhower's Advanced H.Q. was now in Frankfurt, and here we spent a night in Tedder's house—he was away—in a small company which included Ivone Kirkpatrick. Kirkpatrick, who was now Eisenhower's Political Adviser, had been First Secretary of the British Embassy in Berlin at the time of Chamberlain's negotiations with Hitler, and had been involved in their meetings at Bad Godesberg and Munich. His view was that the outcome had been inevitable; we were simply not ready to 'take on' Hitler at the time. The next day we drove through a number of towns, again stopping in Heidelberg, where I spent some time in bookshops vainly looking for some medical texts. We then made for Munich, where we spent the night. I had known the city well in pre-Hitler days, but now it was a sad picture of destruction. I had a long talk with Heinz Heck, the Director of the Zoo, a friend from those pre-war years. He had stayed in Munich during the war and had continued with his cross-breeding experiments in order to achieve 'throw-backs' to the primitive horse and to the prototype European cattle (the Aurochs). As a 'practical' geneticist, he was at pains to decry Hitler's racialist theories. On the other hand, he kept referring to the numerous Russians and Jugoslavs— freed slave-labour—who were wandering around gazing at his animals, as 'Urmenschen' (primitive men). It was all very odd. There were also a lot of people still wearing concentration camp clothes. Dachau was only twenty miles or so from Munich.

From there we flew to Berlin, where we spent a couple of nights with Wiggles, now the British Air Officer in the combined military command in charge of the city. The record which Kingston made at the time gives a vivid picture of what it was like (although for some reason in places he writes as though he were on his own).

'. . . it was an amazing and disturbing sight: millions of inhabitants homeless and aimless amid this vast destruction. One could not see where the people sheltered, though, after dark, hundreds of lights from lamps and candles perched high in the corner of a ruin gave some indication where at least a few of them were making their homes. It was clear the people of Berlin had been through the mill and they were showing signs of great stress and strain and hunger and there must have seemed little hope for them. I felt the worse because of the contrast between the life of the Berlin people and that in the Air Officer Commanding's quarters where I was staying, a lovely mansion with service and food beyond anything I remembered since before the war began: in particular, breakfast in bed served by attractive blonde German servants—not simply bacon and two eggs, but a choice of ham or bacon and two eggs; not merely marmalade, but light or dark honey; and not only milk but milk or cream.'

(The only feature of this magnificence that Kingston forgot to note is that the floor rugs in Wiggles's house were piled one on top of the other. Before he took the place over, someone had been 'collecting'.)

'I was fortunate to tour round the ruins of Hitler's Chancellery with an escort who spoke Russian and German and knew the building in detail. Even the ruin of the long forbidding and once notorious corridor from the main entrance made one realize the effect it must have had on visitors in Hitler's heyday. The Chancellery gardens were badly battle-scarred from the fighting just before the collapse of Germany. In a corner was the now historic Hitler's bunker with several Russian armed guards at the entrance. Admission was forbidden but my escort sought out the Commander of the Russian guard and a

lengthy conversation followed between the two. After the passing of
a box of cigarettes, the Commander sent for the German engineer who
had been responsible for the maintenance of the bunker in Hitler's
time and gave orders for him to show me round. The engineer pointed
out every detail of the bunker and described the life within it during
Hitler's last days. As we came out he pointed to the scarred patch near
the door where the bodies of Hitler and Eva Braun had been cremated.
We stood and contemplated in this environment how Hitler and his
High Command conducted their affairs during those last critical weeks
and days when the end must have been clear to them all. How could
any High Command retain the grip which it did on the German armed
forces under such hopeless and impossible conditions?

'Notwithstanding all the tragedy and horror of Berlin, the place
seemed crazily out of balance. On the one hand were such devastation
and suffering, and on the other were the German characteristics which
helped them endure defeat. This was apparent, for example, at the
Opera: in the midst of such shambles, only the Germans could produce
a magnificent full orchestra and a crowded house of music-lovers.
As we sat in grand style in the Führer's old box, our own civilization
seemed a very topsy-turvy thing. It seemed incredible that even the
foyer parade in the interval could be so fashionable so soon after
defeat and in the midst of such suffering and hunger.'[1]

Berlin made me wish again that I had written that article for Cyril
Connolly.

Towards the end of August, I made my last trip into Germany and
Austria, this time with Raimund von Hofmannsthal, before beginning
work in earnest on the results of the strategic bombing. I had met
Raimund at Schloss Kammer on the Austrian Attersee before the war,
when I was spending a month with the Melchetts in a neighbouring
'castle' which they had rented for the season. Schloss Kammer, which
had been his home when he was married to Alice Astor, had been a kind
of social and intellectual centre before the 1938 Anschluss. He and Alice
had parted, and he was now married to Lady Elizabeth Paget, Diana
Cooper's niece. When Diana and Duff Cooper took over the British
Embassy in Paris, he was frequently there. He had enlisted as a G.I. in
the American army, and had thus assumed American nationality, but in
some extraordinary way his lowly military status proved hardly any
obstacle to his freedom of movement, which was a blessing and a joy to
those of his many English friends who also had the good fortune to
enjoy Diana's and Duff's hospitality. Raimund told me one day that a
number of important refugees were staying in Schloss Kammer and that
they would be able to give me useful information about the background

to the abortive attempt on Hitler's life in July 1944. He had another reason for wanting to return to Austria. He wanted to find out how a small schloss, owned by his mother, had fared in German hands.

Having arranged for him to be assigned to me for 'intelligence' duties for a fortnight, we set off by road for Frankfurt. By this time Germany and the territories it had previously dominated were divided into different control zones, and passes were necessary to move about freely. This was awkward, as many American soldiers, including officers, had never before seen an R.A.F. uniform and, what was worse, Raimund was travelling in civilian clothes. Our appearance immediately invited suspicion.

This was the only occasion when I arranged to take part in an interrogation of one of the German military leaders—Field Marshal Kesselring. I had followed his career from my first tour in the Mediterranean theatre, and until the end of the war regarded him, correctly or incorrectly, as Tedder's opposite number. It was not just a morbid wish to see him face to face; I had serious questions to put to him. But the meeting, in a bare interrogation room, turned out to be a sad affair, and in the end I did not even bother to read the usual formal report that someone prepared of the interview, which was conducted with the help of an interpreter. The Field Marshal, stripped of all badges of rank, in a drab unpressed uniform, nonetheless still carried himself with dignity. I was introduced as Tedder's planning adviser, and evoked some surprise when I said that what I wanted to know first were Kesselring's views about any mistakes which he thought Tedder had made in the past two or three years. The reply, in effect, was 'none'. I got the feeling that here was a case of 'dog does not eat dog', and that it was impertinent for an obvious civilian to ask a military leader to criticise the adversary who had played a major part in his downfall. The only note I made of the interview related to the Ardennes offensive, about which Kesselring observed that the Allied air chiefs had every reason to be disappointed in the results of their attempts to cut the rail lines of communication by which forward troops were served. There seemed no point in telling him that these attempts were not as Tedder and I had hoped they would be. Feeling rather ashamed of having asked for the interview, I cut it short as soon as it was polite to do so.

The rest of my trip with Raimund had an element of farce about it. The high point of the tour was to have been our talks in Schloss Kammer with an ex-Hungarian officer, Herr von Jessenky, who now occupied it with his American wife. They were hosts to a group of high-ranking refugees who had fled from the Russians as they advanced into the Balkans and Austria.

The park gates were open, and about half-way along the drive Raimund yelled to my driver to stop. We had passed a woman, wearing traditional Austrian dress, who was walking slowly across a field at the side of the road. Raimund leapt from the car, rushed up and embraced her, and they then fell into deep conversation. When he returned, he told me that she was Mme von Jessenky, and that she had lived there throughout the war. We drove on, with Raimund becoming more and more tense, muttering how awful it would be talking to people who, at the least, had been Nazi collaborators. I myself was only eager to learn what I could. We drove into the courtyard of the Schloss, and Raimund mounted a staircase leading to the *piano nobile*. When he returned after about ten minutes, he had his arm round von Jessenky's shoulders. After the formal introductions, we went upstairs to a small room overlooking the Attersee. Von Jessenky spoke perfect English, and after some pleasantries said we must have something to drink to celebrate the occasion. He rang a bell and in came a servant with champagne and glasses. I became embarrassed and, remembering the reason for our presence, asked whether I could put certain questions which I understood he was ready to answer. 'Fine', came the answer, 'but we're in no hurry'; he was sure that both he and the others in the castle had a lot to tell which I would find of interest. There followed some talk of his adventures when fighting the Russians, interspersed with much gossip about people known to Raimund. But I got no answers to such questions as I was able to put in edgeways. He then insisted that the best way to meet the rest of the company was to dine and spend the night in the castle. This we agreed to do.

Dinner was unlike anything I had seen during all the years of the war. There must have been at least eighteen of us round the table in a large dining room. Amongst them was Count Karolyi, who had once been Prime Minister of Hungary, and who told me that he had been up at Christ Church in the early 1900s; Count Berchtold, the son of Austria's Foreign Minister at the time of the First World War; and also a number of other people whose names I would no doubt have recognised had I been versed in a middle-European *Who's Who*. A one-star American general had also turned up as a guest from the outside world. Dinner was a splendid affair. Wine flowed freely, the food was excellent, and many of the guests had their personal servants standing behind their chairs. I sat next to an oldish woman who, seemingly like everyone else, spoke fluent English. She asked what had brought us to Schloss Kammer, and when I told her, she said in an undertone, 'Whatever else, don't believe a single word anybody tells you here. I'll show you something after dinner.' When we rose, she led me to a small room and pointed to a pile of uniforms of various kinds, several bearing the swastika. 'These', she said, 'were being worn recently by some of the people with whom you have just been dining.'

I was then made to take a hand in a game of poker. But as the evening wore on it became clear that I was going to leave next morning without discovering whether any Germans other than Albert Speer had had a sense of the impending and inevitable breakdown of the German economy, and whether any of the officers who plotted to take Hitler's life had been influenced by this consideration. The trip ended with Raimund getting into trouble next day with the American military authorities, out of which I managed to help him, but with some difficulty.

During the whole of this period, the work of the B.A.U. continued. But a question-mark hung over its future, and pressures were being brought to bear on the authorities to create a more powerful organisation to analyse the contribution made by the air-war to the defeat of Germany. Any number of other enquiries were proceeding. Evidence was being gathered about war crimes. The horrors of the concentration camps were coming to light. Dick Crossman, who was then a member of the Political Warfare Executive, invited me to join a small audience to see a run-through of a film that had been made of one of the camps. What I saw on the screen was more horrible than the worst kind of nightmare. The Allied officers who gave filmed evidence first identified themselves with placards on which were printed their army numbers. These they had to repeat verbally, adding their name, age, place of birth, and so on. When I asked Dick why this was done, the reply was simple. 'Those films are going into archives. One day there will be people who will stand up and say that there were no such things as concentration camps, and that the whole story was a frame-up by Hitler's enemies. We can't be too careful.' I wonder where those films are today. Even if not on such a scale, other horrors have since been perpetrated, and are still being perpetrated. Perhaps it would help the survival of the human species if every now and then there were an obligatory showing of films of the kind that I saw that day, to remind us that man's inhumanity to man achieves nothing.

Dr. Samuel Goudsmit, the scientific head of the American Alsos Mission, whose main purpose was to discover how close the Germans had got to the secret of the atom bomb, sought me out to see whether any of our interests coincided. I was more beguiled by what he was discovering than he was in my enquiries. There was the vast organisation which went by the initial letters F.I.A.T., an omnivorous squirrel which collected any information relating to Germany's military and economic affairs during the war, with some of whose key members I kept close contact. Bob Robertson was around, and infected me with his concern about the danger that unimaginative and short-sighted officials would interpret the Potsdam directive about the re-establishment of German scientific education and research in such a way that the country would become an educational and scientific desert. Disastrous as Hitler's policies had been in this particular area of national enterprise, the consequences of continuing them into the post-war as a form of retribution would in the long run have been even worse.

While engaged in all these matters, I was also following as best I could the presumed Whitehall negotiations for the setting up of a British Bombing Survey Unit. The trouble was that surveys had become competitive. No-one had suspected me of any ulterior motives when I started to search in the Western Desert for information that could be of use in future planning, nor was the venture regarded as being purely British. My Bombing Survey Unit in Sicily was to all intents and purposes an Anglo-American body, and its findings went to Tooey Spaatz as quickly as they did to Tedder. But in France, a United States Air Evaluation Board had been set up in parallel with the B.A.U. Fortunately, however, the relations between the two bodies were amicable throughout. Indeed, some American personnel cooperated with B.A.U.'s staff in the field to the end. But it was not long before the B.A.U., which came into being in the atmosphere of controversy which characterised the planning phase of *Overlord*, was being viewed with suspicion both by the Air Ministry and by Bomber Command. In November 1944, George Ball, who later became Deputy Secretary of State of the United States, and who will go down to history, if for nothing else, as a staunch opponent of his country's Vietnam policy, came to discuss the new Evaluation Board. He told me that while General Fickel was titularly in charge, he himself would be keeping an oversight on its activities and progress. The authorities in Washington, he said, wanted to be assured that the Board presented an independent statement about the results of the policy to attack railway targets. The record that I kept of this conversation goes on to say that we both agreed that it was essential to clear up the misapprehensions which still existed about the matter, and about the particular part that I had played in the development of the plan. Ball indicated that, incredible though it might seem, there were those in Washington who believed that I had mesmerised Tedder, Eisenhower and Portal into accepting a policy which, if I had not been there, they would have rejected. But since this attitude existed, the Americans had to make an independent assessment of the merits of the policy. I agreed that our two groups, together with our French colleagues, should hold weekly meetings, and that all primary data should be freely available to both the British Unit and the American Board.

This agreement held until the end of the war. At the start, too, members of the Operational Research Sections of R.A.F. Bomber and Coastal Commands, and also of Mary Coningham's 2nd Tactical Air Force, were attached to us. But soon after George Ball had made his arrangements with me, the O.R.S. staff from the two Commands were withdrawn. Their respective C.-in-Cs. wanted independent assessments. Not long after, the French contingent under Ephrussi withdrew. The French General Staff had started to suspect that I was drawing conclusions of seemingly major military significance from the data that my French scientific colleagues were helping to collect, and that as a matter of policy these were being withheld from them. In spite of all these rumblings, an Air Ministry representative at one of our joint Anglo-American meetings declared as late as March 1945, so the Minutes read, that the work of the B.A.U. was 'absolutely vital for the development of future air weapons. On it would depend the formulation of future requirements, and also of future Air Staff policy'. But, he added, the language of the reports, of which the B.A.U. completed about fifty on a variety of topics, was often beyond the 'limited intellectual capacities' of their readers in the Air Ministry.[2]

I fear that the capacities, whether intellectual or otherwise, of those whose business it was to see that an organisation more powerful than the B.A.U. would continue to study the results of the air war, were also unequal to their simple task. Tedder had been convinced from the start that the job had to be done. Bottomley was persuaded. All the Chiefs of Staff swung into action behind Portal and approved the idea—but provided only that the responsibility for the survey rested on the shoulders of someone who had had nothing to do either with the determination or the execution of Air Force policy. In the view of Sir James Grigg, the Secretary of State for War, even S.H.A.E.F. had to be excluded from the enquiry, as should also the Operational Research Sections of the Services. There could not have been a greater nonsense. It was once again like Churchill, when deciding on the merits of a bombing policy, calling on Mr. Justice Singleton for his judgment. The story is told in some detail in Volume 4 of Webster and Frankland's History, but in terms which reflect the echoes of the old pre-*Overlord* dispute about bombing policy, and also in terms which, I fear, reflect the unfamiliarity of the authors with what constitutes a scientific outlook. According to them, I wrote to Bottomley in September 1944 urging that 'technicians and scientists'— in that order—should be used to ascertain the respective merits of area and precision bombing. I have failed to trace a copy of the letter, and I can only imagine that the authors of the History paraphrased what was in it. The word technicians has a strange ring, and Webster and Frankland must have had a queer idea of what the scientific staff with whom I worked were like. They also write that it was suggested that 'M.E.W. should supply 100 technicians drawn from M.E.W. itself, the supply departments and industry'. But what technicians? R.E.8, the division of Stradling's Department that dealt with the overall effects of air-raids, was, they write, 'reinforced by valuable United States technicians'.[3] I was a 'founder' member of Stradling's outfit, and I cannot imagine who these 'technicians' were. Reading Webster and Frankland's account of the lengthy exchanges which took place on the subject, it would seem that the people concerned believed that they were dealing with some routine matter of domestic engineering, or some enquiry that could be left to run-of-the-mill accountants.

Who advised the Prime Minister I cannot think. Perhaps it was the Prof, perhaps he just used his own good sense, but Churchill was adamantly opposed to all the grand schemes that were put to him, some of which were on a scale to match the United States Strategic Bombing Survey (U.S.S.B.S.).[4] On paper this was headed by a few tycoons employing a staff of more than a thousand. In fact, their enquiries were directed by a handful of competent professional men. The final proposal which was put to Churchill and which was also unrealised, was that there should be a British Bombing Research Mission headed by Lord Trent, the head of the chain of Boots Chemist shops, and during the war a Regional Commissioner for Civil Defence, with Sir Thomas Merton, Treasurer of the Royal Society, as its scientific adviser. I do not know what qualifications Lord Trent had for the job, but Thomas Merton, whom I respected highly, could only have allowed his name to go forward from a sense of duty. He was a physicist whose scientific work had been mainly in the field of spectroscopy. He was also a successful inventor, and had used his inherited wealth mainly to add to the family's art collection. But the one thing he was not was a man who could have supervised the rough and tumble work which would have been the business of a bombing survey, part scientific, part social science and economics, and all without boundaries. Merton's world was beautifully ordered within an elegant frame.

The debate about how the British enquiry should be organised kept on being bedevilled by confusing the need to eliminate from it any hint of prejudice with the desirability that the assessment of the facts should be both independent and authoritative.[5] The latter two concepts were also confused, and the official History merely repeats the confusion. There was certainly prejudice. For example, we are told that Bufton urged that the officer who was to be put in charge of the projected organisation 'must believe in the potentialities of strategic bombing'.[3] It is interesting that there were men about who could so honestly and so explicitly declare their prejudices. There also seems to have been a fear that if I were connected with the projected survey, there would be a danger of the 'books being cooked'. By implication, I am among those who Webster and Frankland say 'were anxious to obtain some control over the investigations'.[6] Suspicion certainly persisted, and much depends on the meaning that was attached to the word 'control'. Professor Nicholas Kaldor,* the Cambridge economist, had been recruited to the staff of the American Strategic Bombing Survey, after which he became a member of the British team. In 1959, Sir Charles Webster sent to him for comment a draft of what is now Annex 5 of Volume 4 of the official History, an Annex which gives an account of the history of the various bombing surveys which were carried out. I never saw the draft, so I do not know which, if any, of Kaldor's comments were taken into consideration in the final version. But Kaldor did send me copies of the correspondence. The original draft apparently included 'implied slurs' on me, because I supposedly tried 'to influence the views' of people like Yates and Kaldor —slurs which Kaldor said were quite unjustified. To this Sir Charles replied that he intended no reflection on my integrity, but since I must have embarked on the investigation 'with certain preconceived ideas about it', it would have been better if the survey had been immune from my influence. I had not met Kaldor before he joined the B.B.S.U., nor had he any idea of the part I had played in the controversies about bombing policy. The idea that I could have set out to corrupt his views was somewhat bizarre. Equally ridiculous was the implicit belief that scientists like Frank Yates or Cliff Emmens would have been susceptible to devious persuasion. The people who were involved in the debate simply did not understand that scientists, economists and statisticians who would have to make the enquiries would be working in the same atmosphere of mutual criticism as characterised their work in their universities. Their job was to gather the best facts there were, and to interpret them in the best way possible.

As I reflect on the discussions of thirty years ago, I find it depressing that men like Sir James Grigg, a civil servant who was regarded so highly that he was made a Cabinet Minister, were so ignorant of the nature of scientific enquiry. I shall say nothing of professional historians. No honest scientist, certainly no experimental scientist, embarks on any enquiry *without* preconceived ideas. What he does is test his preconceived ideas against the facts that emerge from his enquiry, expose them as false if they are false, revise them as necessary, or confirm them if they accord with the facts. As Karl Popper has put it: 'In the search for knowledge, we are out to find true theories, or at least theories which are nearer than others to the truth—which correspond better to the facts; whereas in the search for theories that are merely powerful instruments for certain purposes, we are, in many cases, quite well served by theories which are known to be false.'[7] That kind of 'knowledge' was never my concern nor that of the men who worked with me, even if, as history

---

* Now Lord Kaldor.

has shown, it was the concern of others who were involved in the formulation of bombing policies.

As an independent scientist, I would have been no more competent to assess the accuracy or honesty of Thomas Merton's spectroscopical researches than he would have been to assess, from the same point of view, that of my work on the biological effects of explosions or, say, Frank Yates's statistical procedures in dealing with bomb damage. If Sir Thomas or Sir George Thomson, the physicist who was then Scientific Adviser to the Air Ministry, and who is also mentioned by Webster and Frankland, in fact agreed to what the authorities wanted, they must have done so in the realisation that the assessment of what the strategic air war had achieved had become a political matter—not because they thought that their names would have added scientific validity, as opposed to respectability, to the findings. If the answer had turned out, as it did, that area-bombing had not achieved what was expected of it, the Prof would have been there to say that Merton's judgment had been corrupted by someone, and that Thomson knew nothing about the matter. For in this field the Prof was a politician, not a scientist. And in any event, Harris, in his autobiography, had already stated his conviction that the area-bombing of German cities had achieved its declared purpose.[8]

The whole idea that scientists who are involved in the evolution of a situation that needs to be analysed should not take part in the final process of drawing conclusions is hostile to the method of science. Can one imagine—to jump forward a few years—Watson and Crick, or Linus Pauling or Rosalind Franklin agreeing to turn their attention to some problem other than the elucidation of the data that they had assembled about the likely molecular structure of D.N.A., in order to leave the final judgment to some 'independent' who was not necessarily even informed about the nature of the problem to be solved, or about the basic sciences on which the solution depended? The very idea belongs to the Wonderland that Alice knew.

The man in the middle of the debate about the prospective enquiry, and who was fielding all the brickbats as they flew around, was Claude Pelly. On the dissolution of Leigh-Mallory's Command, he had been posted as head of an embryo British Bombing Survey Unit. When the inevitable at last became obvious, 'the Air Ministry', to quote Webster and Frankland, 'did the best it could to combine its scanty resources into a working organisation, late in the day as it was. It was also now necessary to join forces with S.H.A.E.F., where the B.A.U. under the scientific direction of Professor Zuckerman had been doing all it could to make investigations by a few teams manned to a large extent from his staff ... Professor Zuckerman thus became scientific adviser to the B.B.S.U.'[9]

There is no need to spell out the story of the B.B.S.U. In addition to what has been recorded by Webster and Frankland, a brief account of the organisation is given in the preface* to the 'Overall Report'. The publication, and then very limited confidential distribution of this volume, which I wrote, and which appeared under the title, 'The Strategic Air War Against Germany 1939–1945', was deferred for months and months, in spite of the fact that Tedder had succeeded Portal as Chief of the Air Staff at the beginning of 1946. The reason was that some members of the Air Council were worried lest certain sections of the Report did not give as favourable a picture of the contribution of the strategic bombers to the Allied victory as they would have liked. Nor, unlike the corresponding American reports which were made public almost immediately after they were completed, were the B.B.S.U. Reports ever given an open circulation. It is not surprising that it became a matter for regret that they 'could not be released', as Webster and Frankland put it.[10] Air Force nerves were then very sensitive to any comment that could be construed as critical of bombing policy. Years later I sought and was granted official permission to publish the anonymous B.B.S.U. Overall Report under my own name, and to cite the documents on which it was based, but by then my interest had flagged, and I did not proceed with the idea. I have therefore thought it of interest to reproduce, as Appendix 6, some paragraphs with which I concluded that particular volume.

In general, what was said was that the three major factors that had been associated with Germany's defeat were, first, the over-running of her territories by the armies of the Allies; second, the breakdown of her war industry, mainly as a consequence of the disruption by bombing of her communications system; and, third, the drying up of her sources of liquid fuel, and the disruption of her chemical industry, which resulted from the bombing of synthetic oil plants and refineries. But I also warned that it was difficult to consider these factors in mutual isolation.

What, I believe, irritated Tedder's Air Council colleagues most, and therefore made them wish to suppress the Report, were what they took to be my own assessments of the shortcomings of the strategic air war. 'To those who would judge the matter in a light divorced from the day-to-day struggles of the war,' I wrote, 'the main faults of commission in the combined bomber offensive would undoubtedly appear as the launching of the offensive against German aircraft assembly plants, and the continuation of "area attacks" on German towns beyond the point where they were necessitated by the operational limitation of inaccuracy in navigation and bombing. Even the more accurate and devastating raids on the Ruhr that took place towards the end of the war were an extravagant means of achieving a fall in steel production compared to the

* Appendix 5.

direct attack on communications. The continuation of the oil offensive as top priority after September, 1944, and the wholesale use of heavy bombers in a tactical role, where their effects appear to have been mainly on morale, would no doubt appear as lesser faults of commission. Conversely, our main fault of omission would emerge as the failure to follow up the pre D-Day offensive against the communications system of France and the Low Countries with an offensive against rail and waterway targets in western Germany.'[11]

In short, the R.A.F. had embarked on a policy of diffuse area bombing, because its techniques at the time did not allow of precision attacks, and it continued with area bombing long after its techniques permitted of precision bombing.

The major conclusions which the British and American survey teams reached were very similar. The Reports which both teams produced have been the raw material for many histories, including that of Webster and Frankland. Their four-volume work provides a useful account of most, but not all, of the official documents and minutes which passed between various authorities during the different phases of the build-up of the R.A.F. and of the bombing of Germany.[12] The general conclusions which Webster and Frankland reached about the effects of the bomber offensive hardly differ, except in emphasis, from those drawn by the British and American Surveys. This is not surprising since, as they point out, 'one of the major sources of the conclusions reached ... on the results of the strategic bombing offensive' were the American and British Surveys.[13]

In a leading article following the publication of the official History in 1961, the Editor of *The Times* wrote that, 'official history is a contradiction in terms: history is individual and objective or it is nothing'.[14] On this, Sir James Butler, the general Editor of the series of British official war histories, commented that, according to his understanding, 'an official history is commissioned and sponsored by a government which opens its records for the purposes and assumes responsibility for the competence of the historian or editor'.[15] There is, of course, a belief that official histories are authoritative histories, since it is often assumed that official records tell everything that can be told, and that all files, when consulted after a period of years by historians, contain all the records that they always did. As a contributor to official files over a lengthy period in the post-war years, I am not certain that either proposition is watertight. And I certainly know that some documents had already been removed from the Chief of the Air Staff's files when these were opened to me long before the official historians got to them.

To some extent the editorial comment, that history is nothing if it is not individual, was satisfied by the fact that the junior author, Frankland, knew from first-hand experience as a navigator something of Bomber Command's operations. Webster and Frankland, however, play on the word 'authoritative', pointing out that while there is an 'authoritative' account of the achievements of the American Air Forces—to wit, the work of U.S.S.B.S.—there is no comparable British one, partly at least because at the time the B.B.S.U. reports were not allowed to see the light of day. In consequence, the authors expressed the hope that their work would at least help to fill the gap.[16] To the extent that it provides an admirable resumé of official documents, the official History does fill the gap. But nonetheless, it is not Holy Writ, and it certainly does not tell the full story. This is no fault of its authors, whose remit was to deal solely with the *strategic* air offensive; that is to say, what was construed as the bombing of Germany itself. Unfortunately this means that while their work provides a fair picture of the policy debates that marked 1944, it does so with an undertone which implies that air-support for *Overlord* was more 'tactical' than 'strategic'. In one passage, there is almost an implication that it was odd for the B.B.S.U. to consider what had happened to the Italian and French railways when discussing the collapse of the German communications network.[17] I myself was never able to tell what was strategic and what was tactical in the use of the air forces—I have written about the two terms elsewhere[18]—and I suspect that if my views on the subject were in any way abnormal, I could not have enjoyed the confidence of Tedder in the way I did.

Almost every history of the air war, or indeed of any aspect of the war, almost every biography or autobiography, tells a story which, either in emphasis or in other ways, gives a different slant to the picture of what happened, or some different view of the same event. Tedder's own memoirs[19] devote a considerable amount of space to the battles he fought to get the railway network accepted as a major objective for attack. His own account about the effectiveness of the communications offensive, and about its critical significance in relation to our re-entry into Europe, is no different in intent from the one I have presented in this book. Eisenhower, in his *Crusade in Europe*, deals with the same issue in the same way, but in less space.[20] In his *Memoirs*, Monty does not refer at all to the communications offensive and to the paralysis of the railways on which the German forces and economy depended, although he had referred to it briefly in his earlier book, *Normandy to the Baltic*.[21] According to him, Tedder became the coordinator of air operations only 'because of the never-ceasing rows between the lords of the air, each with his own strategic conceptions and with great jealousies between them'.[22] In his *A Soldier's Story*,[23] Bradley hardly refers to the pre-D-Day bombing programme, an issue which Tedder and Leigh-Mallory regarded as critical to the success or failure of Bradley's armies in achieving

a lodgment in, and then breakout from, Normandy. Each of these
Commanders-in-Chief had his own priorities, his own concerns.

Consider the different accounts of the lay-on of preparatory bombing
before Montgomery's first attempt to break through Caen. He does not
refer to this bombing in his *Memoirs*, but devotes two pages to it in
Normandy to the Baltic.[24] Both he and de Guingand[25] state that he had
asked directly for Bomber Command's assistance, which Harris agreed
to at once. But they do not mention either Leigh-Mallory or Tedder, to
whom the request would have had to have been made and who would
have had to agree to it before it went to Harris. Montgomery and de
Guingand then go on to talk about the results of the bombing. I have
described what I saw happening, as it were, from hour to hour. Monty
says, 'Investigation showed the tremendous effect of the heavy bombing
on the enemy; some German defenders were found still stunned many
hours after the attack had been carried out. The troops in the defences
north of the town were cut off and received no food, petrol or ammunition as a result.'[26] De Guingand supports this statement by saying that
'The defenders had been completely stunned, and cut off from their
supplies and reinforcements', and that they suffered 'considerable
casualties in both men and material'.[27] The account of the operation
which Kingston and I provided, in effect an eye-witness account, does
not bear out these statements at all.[28] And while he refers to the meeting
which took place on 15 June, de Guingand does not mention the fact
that Tedder summarily dismissed the A.E.A.F. team which had come
over to discuss with Monty's generals the plan of the projected operation
against Caen. Nor does Monty.

History, at least recent history, depends on the position one occupied
at the time of the actual event. My own view of events was through a
'window' which, by chance, was opened at the start of the war to my
interested and scientific eyes. I saw no more than I have described in this
book. But from the period of *Overlord* to the end of hostilities I learnt
that what emerged from a dispassionate scientific analysis of the confused
events of war counted for no more in the debates in which I became
engaged than the in-built convictions of various members of what were
called the intelligence and planning communities. In a piece which I
started preparing for Tedder in November 1944, at a time when the
Combined Strategic Targets Committee in London were using their hazy
crystal ball to decide the targets for the heavy bomber forces, I wrote:

'In war, the task of defining the major operational policies by which
the immediate history of tomorrow will be determined is far more
difficult, and in general far more unscientific than even the writing of
history. It is more difficult because here the problem is to relate lessons

from the past, themselves usually unscientific, to the framework of an undefined and only "guessed-at" future. While it may remain in general true that the present is written in the past, and the future in the present, unexpected changes may completely transform any prediction that is made about the immediate future character of either the whole or a part of the total situation. At the start, therefore, the determination of operational policies is vastly more complicated than any after-the-event historical analysis of the policies.

'In determining policies in war operations, there is, moreover, no general method to follow, in the sense that we possess a scientific method which is a necessary process in the determination of tomorrow's scientific events. If there is any general method of approach it is that of *a priori* reasoning, a method which is useful as long as the data which it handles are precise, and as long as there is an opportunity to check the conclusions. Another difficulty with which one has to contend is that on the scale with which planning occurs in the wars of today, the personnel whom chance and other factors have brought together, at least at the lower levels, to determine policies are usually, and perhaps naturally, less competent evaluators of events than the historians who emerge through the slower selective processes of peace.'

I then went on to elaborate this thesis by reference to the history of the dispute about the use of heavy bombers in relation to *Overlord*, and about what had emerged at the time about the outcome of the offensive. Later I developed the same general theme in the concluding paragraphs of the Overall Report of the B.B.S.U., but adding,

'One should not, however, be under any illusions about any extended value of scientific method. Short of divine inspiration, all it represents is the most reliable objective method of deriving the best conclusions from any given body of facts. But operational facts in war are usually compounded of a very much larger number of variables, mostly incapable of measurement, than those with which the scientist deals in the laboratory, and all that scientific method therefore permits in the elaboration of policy is the estimation of which of two or more alternative courses of action is likely to yield better results. It is a safer weapon to use than the establishment of a case merely on the basis of authority because it often does allow of some kind of empirical test in order to check a theoretical deduction. Where a situation is in itself inherently complicated, even the few facts gained from a small experimental test, or an observational study, provide a more solid basis for a course of action than speculation. But the dangers of the method are that it can be stretched too far by attempting too great a logic.'[29]

The purpose of the field-work in which I had become immersed as soon as the German bombing of England provided an opportunity to investigate 'the natural history of destruction', and then of the surveys in which I became engaged in the battle zones of the Mediterranean and Northern Europe, were my attempts, first, to check the results of experimental studies of the wounding mechanism of the blast and fragments from bombs, and then to check the validity of the *a priori* reasoning about the functional consequences of destruction which formed the basis of the bombing plans in which I was concerned. To that extent the war was to me an extended and continuing series of experimental situations. Two years after its end, when apparently none of the other people who had been concerned in the post-war analyses of the results of bombing had any further interest, I even took the trouble to do an enquiry, the results of which I published in a brief article, into the recovery, directed by Louis Armand, of the French railway system.[30] To me that was also a necessary part of the scientific analysis which had begun five years before in Sicily.

Before they embarked on their enquiries, the staff of the U.S. Strategic Bombing Survey had been briefed about the objectives of the bombing offensive by the chiefs of the American Strategic Air Forces, by the very men who had been consistently opposed to the diversion of any major effort from attacks on ball-bearing, chemical and oil installations, to Germany's communications network. It is of interest, therefore, that in the official history of the Army Air Forces in World War II, we read that —on the basis of the findings of the U.S.S.B.S.—'with or without other forms of attack, Germany would surely have collapsed within a short period because of her transportation paralysis, a result of her enemy's air power . . .', that 'it was clear toward the end of the war that the transportation campaign had paralyzed Germany', and that 'the attack on transportation was the decisive blow that completely disorganized the German economy'. It is also interesting that the official American historians declare that the plan to attack communications 'had been projected not so much for its strategic effect on Germany's economy, which proved to be the most notable result, as for its influence on land battles, where its effects had usually been disappointing', and that 'the over-all success was so great that, in retrospect, it seemed reasonable to suggest that the attacks on Germany proper should have been begun sooner, thus saving the French and Belgium systems and bringing about at an earlier date the long-sought progressive dislocation of Germany's war-making capacity'.[31] What the American historians fail to observe is that what they proclaim would have been the best course of action was, in fact, from the start an intrinsic part of the plan for which Tedder had been fighting, and which the American and British bomber chiefs and their servant body, the Combined Strategic Targets Committee, were determined to obstruct.

But the last word about the disruptive effects of the bombing on Germany must, in fairness, be that of Albert Speer, Hitler's Armaments Minister, members of whose staff gave considerable help to the American and British survey teams in their post-war enquiries. Speer was in no doubt about what was happening. As early as 11 November 1944, he had informed Hitler that the attacks on the railway system were creating a situation which could make it impossible for Germany to continue the war.[32] He repeated the warning to Hitler in December.[33] In the same month he made a major address to his organisation about the transport crisis, and said that there was now 'clever and far-reaching planning' behind the attacks that had been made on the German railway system, and that Germany had 'been lucky in that the enemy did not make methodical use of this detailed planning until the last half or three-quarters of this year', instead of, as he also implied, going on blundering.[34] But he was certainly wrong in believing that the plan was being executed methodically. He did not know about our arguments with the London planners.

Speer has also provided us with a vivid picture of the effectiveness of our attacks on the chemical and synthetic oil plants, and also of the misery caused by the bombing of German cities. In the course of the interrogations of German leaders during the first year after the war, he himself was asked what would have been the consequences if attacks on the ball-bearing factories had been concerted and continuous—and presumably 100 per cent successful. His answer was the only one to be expected—within a few months armament production would have been brought to a standstill. So it also would have been if every member of the German labour force had been killed, or if every German city had had its water-supply cut off. The whole of Germany's economic life would also have come to a grinding halt if all its cities had been torn apart at a rate faster than essential reconstruction could have been undertaken. But, as Speer also pointed out, the Allies instead allowed Germany to adjust itself to their strategy of bombing cities.[35]

Germany had suffered from transportation difficulties as early as 1941. These were solved. But then came the heavy bombing attacks that began with *Overlord*. 'In spite of the steadily rising demands of the war,' Speer writes, 'traffic continued to flow in the future, or at least until the systematic air raids of the fall of 1944 once again throttled traffic and made transportation, this time for good, the greatest bottleneck in our war economy.'[36]

As a memento of some talks he and I had when I was gathering some of the material for this book, Speer gave me, suitably inscribed, the original second copy of the long Minute on the subject which he sent to Hitler on 11 November, and a translation of which is reproduced in full in the British official History. It is an interesting possession.

As Tedder constantly insisted, transportation *was* the common denominator. The questions are no longer of more than academic interest, but it has been suggested that the end of the war could have been accelerated if the Allies had begun earlier and then intensified their attacks on, for example, the synthetic oil plants.[37] It might well have been if this had been operationally possible—which I doubt. But such plants, or ball-bearing factories, or tank plants, are not self-contained. They convert raw materials, vast amounts of raw materials, and use millions of tons of coal and iron ore. These are rarely found where the manufacturing plants are built. It all seems so obvious now. Raw materials, even manufactured goods, even synthetic aviation spirit, have to circulate to mean anything, either to a peace-time or to a war economy. Movement is and always will be a 'common denominator', however much target systems adjust themselves, for example by going underground, to the weapon systems by which they are threatened. In my view it was operationally feasible from early 1944 onwards progressively to destroy the railway network on which Germany was utterly dependent, by moving in from the periphery of occupied France and the Low Countries into the complex of Germany's own 'arterial' system. It would certainly have been far easier to do this than to make the deeper penetration raids which would have been demanded by attacks on chemical or ball-bearing plants. But, of course, to those airmen and planners, not to mention historians, who had a built-in conviction that there was or is such a thing as a strategic air-war, such a plan of operation would have had to be rejected—as it indeed was—because by their definition it was tactical.

CHAPTER 18

A TANGLE OF INTELLIGENCE AND COMMAND

EXCEPT IN out-and-out military dictatorships, the civil power always, or at any rate in theory always, stands over its military authorities, however great an influence they may bring to bear on national policies. In turn, the cohesion of the military machine is dependent on its rigid hierarchical structure. For, whatever their rank, whatever their service, military men are implicitly assumed to possess the qualities necessary to make those over whom they stand obey the commands which they are given. Discipline, but obviously discipline of the kind that does not stifle initiative, simply has to be the rule—otherwise the whole system would collapse. A Divisional Commander cannot have the delegated authority to make plans and operate independently of the Corps to which he is attached, any more than a Corps Commander can divorce himself from his Army Commander. Heated debate can take place about what plan of action to adopt, but once a decision has been taken at the appropriate level, debate is supposed to end. Montgomery, backed by the British Chiefs of Staff as well as by Churchill, disagreed strongly with Eisenhower about his plan that Bradley, with three American armies under his command, should take the lead in the final thrust into Germany. As soon as Washington had declared its support for Eisenhower, and as soon as Montgomery's objections had been overruled, he had to abide by the decision, even though, as he himself admits in his *Memoirs*, his subsequent communications with Eisenhower—for all their protestations of friendship and loyalty—were on occasion marred by a note of irritation.[1] In the situation which prevailed, it was unthinkable that he, any more than any other army commander, could have emulated Nelson and put a spyglass to a blind eye.

Needless to say, while I was thoroughly aware of the sparring that was going on between the Army Commanders, I saw none of it at first hand. I do, however, well recall the consternation in Tedder's office when, after the German counter-offensive in the Ardennes had been halted, news arrived of the Press conference which Montgomery gave on 7 January 1945, and which, as reported in the newspapers and over the radio, gave great offence to the American generals, and in particular to Bradley, all of whom felt that they had been 'deliberately belittled'.[2] At about the same time Monty was also involved in discussions about getting Tedder 'out', although his own record of his attitude to this proposal, to which he writes that he was opposed when he discussed it with Eisenhower,[3] does not agree with what Alanbrooke recorded in his diary: namely, that Monty 'was all for such a plan which might go some way towards putting matters straight'.[4] Putting what 'matters' straight is not stated; perhaps he meant his relations with the top American generals, with whom Tedder was always on the best of terms. Monty, reigning so serenely in his remote fastness, was certainly not loved by them, and Tedder never disguised his dislike of the man. Given that personal dislikes ever mattered to Monty, I suspect that he returned the feeling.

But while I knew of dissension in Army circles only at some remove, I certainly had a ringside view of the in-fighting that went on between the generals and marshals of the air. And I can quite easily believe that it was more bitter and at times more ruthless than the quarrels between their opposite numbers on the ground. (Whether similar disputes ever occurred in the hierarchy of Allied admirals, I do not know.) This was partly because the air forces of the Second World War had little experience on which to base themselves—after all, they were to all intents and purposes a new service. When Monty wrote that there was 'really no strategy at all' for our armies after the Normandy campaign, with each of them going as far as it could 'until it ran out of gas or ammunition, or both',[5] I suspect that what he meant to imply was that his own designs had not prevailed over those of Eisenhower. But there certainly was no clear-cut and coherent strategy or conception of function for the air forces, except in the case of Coastal Command, whose job was to help keep our sea-lanes open, and of the functional Commands which dealt with Transport, Training and Maintenance. Otherwise the strategic focus of the air necessarily changed with circumstances. During the Battle of Britain there was no question of what came first. Fighter Command then had the supreme task of defending the country and of destroying intruding enemy aircraft. But once that battle had been won, the emphasis of the air effort not surprisingly shifted, with the functions of the Air Force multiplying as the industries on which they depended succeeded in satisfying the varied and enormous demands made on them. Night-fighters, fighter-bombers, medium bombers, a host of aircraft for different specialized tasks then made their appearance. But by the time of *Overlord*, it was Bomber Command which without question had captured the limelight, and with the American Air Force also building up apace, it was the bomber barons who had now moved to the centre of the stage.

Leigh-Mallory had known the danger and glamour of the air duels which characterised the emergence of the air forces of the First World War. In the Battle of Britain he had commanded No. 12 Group of Fighter Command, and so had shared in that enduring tribute of Winston Churchill: 'Never in the field of human conflict was so much owed by so many to so few'.[6] With Sholto Douglas's move in the spring of 1943 to the Middle East to replace Tedder, Leigh-Mallory had been appointed C.-in-C. of Fighter Command. But in spite of his brilliant record, he did not stand a chance in the environment of *Overlord*. He had known as far back as March 1943 that he was slated to be Air Commander-in-Chief for the invasion. But even after his formal appointment on 20 August of that year, he had no idea what forces would be placed under his command. It was not until 16 November, after weeks of wrangling, particularly about who was to take command of the American fighter-bombers, that he received a directive which put under his command the R.A.F. Tactical Air Force, the United States 9th Air Force and, initially, 'such forces as may be allotted to the Air Defence of Great Britain'.[7] Even so, it was clearly stated that his command of the United States 9th Air Force was not to begin until 15 December.

At no time was there any question of the strategic air forces coming under his command. On the rare occasions when the heavy bombers undertook operations in connection with *Overlord*, they did so on the authority of Tedder, Eisenhower's Deputy, not on that of Leigh-Mallory, even though he was C.-in-C. of A.E.A.F. From Leigh-Mallory's point of view, everything depended on his close cooperation with Tedder. Even if they had been on the best of terms, which they were not, this was difficult, since the A.E.A.F. H.Q. was at Stanmore, while Tedder had his own small staff at Supreme Headquarters at Bushy Park, about twelve miles away. The first A.E.A.F. Bombing Committee that was set up in Norfolk House supposedly advised on the use of *all* available forces. It is unnecessary again to spell out its failures. Much later another effort was made to convene at Stanmore a joint bombing committee consisting of representatives of all the forces involved. Leigh-Mallory took pains to 'roll out the red carpet', and to make offices available in Bentley Priory. Brigadier General Cabell, representing the U.S. heavy bombers, did once turn up to sit in the office that had been prepared for him, but the committee never met. Only Colonel de Russy, an emissary from the 8th Air Force, seemed to have the manners not to treat Leigh-Mallory's headquarters as a place to be avoided whenever possible.

Leigh-Mallory never had the staff to control what was going on. For example, he was supposed to coordinate attacks on the German coastal defences. Yet at a meeting which he called on 13 May,[8] it emerged that the Anglo-American Intelligence agency responsible for advising the various Commands about particular targets did not have a single gunner on its staff. My job had been to assess the damage that batteries suffered, using the kind of criteria that I had devised for Pantelleria; not to say which batteries should be attacked and when. Moreover, if Leigh-Mallory was frustrated in bigger issues both by Tedder and by the Commanders of the strategic air forces, he was also squeezed from below in his control of the tactical air forces. The first idea had been to appoint Mary Coningham as his subordinate. This proposal, however, was violently opposed by General Brereton, Commander of the U.S. 9th Air Force, who flatly refused to serve under Coningham. A compromise was then reached whereby Coningham would act in a dual role, analogous to that of C.-in-C. 21 Army Group, both during the assault phase and until such time as Leigh-Mallory established himself in France, when he would revert to the sole position of Commander of the 2nd Tactical Air Force. Coningham consequently saw himself as Monty's opposite number in the opening phases of the invasion, and indeed he did become Commander of the Advanced A.E.A.F. for a short time. But he was adamant that Leigh-Mallory should not get in his way. His argument was that during the first few days after the landings Monty might want to make immediate demands for air support, whose implementation would be delayed if there were any intermediate and unnecessary links in the chain of command. When Leigh-Mallory refused to accept this arrangement, Coningham appealed to Monty, who then insisted to Eisenhower that he had to have only one commander on whom to call for air support. Eisenhower agreed that Coningham was to be that man. But almost within days, Monty failed to adhere to the arrangement. While he had been ready to accept Mary as his equal in the desert, he was certainly not going to do so in the Normandy campaign where, as he says in his *Memoirs*, he (Monty) was now 'working direct to Leigh-Mallory'.[9] In the desert, Mary had perforce to live as austerely as did Monty. In Northern Europe he was able to indulge in a more luxurious and agreeable way of life, and one which Monty, I suspect, regarded with genuine distaste. And, as I have already said, Monty preferred to deal with Broadhurst, and when it came to the use of the heavy bombers, Tedder was there to trump Leigh-Mallory.

The Advanced A.E.A.F. was wound up on 5 August 1944, and it was not many weeks later that Leigh-Mallory was killed. Poor Leigh-Mallory, he could not have derived much pleasure or satisfaction from being Commander-in-Chief of the A.E.A.F. He did not stand a chance either in the jungle where Commanders brought in from the Mediterranean knew all the call-signs, nor in the higher, more rarified atmosphere where the Commanders of the heavy bombers mused about the destruction of Germany. His job seemed to me lonely and friendless. While I sometimes saw Tedder and Spaatz together, I never once saw Tedder alone with either Harris or Leigh-Mallory. So far as I could tell, they met only at the Commanders' meetings. I cannot recall any occasion when I was at a luncheon or dinner table with any two of them at the same time.

I always felt that L-M bore himself with dignity in the adverse currents of the impossible situation to which he had been appointed. It simply was not his world. Normandy was not Dieppe, when he had commanded the Air, and the Combined Chiefs of Staff who were responsible for his appointment could not have realised how different the two were going to be. Fortunately for me, while Leigh-Mallory had to be wary of Tedder all the time, he never resented my close relations with him. L-M realised that the advice that I gave him was the same as that which I tendered to Tedder.

When in Algiers, Eisenhower had done much to stamp out Anglo-American bickering, and Tedder too knew how to suppress the national prejudices that were often not far beneath the surface. This task was much more difficult during the *Overlord* campaign, partly because vastly bigger forces were engaged, and partly because of the geographical isolation of different headquarters, within which the antipathies of different Commanders-in-Chief were constantly reinforced by their respective staffs. The frigid atmosphere of Leigh-Mallory's Commanders' meetings was as a rule matched before and after the formal proceedings by the exchanges between the Commanders' aides, the A.E.A.F. staff, and our military and naval liaison officers. For example, literally just two weeks before D-Day, Oxland asked whether the Army was counting on the use of Bomber Command on the nights of D-Day and D + 1, at the same time warning that it should not be assumed that Bomber Command did not have more urgent tasks on its hands. Not many days before this, Cabell, speaking for the U.S. 8th Air Force, proposed that the armies should put their various problems directly to the Air Commands, who would then decide the best way to meet the calls. This, incredible though it may now seem, was at an A.E.A.F. meeting[10] chaired by the powerful American general, Freddie Smith, who, like most of the other staff officers from the various Commands who were present, thought the idea a good one. It took me, a civilian, to protest that the proposal made nonsense of the integration of the air effort for *Overlord*, and that were it accepted, A.E.A.F., of which Smith was the Director of Operations, would be utterly bypassed. At this same meeting, Colonel Maxwell, who as the representative of the U.S. 8th Air Force later co-chaired with Bufton the Combined Strategic Targets Committee, gave the strongest possible indication that plans were already being laid to send about two-thirds of the American heavy bomber forces against targets in Germany on the third day after the landings. 'Don't', said Maxwell to the Army representatives, 'count on us to be with you after D-Day.'

A.E.A.F. was not only a threat to the independence of the strategic air forces, it was also a focal point for U.S./U.K. bickerings, which the separate Commands, manned by their own nationals, were obviously not. The introduction of the 'points system' into Leigh-Mallory's headquarters, an administrative manoeuvre which I have already described, did little to help the situation. Suspicion continued to simmer, and there were two or three American officers who did not mind telling me to my face that without my presumably nefarious influence over Tedder, Leigh-Mallory and Wigglesworth, matters would not have been as bad as they were.

There was one officer, a Lieutenant-Colonel Burt, who certainly had no inhibitions on this score. I never did find out exactly who he was. Rumour had it that he had been on Arnold's staff in Washington, and that he had been posted to the A.E.A.F. to report directly to Arnold about Leigh-Mallory. Seemingly only a young lieutenant-colonel, he was clearly a powerful figure, and sometimes I got the impression that even Vandenberg deferred to him. He was obviously wealthier than most of our colleagues, and in London he lived in great elegance.

One night, together with Colonel McKinnon, Kingston's American 'shadow', I went back to Burt's luxurious apartment, and spent some hours listening to his complaints. The basic trouble, he said, was that the British wanted to dominate the scene, and that the Americans had not been consulted about the Transportation Plan in its early stages—which unfortunately was true—even though its implementation demanded their full cooperation. I had been totally at fault, he continued, in not 'processing' the plan through proper channels. It was mainly because of this that General Arnold had agreed that the U.S. Strategic Air Forces could interpret the *Pointblank* directive more liberally than the written words implied. It could now be taken to mean that the Americans could use bombs 'to destroy the will of the German people to resist'. While the primary task set by the *Pointblank* directive was to destroy German fighter factories, once this was done, the U.S. heavy bombers would strike at whatever targets they chose in Germany.

Burt had more to say. I was the prime enemy of the concept of an independent Strategic Air Force. The *Overlord* dispute was dangerous because it was driving a wedge between the United States and Great Britain, which would become a serious matter when we came to the real battle—against Russia. And we had to get rid of Wigglesworth, since he was extremely rude both to the Americans and British, and, in his position as Chief of Staff, failed to get the ideas which I put directly to the top people, properly discussed. Poor Wiggles. There could never have been a more forthright, unpretentious and honest man. And so Burt, McKinnon and I rambled on into the early hours.

When I first met Tooey Spaatz in the Mediterranean theatre, he seemed just as interested in army-support operations as in what was regarded as strategic bombing. But those were early days, and as the American Air Forces built up, and certainly by the time of the invasion, the focus of his interest had moved considerably. Whatever the differences in view between those in the R.A.F. who proclaimed the merits of generalised area bombing, and those who defended policies of selective bombing, there was never any doubt that both sides were at one in upholding the doctrine that wars can be won by bombing the enemy's homeland.[11] It did not matter whether or not Eisenhower or Tedder believed any of this, which I am not certain they did, or whether the Russians then believed in so-called strategic bombing, which I doubt very much. The Trenchard doctrine had provided the United Kingdom with an independent air force, and this is what fascinated the people round Tooey. The American Air Forces now had their chance to become independent. The enemy's ability and will to resist could be undermined by raining bombs on his homeland. Armies were wanted as occupying forces, not to fight it out on the ground.

But if the British and American bomber chiefs were secretly at one in this belief, they agreed in little else. Harris insisted to the end that Bomber Command could defeat Germany by laying waste to her cities through wide-ranging night attacks. In spite of the fact that the strategy he pursued gradually ceased to have Portal's support, he was in too powerful a position, too well protected by Churchill, too valuable a leader, either to be dismissed or to have his resignation called for—even though, at his level, neither was unknown in those days. And so area bombing went on, culminating in the devastating attack on Dresden on 13 February 1945, an attack which Sir Robert Saundby, then the Deputy Commander-in-Chief of R.A.F. Bomber Command, has since described as a great tragedy. In the light of the facts that are now available, he has written that few will believe 'that it was really a military necessity. . . . It was one of those terrible things that sometimes happen in wartime, brought about by an unfortunate combination of circumstances.'[12] Dresden, as I have already said, was the turning point when the powerful support which Harris had enjoyed was almost summarily withdrawn. Even so, he could write, more than a month later, and only a few weeks before Hitler's suicide, that he still maintained that his task, 'the progressive destruction and dislocation of the German military, industrial and economic systems', could best be achieved by the elimination of German industrial cities.

He made this protestation of faith in a long letter, dated 29 March

1945, in which, at Bottomley's request, he made plain what he thought about Churchill's original Dresden Minute, and in particular about the charge that he had been engaged in terror-bombing. What is equally surprising is that in this letter (about which the official History is silent) he also admitted that the dislocation of transportation had a more profound effect on a country's ability to recover from bombing than the destruction of buildings (his actual words were that it 'makes any sort of recovery almost impossible'). But the belief in destruction *qua* destruction was so engrained at the time that Harris could also write that he personally would not regard 'the whole of the remaining cities of Germany as worth the bones of one British Grenadier', adding as a postscript that 'the feeling . . . over Dresden could be easily explained by any psychiatrist. It is connected with German bands and Dresden shepherdesses.'[13]

Tooey Spaatz had no faith, as such, in the destruction of cities, although he was not averse to spreading terror. Long before Dresden, as I have already said, he had been urging widely dispersed bombing attacks over Germany in order to demonstrate to the German people the might of American air power. His basic belief was in deep-penetration daylight raids into Germany, and in particular attacks on Germany's oil installations. About a week before D-Day, Tooey had given me as his view that Harris was 'all washed-up', that the German night-fighters and ground defences had made night bombing too expensive, and that the chance to attack the nodal points of the railway system of Northern Europe had come just in time for Bomber Command. Harris, he said, had found salvation in the demonstration of his Command's ability to destroy railway targets in occupied territory.

On this occasion Tooey went even further, and admitted that the attacks on the railway system were having a profound effect. As he saw it, the pity was that his staff had not thought of the oil plan earlier than February 1944, and that they had then done so only in opposition to the Transportation Plan. Another misfortune was that, at the time, they were according a higher priority to attacks on ball-bearing factories than to raids on synthetic oil plants. In his view a combined oil and railway offensive, launched as soon as the German day-fighter defences had been sufficiently weakened, might have shortened the war. This was only too true. But when oil plants were first suggested as targets, the day of the invasion was approaching, and all the so-called experts had agreed that attacks on oil could not affect the issue of *Overlord* for the first six months.

However different their views about bombing strategy, for the bomber chiefs two wars were nonetheless in progress almost to the moment of Germany's surrender—their own, and the Anglo-American and Russian land campaigns. Anything connected with *Overlord* was tactical, a diversion from the real war. A contemporary letter which I happened to find among my B.B.S.U. papers, written by a high-ranking R.A.F. officer, quotes another as saying that *Overlord* had been an unnecessary 'boating expedition'. In retrospect it seems fantastic that in the days when *Overlord* was being planned, it was necessary to argue that it was logical, or at least desirable, that the commitment of millions of Allied troops to an invasion of the Continent should be made part and parcel of the same war as that which Bomber Command and the U.S. Strategic Air Forces were waging against Germany. During my time in the Mediterranean, I had had practically no experience of military controversy, either between or within the separate Services, or between the British and Americans. I had not appreciated the reality—that different factions within the Allies were in fact fighting personal wars. The strategic air forces were almost sovereign powers engaged in some conflict of their own. Contemporary documents make this only too plain. For example, as late as March 1945, only two months before Germany surrendered, Bufton had issued a memorandum in which he differentiated between 'our strategic requirements and those for the support of our armies in the west'.[14] An Air Staff paper had made the distinction even clearer at the end of January:

'Strategic aims', it read, 'particularly as affecting the VIIIth Air Force and Bomber Command, have been largely subordinated to the short-term semi-tactical requirements of the armies on the western front. ... If SHAEF could be persuaded to discontinue attritional attacks on communications targets deep into Germany, and were satisfied with a concentration of attacks on communications areas more directly affecting the battle on the western front, it is possible that there would be sufficient effort to attack systematically the most important tank plants.'[15]

With all the cross-currents that beset the planning staffs of the different air commands, it was not the least bit surprising that Speer was able to add a grain of comfort to an otherwise despairing report, which he had sent to Hitler shortly before D-Day, about the results of the bombing raids that had been started against the German synthetic oil plants. 'The only hope', he wrote, 'is that the enemy, too, has got an Air Staff',[16] the implication being that if we had one, it would be bound to turn its attention from targets that really mattered to others which were less significant. Had he only known, he need not have worried. We had a surfeit of air staffs, presided over by chiefs who were not called 'the air barons' for nothing. They ruled their commands like feudal lords, rarely changing their conventional views or their personal allegiances. What mattered was the ability to destroy. To all sides in a conflict, the goal of war must always be victory, but victory has over the course of history almost always been associated with destruction, so much so that destruction has become a kind of vested characteristic of war. It is easy for those who were not involved in the Second World War, or who were not directly touched by the armed conflicts that have occurred since 1945, to be self-righteous about the death and destruction brought about by bombing, or to suppose that a country which has been hurt can, as it were, be expected to turn the other cheek. When Britain was being bombed in 1940 and 1941, the cry was always for retaliation. When the V-weapons started flying, the cry was for retaliation. On both the German and our own side the hope of the bomber chiefs was that the enemy's surrender could be achieved through destruction—through retaliatory raids, through sustained bomber offensives, or through rocket bombs. Harris and Spaatz were even competing with each other for public recognition of the number of bombs they were dropping, regardless of the targets at which they were aimed. For example, in one of Spaatz's journal notes dated 3 June 1944, one reads that he had lunched that day with Leigh-Mallory and that Harris, who was also there, was 'very noticeably enraged by the fact that our statement in newspapers of bomb tonnage dropped during month of May by U.S. Strategic Air Forces exceeded that reported as dropped by R.A.F. Bomber Command'. When, after the war, the nuclear bomb came, the concept of winning through destruction assumed an even greater force. As the Vietnam war dragged on, and as intensive and extensive bombing by the U.S. Air Forces with conventional bombs failed to bring about the collapse of 'the enemy' in an area smaller than that of Europe, Curtis LeMay, the Chief of Staff of the U.S. Air Forces, was widely reported as having declared that the right policy was to use nuclear weapons to 'bomb them [the North Vietnamese] back into the stone-age', an observation which drew from a prominent member of the National Security Council the rejoinder, 'spoken like a true stone-age general'.

The concept of a strategic air war had, of course, never been put to the test before the Second World War, and the belief that Germany could be forced to capitulate as a result either of diffuse bombing or of the bombing of particular elements in her economic system was more an expression of hope than an idea based on experience. The whole thing was so speculative, that while I accepted the fact that once it had been started such bombing was going to continue, I came to regard the strategic options which bombing implied as something to be decided on the basis of empirical study—which is what the Hull and Birmingham enquiry was—and not as matters which could be argued about as from first principles. That is why I continued to puzzle about the curious structure of the planning and Intelligence air-force staffs with which I had been dealing in the final year and a half of the war, and by the almost inbuilt inability of some of their members to appreciate what constituted evidence. The minutes of the final meeting of the Combined Strategic Targets Committee had recorded Colonel Maxwell as congratulating his colleagues for having transformed the process of target selection from the stage of guesswork to that of scientific method.[17] This seemed to me an utterly ridiculous claim. I have little idea what the members of that particular Committee—to which, in effect, the bomber chiefs had delegated all authority in the selection of targets from the beginning of October 1944 until the end of the war—have done since, but at the time they were all relatively young men, working hand-in-glove with like minds in the Commands. They heard and saw only what they wished to hear and see. There were always pieces of Intelligence to support whatever preconceived idea was the vogue. After all, whatever the targets which we bombed, the German messages that we intercepted were hardly likely to tell us that the attacks had made life easier for the victims. Speer was not going to send messages to Hitler to say that an area-attack on a big city had improved its lot, or that bombing raids on chemical and oil plants or on the railways had made life easier for him in his job as Minister of Armaments. It was always possible to select 'Intelligence' which fitted into either Harris's scheme of things or that of Spaatz. As I put it in the final chapter of the B.B.S.U. Overall Report—years before one could even whisper the word ULTRA—Intelligence staffs usually 'started with the same basic information, but interpretations were often coloured by pre-conceived ideas or by wishful-thinking, so much so that an archivist today would scarcely believe that certain completely conflicting reports, kept as historical documents, were based upon the same material.'[18]

Maxwell may well have congratulated his colleagues for introducing scientific method into the selection of targets, but I doubt if any one of them could have written a respectable essay about the nature of the method. They formed a group which had been brought together through the accident of war, to hand down judgments on matters which affected life and death on a vast scale. And who, in fact, were they? Some were regular officers who had been moulded by doctrine, and who lived in a military environment of faith which was the very antithesis of the critical one in which science thrives. Others were wartime officers. Among them was one who in civilian life was a coal merchant, another came from a firm of publishers, a third was connected with a brewery, a fourth was a young lawyer, a fifth was a junior administrative civil servant, and a sixth was a member of a tobacco firm. Not one had ever done any research himself into the physical and functional effects of bombing. It is possible that a few would have understood the analytical processes whereby substance had been given to quantitative concepts of unit factors of destruction. But not one seemed to accept that as more and more technology was applied to the apparatus of war, battles became more and more a series of experimental situations. My own opinion remains that far from having brought scientific method to bear on the selection of targets, they had obstructed it, and so prolonged the agony of war, both for the victors and for the defeated.

As I have said, the people concerned heard and saw only what they wished to hear and see. From the economic heights commanded in those days by the young Kindleberger and by the young Lawrence, supported by their equally academic and inexperienced staffs, it had been handed down by a process of simple subtraction that military traffic consumed only a small part of the available capacity of the railways. *Ergo*, it would always be possible to deal with military requirements, however much the capacity of the railways was reduced. To the theoreticians, this logic, unrelated to practical experience, was more reliable than the hard practical lessons which the campaign in the Mediterranean had revealed. It is true that none of them ever withheld praise for the successful bombing of individual rail targets, but I cannot recall a single member of the Strategic Targets Committee drawing the right conclusions about the strategic significance of the programme of attacks on transportation as a whole. If I am wrong here, all I can say is that if one of them did, then he was not prepared to question publicly the uniformly negative appreciations that were put out by the hierarchy of Intelligence agencies.

It was not as though these appreciations were backed by ULTRA intercepts or by agents' reports. The very reverse. I have already said that the Intelligence digests that were served up to the top Air Commanders had already been processed through the 'interpretation sieve' and that, because they did not make sense to me, I had demanded to see for myself such basic Intelligence material as came to A.E.A.F. Of course, I was only at the user end of ULTRA. Hugh Trevor-Roper, who was in the middle of the intercept machine, has now told us, in his fascinating book, *The Philby Affair*, how arbitrary and how misleading the ULTRA information that was fed out could be. Even the intercepts which went each day to the Prime Minister himself were arbitrarily selected. What is more important is Trevor-Roper's unequivocal statement that 'Secret intelligence should be the continuation of open intelligence by other means', and that its credibility depends 'on its demonstrable coherence with its known or knowable content'.[19] It was this which was so conspicuously lacking in the Intelligence appreciations of the offensive against the communications network.[20]

There can hardly be a better illustration of the consequences of the rivalry that prevailed between Intelligence agencies than our blindness to the imminence of the German counter-attack in the Ardennes. The

Intelligence staff of the American 1st Army had said that it was going to happen. Bradley knew of their fears, but he freely admits in his memoirs that his mind was fixed on the winter offensive he was about to mount, not on the possibility that the Germans were going on the offensive. More than that, he bluntly dismisses as 'pure nonsense' the complaint that was made later by the 1st Army that its warnings had been ignored, at the same time as he stated that he readily accepted the responsibility for the 'calculated risk' which he had taken in spite of the murmurings that must have been passed to the Intelligence staff of his Army Group.[21] Eisenhower makes plain—as also does Tedder[22]—that he did not know of the 1st Army's 'gloomy Intelligence estimates'.[23] The explanation seems simple. S.H.A.E.F.'s Intelligence staffs were not geared to listen to what was coming from the 1st Army. If the estimate was that the Germans had six fresh divisions to throw into a counter-attack, why not add a marginal note—'and the kitchen sink too'? When I told Tedder what I had read, I had added that the people concerned should be put against a wall and shot.

To return to the Intelligence assessments of the results of our bombing, clearly Harris was not alone in his faith in area-attacks, and I doubt if any of his staff officers would have survived long if they had argued against the policy that he so powerfully supported. Equally, when Tooey Spaatz remarked to me that Harris was 'all washed-up', he was merely repeating the current chit-chat circulating among those closest to him. Indeed, few leaders could possibly have furthered the causes or plans for which they are either celebrated or condemned by history had they not been surrounded by men who thought the same way as they did, or who at least professed to think the same. It has been said that a new Minister appointed to a Government Department has only a limited period of freedom before he becomes a slave to a past within which his civil servants are inevitably working, and which automatically constrains his room for manoeuvre. Eisenhower and Tedder were among the few military leaders whom I then knew who had the courage to insist on policies which their top staff openly opposed. If the views of S.H.A.E.F.'s Intelligence staffs about the Transportation Plan had been proved right by history, the contrary decisions taken by the Supreme Commander and his Deputy would now have to be judged as totally irresponsible and irrational. Fortunately, the staffs were proved wrong.

It would, of course, be asking too much to suppose that all the operations of the secret Intelligence agencies of the world now abide by the criteria formulated by Trevor-Roper. But with the post-war development of systems analysis as a logical extension of operational research, I can hardly imagine that the selection of strategic objectives would ever again be left to the kind of naïve economic analysis which was the fashion when, during the Second World War, strategic bombing sought to come into its own. But one now has to ask what meaning the concept of strategic bombing has anyhow in a nuclearised world.

Almost immediately after Pantelleria, and more than once after we had returned to London for *Overlord*, Tooey had urged me to go to Washington to discuss my views about the potentialities and planning of bomber offensives. Unfortunately, there was never time to do as he asked, and I was unable to make the visit until the early part of 1946. By this time Tooey had returned from his brief tour in the Pacific as overall Commander of the U.S. Air Forces in the theatre, and had succeeded Hap Arnold as Chief of Staff.

I had thought first of spending a few days in New York, but it was not as stimulating as I had hoped, and I soon left. It was certainly not the New York I had known before the war. I particularly missed Ira and Lee Gershwin, who by then had settled in California, but John and Maria Rogers were there, as were also Marion and E. E. Cummings, whose wry conversation about the madness of the world fascinated me as it always had.

In Washington the British Military Mission had booked me into a small hotel of somewhat ancient vintage. As soon as I arrived, I telephoned Tooey, who asked me to join him in the Pentagon, that vast headquarters of the American armed services, which I was to get to know well in later years. Tooey was standing outside the door of his office, and suggested that, rather than stay there, we should go to his official residence in Fort Myer, the big Air Force residential camp on the outskirts of Washington. On the way he took me to see the house which he and his wife Ruth had bought in Alexandria. We were alone for some time before dinner, speculating about what was going to happen now that the war was over. I was a little taken aback when Tooey suggested that before I left Washington I should see Curtis LeMay. He wanted me to persuade LeMay that nuclear weapons were going to prove far more effective agents of destruction than fire bombs, which, as Commander of the forces which were engaged, LeMay had used to lay waste to 15 square miles of the Tokyo complex. In this operation, on 10 March 1945, nearly 84,000 Japanese lost their lives. I did not go to see LeMay.

Tooey had invited Hap Arnold, and Jimmy Doolittle and General Brereton, together with their wives, to meet me at dinner. I had met Arnold only once before, when he attended one of the pre-D-Day Commanders' conferences. One of the odd memories of that dinner is of the three ladies doing all the waiting at table and then washing up—I would have expected a host of military servants for the top brass of the American Air Forces. We went on talking about the same general matters that Tooey and I had been discussing before dinner; about Anglo/U.S. cooperation and the transformation that had occurred in the apparatus of war, and in the significance of the Air. I do not recall any mention of the U.S.S.R. on that occasion. At the end of a long evening, Hap Arnold drove me back, but stopped a block away from my hotel. He started talking again, and very seriously, about the atom bomb. As though I had some unique way of seeing into the future, he asked what I thought was now going to happen. I could only reply by saying that I knew less than he did, since he had been one of the main people concerned in the development of 'the bomb', and certainly in authorising its use over Hiroshima and Nagasaki. He seemed a deeply worried man.

As we talked, I could not help thinking of a meeting which I had had in my B.B.S.U. office at the foot of Whitehall some weeks before, with the great Theo von Karman of the California Institute of Technology, the scientist/engineer in whose advice about the design and equipment of their Air Forces the Americans had complete confidence. Von Karman, who was Hungarian by birth, and a Foreign Member of the Royal Society as well as a member of the American National Academy of Sciences, had arrived in my room with a bodyguard of colonels. All took notes of our conversation. Von Karman knew that I was ignorant about matters relating to aeronautical design or the design of armaments. What he wanted to find out was what I had learnt about the significance of destruction in war. 'If you had been one of the dead', he asked, 'would it have made any difference to you whether you were incinerated in Hamburg or in Hiroshima?' He seemed to think not. It was the means of destruction, of death, on which all discussion focused in those days. Some of the scientists concerned in the development of 'the bomb' may have known about the biological effects of radioactivity, but if they did, these were secondary considerations at the time. What mattered was the enormous explosive and thermal power of 'the bomb'. As Prime Minister representing the U.K. at the end of the Potsdam Conference in July 1945, Attlee shared the responsibility of agreeing with President Truman that 'the bomb' should be used. According to him, not one of the politicians who took the decision to use it was aware of the fact that nuclear explosions differed from the burst of conventional weapons, except in their greater force. 'We knew nothing whatever at that time about the genetic effects of an atomic explosion. I knew nothing about fall-out and all the rest of what emerged after Hiroshima. As far as I know, President Truman and Winston Churchill knew nothing of these things either, nor did Sir John Anderson, who coordinated research on our side. Whether the scientists directly concerned knew, or guessed, I do not know. But if they did, then, so far as I am aware, they said nothing of it to those who had to make the decision.'[24] In fact, the scientists who at the time tried to put a brake on the use of the bomb, men like Szilard, Seaborg and Franck, did so because they could see no end to infinitely destructive conflict if nuclear weapons were developed. Issues such as the danger of radioactive environmental contamination, of possibly disastrous genetic changes, of radiation-induced cancer, did not come to the forefront of discussion till the fifties, when the testing of new atomic weapons made such matters obvious to all. It was the widespread realisation of the hazards of fall-out that then played so prominent a part in the run-up to the Partial Test Ban Treaty of 1963.

But in 1945 what mattered was destructive power. And it still matters. Even if wars have hardly ever been won by pitting one unit of destructive power against another, destruction, as I have said, is a kind of vested interest of war. Today, the threat that destruction could escalate to the level of global annihilation has become the true meaning of what is known as the concept of 'deterrence'. Dick Crossman once told me that during the course of a public relations tour of an American nuclear control centre, in a period when relations between the West and the U.S.S.R. were at a low ebb, he was advised that if only the politicians would give the go-ahead and keep out of the way, 'the whole thing could be settled in an afternoon'. An American friend, an official very high in the Washington hierarchy, also told me of a time when he attended a briefing at which maps were displayed showing the targets for potential nuclear strikes, both in the U.S.S.R. and China (I have no doubt at all that reciprocal maps exist on the other side). At the end of the proceedings, the Commanding General asked whether there were any questions. One junior general had the temerity to ask what would happen 'if we are not at war with China, only with Russia?' The answer was to the point: 'Say, do you want to foul up our targeting arrangements?' The comment on that answer that should have been made is also straightforward. If ever those arrangements were put into effect, it would be a miracle if anything was spared from destruction. Strategic air war becomes a meaningless concept were it ever to imply the use of nuclear weapons. There would be destruction, yes—destruction on a scale that would never be seen again. But there would be no victory.

The day after Tooey's dinner, Larry Norstad, who was back in the Pentagon, said that before leaving Washington I should make a point of calling on Brigadier General Groves, the military head of the Manhattan Project organisation which had been responsible for the development of 'the bomb'. Larry told me that Groves, who was an M.I.T. graduate, was what he called 'a wooden engineer' because of his subsequent low placing in his passing-out year from West Point, and that he had been involved in the building of the Pentagon. 'Some of us', said Larry, 'are beginning to think it's a pity he did not get his two projects mixed up.' I duly saw Groves, and made whatever observations seemed appropriate about his successful direction of an enormous team of scientists and engineers. I then remembered that the newspapers were full of appeals for funds to mount a new campaign to 'conquer' cancer, and mildly asked whether he believed that if he were put in charge of the campaign he would succeed in eliminating that eternal scourge of mankind. 'Yes,' Groves replied slowly, 'if only I could stop you scientists working on things in which you become interested.' That was neither the first nor the last illustration I have been given of the way those who are not creative scientists sometimes look at the scientific process.

I also spent some time with Paul Nitze, whom I had first met when he was a member of the United States Bombing Survey team in Europe, and who was then completing the final report of the corresponding study which the Americans had made of the use of air-power in the Pacific. The main purpose of our talks was to uncover, if possible, any common factors between the two air-wars. While one of the major causes of Japan's defeat was the decline in her imports of raw materials due to shipping losses, one of the significant conclusions which the American team drew was that a focused attack on parts of Japan's rail network would have produced a 'strangulation' which 'would have more effectively and efficiently destroyed the economic structure of the country than individually destroying Japan's cities and factories'—including oil refineries.[25]

John Fulton, whom I had telephoned when I landed in New York, had arranged that I should meet the medical authorities who had been involved in the war, and joined me in Washington to make quite sure that I did. The organisation of the wartime scientific effort of the United States had been controlled by the Office of Scientific Research and Development (O.S.R.D.), over which presided Vannevar Bush, the distinguished M.I.T. engineer, and J. B. Conant, the President of Harvard, who had been one of the wartime guests of the Tots and Quots. These two men were to do much to bring science into American government. The head of the medical division of O.S.R.D. was my old Baltimore friend, Lew Weed, of the 'Hamilton Street Club'. He and John arranged a dinner for me to meet some of their colleagues, but the occasion was one of such celebration that the next day I could remember little of the conversation. Late that night John and I took a train for New Haven, and the next morning he put me up to address a large class at Yale. He introduced me as a kind of scientific war-hero, but I fear that my performance was somewhat maudlin.

When I got back to London, I tried hard to wind up my military concerns in order to give my full attention to the many new interests which were flowing from the wartime involvement of scientists in the affairs of the nation. I was not alone in believing that their services were going to be just as much in demand in the period of reconstruction as they had been in the war. In addition to the time I had to devote to the B.B.S.U., I was also called upon to give the occasional lecture on the air-war or on operational research to service institutions, including the Imperial Defence College. What then became obvious was that not many scientists, perhaps extremely few, had become involved, as I had, in operational planning. During the early days of *Overlord*, there was an occasion when John Cockcroft and Basil Schonland* invited me to a meal to discuss how it was that while some scientists like R. V. Jones and Bob Robertson played a critical part in the secret world of technical intelligence, in which their task was to glean as much as possible about developments in enemy armaments from snippets of data, I seemed to be the only working research scientist who was admitted into inner planning circles—except, of course, for the Prof with his special relationship with Churchill. I had no answer. That was the way things were—brewers and lawyers and bookbinders, but scientists?—no.

'If', as I said in a lecture many years later, there ever was 'a world in which situations do not repeat themselves like some mass production model, it is the military world.'[26] But it is nonetheless a world which is quickly fixed in a mould by the weapons it generates, a world where, to use the apt expression, one is only too easily 'painted into a corner' by one's own creations. In a letter I wrote to Kingston-McCloughry when I was trying to finish my work with the B.B.S.U., I said that at the start of the war 'we were incapable of bombing accurately'. This meant that we had to rely on 'stick-bombing'. 'Stick-bombing in general assumed small bombs, since aircraft could not carry vast loads. Small bombs meant relatively small foci of damage, and small foci of damage limited the choice of target systems to built-over-areas whose destruction could not have had much effect upon war industry. The more one attacks a bad system, the more you have to justify your actions so that the bad system becomes a good system. We were definitely caught up in this vicious circle.'

I developed the same theme in greater detail in a lecture which I was invited to give early in 1957 to N.A.T.O., at a meeting over which Larry Norstad, then Supreme Allied Commander, presided. But on that occasion, I also emphasised that 'the accelerating speed and growing power of new invention can possibly be a hindrance to clear thinking in the military field'. While particular tactics may call for particular weapons, it is usually the weapon which dictates the tactics; and inevitably strategy then becomes conditioned by what is practically possible. 'For example,

---

* Schonland, who was knighted in 1960, became head of the Operational Research team attached to Montgomery's 21 Army Group in 1944. He was Director of Harwell from 1958 to 1960.

weapons systems which might be pre-eminent in range and destructive power might impose inefficient strategies both from the point of view of cost and of results—in the same way as good strategy may be nullified by inefficient weapons, using the word "weapon" in its broadest sense, and using the term "inefficient" as implying inadequate for the purpose in view.'

This lecture was the opening address to a conference on 'Operational Research' of which in those days I was still regarded as one of the founding fathers. An essential part of my message was that 'regular officers should be partly responsible for operational research because it is to such men, when they reach the higher levels of command, that we have to look for the proper appreciation of scientific method in the determination of policy in a technological age.'[27] I had urged the same message immediately after the war in an address at the R.A.F.'s major armaments school at Manby in Lincolnshire. A lot of senior officers turned up—I appeared to have been forgiven my transgressions against the R.A.F.— but it took many years, indeed I had to wait until I became Chief Scientific Adviser on Defence more than fifteen years later, before some action was taken to implement my message. And I sometimes wonder if the action that was taken is yet effective.

I then had another reason for hoping that professional military people would become involved in operational research. Creative scientists are rare. Major turning-points in science are few and far between. Most scientists are hewers of wood and drawers of water and, in general, some become 'more equal than others' only in terms of rank or authority. One simply cannot order up so many assorted scientists to do a job, or command them to make a 'break-through'. Operational problems, I discovered, savoured more of the characteristics of biological enquiry than of those encountered by chemists or physicists. I had a fear that scientists who were accustomed to the handling of only strictly controlled situations, and who had little taste for others—for example, 'pure' mathematicians, or mathematical physicists, or theoretical biologists—would have little to contribute to the solution of the kind of issues that were of overriding importance to the good military leader or politician. I had had my fill of idle questions about the number of pounds of explosive that were needed per yard of front to assure an advance of a hundred yards, or of talk about the excess capacity of railways, or of the number of hours it took to repair a broken line or bridge. War generated an inflexibility of outlook, and the more remote from the scene of action, the more inflexible the desk warriors became.

In February 1945, shortly after von Rundstedt's counter-offensive in the Ardennes had been turned, I had written: 'In the efforts of generals and others to save the lives of their soldiers by making warfare more remote, they have automatically increased the amount of iron and chemical necessary to kill a man. Let us assume an annual production of iron of 200 million tons a year, of which, say, 50 million tons are used in munitions. Let us then assume 200 million tons of explosive. If 50 million men and women were killed a year (these were figures 'pulled out of a hat' in order to make the point) that would mean 5 tons per person destroyed. But 1 gram is enough to kill a man. The rest produces devastation. So in order to save lives now, we make it more difficult to survive afterwards.'

In a way I was merely echoing Tacitus—'when they make a wilderness, they call it peace'.[28] And when I wrote those words, Vietnam was still far away. So were hydrogen bombs. Survival today depends on mutual deterrence, on fear of mutual annihilation, but the arms-race is nonetheless urged on by the momentum in the system.

CHAPTER 19

THE END OF ONE EDUCATION

IT WAS the winter of 1946 before I finally shook off my responsibilities for the B.B.S.U. The organisation had by then been disbanded, and the task of producing the reports of some of its panels, as well as the Overall Report, had been accepted as a labour of love by senior members of the Unit. By then I had other things to think about. Before the war had ended, Stradling had been invited by Duncan Sandys, then Churchill's Minister of Works, to become head of a new scientific division that was about to be formed in his Department. The purpose of this proposed organisation was to provide a scientific background to plans for the rebuilding of our bombed cities, and Sandys had decided that it should be furnished with an advisory committee, which he asked me to join. I agreed, but he was no longer Minister when Churchill's Government was replaced by Attlee's after the July 1945 election. I also became a member of another Governmental committee which was set up in December 1945, with wider responsibilities. Its chairman was Sir Alan Barlow of the Treasury, and its task was to propose measures whereby the country's scientific strength could be rapidly increased. Barlow's Committee was small, and since I was in Whitehall much of the time, it was thought convenient to have me as one of its independent members.

Indeed, before this Committee was established I had undertaken to prepare for Herbert Morrison, who was now in Attlee's Cabinet as Lord President of the Council, a plan for a 'Science Secretariat' to help direct the country's scientific effort. Morrison's request that I should do this came after a meeting I had arranged for him with a few members of the Tots and Quots, including Mark Oliphant, one of Rutherford's team at the Cavendish Laboratory in Cambridge. Mark, who had played a major role in the development of the magnetron, on which short-wave radar depended, had been head of Birmingham University's Department of Physics from before the war, and it was he who had transmitted to the responsible governmental committee Peierls's and Frisch's famous short paper which explained how an atom bomb could be made. The others who helped me were Blackett, Bernal and Waddington. The final draft of the document (which is reproduced as Appendix 7) was submitted to Morrison in September 1945. It presages a great deal that has happened since in the organisation and support of British science, and I cannot but be amazed by the extent to which today's debate about the place of science in national affairs echoes what we said more than thirty years ago, and how little the problems have changed.

There was also my Extra-Mural Unit in Oxford that had to be wound up. Another urgent question which I had to answer was whether to remain in Oxford with Le Gros Clark under new terms which he wished to dictate, or to assume my duties as head of the Department of Anatomy in the University of Birmingham. Our son Paul had been born little more than a month after V.E. Day, and a decision on the matter could not be delayed, since 3 Museum Road was going to prove too small for us, whether or not we left Oxford.

I had managed to keep abreast with such developments as had occurred during the war in my own fields of academic research, and I wanted to return to the laboratory. That, and the intellectually exciting prospect of helping to deal with a mass of national problems in the civil field, left me in no doubts that I had to decline Tedder's invitation to abandon university life and join him as scientific adviser to the Air Ministry. He made this suggestion shortly before he succeeded Portal as Chief of the Air Staff on 1 January 1946. 'I shall need your help', he said as we dined in the Athenaeum and speculated about the consequences of the emergence of the atom bomb, about which neither of us knew much. 'I don't know whether my job is going to be to bury the R.A.F. or to keep it going.' But even the thought that from then on I would see less of him and my other military friends could not make me change my mind.[1] Like Mountbatten, Tedder had revealed to me new horizons of experience, and had made me learn much about the ways of the world. He had, in effect, directed the finishing school of the first phase of my life. He had come to trust me, and I had learnt to respect both his critical judgment and his patience in dealing with the powerful and often wayward air barons with whom he had to live. No-one can compromise about what is the best available truth in new scientific knowledge. But compromise had proved essential in dealing with the Titans who bore the direct responsibility of command in the war. Command turned simple men into *prima donnas*. Tedder knew this, and I did not. What I had learnt from our association was that the most obviously rational propositions had often to be fought for, and that one had to learn to move in a world where what was manifestly black had sometimes to be treated as white.

The Services may have been beholden to the scientist and engineer for their equipment. But for most military leaders that is where the relationship stopped. What was done with the 'hardware' which the scientist and engineer designed was another matter. Not long after I had moved to Birmingham, the University was host to an international conference of physicists. Mark Oliphant induced me to attend one of its receptions so that I could meet some of his friends. Among them was Robert Oppenheimer, then the leading member of the community of American and refugee scientists who had been involved in the development of 'the bomb'. This, of course, was well before the fateful dispute which he was to have with Edward Teller and the military authorities, and which ended in his removal from American official science. Mark drew Oppenheimer and me into a quiet corner in order to discover whether I knew anything about the intentions of the American or British military. What they particularly wanted to know was whether I had heard any talk about the further development of the bomb. I had not, but nonetheless I had no hesitation in saying that if Oppenheimer was not already in the confidence of his military chiefs, he was unlikely ever to be, however much they appreciated his achievement in a field which had now become central to their thinking. In the circumstances, I warned him to be wary of what gossip he was likely to pick up about U.S. military intentions. I assumed that he knew about their views of the Russians. After all, 'Bolsheviks' had been under American beds even before the Wall Street collapse of 1929. One of the current jokes when I was at Yale in the early thirties was that Mrs. Angell, the President's wife, got down on her knees every night to make sure that there was no bearded figure lying in wait under her bed to spring on her while she slept.

Although I never again worked directly with Tedder, I saw him as often as I could until his death in 1967. I have often heard it said that at heart he was an academic, and not a professional soldier, and that after reading History at Cambridge, it was only the First World War that prevented him from becoming a don. In fact, after taking his degree, he was appointed to the Colonial Service, and was then posted to Fiji. From there, on the outbreak of war in 1914, he made his way back to England to join the Army, from which he transferred, in 1916, to the Royal Flying Corps. I do not believe Tedder was an academic type, but he was, in a sense, an intellectual. I thought I knew and understood him well, but in his autobiography he revealed to me new aspects of events in which I had been directly concerned, and about which I had assumed that I was aware of all that was to be known. Tedder wrote remarkably few minutes in comparison with, say, Dickie Mountbatten. When, in the stormy period after *Overlord*, I asked him why this was so, his reply was, 'What's the point of circulating minutes? There never will be a true history of what's happening.'

Of all the military men I met during the war, only Tedder would have talked about the Punic Wars on the night we invaded Sicily. Someone with my kind of background distracted him from the run-of-the-mill affairs with which he had to deal. He was certainly fascinated by the way a scientific approach helped in dealing with matters which were otherwise tackled along conventional planning lines. Leslie Scarman, his Principal Staff Officer, was also like a breath of fresh air; Leslie, who in due course was to become head of the Law Commission and then a Lord Justice of Appeal. It is true that Monty surrounded himself with a bevy of young men, among whom were academics like E. T. (Bill) Williams, his Chief Intelligence Officer and now the Warden of Rhodes House in Oxford, and Tom Howarth, today Senior Tutor of Magdalene College, Cambridge. But from all I have been told, Monty was too focused on himself in those days, too single-minded as a military man, to seek relaxation in their intellectual interests.

Tedder was a modest and reticent man. His bantering tone and sardonic humour disguised a sensitive core which his pencilled landscape sketches so often revealed. Toppy used to call him 'Bomb', a nickname which I disliked. Most of the staff called him 'Chief'. Unlike other Commanders in his circle, most of whom, like Eisenhower (Ike) or Spaatz (Tooey), were known by their christian names or by nicknames, Tedder was called by his surname by all except Eisenhower, who called him Arthur. Starting at the end of 1943, Tedder kept what he called a 'line book' into which was entered and duly signed, any extravagant remark that one may have made—'shooting a line' was a popular expression in those days. 'Put it in the book', the shout would go up from him or Toppy. Most of the entries are in very light vein, and fail to recapture the atmosphere in which the remarks they enshrine were made. For example, there is one signed by Eisenhower, which says, 'I always await orders, Lady Tedder'. The first remark of mine which appears is, 'I like the simple things of life'.

But one entry is far more revealing about Tedder himself than are any of the others. On the fly-leaf of the book is pasted a letter which Tedder had received from Montgomery only a year after the end of the war. It dealt with a forthcoming conference of Army Commanders, which Tedder was rather peremptorily invited to attend, and at which Monty declared that he was going to lay down 'a common doctrine of war'. I am sure that what made Tedder regard the letter as 'a line' was the statement that the doctrine which Monty was going to enunciate 'will be the Army teaching in broad outline'. 'There will', he wrote, 'be no argument about it.' Monty's letter epitomised the reverse of the way Tedder operated. Tedder listened and questioned. It was certainly irony that made him sign a 'line' which said that he 'always agreed with his staff'. But whatever else, he never laid down the law.

After the war, Tedder and Toppy sometimes stayed with us in Birmingham, where his son John, now Professor of Chemistry in the University of St. Andrews, had settled as a research worker. On a visit in 1951, Charles Laughton was one of four players (the others were Charles Boyer, Agnes Moorehead and Sir Cedric Hardwicke) who were giving a reading at a Birmingham Theatre of *Don Juan in Hell*—Charles's own arrangement of Act III of Bernard Shaw's *Man and Superman*. This was before he satisfied his ambition to play *Lear* at Stratford, and he came round one night after the show. Tedder and Charles were fascinated by each other, and in due course I encouraged Charles to read from the Bible. He chose Daniel, and I can still hear him intoning:

'Then Nebuchadnezzar came near to the mouth of the burning fiery furnace: he spake and said, Shadrach, Meshach, and Abed-nego, ye servants of the Most High God, come forth, and come hither. Then Shadrach, Meshach and Abed-nego came forth out of the midst of the fire. And the satraps, the deputies, and the governors, and the king's counsellors, being gathered together, saw these men, that the fire had no power upon their bodies, nor was the hair of their head singed, neither were their hosen changed, nor had the smell of fire passed on them. Nebuchadnezzar spake and said, Blessed be the God of Shadrach, Meshach, and Abed-nego, who hath sent his angel, and delivered his servants that trusted in him, and have changed the king's word, and have yielded their bodies, that they might not serve nor worship any god, except their own God. Therefore I make a decree, that every people, nation, and language, which speak any thing amiss against the God of Shadrach, Meshach, and Abed-nego, shall be cut in pieces, and their houses shall be made a dunghill: because there is no other god that is able to deliver after this sort. Then the king promoted Shadrach, Meshach, and Abed-nego, in the province of Babylon.'[2]

We went to bed late that night.

I do not know what it was that drew Eisenhower and Tedder together. Perhaps it was the quality of 'goodness' which people found in Eisenhower that made him realise Tedder's virtues. Ike was not a patch intellectually on Tedder, and Tedder shared none of Ike's liking for card games or golf. The last time I saw Eisenhower was at Tedder's suggestion, shortly after the general had decided to embark on his campaign for the Presidency of the United States. I had gone merely to pay my respects, but Ike started to tell me about the things that had to be put right, and the things that needed to be done, in order to preserve freedom and democracy. At one moment I interrupted and asked whether he remembered the British cartoonist, Low, and his favourite figure, Colonel Blimp. When he said he did, I remarked that what he was saying about preserving democracy sounded very much like the Colonel saying to another colonel in the turkish baths, 'Gad Sir, Lord Beaverbrook is right. The Tory party must save the Empire if it has to strangle it in the attempt'. For the Empire, I asked whether we had to read democracy. Ike was not pleased.

The Tots and Quots were very much alive when the war ended, and for a brief period some of us thought that we could again hold together. But this was not to be. There was a dinner to which Joliot-Curie came to discuss the organisation and future of science in France, and the re-establishment of the Anglo-French Society of Science which we had all but launched at the start of the war. There was another dinner which was attended by Laugier and Pierre Auger, another of our French colleagues, and by Harlow Shapley, the Director of Harvard Observatory. On this occasion we discussed the U.N.E.S.C.O. Conference which was then taking place in London. Laugier, who was to become Deputy to Trygve Lie, the first Secretary-General of the United Nations, warned that unless powerful action were taken, the Preparatory Commission which had been charged to set up a framework for the projected U.N.E.S.C.O. was unlikely to include a single scientist. We accordingly decided that it was all the more urgent that bilateral and multilateral arrangements on scientific matters should be made with other countries, in the know-ledge that once established, they could be absorbed into any future U.N.E.S.C.O. We therefore proposed that an international conference should be convened in Paris in order to stimulate action. Shapley and Laugier suggested that the Tots and Quots should take the initiative in selecting delegates—a remarkable indication of the international esteem which our private dining club then enjoyed. In fact, the club did not take up the suggestion, but left the task to individual members, one of whom, Julian Huxley, in due course became the first Secretary-General of U.N.E.S.C.O.

After a few more dinners, the club ceased to exist, partly because its members had become less tolerant of each other's political opinions, and partly because I simply did not have the time, or the patience, to continue convening the dinners. I sometimes regretted that the club died. But it had had its day, and had served its purpose. When we began we were a group of relatively young, outspoken men, few of whom were known outside our own university departments. To our elders we no doubt appeared as a pack of 'Young Turks'. If anyone had suggested to the original Tots and Quots that among their numbers was a future President of the Royal Society, or that a few would end up in the House of Lords, it would have been regarded as a silly joke. But all of us had matured by the time the club died, and several had had to shoulder major responsibilities. We had indeed become part of a new Establish-ment. Operational research was, to a significant extent, the creation of our members. We stimulated the appointment of scientific advisers to Government Departments. And we helped give substance to the concept of social responsibility in the application of science. We may not have started out to do any of these things, but if we helped to bring them about, then, as a survivor, I am happy to share in the legacy of credit.

The casual nature of my connection with the Ministry of Home Security was, I suppose, the reason why no-one seemed to have noticed that I was never formally attached to any of the military staffs with which I later worked. I had therefore been able to travel independently through the war years, neither having had to subcontract my judgment to others, nor bow to doctrine which I could not accept. Consequently I was as much a free man at the end of it all as I had been at the start. But if still free, the freedom which I was to enjoy in the post-war years certainly differed from what I had known before destruction became part of my daily life.

For with the fighting over, it did not take long to discover that a scientist could not expect to be as free in the public arena as he could in a university. And from then on I was to live in both. In 1946 I moved to Birmingham, where I was able to build up a Department of Anatomy which became one of the strongest in the country. That was an academic enterprise. But the attempt—in a wider sphere—to revitalise the Zoological Society of London, whose Honorary Secretary I became in 1955, was nothing like as easy, and was to bring me and the Society's Council into a head-on conflict with some of its subscribers, a conflict which was to end in the Law Courts. The decision in our favour then left me with a moral responsibility to embark on a vigorous search for funds with which to replace the derelict buildings of this national institution and also to provide it with the research facilities it needed to justify the terms of its Royal Charter.

I have no doubt at all that the effectiveness of my University work, like that of the services which I was giving to the Zoological Society, gained from my simultaneous involvement in committee work in Whitehall. In 1946 the Government set up an Advisory Council on Scientific Policy, and I became its Deputy Chairman and Chairman of its Scientific Manpower Committee. I was also appointed Chairman of another body which went by the name of the Natural Resources Committee. This voluntary government service went on for fourteen years, and provided a fascinating education, which quickly revealed that it is far more difficult to reconcile the diverse aims of peace than to resolve the disputes of military planning, where, whatever the argument, victory was always the single and overriding national purpose.

In 1959 I accepted a full-time appointment as Chief Scientific Adviser to the Ministry of Defence. It was agreed, however, that in filling this post, I should not have to relinquish my Chair of Anatomy in the University of Birmingham, and that I could continue with the campaign to help modernise the Zoological Society.

I could not see myself being an effective scientific adviser were I not actively participating in research; that to me was the best way to keep a critical spirit alive. In 1964 the responsibilities of the post were widened and I was also named Chief Scientific Adviser to the Government as a whole.

Hard practical experience as a full-time Government servant showed me what is entailed when vast resources are committed to a particular technological development, such as an advanced aircraft, which in the end has to be cancelled. I was to learn that the military trappings of the past, and the interests by which they are sustained, do not necessarily relate to the political realities of today. I was to discover that the debate about nuclear weapons, which, like the negotiations in which I became involved and which led to the Partial Test Ban Treaty of 1963, was far from straightforward, however obvious the issues seemed. I was to realise that industrial success is not just a matter of embarking on more Research and Development. I became very conscious of the fact that there is far more to the social responsibility of scientists than mere declarations in favour of world peace, of world plenty, of an end to famine and of an unpolluted rather than a destroyed environment. And I was to find out that statements of the obvious by academics who are temporarily recruited to Governmental advisory bodies are not necessarily blueprints for action; that different constraints affect freedom in every field of social endeavour; and that the public arena is a dangerous place for the inexperienced idealist. Like others, I now have my doubts whether scientists, who had rightly been lauded for what they had done to help win the war, have since lived up to what was expected of them, and to the promise which was theirs. Some of our hopes have certainly come true; others, alas, have turned sour.

It will not be easy to tell the story of those post-war years.

GLOSSARY

Codenames:

AIMWELL	Projected raid on Alderney, August 1942
BLAZING	Projected raid on Alderney, May 1942
BUGLE	Allied air attacks on communications in the Ruhr, March 1945
CHARNWOOD	Allied attack on Caen, 7 July 1944, employing tactical bomber forces
CLARION	Plan for a one-day widespread air attack on communications throughout Germany, February 1945
COBRA	Break-out by American forces near St. Lô, 25–29 July 1944
CORKSCREW	Allied attack on, and capture of, the Island of Pantelleria, June 1943
CROSSBOW	The German V-weapon system, and Allied operations against it
FORTITUDE	Cover plan for OVERLORD, designed to indicated an invasion in the Pas-de-Calais area
GOODWOOD	British 2nd Army attack S.E. of Caen, 18–21 July 1944
HABBAKUK	Plan to construct aircraft-carriers from reinforced ice
HUSKY	Allied invasion of Sicily, July 1943
NEPTUNE	The assault phase, and naval aspect, of OVERLORD
OBOE	Radar aid for blind bombing
OVERLORD	Allied invasion of Europe, June 1944
POINTBLANK	Directive for the conduct of the Combined Bomber Offensive, issued on 10 June 1943
TOTALIZE	First phase of attack towards Falaise by 1st Canadian Army, 8–11 August 1944
TRACTABLE	Second phase of attack towards Falaise by 1st Canadian Army, 14–16 August 1944
ULTRA	Intelligence obtained by means of deciphering German 'Enigma'-coded messages.

NOTES AND REFERENCES

The following abbreviations have been used to designate sources which have been referred to three or more times.

B.B.S.U. Overall Report = B.B.S.U., 1946, *The Strategic Air War against Germany, 1939–1945.*
Bradley = Bradley, O. N., 1951, *A Soldier's Story*, London: Eyre & Spottiswoode.
B.S.U. Report No. 4 = B.S.U., 1943, Air Attacks on Rail and Road Communications. 28 December. [Sicily Report]
Clark, 1962 = Clark, R. W., 1962, *The Rise of the Boffins*, London: Phoenix.
Clark, 1965 = Clark, R. W., 1965, *Tizard*, London: Methuen.
Craven & Cate = Craven, W. F. and Cate, J. L. (Eds), 1951, *The Army Air Forces in World War II*, v. 3, Chicago: University of Chicago Press.
Eisenhower = Eisenhower, D. D., 1948, *Crusade in Europe*, London: Heinemann (New York: Doubleday, 1945).
Ellis = Ellis, L. F., 1962, *Victory in the West*, v. 2, in series *History of the Second World War*, London: H.M.S.O.
Harris = Harris, Sir Arthur, 1947, *Bomber Offensive*, London: Collins.
Harrison = Harrison, G. A., 1951, *Cross-Channel Attack*, in series *United States Army in World War II*, Washington, D.C.: U.S. Govnt Printing Office.
Montgomery, 1947 = Montgomery, Viscount, 1947, *Normandy to the Baltic*, London: Hutchinson.
Montgomery, 1958 = Montgomery, Viscount, 1958, *Memoirs*, London: Collins.
Kingston-McCloughry = Kingston-McCloughry, E. J., 1955, *The Direction of War*, London: Cape.
Pogue = Pogue, F. C., 1954, *The Supreme Command*, in series *United States Army in World War II*, Washington, D.C.: U.S. Govnt Printing Office.
Tedder = Tedder, Lord, 1966, *With Prejudice*, London: Cassell.
Webster & Frankland = Webster, Sir Charles and Frankland, N., 1961, *The Strategic Air Offensive against Germany, 1939–1945*, 4 vols, in series *History of the Second World War*, London: H.M.S.O.

Notes to pages 25–30

Chapter 2
1. The account given of Trotter by W. R. Merrington, in his *University College Hospital and its Medical School* (Heinemann, 1976), implies that Trotter's sarcasms were meant kindly. That is not the impression they made on me. Nor do I believe that the book for which he is so famed—*Instincts of the Herd in Peace and War*—is as intellectually distinguished as it is said to be.
2. Zuckerman, S., 1926, Growth Changes in the Skull of the Baboon, *Proc. Zool. Soc., Lond., 15*, 843–73.
3. Huxley, J. S., 1932, *Problems of Relative Growth*, London: Methuen.
4. Margaret Gardiner, in a charming memoir on Wystan Auden published in Volume 3 of *The New Review* (1976), describes some of John Layard's eccentricities and relates how he tried to commit suicide by shooting himself in the head.

This unsuccessful attempt seems to have fascinated Christopher Isherwood, for he uses the episode in two of his books. In *The Memorial* (The Hogarth Press, 1932), it is Edward Blake who puts a pistol to the back of his mouth and fires. He survives and, managing to stagger downstairs to the street, gets a taxi to take him to a psychoanalyst's office, where he collapses. In the more widely known *Mr. Norris Changes Trains* (The Hogarth Press, 1935), it is the Baron Kuno von Pregnitz who, pursued by the German secret police in Berlin, is finally run to ground in a public lavatory at the Zoo station, where he, also unsuccessfully, shoots himself. The other aspect of John Layard, the fact that he was a disciple of Homer Lane, the psychologist, is used in *Lions and Shadows* (The Hogarth Press, 1938) where Christopher Isherwood gives him the name Barnard. And finally, there is a very faint hint of Layard in Peter Wilkinson's elder brother, who appears in Christopher Isherwood's *Goodbye to Berlin* (The Hogarth Press, 1939), and who is described as being 'a scientist and explorer' who has been on an expedition to the New Hebrides—as Layard had been. Isherwood refers to the influence John Layard had on him and Auden in the opening pages of his *Christopher and his Kind* (Methuen, 1977).

5. When he died in 1956, F. J. F. Barrington, who had been a Fellow of the Zoo-logical Society since 1920, bequeathed to it a thousand pounds for the mainten-ance and development of its Library, and a collection of nearly 450 volumes of periodicals and separate works.

Chapter 3

1. Zuckerman, S., 1929, The Social Life of the Primates, *The Realist, 1*, 72–88.
2. Zuckerman, S., 1930, The Menstrual Cycle of the Primates, I. General Nature and Homology, *Proc. Zool. Soc., Lond.,* 45, 691–754.
3. Williams-Ellis, Clough, 1971, *Architect Errant*, London: Constable.
4. Parkes, A., 1966, *Sex, Science and Society*, London: Oriel Press.
5. Zuckerman, S., 1953, The Breeding Season of Mammals in Captivity, *Proc. Zool. Soc., Lond., 122*, 827–950.
6. Woolf, L., 1967, *Downhill All the Way*, London: Hogarth.
7. Higham, C., 1976, *Charles Laughton*, London: W. H. Allen.
8. Fleming, P., 1933, *Brazilian Adventure*, London: Cape.
9. Zuckerman, S., 1932, *The Social Life of Monkeys and Apes*, London: Kegan Paul; New York: Harcourt, Brace.
10. Zuckerman, S., 1937, *La Vie Sexuelle et Sociale des Singes*, Paris: Gallimard.
11. Dart, R., 1959, *Adventures with the Missing Link*, London: Hamish Hamilton.
12. Zuckerman, S., 1933, *Functional Affinities of Man, Monkeys and Apes*, London: Kegan Paul; New York: Harcourt, Brace.

Chapter 4

1. Yerkes, R. M. and A. W., 1929, *The Great Apes*, London, Milford: Yale Univer-sity Press.
2. [Zuckerman, S.] 1929, *The Spectator* (28 December), p. 981.
3. Kellogg and Kellogg, 1933, *The Ape and the Child*, New York: Whittlesey House.
4. Zuckerman, S., 1935, The Ascheim-Zondek Diagnosis of Pregnancy in the Chimpanzee, *Am. J. Physiol., 110*, 597–601.
5. Dupee, F. W., and Stade, G. (Eds), 1972, *E. E. Cummings Selected Letters*, London: Deutsch.
6. Levant, Oscar, 1968, *The Unimportance of being Oscar*, New York: Putnam's.
7. Gissing, G., 1903, *The Private Papers of Henry Ryecroft*, London: Constable.

Chapter 5

1. Lanchester, E., 1976, Introduction to *Charles Laughton*, by C. Higham, London: W. H. Allen.
2. Harrod, R. F., 1959, *The Prof.*, London: Macmillan.
3. Thomas, Hugh, 1973, *John Strachey*, London: Eyre Methuen, p. 125.
4. Ayer, A. J., 1936, *Language, Truth and Logic*, London: Gollancz.
5. Zuckerman, S., 1936, Philosophy and Science, review of *Language, Truth and Logic*, *New Statesman* (11 April), p. 572.
6. Zuckerman, S., 1938, Uterine Bleeding after Neural Lesions, *Les Hormones Sexuelles*, Paris: Hermann, pp. 121–37.
7. Zuckerman, S. and Groome, J. R., 1937, The Aetiology of Benign Enlargement of the Prostate in the Dog, *J. Path. Bact.*, *44*, 113–24.
8. Zuckerman, S., 1936, Treatment of Enlarged Prostate with Male Hormone, *Lancet*, *230*, 439–40.
9. Zuckerman, S., 1936, Inhibitory Effect of Testosterone Propionate on Experimental Prostatic Enlargement, *Lancet*, *231*, 1259.
10. Zuckerman, S., 1936, The Endocrine Control of the Prostate, *Proc. R. Soc. Med.*, *29*, 1557–68.
11. Zuckerman, S., 1940, The Histogenesis of Tissues sensitive to Oestrogens, *Biol. Rev.*, *15*, 231–71.
12. When we first met, George Corner was Head of the Department of Anatomy in the University of Rochester. He then moved to the Carnegie Institution of Washington in Baltimore. In 1952, he was appointed George Eastman Visiting Professor in Oxford, and today he is the Executive Officer of the American Philosophical Society, the oldest learned society of the United States.
13. Clark, W. Le Gros, 1968, *Chant of Pleasant Exploration*, London and Edinburgh: E. & S. Livingston, p. 134.
14. Bernal, J. D., 1938, *Nature, Lond.*, *142*, 685.
15. Liddell Hart, B., 1965, *Memoirs*, 2, London: Cassell, p. 185.
16. Williams-Ellis, Clough, 1971, *Architect Errant*, London: Constable.

Chapter 6

1. Clark, 1962, 56.
2. Zuckerman, S. and Groome, J. R., 1940, An Experimental Study of the Morphogenesis of Intersexuality, *J. Anat.*, *74*, 171–200.
3. Crowther, J. G., 1970, *Fifty Years with Science*, London: Barrie & Jenkins.
4. Anon, 1940, *Science in War* (Penguin Special No. 74), London: Penguin Books.
5. After a short stay in London, both Longchambon and Laugier went to the United States, where they remained for a few months. Longchambon then found his way back to France, while Laugier accepted an invitation to a professorship at the University of Montreal, the largest French-speaking University outside France. The preface to a book that he brought out early in 1942 under the title of *Service du France au Canada*, a copy of which he managed to get to me almost as soon as it appeared, referred to the 'acceuil fraternel et de l'emouvante amitié de mes collègues scientifiques anglais' when he reached England. One of the essays in the book is entitled 'La Science au service du combat'—the matters which Bernal and I had discussed with him and Longchambon before the fall of France. Both of them became Ministers in de Gaulle's first Government set up in 1944, and Laugier, who died in 1973 at the age of 85, became the first Under-Secretary of the newly formed United Nations, a post which he held from 1946 to 1951. He was a charming man with a taste for elegant living which, in his last years in Paris, he

was able to enjoy in a house on whose walls were more Picassos than I have seen anywhere else, and where a set of chairs was covered in tapestries designed by Miró.

6. In his *Fifty Years with Science* (op. cit.), Crowther gives a different account of the arrival of the French scientists, saying that he was alone when Laugier and Longchambon came to his flat. Since this differed from the notes of the club which were in my hands, and from the account given by Ronald Clark in his *The Birth of the Bomb* (Phoenix House, 1961), I wrote to Crowther in 1973 pointing this out, and giving my account. In his reply he wrote: 'You are right about the arrival of Laugier and Longchambon. I remember we received them in my flat because you were otherwise engaged earlier in the day, and I must have mixed the occasion up with others when nothing effective was done because you were out of the country.'

7. Zuckerman, S., 1939, 'The effects of direct concussion on monkeys in underground shelters', Ministry of Home Security, A.R.P.D., Research and Experimental Branch, December. R.C. 65.

8. Greenwood, M., 1940, 'Comments on paper R.C. 65'. Ministry of Home Security, A.R.P.D., Civil Defence Research Committee. 15.1.40. R.C. 65A.

9. Hansard, House of Commons Debates, 10.11.32. *270*, cols 631–2.

10. Haldane, J. B. S., 1938, *A.R.P.*, London: Gollancz, p. 31.

11. Office of the Lord Privy Seal, 'Sectional steel shelters; report upon the investigations of the standard of protection afforded'. H.M.S.O., July 1939 (Cmnd 6055).

12. Zuckerman, S., 1940, 'Brief report of experimental work on the physiological effects of blast'. [Ministry of Home Security Research and Experiments Branch] June. R.C. 108.

13. Ministry of Home Security. Civil Defence Research Committee. Minutes of the 11th Meeting held on 28th June 1940, at the National Physical Laboratory, R.C. (Minutes) 11.

14. R. H. Fowler was Professor of Mathematical Physics and a ballistics expert. He coordinated war research with Canada and then with America from 1939 to 1942, for which work he was knighted in 1942. He was also a full-time member of the Admiralty's Research Section. He died in 1944.

15. Zuckerman, S., 1941, The Problem of Blast Injuries, *Proc. R. Soc. Med., 34*, 171–188.

16. Krohn, P. L., Whitteridge, D. and Zuckerman, S., 1942, Physiological Effects of Blast, *Lancet*, i, 252.

17. E.M.S. GEN. 331. 8 June 1940, signed F. R. Fraser.

18. Zuckerman, S., 1940, Wounds from bomb fragments, *Br. Med. J.*, ii, 131 (L).

19. Cranz, C. and Becker, K., 1921, *Handbook of Ballistics, 1*, London: H.M.S.O. (trans. of 2nd German edition).

20. Zuckerman, S. and Black, A. N., 1940, 'The effects of impacts on the head and back of monkeys', Ministry of Home Security. Research and Experiments Department. 26.8.40. R.C. 124.

21. Black, A. N., Christopherson, D. G. and Zuckerman, S., 1942, 'Fractures of the head and feet'. Ministry of Home Security. Research and Experiments Department. 12.8.42. R.C. 334.

22. Fisher, R. B., Krohn, P. L. and Zuckerman, S., 1941, 'The relationship between body size and the lethal effects of blast'. Ministry of Home Security. 10.12.41. R.C. 284.

23. Green, F. H. K. and Covell, Sir Gordon, 1953, *Medical Research. History of the Second World War*, London: H.M.S.O. (Chapter 11).

24. Black, A. N., Burns, B. Delisle and Zuckerman, S., 1941, 'An experimental study of the wounding mechanism of high velocity missiles'. Ministry of Home Security. 25.10.41. R.C. 264. *and Brit. Med. J.*, ii, 872.

25. Burns, B. Delisle and Zuckerman, S., 1942, 'The wounding power of small bomb and shell fragments', Ministry of Home Security. Research and Experiments Department, 17.11.42. R.C. 350.

26. Clark, 1962, 211–12.

27. Macrae, R. S., 1971, *Winston Churchill's Toyshop*, Kineton: Roundwood Press.

28. The following were at one time of another members of the Oxford Extra-Mural Unit: *Laboratory*: Dr. P. L. Krohn, Dr. B. Delisle Burns, Col. P. Libessart, Dr. Georges Ungar, Dr. C. W. Emmens, Miss B. G. Hunt, Miss E. M. Alden, Miss P. Batty Shaw, Capt. Fulleringer; *Central office*: Dr. Pamela Blake, Dr. J. W. B. Douglas, Dr. H. Grüneberg, Miss A. M. Vidal-Hall; *Casualty Survey* (London): Dr. T. McKeown, Dr. J. Bull, Dr. A. Davies, Dr. T. R. C. Fraser, Dr. K. K. Conrad, Dr. G. E. C. Kennedy, Dr. M. Lubran, Dr. Hildred; (Provinces): Dr. C. C. Spicer, Dr. R. Powell, Dr. C. W. M. Whitty, Dr. D. M. L. Doran.

29. Zuckerman, S., 1952, 'Vulnerability of Human Targets to Fragmenting and Blast Weapons', in *A Textbook of Air Armament*, Ministry of Supply, Ref. TAA/2/12/51.

Chapter 7

1. Zuckerman, S. *et al.*, 1941, Ministry of Home Security. Research and Experiments Department. Casualty Survey; Analysis of Reports nos 1–111.

2. Zuckerman, S., 1941, The Field Survey of Air-Raid Casualties. Ministry of Home Security. Civil Defence Research Committee. 5.11.41. R.C. 270.

3. Hill, A. Bradford, 1941, 'An appreciation of statistical data relating to air raid casualties, collected and analysed for the Research and Experiments Department of the Ministry of Home Security'. Ministry of Home Security, Civil Defence Research Committee. 31.10.41. R.C. 268.

4. Blake, P. M., Douglas, J. W. B., Yates, F. and Zuckerman, S., 1942, 'A Comparison of the Numbers of Casualties caused by German Bombs of Different Sizes'. Ministry of Home Security. Research and Experiments Department. 26.10.42. R.E.N. 182.

5. Webster & Frankland, v. 1, 320–1.

6. Webster & Frankland, v. 4, 143–5.

7. Butt Report To Bomber Command, 18 August 1941, given as App. 13 in Webster & Frankland, v. 4, 205–13.

8. Webster & Frankland, v. 1, 331–2.

9. Birkenhead, the Earl of, 1961, *The Prof in Two Worlds*, London: Collins, p. 249.

10. Webster & Frankland, v. 1, 337.

11. Bernal, J. D. and Zuckerman, S., 1942, 'Quantitative Study of Total Effects of Air Raids' [Hull and Birmingham Survey] Ministry of Home Security. Research and Experiments Department. 2770. (8.4.1942).

12. Air Ministry, 'The Total Effects of Air Raids (Ministry of Home Security Report 2770).' A.I. 3(c) (Air Liaison) Commentary. 2836 (5.5.42).

13. [Emmens, C. W.], 1943, 'A note on the Meaning and Measurement of the Morale of Towns in Relation to Air Raids'. 8.2.43.

14. B.B.S.U. Towns Panel, 1946, 'Report on the Effects of Strategic Air Attacks on German Towns' (November).

15. B.B.S.U. Overall Report, p. 7.

16. Sir Henry Tizard, F.R.S., Secretary of the Government's Department of Scientific and Industrial Research from 1927 to 1929, and from then until 1942, Rector of Imperial College, London, had been a friend of the Prof for years, but the two had fallen out before the war when both were members of a secret technical committee which was responsible for developing measures of air-defence, and in particular radar. This Committee for the Scientific Survey of Air Defence was known as the Tizard Committee. The two remained on bad terms throughout the war and never became reconciled.
17. Snow, C. P., 1961, *Science and Government* (The Godkin Lectures), London: O.U.P.
18. Snow, C. P., 1962, *A Postscript to Science and Government*, London: O.U.P.
19. Clark, 1965, 312.
20. Clark, 1965, 311.
21. Clark, 1965, 308.
22. Harrisson, T., 1976, *Living Through the Blitz*, London: Collins.
23. Webster & Frankland, v. 1, 337.
24. R. V. Jones, F.R.S., as a former pupil, knew the Prof well. During the war he was Assistant Director of Intelligence at the Air Ministry, and is now Professor of Natural Philosophy at the University of Aberdeen.
25. Jones, R. V., 1961, Scientists at War, *The Times*, 6, 7, 8 April, and correspondence, 8, 12, 17 April.
26. Getler, M., 1973, *Washington Post* (15 August).
27. Tedder, Marshal of the Royal Air Force the Lord, 1947, *Air Power in War*, London: Air Ministry.

Chapter 8
1. Fergusson, B., 1961, *The Watery Maze*, London: Collins.
2. Lampe, D., 1959, *Pyke. The Unknown Genius*, London: Evans Bros.
3. Lucas Phillips, C. E., 1965, *The Cockleshell Heroes*, London: Heinemann.
4. Harrison, M., 1965, *Mulberry*, London: W. H. Allen.
5. Zuckerman, S., Scientific Liaison Officer, to C.C.O., 1942, 'Operation BLAZING and AIMWELL', 10 June.
6. Lord Mountbatten has reminded me that the concept of *Habbakuk* comprised two objectives: the first to serve as a mid-Atlantic airfield for anti-U-boat operations, and the second as a fighter airfield stationed off North-West France to support our projected invasion of the Continent. The first objective was pre-empted by the Portugese Government allowing us to use the Azores, and the second by providing our fighters with additional fuel capacity.
7. Minutes of 31st meeting of the Bombing Committee held at Air Ministry, on 21 October 1942. S.35062.

Chapter 9
1. Effect of Air Raids on Tripoli. 15th June, 1940–23rd January, 1943 [S. Zuckerman to Air Officer Commanding-in-Chief, Royal Air Force, Middle East. 6 March 1943].
2. [Zuckerman, S.] 1943, Observations on the Effects of Air-Raids on Tripoli Town and Harbour, on shipping and on Military Targets in the Field. 15.6.43. [Tripoli Report].

Chapter 10
1. Eisenhower, Gen. D. D., June 1943, Pantelleria Operations Dispatch.
2. Zuckerman, S. to Spaatz, Lt.-Gen. Carl, 1943, Operation CORKSCREW, Estimation

of the Bomber Effort Required. (2 June) [Also issued as App. II to Pantelleria Report (Note 4)].

3. Zuckerman, S. to Norstad, Brig. Gen. L., A.C.O.S., A-3, 1943, Operation CORKSCREW, Progress Reports Nos 1–12. 30 May to 11 June. [Also issued as App. IV to Pantelleria Report.]

4. Zuckerman, S. to Spaatz, Lt.-Gen. Carl, 1943, Operation CORKSCREW. Analysis of Relation between Bomber effort and Effects Achieved. (20 July) [Pantelleria Report]

5. Tedder, pp. 442–3.

Chapter 11

1. Winterbotham, F. W., 1974, *The Ultra Secret*, London: Weidenfeld.

2. In his *Blast of War* (Macmillan, 1967, p. 369) Harold Macmillan quotes a statement that Tedder was in Malta with Generals Eisenhower and Alexander and Admiral Cunningham on the night of the Sicilian landings. Tedder had visited Malta two days before, but as he makes abundantly clear in his *With Prejudice* (p. 448) his D-day H.Q. had to be La Marsa because that was where his subordinate air-commanders were stationed, and because he could not operate his forces from Malta. He had in fact failed to persuade Admiral Cunningham that a unified H.Q. for the invasion should be set up on the African mainland.

3. Peter Rodd was a friend whom I had first met at Rolls Park which, as I have already mentioned, was the Spearman's house. He was a brother of Lord Rennell, and at the time was married to Nancy Mitford, the novelist.

4. B.S.U. Report No. 5, Ground Survey of the Results of Attacks on Airfields in Sicily and Southern Italy, 16.5.44.

5. B.S.U. Report No. 3, Analysis of Air-Raids on Palermo (30 December 1943).

6. Palmer, A., 1962, Casualty Survey, Cassino, Italy. Chapter 8 of *Wound Ballistics*, Ed. J. C. Beyer, Washington, D.C.: Office of the Surgeon General, Department of the Army.

7. My Sicily Report (B.S.U. No. 4) was given a fairly wide circulation and in due course became the basis of a major and controversial part of the air plan for the invasion of northern Europe. What I had written about attacks on railway targets, other than big centres or marshalling yards (on which many came to suppose that I had some kind of fixation) suffered a lot of misrepresentation in the arguments which were to develop. But in fact the term 'marshalling yards' was rarely used in what I wrote. As this report is referred to in several official and other histories of the war, and since it has never been published, I have thought it worthwhile to include its opening few pages of 'General Conclusions' as Appendix 3.

Chapter 12

1. B.S.U. Report No. 4.

2. Operation Neptune; Air Attacks on Railway Targets. COSSAC/2301/Ops (Third draft) 3 November 1943.

3. Harris, p. 149.

4. Joint Planning Staff NEPTUNE, 1944, Study No. 6, 'The Delay of Enemy Reserves during the Initial Stages of Operation NEPTUNE. 4.1.44.

5. Minutes, 1st Meeting of Allied Air Force Bombing Committee, 10 January 1944.

6. Air Marshal Peck, A.C.A.S. (General), 2 February 1944, CS 19639/D.A.T.

7. Kingston-McCloughry, p. 128.

8. Minute from the Chief of the Air Staff addressed to the Assistant Chief of Air Staff (Policy), 5 January 1944.
9. According to this appreciation, all the evidence indicated 'that the combined bomber offensive is achieving a profound effect upon Germany's war economy and upon the morale of her people. In the continuation of the offensive towards a decision, time is a vital factor. The offensive should be pressed on in accordance with the existing directifs with all vigour and its intensity increased.' (Report by Chief of the Air Staff and Commanding General, U.S. 8th Air Force on Progress made by the R.A.F. and U.S. 8th Air Force in the Combined Bomber Offensive. 7 November 1943.)
10. Harris, Chapter 9 *passim*.
11. Harris, A. T., 1944, 'The Employment of the Night Bomber Force in Connection with the Invasion of the Continent from the United Kingdom'. BC/MS 31156/C-in-C, 13 January 1944.
12. Comments on Bomber Command Memorandum for the Employment of Night Bombers in Connection with 'Overlord'. D.C.A.S., 27 January 1944.
13. Harris, p. 215.
14. Minute, D.C.A.S. to C.A.S., 23 January 1944.
15. The original Minute, which is quoted in full in Webster and Frankland's History (v. 3, p. 112) reads as follows:
   'General Ismay for C.O.S. Committee.
   'It seems to me that the moment has come when the question of bombing of German cities simply for the sake of increasing the terror, though under other pretexts, should be reviewed. Otherwise we shall come into control of an utterly ruined land. We shall not, for instance, be able to get housing materials out of Germany for our own needs because some temporary provision would have to be made for the Germans themselves. The destruction of Dresden remains a serious query against the conduct of Allied bombing. I am of the opinion that military objectives must henceforward be more strictly studied in our own interests rather than that of the enemy.
   'The Foreign Secretary has spoken to me on this subject, and I feel the need for more precise concentration upon military objectives, such as oil and communications behind the immediate battle-zone, rather than on mere acts of terror and wanton destruction, however impressive. (Initialled W.S.C. Prime Minister's Personal Telegram Serial No. D. 83/5, 28.3.45.)'
   Not surprisingly, the Air Staff, beginning with Portal, were incensed by the charge of 'terror-bombing'. In their eyes, all that Bomber Command had been doing throughout the war was implementing a policy of area-attacks on cities which had been endorsed by the political authorities—who now seemed to be trying to absolve themselves from their share of moral responsibility for attacks on centres of population. Bottomley immediately set out the framework of a rebuttal which he instructed Bufton to translate into a measured reply (D.C.A.S. to D.B.Ops. 28 March 1945). On the same day he also wrote to Harris giving the substance of the P.M.'s Minute on which he wanted comments (Bottomley to Harris, C.M.S. 608/D.C.A.S., 28 March 1945). Harris's lengthy reply, to parts of which I refer in Chapters 12 and 18, is dated the 29 March (A.T.H./D.O./4B). It is of interest that no reference is made by Webster and Frankland to the fact that there had been exchanges between the Air Ministry and Harris before Portal induced Churchill to substitute for his original Minute one which did not speak of terror-bombing. It is equally interesting that David Irving, who made extensive enquiries into the Dresden raid, says that Harris claimed he had not

been informed 'about the wording of the Prime Minister's first minute'. Irving, who was clearly misinformed, adds that had he been, it was unlikely that Harris 'would have commented on it' (1963, *The Destruction of Dresden*, London: Kimber, p. 232). Since I knew of the existence of Harris's letter—from which I had quoted in the Overall Report of the B.B.S.U. (p. 27)—I was not in the least surprised to find that it was available for reference in the Public Record Office.

In his autobiography, Harris writes: 'Here I will only say that the attack on Dresden was at the time considered a military necessity by much more important people than myself, and that if their judgment was right the same arguments must apply that I have set out in an earlier chapter in which I said what I think about the ethics of bombing as a whole'. (Harris, p. 242.).

The altered Minute which Portal persuaded Churchill to substitute was issued on the 1 April 1944, and reads as follows:

'General Ismay for C.O.S. Committee C.A.S.

'It seems to me that the moment has come when the question of the so called "area bombing" of German cities should be reviewed from the point of view of our own interests. If we come into control of an entirely ruined land, there will be a great shortage of accommodation for ourselves and our Allies: and we shall be unable to get housing materials out of Germany for our own needs because some temporary provision would have to be made for the Germans themselves. We must see to it that our attacks do not do more harm to our-selves in the long run than they do to the enemy's immediate war effort. Pray let me have your views. (Initialled W.S.C. Prime Minister's Personal Minute Serial No. D.89/5. 1.4.45.)'

16. The paragraph relating to the A.E.A.F. Plan, in the Initial Joint Plan of the 1 February 1944, reads as follows:

'It has been agreed that the Army's requirement for the delay and disorgan-isation of rail reinforcements into the assault area cannot be made by the cutting of specific lines during the later stage of the preparatory phase. Not only would many of the essential targets in question be unsuitable for air attack but it is doubtful if the air effort would be available at a time when other commitments will be heavy. It has therefore been agreed that the only practicable method of achieving our object will be to impose a general reduction on the whole rail movement potential over a wide zone extending from Brittany to Flanders and probably into Germany. This will entail attacking a large number of rail centres to bring about a general paralysis of the system. This Operation will necessarily be spread over a considerable period of time and must be initiated in the preliminary phase.'

17. Slessor, Sir John, 1956a, *The Central Blue*, London: Cassell.
18. Slessor, Sir John, 1956b, in *The Listener*, 22 November, p.836.
19. Minutes, 2nd Allied Air Commanders' Conference, 26 May 1944.
20. 'Overlord. The Employment of Bomber Forces in Relation to the Outline Plan. AEAF/MS 22007/Air Ops, 11 February 1944 (issued under covering letter signed Kingston-McCloughry, 12 February 1944).
21. Harris, A. T., 1944, Memorandum by AOC-in-C, Bomber Command on Paper Entitled: 'OVERLORD'—Employment of Bomber Forces in Relation to the Outline Plan'. BC/MS 31156/Air/C-in-C, 14 February.
22. Draft Minutes of AEAF Bombing Committee Meeting, 15 February 1944, *and* Craven & Cate, v. 3, 75.
23. Tedder, p. 508.
24. Waugh, E., 1928, *Decline and Fall*, London: Chapman & Hall.

25. War Cabinet Joint Technical Warfare Committee. Sub-Committee on the Effect of Interruptions of Lines of Communication. W.O.T.W./P(44)1. 1 February 1944.
26. War Cabinet Joint Technical Warfare Committee. Sub-Committee on the Effect of Interruptions of Lines of Communication. W.O.T.W./M(44)1. 5 February 1944.
27. War Cabinet Joint Technical Warfare Committee. Sub-Committee on the Effect of Interruptions of Lines of Communication. Interim Report. W.O.T.W./P(44)23. 10 April 1944.
28. Zuckerman, S. to Ellis, C. D., 24 April 1944.
29. Joint Technical Warfare Committee. 'Observations on Interim Report on Effect of Interruptions of Lines of Communication'. 5.6.44.
30. [Paper by the Enemy Objectives Unit of the United States Economic Warfare Department. EOU/EWD. Air Ministry file CMS. 439.]
31. United States Strategic Air Forces in Europe, 1944, 'Plan for the Completion of the Combined Bomber Offensive—March 1944', 5 March 1944 *and* Harrison, p. 219.
32. 'Operation "Overlord"; Delay and Disorganisation of Enemy Movement by Rail', 6 March 1944. [Signed W. S. Wigglesworth, J. H. Ewing, C. [*sic*] L. Lawrence, C. P. Kindleberger.]
33. Verbatim Minutes of a Conference held . . . on Friday, 25th February, 1944, to discuss attacks on Enemy Rail Communications.
34. Napier, Major-General C. S., Mov. & Tn. 'Air Attacks on Railways', 26 February 1944 [to Air Vice-Marshal H. E. P. Wigglesworth].
35. Minutes of the Sixth Meeting of the Allied Air Force Bombing Committee held . . . on 24/1/1944. B. Ops. AEAF/MS 697/Air Plans. 28 January 1944.
36. Harris, p. 200.
37. Tedder, p. 509.
38. Minutes of a Meeting held on Saturday, March 25th, to Discuss the Bombing Policy in the Period before 'Overlord'. CAS/misc./61.
39. Tedder, A. W., 1944, 'Employment of Allied Air Forces in Support of "Overlord" '. DAC/MS. 100, 24 March.
40. Bufton, J. O. [*sic*], D.B.Ops[Minute to DCAS]24 March 1944. D.B.Ops.23082.
41. Craven & Cate, v. 3, 81.
42. Harrison, p. 223.
43. Spaatz to Arnold, 26 March 1944, U. 60193.

Chapter 13
1. Letter COSSAC to C-in-C, 10.1.44 (TLM/MS 136/15).
2. Tedder has given his account of these meetings in his autobiography. He had good reason to write: 'I shall never forget those meetings in the Map Room when we wrangled for hours about the Transportation Plan. Even at the end of them I was far from sure that the Prime Minister fully understood our purpose. I could not help noticing, as the meetings dragged on into the early hours, and the decisions were postponed from week to week, how tired he was and how the rush of events since 1940 had undermined his strength.' (Tedder, p. 532.)
3. Crossman, R. H. S., 1975, *Diaries of a Cabinet Minister*, v. 1. London: Hamish Hamilton.
4. War Cabinet Defence Committee (Operations) Minutes of Meeting held on Wednesday, 5 April 1944, D.O.(44) 5th Meeting.
5. Craven & Cate, v. 3, 79.
6. Saunders, H. St. G., 1954, *Royal Air Force 1939–1945*, v. 3, London: H.M.S.O., p. 87.

7. A.C.M. Tedder to Chief of the Air Staff, 12 April 1944.
8. War Cabinet Defence Committee (Operations) Minutes D.O. (44) 6th Meeting. 13 April 1944.
9. War Cabinet Defence Committee (Operations) Minutes D.O. (44) 7th Meeting. 19 April 1944.
10. War Cabinet Defence Committee (Operations) Minutes D.O. (44) 8th Meeting. 26 April 1944.
11. The exchanges referred to here can also be found in Webster & Frankland, v. 3, 37–8, Harrison, pp. 222–3, Ellis, v. 1, 100–1, and Eisenhower, pp. 255–6. I used to believe that Eisenhower would resign if the AEAF Plan were not accepted, and official histories do say that he had indicated that he would give up his post if he could not have control of the strategic air forces. Harrison, p. 220, Pogue, p. 124, Eisenhower, p. 244.
12. War Cabinet Defence Committee (Operations) Minutes D.O. (44) 9th Meeting, 3 May 1944.
13. Prime Minister to President Roosevelt, No. 669, 7 May 1944.
14. President Roosevelt to Prime Minister, No. 537, 11.5.44.
15. Prime Minister to General Ismay for C.O.S. Committee, and General Eisenhower, Minute D159/4. 16 May 1944.
16. B.A.U. Report No. 1, The Effects of the Overlord Air Plan to Disrupt Enemy Rail Communications, 4 November 1944.
17. Notes of meeting held in the Air C-in-C's Office, H.Q., AEAF on Saturday, 6th May, 1944, to Discuss Bombing Targets (TLM/MS 136/15. 11 May 1944).
18. Effects of Recent Attacks on Rail Centres . . . in the Bridgehead Area. 24 May 1944.
19. Effects of Recent Attacks on Rail Centres in France, Belgium and Western Germany. SHAEF G-2 (Intelligence) Division to Group Captain C. W. B. Urmston, 25 May 1944.
20. The Use of Air Power against Transport and Military Supplies. SHAEF G-2 (Intelligence) Division. 7 June 1944.

Chapter 14
1. 9th AF HQ to AEAF, 1944, 'Report on Precision of Assessable Bombing Missions—Crossbow Targets—1 December 1943 to 4 January 1944'. 20.1.44.
2. D.B. Ops, 1944, 'Potential Effort of Bomber Command against Short Range Targets'. 30 January.
3. Meeting called by Air Commander-in-Chief AEAF, 31 January 1944 (AEAF/22004).
4. Leigh-Mallory's Dispatch, 1946, *London Gazette* No. 37838, Fourth Suppl. 31 December.
5. Fergusson, B., 1961, *The Watery Maze*, London: Collins.
6. Another Oxford zoologist friend, Christopher ('Cub') Hartley, who had also joined the RAF, was more closely involved in the implementation of this idea. He was first given the task of flying a Typhoon against a captured Würzburg, to test a specially devised 'homer'. The test having proved successful, sorties were then flown to probe the German defences across the Channel. These proved to be far too efficient. The Würzburg which was being monitored by the homer either went off the air before the Typhoons could get airborne, or after the station had identified a high-speed plot making straight for it. The plan was therefore abandoned. In the end, the Würzburg stations were taken out by Typhoons

attacking from the rear. Chris remained in the RAF after the war, ending his Service career as Air Chief Marshal Sir Christopher Hartley.

7. Minutes, 2nd Allied Air Commanders' Conference, 26 May 1944.
8. In a letter dated 29 July 1976, Lord Ritchie-Calder had this to say about Harry Lucas. 'I have been thinking a lot about Harry Lucas, who came to me through you and the Tots and Quots. I was surrounded by zealots and I needed a sceptic. I was beset by romantics and needed a cynic. The acerbic Harry seemed an admirable deputy. He was, but not in the terms I had meant. He became my conscience. He had a total concern. He, like me, was determined that propaganda would not make policy (as it did in the First World War) but that policy would make propaganda, and would honour the pledges. We called it the Unwritten Treaty. He worked himself to death—and drove me just as hard.'
9. Minutes, Allied Air Commanders' Conference, 3 June 1944.
10. AEAF Historical Record, 3 June 1944.
11. Minutes, Allied Air Commanders' Conference, 8 June 1944.
12. Zuckerman, S. to Air C-in-C, 1944, 'Observations—suggested by G-2 SHAEF Plan of Attacking some 87 Bridges in Occupied Territory', 14 June.
13. Minutes, 14th Allied Air Commanders' Conference, *and* AEAF Historical Record, 14 June 1944.
14. AEAF Historical Record, 16 June 1944.
15. AEAF Historical Record, 21 June 1944, *and* Craven & Cate, v. 3, 530.
16. Minutes, Allied Air Commanders' Conference, *and* AEAF Historical Record, 20 June 1944.
17. AEAF Historical Record, 14 June 1944.
18. AEAF Historical Record, 15 June 1944.
19. Kingston-McCloughry, pp. 146–7.
20. Tedder, p. 552 *et seq.*, 565.
21. Montgomery, 1958, 257.
22. Minutes, 16th Allied Air Commanders' Conference, 16 June 1944.
23. Kingston-McCloughry, p. 148.
24. Kingston-McCloughry, E. J. and Zuckerman, S., 1944, 'Observations on RAF Bomber Command's Attack on Caen, July 7, 1944', 14 July.
25. Tedder, p. 560.
26. Tedder (p. 565) refers to the report in his autobiography as follows: 'Zuckerman's preliminary report on the bombing of Caen during the first combined operation indicated that it had been of little value except on morale, and one of the lessons which he drew on that occasion was that the Army machine had not informed its various cogs correctly about the purpose of the heavy bombardment which was laid on as a prelude to the assault.'
27. Bradley, p. 340.
28. According to Ellis (v. 1, 378–82), the area was defended by German 84th Corps (Infantry). The front line was held by Panzer Lehr Division, 5th Para. Reg. and—at the Périers end—17th S.S. Panzer Group.
29. Kingston-McCloughry, pp. 147–8.
30. B.A.U. Report No. 44, 'The German Retreat Across the Seine in August 1944'. [June 1947].
31. Montgomery, 1958, 254.
32. Montgomery, B. L., C-in-C, to Comd First US Army, Comd Second Br. Army, 14 April 1944 (21 A Gp/1001/C-in-C).
33. Montgomery, 1958, 256.
34. Montgomery, 1958, 257.

35. Montgomery, 1958, 255.
36. Bradley, pp. 329, 317.
37. Bradley, pp. 321–2.
38. Kingston-McCloughry, pp. 144–5.
39. Montgomery, 1958, 16.

Chapter 15

1. Zuckerman, S., 1944, 'An Appreciation of the Results, up to D+30, of the Overlord "Transportation Plan" '. 25 July.
2. Tedder, pp. 577–8.
3. Wilmot, C., 1952, *The Struggle for Europe*, London: Collins, p. 542.
4. Valéry, P., 1936, La Politique de l'Esprit, *Variété*, v. 3.
5. Pogue, pp. 272–3.
6. Tedder, p. 604, *and* Craven & Cate, v. 3, 640.
7. Tedder, p. 609, *and* ill. facing p. 541.
8. B.A.U. Report No. 1, 1944, The Effects of the Overlord Air Plan to Disrupt Enemy Rail Communications, 4 November.
9. Tedder, p. 610.
10. Notes of a conference held at SHAEF (Main) on October 26th, . . . 1944 to discuss Future Bombing Policy.
11. Tedder, p. 601.
12. Webster & Frankland, v. 3, 85–8.
13. Tedder, Marshal of the Royal Air Force the Lord, 1947, *Air Power in War*, London: Air Ministry Pamphlet 235 (Lees-Knowles Lectures).
14. B.B.S.U. Overall Report.
15. Tedder, p. 612.
16. Tedder, p. 613.
17. Harris, A. T., 1944, 'The Employment of the Night Bomber Force in Connection with the Invasion of the Continent from the United Kingdom' (BC/MS 31156/ C-in-C). 13 January 1944.
18. Comments on Bomber Command Memorandum for the Employment of Night Bombers in Connection with 'Overlord'. D.C.A.S., 27 January 1944.
19. Further Comments by Air Staff in the Light of Experience of Bomber Command's Operations in Support of 'Overlord'. (D.B. Ops 26715 B. Ops 6485A) [under covering note to A.C.A.S. (Ops) signed S. O. Bufton, D.B. Ops, 28 June 1944]

Chapter 16

1. Otto Skorzeny was the young Austrian S.S. officer who had rescued Mussolini from a hotel in the Italian Alps, and flown him to Vienna. In December 1944, he was given an assignment to organise a special brigade of two thousand English-speaking German soldiers, dressed in American uniforms, and to infiltrate them in captured American tanks and jeeps behind the American lines. Here they were to cut communications, misdirect traffic, and generally to cause confusion. Small units were also to penetrate to the Meuse and to hold the bridges until the main German troops arrived. Although a German officer who was captured was found to have on him several copies of Operation *Greif* as it was called, and the Americans therefore learnt what was happening, this does not seem to have stopped the confusion. Indeed, if anything, it accentuated it. Some of the captured Germans told Intelligence officers that a few of Skorzeny's men were on their way to Paris to assassinate Eisenhower. Although this does not appear to

have been true, it did mean that Eisenhower, to his great annoyance, was given a special guard, and that for several days thousands of American soldiers were stopped by the Military Police and made to prove their identity.

2. Speer to Borman, 6 November 1944, *in* Tedder, p. 637.
3. Tedder, p. 669.

Chapter 17

1. Kingston-McCloughry, pp. 192–3.
2. Minutes of Eighth Meeting of USAAF Evaluation Board and Bombing Analysis Unit, held at Butte Rouge on Monday, 5th March, 1945 at 14.00 hours.
3. Webster & Frankland, v. 4, 42.
4. A somewhat strange history of the American organisation has been published by David MacIsaac, an officer of the United States Air Force, under the title *Strategic Bombing in World War Two* (New York: Garland, 1976). The author had apparently not known of the existence of the USSBS until the early 1960s, and is clearly not as well informed as he might be about the origins of field enquiries into the destruction of war—in places he writes almost as though they were a peculiarly American invention. But he does provide some interesting information about the determination of the American Air Forces not to collaborate with the British in any examination of the effects of the air war, and also of their anxiety lest the US Navy share in their labours. Here he quotes (p. 39) a remark by General 'Larry' Kuter, that the US Navy's 'participation in the higher levels of such a committee [the controlling body of USSBS] might well be diplomatic on the part of the Army Air Forces but quite possibly might impair the paramount interests of the AAF', which he does not define. Lt.-Col. MacIsaac also provides some, to me, hitherto unknown information about exchanges which Spaatz is said to have had with Eisenhower. For example, there is a statement (p. 77) that 'Two days after D-Day the supreme commander agreed that oil was now [to be Spaatz's] number one priority'. The book is liberally documented, but no indication is given of the source of this piece of 'knowledge'. Tedder's autobiography is cited in the list of references, but Tedder makes no mention of any such agreement. Had there been one, he, and I in turn, as well as others, would assuredly have known of it unless, of course, Eisenhower had been 'double-dealing' his Deputy who, both as such, and on behalf of the Joint Chiefs of Staff, was then in control of the US and British strategic air forces. Oil targets were not accorded a higher priority than transportation until mid-September. It is a pity that the author did not check a statement which imputes duplicity on Eisenhower's part, by reference to official Chiefs of Staff documents. It is, of course, possible, that MacIsaac relied on Spaatz's informal diary (p. 78). Spaatz's desire, like that of Harris, to defeat Germany on his own, was no secret, but however much both of them managed in practice to wriggle out of the framework of the directives to which they were bound, neither could surely have been disloyal on paper to the Command structure under which they were operating. Even Harris was able to cite tactical considerations as a reason for attacking one city rather than another that had been designated by his C-in-C, Portal.

MacIsaac also makes plain that the vast team of 'business executives, corporation lawyers, bankers, industrial production experts, and economists' who, with their minions, made up the staff of USSBS, were briefed by airmen about 'what strategic bombing had been *envisaged* to become' (p. 157). According to the author, too, 'it had too many people involved in measuring the effects of bombing aircraft factories and too few engaged in the fields of land transportation or industrial area attacks' (p. 158). What he does not say is that USSBS, made up and directed, as it was, by novices in the field of enquiry into which they were plunged, did its work very hurriedly and finished it in a matter of months, whereas the BBSU which had direct access to operational directives—this was decidedly better than being briefed—had, in effect, started its work years before it was formally set up, and completed it in much more leisurely fashion.

5. While the British official History relied for the bulk of its information about the effects of bombing on the British and American Surveys, it imputes prejudice of one sort or another to both, particularly because they did not conclude that RAF Bomber Command's policy of area attacks achieved more than they were able to discover. The British History provides a fair account of the exchanges in which Sir Arthur Harris defended his own policy, even against the contrary instructions of Sir Charles Portal, the Chief of the Air Staff, and leans heavily on Sir Arthur's side, for whose formidable stand the work is in effect an *apologia*.

It also makes some disparaging but unsophisticated comments on the way the survey teams collected and analysed their statistical data, without at the same time providing any indication as to how its authors, Webster and Frankland, would have done the job themselves—assuming that the work which would have been entailed was within their competence. In spite of this, they nonetheless concluded that 'the figures of the surveys, if neither is an exact computation of the effect of area bombing, are sufficiently accurate to show the general effect. . . . There is indisputable evidence that area bombing did not produce any sensible effect on German production of armaments until the closing months, when the attack was at its greatest height' (v. 4, pp. 53–4).

Elsewhere (v. 3, p. 288) the authors also write that 'Huge areas in many great towns all over Germany were severely stricken and some were devastated, but the will of the German people was not broken nor even significantly impaired and the effect on war production was remarkably small. It was not only that the damage could be repaired more readily than had been supposed. The German war economy was more resilient than estimated and the German people calmer, more stoical and much more determined than anticipated.' Webster and Frankland also note (v. 3, p. 89) that 'while the German air defences had been effective, the general area offensive had been a largely self-defeating policy, and that after the German air defences had ceased to be effective, it had been revealed as an uneconomic and even irrelevant policy'. On the other hand, there are some statements made in Webster and Frankland's massive tomes about the area attacks which are anything but as clear-cut as those I have quoted, and which indeed give a contrary impression.

Webster and Frankland agree that the decisive attacks by the U.S. and British heavy bombers were those levelled against the communication network and the synthetic oil plants. For example, they write (v. 3, p. 255) that 'even before the Ruhr was cut off the attack on communications had had devastating effect on the whole of the German economy. Little coal had got out of the Ruhr and everywhere industry was demanding coal from central Germany and the Sudentenland and from such stocks as still existed. This condition was made progressively worse in March and completed in April by the tactical air forces, which ranged over Germany without meeting any effective opposition and made movement both by rail and road almost impossible in large areas.' They also admit (v. 3, p. 261) that 'the strategic offensive against communications was less successful and produced its results more slowly because of the manner in which it was directed . . . the immense power of the strategic forces was not used in the attack on communications in such a manner as to produce the most rapid end to the resistance of the enemy.'

6. Webster & Frankland, v. 4, 41. Far from this being the case, at my meeting with George Ball in November 1944, I had declined his invitation to chair the meetings between the American, French and British teams because I wanted to be released from the work I was doing as soon as possible. Indeed, by the time the survey started, in which I perforce did become immersed, I was already deeply involved in other matters.

7. Popper, K., 1963, *Conjectures and Refutations*, London: Kegan Paul.

8. Harris, Chapter 12, *passim*.

9. Webster & Frankland, v. 4, 45.

10. Webster & Frankland, v. 4, 48.

11. B.B.S.U. Overall Report, p. 166.

12. Webster and Frankland state (v. 4, p. 46) that the BBSU Overall Report 'is not documented' and that therefore 'it is not always possible to ascertain on what evidence judgments are based'. If the two authors had really wished to find out, they had only to enquire. The Overall Report was based on the separate reports which the BBSU Panels had produced. References were not given in its opening chapter to the various statements that had been made by different parties in the debates about bombing policy. These were all kept in an annotated copy, and Pelly took the precaution of having all the relevant documents copied and the copies certified by one of the Air Ministry's legal officers. Pelly kept the documents until shortly before his death in 1972. I, too, have certified true copies.

13. Webster & Frankland, v. 4, 40.

14. *The Times*, 7 October 1961.

15. Butler, J. R. M., 1961, *The Times*, 10 October.

16. Webster & Frankland, v. 3, 284.

17. Webster & Frankland, v. 4, 55.

18. Zuckerman, S., 1966, *Scientists and War*, London: Hamish Hamilton.

19. Tedder, *passim*.

20. Eisenhower, p. 255.

21. Montgomery, 1947, 60, 67.

22. Montgomery, 1958, 324.

23. Bradley, p. 340.

24. Montgomery, 1947, 72–4.

25. de Guingand, F., 1947, *Operation Victory*, London: Hodder & Stoughton, p. 401.

26. Montgomery, 1947, 74.

27. de Guingand, F., 1947, *Operation Victory*, London: Hodder & Stoughton, p. 402.

28. Kingston-McCloughry, E. J. and Zuckerman, S., 1944, 'Observations on RAF Bomber Command's Attack on Caen, July 7, 1944', 14 July.

29. B.B.S.U. Overall Report, p. 170.

30. Zuckerman, S., 1948, The recovery of the French railways, in *The Adventure Ahead*, London: Contact Publications, p. 74.

31. Craven & Cate, v. 3, 796–8.

32. Speer to Hitler. Translated as Appendix 35, in Webster & Frankland, v. 4.

33. Speer to Hitler, in Tedder, p. 616.

34. Speech by Speer at Rechlin, 1944, 1 December. Translated as Appendix 36, in Webster & Frankland, v. 4.

35. Speer, A., 1970, *Inside the Third Reich*, London: Weidenfeld & Nicolson, pp. 284–285.

36. Speer, A., 1970, *Inside the Third Reich*, London: Weidenfeld & Nicolson, p. 224.

37. Frankland, N., 1969, Why didn't we win the war six months sooner? *Observer Magazine* (14 December).

Chapter 18

1. Montgomery, 1958, 332.
2. Eisenhower, p. 389.
3. Montgomery, 1958, 326.
4. Bryant, A., 1959, *Triumph in the West*, London: Collins, p. 376.
5. Montgomery, 1958, 324.
6. Churchill, W. S., 1940, Speech, House of Commons, 20 August.
7. Directive to Air Commander-in-Chief, Allied Expeditionary Air Force (COSSAC (43) 81). 16 November 1943.
8. Minutes, Air C-in-C's Meeting, 13 May 1944 (TLM/MS. 136/9/1).
9. Montgomery, 1958, 257.
10. Minutes, AEAF Bombing Committee Meeting, 14 May 1944 (TLM/MS. 136/9/1).
11. For example, in a note which he sent to Sir Archibald Sinclair in January 1944, Portal wrote that 'the Air Staff advocate throwing the weight of Bomber Command round about the weak places in the German structure, whereas the A.O.C. in-C [Harris] believes more in piling the maximum on the structure as a whole'. (Webster & Frankland, v. 3, 77).
12. Saundby, Sir Robert, 1963, Foreword to *The Destruction of Dresden*, by D. Irving, London: Kimber.
13. Harris, A. T., to Sir Norman Bottomley, 29 March 1945 (ATH/DO/4B).
14. Effects of interrupting the export of hard coal from the Ruhr to the rest of the Reich. J.I.C. (45) 60(O)(Final). A.C.A.S.(P), D.B.Ops., 5 March 1945.
15. Air Staff, 1945, [Review of] Strategic Bombing in Relation to the present Russian offensive, 26 January.
16. Tedder, p. 601.
17. Minutes of 28th Meeting of Combined Strategic Targets Committee, 2 May 1945.
18. B.B.S.U. Overall Report, p. 170.
19. Trevor-Roper, H., 1968, *The Philby Affair*, London: Kimber, p. 68.
20. In *My Silent War* (MacGibbon & Kee, 1968, p. 31), the Russian agent Philby who, like Trevor-Roper, was also in the centre of the ULTRA machine, tells us that there was wrangling even in the central Intelligence establishment where intercepts of enemy messages were decoded.
21. Bradley, p. 462.
22. Tedder, p. 623.
23. Eisenhower, p. 372.
24. Williams, Francis, 1961, *A Prime Minister Remembers*, London: Heinemann, p. 74.
25. 'It seems clear that, even without the atomic bombing attacks, air supremacy over Japan could have exerted sufficient pressure to bring about unconditional surrender and obviate the need for invasion. Based on a detailed investigation of all the facts, and supported by the testimony of the surviving Japanese leaders involved, it is the Survey's opinion that certainly prior to 31 December 1945, and in all probability prior to 1 November 1945, Japan would have surrendered even if the atomic bombs had not been dropped, even if Russia had not entered the war, and even if no invasion had been planned or contemplated.' (United States Strategic Bombing Survey, 1946, Summary Report (Pacific War), Washington D.C., U.S. Govt Printing Office.)
26. Zuckerman, S., 1962, Judgment and Control in Modern Warfare, *Foreign*

Affairs (January), *and* 1966, *Scientists and War*, London: Hamish Hamilton, pp. 101–21.

27. Zuckerman, S., 1958, The need for operational research, *Operational Research in Practice*, London: Pergamon, pp. 6–16.

28. Ubi solitudinem faciunt, pacem appellant. *Agricola*, 30.

Chapter 19

1. I continued to see many of my Air Force friends. Kingston, who had independent means, wrote abstruse books on war after he left the RAF, with which he felt embittered to the end because he had not been given adequate recognition of his wartime services. He was not the only senior AEAF officer who felt that way. Another was Mary Coningham. The last time I saw him was at the lecture I gave at Manby in June 1945, when I urged that professional airmen should become responsible for the kind of operational research which civilians had been doing during the war. Two years later, Coningham was 'lost' over the Atlantic when flying to Bermuda. He had ended the European war under a bit of a cloud, and the award he received at its end was a grade below that which he had been granted when he commanded the Desert Air Force. It was as though a man with a university degree had been presented with a certificate declaring that he had passed his school-leaving examinations. Mary, who has been described by Roderick Owen in his biography of Tedder (Collins, 1952) as 'beyond dispute the outstanding Tactical Air Force Commander of the war', felt hurt by all this. After the grand mess-night dinner which followed my lecture, he asked me to intercede on his behalf with Tedder, as Chief of Staff. I did not know why he had been passed over, but I certainly felt that the mighty had fallen.

   Robb and I kept in touch to the time of his death, and during the period of my secretaryship of the Zoological Society of London, he served on its Council. Wiggles retired to the south coast, to live on his pension. We exchanged affectionate messages every year. Like so many others, he died a forgotten man. Claude Pelly, at first so suspicious of me, remained a close friend until his death. His career did not end with the war. He went on to become, first C-in-C of the Middle East Air Force, then Controller of Aircraft in the Ministry of Supply, and finally a member of the Atomic Energy Authority.

   I continued to see Tooey Spaatz, or at least speak to him on the telephone, whenever I was in Washington, and he would invariably try to arrange for us to have a meal or a drink together. We rarely discussed the war, except once when I checked with him the precise dates on which, in the Pacific, he had informed MacArthur and the other Commanders of the impending use of the atom bomb. He was always friendly and would ask after Portal and Tedder. I also saw Larry Norstad from time to time, but our paths ceased to cross after he had finished his term of office as Supreme Commander of NATO.

2. Daniel, Ch. 3, vv. 26–30.

APPENDIX 1

(see pp. 109, 112)

The Tots and Quots

I have given an account in Chapter 3 of the foundation of the dining club which became known as The Tots and Quots. A few years ago a somewhat dramatic picture of the club was presented in a BBC television programme which the late C. H. Waddington, one of its members, had organised. He used to call us 'Solly's Sunday School'. J. G. Crowther, who has written much about the history of science, and who was also a member, has published a record of some of our meetings in his book *Fifty Years with Science* (Barrie & Jenkins, 1970). The part which the club played during the inter-war years in promoting a social conscience among British scientists has been referred to by P. G. Werskey in his monograph 'British Scientists and "Outsider" Politics, 1931–1945' (*Sci. Studies*, 1971, 1, 67–83). Yet another printed reference to the club of which I know is in *Parliamentary Debates, Lords* (Hansard, Volume 324). In a speech which he delivered during the course of a debate on the Common Market, Lord Ritchie-Calder referred to the Tots and Quots as a 'group of then young scientists, destined for eminence in the scientific world and, all of them, for key positions as the "tame magicians" of the war . . .'.

As the club's convenor, the record which I have of its affairs, even if incomplete, is probably fuller than any other that exists. Apart from those whom I have mentioned in Chapter 3, its members in the first phase of its existence included Gordon Childe, J. Z. Young, John MacMurray, the philosopher; Joseph Needham, the biochemist and sinologist* and Hyman Levy, the Professor of Mathematics at Imperial College, and one of the founders of the Association of Scientific Workers, and so of what today is a powerful Trades Union. Several of us were still in our twenties, but some had already published their first, if not their second and third books. Not one of our scientific members was yet a Fellow of the Royal Society; in the end all were.

Our opening 'meet' took place in 1931 at a now defunct, but then well-known Victorian restaurant, Pagani's, in Great Portland Street. We then dined at more or less monthly intervals in a private room in whatever Soho restaurant I chose. As convenor, it was not only my responsibility to decide the menu, but also to agree the topic on which our after-dinner discussion would focus, and to arrange for the opening speaker. But the club did not run in the way some had expected. Gip Wells resigned after our first dinner, saying that he had hoped the whole thing would be fun, whereas we were obviously going to become monastic and deadly serious. We may not have been monastic, but we certainly were serious.

The notes that survive from that first discussion merely say that the number of members was to be limited to twenty, that fourteen had already been nominated, that further elections had to be by unanimous vote, and that the objects of the club would emerge from discussions to which people of different interests would contribute. The question of a name was raised, but not decided until the next dinner when, after a number of conflicting suggestions, Jack Haldane remarked, 'quot homines, tot sententiae'. Lancelot Hogben, who had recently returned from South Africa, then

* Later Master of Caius College, Cambridge.

said 'the quottentots', a play on the word Hottentots, that tribe of primitive South Africans of whom he may just have encountered one or two survivors before all became extinct. And so we became, first, Quottentots, and then finally The Tots and Quots.

Early in 1932, at what may have been the next dinner, Levy opened a discussion on the economic implications of science, by questioning the extent to which science and economics are in fact the prime motivating forces in society. He pointed to other factors, such as natural resources, the genetic material of a population, climatic conditions and the availability of knowledge, which also constrain social development, and asked whether science should be allowed to grow in accordance with the whim of the individual research worker, or whether it should be directed in accordance with trends of social development. Hugh Gaitskell contended that Levy was confusing concepts of economics with those of sociology. According to him, the social values that determine the priority of different economic and scientific questions were in essence arbitrary, and what was best in economic terms could be assessed only with the help of a measuring rod such as money. The fact that both public and private money were being directed to scientific research was an indication of an implicit judgment that research did have a social value. Gaitskell agreed that new scientific knowledge led to technological developments which then transformed the economic field, and in turn the distribution of wealth and labour and, in consequence, social values. But his view was that social and political objectives had a definite primacy over economic or scientific matters. Years later, after the war, Aneurin Bevan expounded the same idea to me when declaiming against Gaitskell, then the Chancellor of the Exchequer.

In view of the dominant position which Gaitskell assumed in the post-war years, I find it interesting that at that time his views did not commend themselves either to Jack Haldane, or Lancelot Hogben, or Desmond Bernal. I may have missed the point they were making, but the notes which I kept imply that their main criticism was that money values do not necessarily reflect social priorities, and equally that scientists, even though they may be professionally wedded by a common method, constitute a diverse group of people who aim at diverse political ends. In other words, scientists were not working towards any single political purpose.

From this dinner a theme emerged which appears to have been taken up again and again. And after another dinner towards the end of 1932, when the question of the ethical content of Marxist theory came in for much discussion, I penned a note in which I asked whether some members of the Tots and Quots were not being drawn to Marxism because of some, to me, uncritical belief in its scientific basis. I wrote that Marxism, as expounded particularly by Dickinson, was likely to end in illiberalism and rigid dogma because of a failure to recognise the 'psychological inequality of people'. As a group, we were 'left of centre', and in time at least two became very left. But most of us were politically naive and one or two were certainly right wing.

At another dinner which took place not long after, the topic for discussion was the popularisation of science, when a disquiet, which some of us still voice, was expressed about the way scientific knowledge is presented by the popular press to the public.

The experience of the first year or two of the Tots and Quots showed all too well that the name by which the club had come to be known was more than appropriate. Every discussion provoked a clash of opinion, and the greater the measure of disagreement, the more stimulating the meeting. Our talks roamed over wider and wider issues, but more and more what we debated was the question of the general significance of science to society, and the conscious role science might play in social development. But I certainly do not remember believing that as a group we thought that we were helping blaze a trail towards some new understanding of these matters, as has been suggested by one or two people who have written about the club. There was nothing evangelistic about our meetings. If any of the club's members felt that way, they kept the sentiment to themselves. Nor was there any sign of C. P. Snow's 'two cultures'. We were not insulated scientists or economists. So far as I was concerned, it was exciting to be in the company of men like Hogben, with his acute mind which challenged everything; with Bernal, with his encyclopaedic knowledge; with Haldane, with his absolute, some would say arrogant assurance; and with Roy Harrod, with his balanced intellectualism. But why mention only these four? All the members had something to impart, and all, or nearly all, had one thing in common—they were totally free in spirit and speech, and were seemingly bound to no dogma.

The club ended its first phase of life not long after I left London for Yale in January 1933. Hugh Gaitskell and J. L. Gray had said that they would convene the dinners while I was away, but these had ceased by the time I returned to England in the summer of 1934. I do not know how many times the club met while I was at Yale, for when I returned I found that either Hugh or Gray had mislaid the club's Minute Book. In the club files that have survived, there is a letter sent to me in America, in which Dick Lythgoe wrote that 'The Tots and Quots is rather thin in its meetings. Only 6 last time and Sir Frank Smith as the guest of the evening! A perfectly bloody dinner at Brices'. Sir Frank Smith was the Secretary of the Government's Department of Scientific and Industrial Research, the biggest of the Research Councils at the time, and one part of which survives in today's Science Research Council. Philip Hart also wrote to me in the same vein.

I thought about reconvening the club when I returned from the States, but did nothing about it. I was far too busy getting started in Oxford, and too beguiled by lighter matters than those that were exercising my more serious friends. Bernal tried to involve me in his concerns, for among the letters which have survived from that period I find a copy of one that I sent him in October 1934, a few weeks after I had settled in Oxford, asking to be excused from serving on the committee of a new organisation, whose functions I felt could best be discharged by some other body he had mentioned, and of which I confessed I had never heard before. In his reply, he referred to a letter that was being prepared for submission to *The Times*, which he wanted me to get signed by 'Oxford scientists'. What it was about I do not remember.

In the next few years I was aware that several of my old Tots and Quots friends were becoming increasingly preoccupied by what was happening in the political world. But Oxford was neither London nor Cambridge. I knew no scientists in my new university who were as politically concerned as were my Cambridge and London friends. Politics in Oxford seemed to me to be more the business of undergraduate societies, of G. D. H. Cole or of the Oxford Labour Club, than of the High Table or Common Room of Christ Church. Today I find it odd to think that at the time I was immersed in my work in the Anatomy Department, Harold Wilson and Edward Heath, together with others of their contemporaries or near contemporaries who were destined to become our political masters, were undergraduates at Oxford. But my steps did not stray into their circles, and I was unware of their existence. So far as I was concerned there was more than enough excitement in my researches and in my varied social life for me to resist the urge to try to do something to help make a better world. But I had many discussions with Bernal when he was writing the book which, more than anything else, made him known to the wider world—his *Social Function of Science* (Routledge & Kegan Paul, 1939). In particular, I suggested to him a scheme for the integration of medical services, in which the research worker would play a dynamic and central part in the organisation, instead of being someone who,

as it were, was there either to provide answers to questions put to him by the practi-
tioner who wrestled with day-to-day problems, or who worked on the periphery of
a health service, and whose discoveries might or might not in due course be thought
to be relevant to the treatment of disease. I am among those whose help he acknowledged in his Preface, and he inscribed my copy of the book

      To Solly
      Quot homines, tot sententiae
           D.

There must have been a bit of the flavour of our old Tots and Quots discussions in
some of what he wrote.

Stephen Toulmin, a scholar well-known for his writings on the philosophy
and history of science, published a discerning article in the *Observer Magazine* of
28 November 1971, which dealt with the dilemmas that scientists have to face when
they ponder on their social responsibilities, and he refers to Bernal's book as a critical
event in the evolution of our ideas about the place of science and scientists in society.
I believe that Toulmin is right when he says that Bernal's conception of the social
function of science resurrected the basic ideas that Francis Bacon advanced in
Elizabethan times. Toulmin saw Bernal as advocating, in the spirit of Bacon, the end
of science as 'a withdrawn and gentlemanly occupation whose sole aim was to create
a fund of pure knowledge that privateer industrialists might then raid, and exploit,
at their own pleasure and convenience. Instead, scientific research should be financed
out of the national budget: in return, the priorities of different research projects
should be decided with at least half an eye on their social utility.' And Toulmin is also
right in saying that 'Though superficially "socialist", the resulting scheme was not
uniquely so: in the event, it prefigured the administrative structure of the scientific
agencies of the United States of the 1960s, at least as closely as it did those of Russia
and the other socialist States.' But as one who lived through those times, I fear that
Toulmin exaggerates when he writes that Bernal's book 'precipitated a storm'. It may
have stimulated a few people to set up a 'Society for Freedom in Science', but in
general the book hardly caused a ripple, and I doubt if at the time more than a handful
of scientists, and even fewer of the general public, bothered to read it. I for one
deeply regretted this. The literature of the period that must have led Toulmin to his
view does not correctly reflect the passive attitude which then characterised the vast
majority of the scientific world.

When in 1938 Bernal and I had written our paper for Hore-Belisha on the mobilisation of science for war (p. 101), he also agreed that we ought to reconvene the Tots
and Quots in order to help alert scientists to the dangers that lay ahead. I have told
how we reconstituted the club (pp. 109–10), and have also summarised the discussion
that took place in November 1939, at out first dinner of the war. The role that we felt
scientists should play in the war effort was again the theme of the next meeting in
December. Our guest on that occasion was Alfred Egerton, a pillar of what most of
us regarded as the scientific establishment, since he was one of the two Secretaries of
the Royal Society. Our other guest, William Slater, who became a member at the
next dinner of the club, opened a discussion about the disorganisation that war had
brought to agriculture, which he felt could have been prevented by responsible
planning and rational scientific organisation. What he wanted to see formed was a
'scientific general council' that would be in close contact with the Cabinet. Egerton
was diffidently unsympathetic. He disliked both the idea of excessive planning in
science and any undue emphasis of its 'social aspects'. In his view, the general
position would be sufficiently improved if the Secretaries of the three Government
Research Councils operated in concert with the Council of the Royal Society, instead

of separately. This view was not shared by most of our members, who felt that even if the Research Councils and the Royal Society did get together, they would still be remote from those responsible for the determination of national policy. Consequently, so we argued, the way to stir action was to make the public aware of the fact that science and scientists were either not being used in the national interest, or were being misused. In putting our message across, we felt that it would be necessary to use all possible means, and also to call on the prestige of the scientific organisations to which Egerton had referred.

It is interesting that a small Scientific Advisory Committee to the Cabinet was in fact formed less than a year later, and that Egerton became its Secretary. The Prof (Lindemann) had told me that he was not going to oppose the formation of this body since it was unlikely to do any harm, while its formation would help silence some of his critics. When it came to action, he, the Prof, was Churchill's Scientific Adviser, and the officers of the Royal Society were unlikely to get in his way. And, indeed, at this distance, I find it difficult to believe that any significant scientific and technical developments of the war owed their existence to the Committee. Even the work leading up to the atomic bomb, over which, theoretically, the Committee had some kind of supervisory function, would have proceeded just as fast if there had never been any Committee. I suspect that very few scientists even knew of its existence.

In the meantime, the Tots and Quots pressed on, and at the next dinner, towards the end of January 1940, we decided to prepare a series of pamphlets or small books to be published as paperbacks. Our guests at the March dinner were the Prof, and Lord Melchett who, in his capacity as Deputy-Chairman of ICI, opened a discussion on the effects of the war on industry and science. Some of the prophecies made at this dinner proved to be so wide of the mark that they may be worth quoting as an illustration of how impossible it was, even for those who were as well-informed about events as anyone could be, to see how the future would unfold.

Melchett, who soon became one of our members, began by suggesting that the war would prove a stimulus because of the need to overtake German industry, and to capture its foreign markets. In view of the unemployment that existed after the 1914–1918 war, he felt that there would be no shortage of manpower after this one, nor any irremedial material destruction. The steam engine had become necessary at the end of the Napoleonic Wars in order to increase the horse-power per man required to satisfy the growing needs of society, but in his view it would be enough to rely on the existing momentum of industry and science to see us through. There was not going to be any problem of shortage; what was wanted was the proper organisation of 'plenty'. His own economic cure was the establishment of stocks of commodities as an insurance against depression and shortages. This would ensure economic stability, and thus political stability.

Harrod, who followed Melchett, argued that the war had little effect on population trends, and that unemployment was essentially a function of the rate of increase of population. While the capacity to repair the losses of war undoubtedly existed, it was impossible to say that there would not be a demand for some new major technical development comparable to a steam engine (as a close friend of the Prof, he probably knew of the 'atom'). And without an increase in the size of the cake, the private property motive would prove a psychological barrier to the organisation of existing plenty.

The scientists were not greatly impressed by Melchett's arguments. Haldane argued that the misuse of scientific ability would inevitably prove to be a serious handicap in the post-war period of competition. Levy went further, contending that the war itself sprang from the economic crisis of the later twenties, which in turn had been the result of a general process of social change. In his view neither accumulations of stocks, nor the emergence of startling new inventions, could provide either the incentive or the knowledge for properly using 'stocks' for the benefit of society. Huxley thought that the rate of population growth was bound to slow down (a curious thing for him to say in view of his dramatisation of the 'population explosion' in the post-war years), and that the adjustment of the scientific and economic systems must come through the development of backward colonial empires, especially by raising standards of living. Bernal then brought the discussion back to a scientific level, again arguing that science was suffering not so much from a process of repression as from mal-direction. Lack of scope for scientific enterprise, he pointed out, is as important as lack of money or brains. The social, economic and industrial disorders of society might be corrected, but their adjustment would be effective only if science were properly used and developed. My Minutes record that at this moment the Prof entered the discussion and, while agreeing the need to spread a proper scientific outlook in society, he reminded us once again that the war had first to be won before we could consider the future of science. There was some disagreement with this view, it being felt that the war would not be won unless science was applied over a wider front than it was at present. The Prof could always be relied upon to stir dissent, even when he stated the obvious.

It was at the dinner on 12 June 1940 (pp. 110–11) that Allen Lane accepted the challenge to publish what became *Science in War*, given that he received the typescript within a fortnight (in fact he got it in eleven days). The club dined again on 10 July, but the hope that there would be a copy at each cover was not realised. The book had been printed, but something had gone wrong with the transport arrangements. It appeared on the bookstalls two or three days later, but from the point of view of the publisher, prematurely. Lord Samuel, who was present at this July dinner, as were three of the party of French scientists who had escaped from France (p. 112), then suggested that parliamentary questions on the issues raised by the book should be prepared. The question of publicity was also discussed, but this turned out to be a work of supererogation. Our little paperback was widely reviewed, and almost invariably favourably. One or two of the anonymous contributors also wrote favourable reviews. Julian Huxley, reviewing it in *Nature* on 27 July 1940, began his article with the words: 'This is a tract for the times, which every scientific worker should read', and ended with 'The publisher in his foreword informs us that "Science in War" was conceived, written, printed, and published in less than a month. This abbreviated gestation, more characteristic of a rodent than of a human being or a book, though very remarkable, has had certain unavoidable defects. The book betrays its composite authorship rather too obviously, and there are a number of misprints . . .'.

The main and customarily anonymous editorial in the same issue of *Nature* was headed 'Men of Science and the War', and was written by me at the invitation of the Editors. I found myself smiling when I recently re-read the piece, particularly at this sentence: '. . . many scientific workers have not been used at all, and others, who have for long been in Government service, or who have been recruited since the War, are not being used to their fullest capacities. The fundamental reason for this (and this is the fundamental defect of the whole organization) is that the functions of science have been generally conceived, to a large extent even by men of science themselves, in altogether too restricted a way. A general scientific point of view is foreign to the direction of the country, and in particular to its administrators. If this defect is to be remedied, men of science themselves must show the way.'

From the moment it appeared, Allen Lane received enquiries about statements made in the book, each of which had then to be routed through me to the particular author concerned. Queries were still coming in after the war. No-one seemed to mind that the book had been issued anonymously, and indeed Lord Samuel, in a review in the *Spectator* on 26 July, correctly said that the book was anonymous, 'not in order to conceal insignificance in the writers', but because almost all of them were actively participating in the war effort; 'to set their names to their contributions would only have been a check on their freedom of speech and an embarrassment'. A second printing, with some of the errors of the first edition corrected, was issued in November, and altogether more than twenty thousand copies were sold. A third printing was called for because of the continued demand, not only in the United Kingdom, but also abroad, but was prevented because of the war-time paper shortage, and because of Allen Lane's understandable preference for new books.

Some of the official leaders of British science regarded the book as a criticism of their efforts. But even though as a group the Tots and Quots were not disturbed by this, I was fully conscious of the need to bear the susceptibilities of the Establishment in mind. For example, I was sent a documented proposal by a scientific worker, of whom I had not before heard, for the creation of what he called 'a scientific corps'; and he hoped that his paper could be included in a third edition of the book. When I told him that it was unlikely that there would be a further edition, I suggested that he might consider sending his article to *Nature*. 'On the other hand,' I went on, 'I am wondering whether there is not a case for your sending it directly to the Secretary of the Hankey Committee—the Scientific Advisory Committee of the Cabinet—before publishing it in "Nature". If the matter were sympathetically considered by them and action was taken, your plans would have immediate effect. If, however, you published your views in "Nature" without consulting them, you might arouse a certain amount of hostility amongst the official scientists who are responsible for the organization you suggest, and by so doing jeopardise the success of your scheme.'

The contract for the book was not lucrative, and the money it earned was used to help pay for our dinners.

The topic at the dinner at which *Science in War* failed to turn up was the situation of French scientists, and the steps that might be taken to help selected ones escape to England. Laugier and Longchambon played a prominent part in this discussion and, mainly because of the energetic work of Louis Rapkine, some useful action followed. One by-product was the Society for Visiting Scientists, which flourished from 1942 until the late sixties, and whose origins can be traced to our discussions, with the main initiative coming from Crowther.

H. G. Wells was among the guests at the next dinner (August 1940) when the topic for debate was the part that science might play in post-war reconstruction, a matter which already preoccupied Julian Huxley, even though none of us had any idea when the war would end, or what would be the state of the world when it did. There is no indication in the record of this dinner that at the time any of us were involved in whatever official or quasi-official talks may have been going on about what culminated in the United Nations. H. G. Wells's views were straightforward and, in the event, more than a little wrong. He saw the world dominated after the war by three major powers—Great Britain and the Empire, the Americas and the Soviet Union. Jack Haldane was concerned that we were not taking the Sino-Japanese dispute into account, and he took the view, which is interesting in retrospect, that further disaster could not be prevented while the eastern and western conflicts remained separate. How right he was.

The following dinner, in September 1940, took place in Magdalen College, Oxford, and once again our topic was the question of publicising the need for the full mobilisation of scientists. Tom Harrisson had prepared for us a memorandum on the subject. Among our guests were two influential journalists; Tom Hopkinson, the Editor of *Picture Post*, and Tom Driberg,* who wrote the William Hickey column in the *Daily Express*. The Ministry of Information was represented by Sidney Bernstein.† The following day, Driberg used his column to give an account of his visit, writing that he had gone to Oxford 'to attend a dinner & meeting of a group of eminent scientists. These scientists are tired of being, like angels, misjudged. They want to correct the popular view of scientists as magicians—untidy, absent-minded, slightly comic miracle-workers with "magnetic eyes". They want to establish more everyday relations with the public, to help organise a scientific approach to current problems. So they invited a Government film chief, the editor of a picture weekly, and myself to discuss possibilities with them. This is of direct practical importance. For instance, shelters: among us was an architect one of whose shelters recently resisted a direct hit—tho' it was only meant to be blast- and splinter-proof. Closer relations between scientists, authorities, public would speed the using of such skill.' ('Bombed to College'. *Daily Express*, 30 September 1940.) Unfortunately, little that was useful flowed from this meeting. Articles which Tom Harrisson prepared for *Picture Post* were rejected, while the *Sunday Express* published only one of what was intended to be a series of pieces about 'relevant science'. The idea had been that members of the club would send me paragraphs, which I would then pass on to a writer on the paper's staff, whose job it was to turn them into chatty pieces without distorting meaning or emphasis.

We next met towards the end of November 1940, at Christ's College, Cambridge, when the theme of our discussion was Anglo-American scientific cooperation. One of our guests was Major Hertford,** then attached to the United States Embassy, who became a constant attender of our dinners.

Because Bernal and I were fully caught up with our field-studies of air-raids, there were no meetings in December or January, and we next met in February of 1941 at the Café Royal in London where, in spite of strict rationing, an excellent dinner was provided. In the interval, however, Henry Melchett, together with some of our other members, had been trying to set up a science-news service in order to bring American and British scientists into closer contact. This idea, which obviously could not be pursued far by the Tots and Quots, was referred to the Social and International Division of the British Association, which in turn referred it to the Ministry of Information. Paul Rotha‡ was at this dinner, and he wanted members of the club to help him produce a series of short films which he hoped would be commissioned by the Films Division of the Ministry of Information, the part of the Ministry with which Bernstein was connected. Some were made.

A month later, in March, we again met for dinner at the Café Royal, our chief

---

* Tom Driberg, who died in 1976, was a writer and journalist who became an M.P., although he continued writing even after taking his seat in the House of Commons. He was created Lord Bradwell in 1976.

† Lord Bernstein since 1969. Now Chairman of the Granada Group, he was in the Ministry of Information's Film Division during the war.

** Major Hertford ended his military career as the General responsible for the management of Sandia Base, New Mexico, the major pre-production laboratory for nuclear weapons.

‡ Paul Rotha was a brilliant pioneer of documentary films.

guest being J. B. Conant, the chemist and President of Harvard University.* Other guests were Dr. O'Brien and Dr. Weaver, two directors of the Rockefeller Foundation; Jack Drummond, the Chief Adviser to the Ministry of Food, and Professor Holford.† John Cockcroft, who was also with us, had just returned from his visit to America as a member of the 'Tizard Mission', which had tried to stimulate American scientific cooperation by revealing some of our most critical and secret information about new developments in radar and the other apparatus of war.

Planning for post-war reconstruction and Anglo-American cooperation were again the main topics of discussion. Dr. Conant referred to his well-known support of the British cause, and made it clear that he was very concerned about Anglo-American cooperation 'both now and in the future'. But he felt 'that we should not give way to wishful thinking and imagine that this cooperation was easily achieved'. To demonstrate the difficulties, he cited ten points which he felt might prevent the full realisation of the desires of those who 'have the cause of cooperation close at heart'. They read with almost the same relevance today as they did when I recorded them for the Minutes.

'1. An underestimation of the difficulties of cooperation, especially in England.

'2. Over-simplification and over-rationalisation of both internal and external United States policy.

'3. The fact that institutions which have a superficial similarity in the two countries may in fact operate very differently—e.g. the Government machine.

'4. Inaccurate reporting of events on both sides of the Atlantic.

'5. The existence in the United States of well defined racial groups many of which have considerable power and many of which oppose cooperation for one reason or another—e.g. the Irish problem.

'6. The confusion between Anglo-American relationships and the relationship of the United States to the British Empire.

'7. The occasional unfortunate effects of sentimental Anglophiles in the United States.

'8. The conflict of various interests between the two countries.

'9. The equating of anti-Axis feeling with pro-British feeling.

'10. The difficulty of getting a country as big as the United States to recognise the privilege of being a world power.'

Eight more months were to pass before America came into the war, and it seems odd that we were even then talking about post-war UK/USA cooperation on a planned basis. Roy Harrod reminded us that post-war cooperation would necessitate a degree of political understanding which obviated the need for excessive expenditure on armaments, and which favoured the kind of economic planning that did not itself provoke political conflict. For example, the location of industry was always dealt with on a national basis, whereas ideally it should be treated as an international undertaking in order to stabilise international economics. It was essential that there should be a regular and steady external investment into those parts of the world that were in need of development. In making this point, Harrod asked Conant how the average United States citizen could be made to understand that investing in under-developed countries was a duty, and not a privilege. The club was certainly looking realistically at the post-war world. But, as Jack Drummond pointed out, that world was still far away. The next two or three months would tell whether we were going to survive

* After the war, Conant became, first the United States Commissioner and then Ambassador to Germany.

† William Holford became Lord Holford in 1965, and died in 1975.

402 *From Apes to Warlords*

at all, and if we were to survive, the United States *had* to help. The critical issue of the day was transport and shipping, and that was where the USA came in.

There was a gap of four months before the next dinner in July 1941, again no doubt because Bernal and I had been too busy chasing bombs and in carrying out the Hull and Birmingham Survey (pp. 140–4). Twenty-five of us sat down to this dinner, among them Lord Woolton, the Minister of Food, Jack Drummond, and Sir Wilson Jameson, the Chief Medical Officer at the Ministry of Health. I noted that an excellent dinner 'which did not contravene the catering laws' was provided. Since our previous meeting the pressure we had been exerting had taken effect, and Jimmy Crowther had been appointed Scientific Secretary to the British Council. He was able to report that at long last a science-news service was going to come into being. We then settled down to a vehement discussion of war-time food policy. Hugh Sinclair opened provocatively by saying that if, as a reply to a recent parliamentary question had indicated, all the Ministry was concerned to do was maintain the country's nutritional level, it was aiming very low. The average level had been abysmal when the war began, and the Ministry's job should be not just to maintain that level, but to raise it. Sinclair went on in this vein for some time in order to goad Woolton and Drummond. He certainly succeeded. Henry Melchett was almost as critical and ended his remarks by saying that before coming to the dinner he had had a drink with a distinguished American, to whom he had mentioned that he was going to meet Woolton. The American had asked him to tell Woolton that he thought him 'a grand guy, as grand a guy as had ever starved a country into submission'. Melchett said that he had asked the American if he had not made a mistake, and if it was not Dalton (the Minister of Economic Warfare) whom he meant. The reply had been, 'Woolton, not Dalton'. Woolton, who in spite of all the banter was obviously enjoying himself, answered that as Minister of Food he could certainly lose the war, but that equally he could not win it. Critics like Sinclair simply did not realise that we were fighting for our very existence. A sharper note entered the discussion when he then berated 'the scientists', who criticised so easily, and it was left to Wilson Jameson to restore calm, which he did by graciously saying that we owed many of our difficulties over food supplies to the fact that Lord Woolton had not been appointed to his office soon enough. Jack Drummond defended his 'boss' by saying that the provision of adequate food for children might well prove to be among the war's most positive achievements, in the same way as history associated nursing with the Crimean War and inoculation with the Boer War. In this belief, events certainly proved him right, even if he did not live to see just how right he was. Jack Drummond, his wife and daughter, were murdered in 1952 while on holiday in France.

The Germans had turned on Russia by the time we next dined in August, and the Soviet Ambassador, Mr. Maisky, was our main guest. Among others there were A. V. Hill, the Biological Secretary of the Royal Society, and Ritchie Calder. The topic for debate was Anglo-Soviet scientific liaison, and I opened the discussion by explaining what had been done to reinforce scientific contacts between ourselves and French and American scientists. Blackett then spoke, pointing out that however important the issue of scientific cooperation, it was less important at the moment than the provision of fighter squadrons, or the opening up of a second front in the west. He referred to various forms of cooperation that were desirable, and to the prevailing ignorance about each other's armaments. He reminded the club of what Dr. Conant had defined as the difficulties which inhibited Anglo-American cooperation, and suggested that ardent Russophiles in England were likely to prove as much of a drawback to Anglo-Soviet cooperation as passionate Anglophiles in the United States were to Anglo-American relations. An even more acute difficulty was the prevailing fear in the UK that the USSR might soon collapse, and the reciprocal fear in that country that we were going to be too slow in opening up a 'second front'. Harry Lucas, who knew that President Roosevelt and Churchill were going to announce the signing of an 'Atlantic Charter' on the following day, urged an immediate and firm statement that neither the USSR nor the UK had any imperialistic ambitions. The Atlantic Charter, which has long since been forgotten, formally stated that neither Britain nor the United States had any aims of territorial aggrandisement; that all people had the right to choose their own form of government; and that peace should bring both 'freedom from fear and want', as well as disarmament of the aggressors, pending the establishment of a wider and more permanent system of general security. Harry wanted a corresponding declaration from the Russians.

Much had been said before Mr. Maisky entered the discussion. After a few preliminary remarks, he observed with a quiet and impressive force which I can still sense as though I had just heard him, that he did not understand the fears that had been expressed about Russia collapsing. He had absolute confidence in the ultimate victory of his country. But, he then added slowly, he did not know what price the USSR would have to pay for victory. Nor, speaking even more slowly, did he know what price we would have to pay for Russian victory. But the greater the degree of collaboration between the two countries, the lower the price would be for both.

John Winant, the American Ambassador, who was the chief guest at our September dinner, was equally impressive, but far more visionary. He brought with him two American professors of economics, Drs. Hansen and Gulick, both temporary civil servants in Washington, who had arrived in England that day, ostensibly to attend a meeting of the British Association for the Advancement of Science. By then Drs O'Brien and Hugh Smith of the Rockefeller Foundation were attending all our dinners, and had become members of the club, as had Louis Rapkine and Ritchie Calder. Our discussion focused on post-war reconstruction, which the club clearly did not regard as as urgent a matter as it did winning the war. But nonetheless we had learnt the hard way about the need to organise scientists. Many interesting but dreamy points were made during the course of the evening, among them that the fundamental problem which would face the world after the war was full employment without depression. Mr. Winant felt that this was a matter for which the USA and the UK could and should start planning straight away. Dr. Basil Schonland, the South African geophysicist, was also at the dinner. Some of his remarks are fascinating in the light of what is happening today. He told us that the prevailing view in South Africa was that Great Britain had done nothing for South Africa and had 'allowed the native population to stew in their own juice'. It was time the United Kingdom and United States got together to consider what was going to happen to the colonial empire. If this were not done now, he felt that the present war would be the last occasion on which South Africa would fight as part of an empire. He certainly owned a good crystal ball.

Three months later, at our last dinner of 1941, Herbert Morrison, who by then had replaced Sir John Anderson as Home Secretary and Minister of Home Security, was the club's main guest. In my record I noted that wines were getting scarce, and that after this dinner we would probably have to make do with some other drink. The subject for discussion was 'How scientific is social science?' a topic that was stimulated by one of Harrod's observations at the dinner attended by Mr. Winant. This had riled Tom Harrisson who, as founder of Mass Observation, regarded its activities as truly scientific—which others of us had denied. As Harrod pointed out, no general laws of the kind that governed science had as yet been revealed by social scientists, and in particular, none that was applicable to economics. And he reminded us that Max Planck, of quantum-theory fame, had first considered taking up the social sciences, but that he had abandoned the idea in favour of an 'easier' career in physics. Herbert Morrison also expressed a certain scepticism about the value of social science, and doubted whether its greater development in the United States had had any effect upon the policies of that country's Government. He agreed, however, that government policies were not tested sufficiently by means of social enquiry, in the same way as he regretted the lack of social knowledge on which to base government policies.

In the record of this dinner, I find the first mention of the term 'operational research'. This is surprising, since the few who are now regarded as having founded the subject were all members of the club: Blackett, Bernal, Waddington—who in 1973 published a book entitled *O R in World War 2* (Elek)—and myself.

In 1942 dinners became infrequent because by then most of us were almost completely immersed in our war-time duties. In addition to our commitment to the Ministry of Home Security, Bernal and I had become scientific advisers to Lord Mountbatten at Combined Operations headquarters. Blackett, who had first been scientific adviser to General Pile, Commander of our anti-aircraft forces, was now scientific adviser to the Admiralty. Waddington had taken up operational research for Coastal Command. But such dinners as I did organise always managed to raise sparks, and rarely did anyone refuse an invitation to be our guest. The club had made its mark, both in civilian and in military quarters, and it almost became a sign of distinction to be invited to one of our gatherings. I do not know about the others, but each dinner added to my own education, and with each dinner I became more and more aware of the many sides there were even to the simplest issue, and of the different attitudes from which each was viewed. The demise of the club is dealt with on pp. 370–1 of the main text.

APPENDIX 2

(see p. 143)

Quantitative Study of Total Effects of Air Raids
[Hull and Birmingham Survey]
Ministry of Home Security
Research and Experiments Department. 2770 (8.4.1942)
Summary of Conclusions

'I. *Social Effects and Morale*

(a) THE FACTOR MOST AFFECTING THE POPULATION IS THE DESTRUCTION OF HOUSES. (In bombing of the kind experienced in Birmingham and Hull, 1 ton of bomb kills 4 people. In neither city did the air-raid death rate increase the normal death rate by more than 35%).

(b) 35 PEOPLE ARE BOMBED OUT FOR EVERY ONE KILLED.

(c) DWELLING HOUSES ARE DESTROYED BY HIGH EXPLOSIVE BOMBS AND NOT BY FIRE.

(d) Large towns have a high capacity for absorbing their bombed out population.

(e) Other raid effects such as stoppage of water or gas have little effect on the population.

(f) Temporary evacuation does not interfere with the work of the town.

(g) Steady employment and a high rate of wages are the major stabilising factors for the population.

(h) THERE IS NO EVIDENCE OF BREAKDOWN OF MORALE FOR THE INTENSITIES OF THE RAIDS EXPERIENCED BY HULL OR BIRMINGHAM. (MAXIMUM INTENSITY OF BOMBING 40 TONS PER SQUARE MILE.)

'II. *Production*

(a) LOSS OF PRODUCTION IS CAUSED ALMOST ENTIRELY BY DIRECT DAMAGE TO FACTORIES.

(b) FACTORIES ARE MORE SERIOUSLY DAMAGED BY FIRE THAN BY HIGH EXPLOSIVE. In Birmingham 30% of factories were damaged—10% seriously (8% by fire and 2% by high explosive).

(c) Most fires could have been prevented at the scale of fire attack encountered.

(d) Machine tools are rarely damaged by high explosives but very extensively by fire.

(e) Indirect effects of raids on labour, turnover, health and efficiency are insignificant.

(f) The direct loss of production in Birmingham due to the raids was about 5% and the loss of productive potential was very small.

(g) Transport activity is only partially interfered with and recovery is rapid in the absence of continuous raiding.

(h) Docking was not interfered with and docking potential was diminished by about 10% in the raids on Hull.'

APPENDIX 3

(see p. 381 *ch* 11 *n* 7)

Air Attacks on Rail and Road Communications [*Sicily Report*]
B.S.U. Report No. 4. 28 December 1943
General Conclusions

1. If the measure of success of air attacks on enemy rail and road communications is taken as the destruction of the means of communication, then the offensive carried out against rail targets in Sicily and Southern Italy must be regarded as an outstanding success. If, however, the measure of success were taken as the complete cutting and blocking of railway-lines and roads, then the offensive could be regarded as having partly failed in its purpose. There is little indication that the attacks prevented the enemy from moving from place to place within the limits imposed by the capacity of the transport at his disposal.

2. The two factors which contributed most to the strategical and tactical success of the offensive were the destruction and damaging of rolling-stock and repair facilities. Largely because of such damage, the Sicilian and Southern Italian rail systems had become practically paralysed by the end of July 1943—as a result of attacks on only six railway centres, Naples, Foggia, San Giovanni, Reggio, Messina, Palermo.

3. The attacks on these six centres appear to have added at least as much to the enemy's supply difficulties in Tunisia as did the losses he incurred at sea.

4. Major damage to the railway system in Sicily and Italy forced the enemy to other means of transport, especially to the use of motor-transport, and helped to consume his petrol supplies.

Local, and possibly a general, shortage of coal may have contributed to the decline in railway traffic. It seems fair, however, to assume that damage to the railway distribution system was a major factor in producing this shortage, since it is improbable that motor-transport would have been used for long hauls that might have been effected by rail—had it been possible to work the railway system.

The dislocation of the electric railway system in Southern Italy was another factor which would have forced the enemy to a greater use of steam trains—given that the railway system had not suffered other critical damage.

5. The enemy managed to maintain a ferry service across the Messina Straits until the end of the Sicilian hostilities. A fairly successful attempt was also made to compensate for the losses in traffic resulting from direct damage to the ferries, by substituting coastal vessels.

6. The damage inflicted on the railway system represented more than a potential loss in traffic flow; it also represented an actual loss in goods.

7. In general, the normal peace-time capacity of a railway system is far in excess of war-time military requirements. After the railways of Sicily and Southern Italy had been severely hit, they were inadequate to deal with the enemy's military needs.

8. Damaging a railway system in the manner that has been described hits the civilian population at least as hard as it does the military, and has serious effects on morale.

9. It is worth noting that the damage suffered by the Southern Italian and Sicilian

railway system will have very lasting effects, and will probably be felt by the civil population long after hostilities have ceased.

10. The strategical effect of destroying the enemy's means of rail communication is best achieved by attacks on large railway centres which contain important repair facilities and large concentrations of locomotives and rolling-stock. The sub-targets (e.g. tracks, rolling-stock, warehouses, repair sheds, etc.) in a large railway area are very concentrated. As a result, the general risk of damage from bombing, if the attacks are carried out in adequate strength, is very high.

The efficiency of a railway system appears to fall very rapidly when bombing simultaneously leads to an increase in the calls upon, and a decrease in the capacity of the repair facilities.

11. In the Italian railway system, repair facilities, and especially major repair facilities, are concentrated in a few large centres such as Naples, Palermo, and Turin. At any given moment, about half of the available locomotives in each compartment of the Italian railway system were also concentrated in a few large centres.

12. The high vulnerability of rolling-stock to concentrated bombing is partly explained by the fact that the direct effects of the bombs are greatly increased by indirect causes, such as spreading fires, etc. etc. The relation between damage to rolling-stock and scale of attack has been determined, and is shown in Fig. 17 of the main report.

13. The only major counter-measure which the enemy used to decrease the risk of damage to the railways was the dispersal of locomotives. The extent to which the dispersal of rolling stock is possible is, however, small, and is determined by the more or less fixed capacity of different railway areas.

14. A far more costly air effort would be needed to achieve a tactical success, in the sense of a sudden blocking of communications at any given series of points, than has proved necessary to produce the strategical effect of reducing traffic potential by the destruction of rolling-stock and repair facilities.

15. In spite of the heavy cost, it may be a vital necessity in certain situations to attempt to disrupt enemy movement suddenly by means of air-attacks. The heavy bombing of Eboli and Battipaglia during the period of the Salerno battle represents a case in point.

16. Since the strategical results that have been discussed above in general outweigh immediate tactical effects, and since they can be achieved by a less costly air effort, it is necessary to consider how soon their effects are felt in the sphere of tactics. Unfortunately no definite answer can yet be given to this question. In the case of the Messina ferry service, the fall in the first three months of 1943 was no more than about 20% of the average level of flow for the last six months of 1942. In April, however, the flow fell 17% in relation to the March figures; in May it fell 42% in relation to the April figures, and in June 50% in relation to the May figures. In the case of southbound traffic from Naples, the fall, after the severe damage inflicted in July, amounted to at least 50% during the following month.

These figures in no sense indicate absolute limits in speed of effect. The latter is largely bound up with the scale of effort that can be applied in any given period of time. Major falls in traffic could have been achieved more rapidly had it been possible to expend a larger effort on large railway centres.

APPENDIX 4

(see p. 304)

Claims and Counter Claims about the Role of Bomber Command

Paras of Memorandum	Statements in C-in-C's Memorandum*	Comments by AEAF*	Comments by the Air Staff (27 January 1944)*	Comments by the Air Staff (28 June 1944)‡
1	*Role of Bomber Command* The Memorandum states without qualification that Bomber Command's task is the destruction of the enemy's industrial centres.	It is presumed that Bomber Command will have its role extended to include, as and when required, the maximum assistance to 'OVERLORD'.	From a date in the preparatory phase of 'OVERLORD' yet to be selected the primary object of Bomber Command will become the support of that operation, and all or part of the forces of Bomber Command will be at the disposal of the Supreme Commander. That support will be, in the words of the directive 'in the manner most effective'. Once the type of support required from Bomber Command has been decided—and this will be done in conjunction with advisers from Bomber Command, it will be the duty of the C-in-C to do his best to fulfil these tasks.	Under the direction of the Deputy Supreme Allied Commander and in accordance with the Combined Chiefs of Staff's ruling, the whole of the forces of Bomber Command have been available for the support of 'OVERLORD' 'in the manner most effective'. This has been fully justified by events. The C-in-C Bomber Command has cooperated wholeheartedly in fulfilling the tasks allotted to him, and the results achieved have far exceeded expectations.

* Source: Comments on Bomber Command Memorandum for the Employment of Night Bombers in Connection with 'Overlord'. D.C.A.S. 27 January 1944.
‡ Source: Further Comments by Air Staff in the Light of Experience of Bomber Command's Operations in Support of 'Overlord'. (D.B. Ops 26715A). 28 June 1944.

Limitation of Bomber Command's Operations

The nature of Bomber Command's operations is limited by the highly specialised aircraft and the complex operational technique employed.

It is not clear why targets in FRANCE should be any less suitable than industrial centres in GERMANY, provided they are carefully selected ones, e.g. railway centres, or towns where the enemy's reserves are concentrated.

Although the heavy bomber force has been developed as an independent strategic force, its task is not necessarily the destruction of enemy industrial centres. The highly specialised equipment and operational technique has been evolved to enable the force to place its bombs accurately on the desired target. Although bombing accuracy so far achieved has only enabled the force to carry out area bombing by night, the aim is still to achieve the most accurate bombing possible; all technical development is to this end. The unavoidable limitations of Bomber Command in support of 'OVERLORD' are due to inability to achieve a high accuracy of bombing and not to the nature and extent of any specialisation which is taking place.

Events have shown that the capabilities of the night bomber force in the support of 'OVERLORD' have not been limited to any appreciable extent; on the contrary Bomber Command have demonstrated their ability to achieve an accuracy and concentration on small targets far exceeding that which can be achieved by the American heavies by day; furthermore, they have achieved such concentrations by night below a 10/10ths cloud base, while the American day heavies in similar conditions have been forced to abandon their task.

The following wide diversity of targets has been successfully attacked: Transportation targets; Coastal batteries; Dumps; Camps; Airfields; Radar stations; Tactical Targets.

The earlier Air Staff comment 'that the aim is still to achieve the most accurate bombing possible' has been justified beyond expectation. The density of attack

Paras of Memorandum	Statements in C-in-C's Memorandum	Comments by AEAF	Comments by the Air Staff (27 January 1944)	Comments by the Air Staff (28 June 1944)
				achieved by Bomber Command throughout its operations in support of 'OVERLORD' has been most creditable and in many attacks such as Juvissy, Mailly-le-Camp, Aunay, etc. an amazing density has been achieved.
3	*Day Operations* Because of training, armament and ceilings when flying in formations, day operations are absolutely out of the question and could in no circumstances be undertaken.	It is not anticipated that our night bombers will normally be called upon for day operations.	Bomber Command have within the last two years carried out daylight raids on Augsburg, Danzig, Creusot and Milan. These were done with little previous daylight training, and if necessary squadrons could again be trained to operate in daylight probably with less than six weeks being set aside for the purpose, especially in view of the shorter ranges involved and the degree of fighter cover which would be afforded in this theatre of operations. Their armament is no less efficient than some squadrons in the Tactical Air Forces; the height at which it would be	The C-in-C's statement that daylight operations were absolutely out of the question and could in no circumstances be undertaken, has been directly contradicted by events. Bomber Command have now carried out a large number of heavy scale daylight attacks with smaller losses than they incur against the same targets by night. The previous Air Staff view as to the feasibility of daylight operations has been proved correct.

necessary to fly would be dependent on the flak opposition in the 'OVERLORD' area. Tactical Air Forces are already operating at heights and below those heights at which our heavy bombers could operate. It is considered, however, that there would be little if any call for the R.A.F. Bomber Command to operate by day since they can be effectively employed at night in support of landing operations. Moreover, American heavy bomber forces in numbers equal to those of R.A.F. Bomber Command will be available for precision daylight attacks.

4-7 *Night Operations—Pathfinder Technique*
It is necessary always to use some form of Pathfinder technique.

Whatever the result obtained through the use of P.F.F. for targets in GERMANY, they should be improved for targets in FRANCE. The Memorandum admits that individual bombing can be successful in suitable conditions such as excellent visibility, bright moonlight and meagre opposition. The con-

Paras 4 and 5 give an incorrect impression of the potential uses of existing navigational aids and marking technique in support of military operations and be-little the accuracy which is to be expected from 'OBOE', H.2.S. or H.2.X. for bombing strips of coastline in preparation for a landing. Results to

The Air Staff comment that the C-in-C had given an incorrect impression as to the use of the existing navigational aids has been confirmed by the 'OVERLORD' operations. Since the C-in-C's paper was written the technique of visual marking with the aid of flares has been developed and results achieved by this technique

Paras of Memorandum	Statements in C-in-C's Memorandum	Comments by AEAF	Comments by the Air Staff (27 January 1944)	Comments by the Air Staff (28 June 1944)
	The aids for the Pathfinder technique are 'OBOE', H.2.S., G.H. The limitations of these aids are emphasised.	ditions might well exist for 'OVERLORD'. In any event, Bomber Command's statement seems to have been written with special reference to targets deep in GERMANY. The limitations of the aids are well realised and there is no suggestion that they should be used in attacks against unsuitable targets. With the exception of H.2.S., greater accuracy with these aids can be obtained against short range targets in FRANCE than against those at longer ranges in GERMANY.	be achieved by H.2.S. alone are shown by the attached chart . . . giving the appearance of Baltic coast near Peenemunde on an H.2.S. screen. The bomb plot and photographs of results achieved in this attack are shown at Appendix B. H.2.S. or H.2.X. are more effective in picking out coastline than in other circumstances. It is therefore incorrect to state that H.2.S. gives its best results when used against 'isolated and densely built-up industrial areas surrounded by open country'. In fact water shows up much better than any other feature on H.2.S. screen. The statement 'It is always necessary to use some form of Pathfinder Technique' is too sweeping. In an emergency and with clear moonlight the heavy bomber force might quite well use visual methods of bombing especially in the coastal areas. The extent of	have been in many cases comparable to those achieved with the aid of 'OBOE'. It is true that some form of Pathfinder technique is always necessary, but this does not necessarily involve the use of 'OBOE', H.2.S. or Gee-H.

413

9–10	*Weather Restrictions* Choice of heavy bomber targets is chiefly governed by weather.	It is agreed that an adequate period must be allowed for the necessary bomber effort to be brought to bear on 'OVERLORD' targets. It should be remembered that the closer ranges of 'OVERLORD' targets permit of considerably greater accuracy of weather forecasts than for targets deep in GERMANY.	coverage of 'OBOE' as shown on the Bomber Command charts is misleading. There is considerable cover provided over the vital coastal area to the West of Paris. It is agreed that weather conditions will restrict the choice of targets but if defences are light, and deep penetration is not required, restrictions on account of weather will not be so great as is general in Bomber Command operations. Night attacks need not necessarily be aided by blind bombing devices. The hooded flare has been developed with a degree of priority to enable targets to be found and visual bombing to be carried out. The comments of A.E.A.F. are agreed.	Weather has not been so great a limiting factor on operations over France as over Germany; owing to the lighter flak defences in France it has often been possible to make accurate and concentrated attacks from below the cloud base. Moreover in a period of extremely bad weather the effort* directed against Germany in support of 'OVERLORD'* has, in June, far exceeded that ever before put out by Bomber Command.
11	*Tactical Restrictions* Employment of the Pathfinder technique limits the number of targets which can be attacked on any night and also the number of consecutive	If the period during which targets are marked is reduced, and the targets are at shorter ranges from this country, it should be possible to raise the	It is not agreed that it is impossible to mark more than two targets during the course of one night without crews and aircraft being used more	The Air Staff view has been fully substantiated. During 'OVERLORD' operations up to 10 targets have been attacked in one night, a Pathfinder

the words between * and * have been scored through.

Paras of Memorandum	Statements in C-in-C's Memorandum	Comments by AEAF	Comments by the Air Staff (27 January 1944)	Comments by the Air Staff (28 June 1944)
	nights over which attacks can be sustained (with present limitations Pathfinders can work 2 targets each night during two nights out of every three for 12 days).	maximum number of targets that can be marked during a single night. In any case it is understood that P.F.F. capacity will have increased by the time of 'OVERLORD'.	than once. Targets can be marked by aircraft fitted with H.2.S., 'OBOE', G.H., and in addition visual identification can be practised with the aid of flares.	technique being employed against each target. The technique of visual marking with the aid of flares has proved highly successful.
12–14	*Maximum Monthly Effort* The Maximum effort Bomber Command can sustain is approximately 5,000 sorties per month assuming normal wastage. This allows of eight full-scale attacks per month.	Presumably this is based on deep penetration operations against targets in GERMANY. Short range operations against targets in FRANCE should allow a considerably greater number of sorties to be carried out.	This paragraph is misleading. Last May, June and July Bomber Command averaged 5,700 sorties a month. These were for the most part long range sorties accomplished with an average operational strength of 52 Squadrons. If the same effort per squadron is expanded, the existing Bomber Command force should be able to put out 7,300 sorties a month during 'OVERLORD'. This figure should be proportionately greater in view of the shorter sorties involved.	The Air Staff view that more than 7,300 sorties a month should be possible during 'OVERLORD' is proved correct by the fact that during the 68 day period between April 14 and June 21, Bomber Command completed a total of 24,154 heavy bomber sorties. This is an average of approximately 11,000 sorties per month, which is more than twice the figure of 5,000 sorties per month which the C-in-C put forward as the effort that could be sustained by Bomber Command assuming normal wastage (total aircraft missing over this period amounted to 641 or 2·6%).

15 *'Fleeting Targets'*

The heavy bomber force is quite incapable of being brought into action quickly against 'fleeting targets'. The time required to refuel, service and bomb up the aircraft, brief the crews and marshal the force is such that with maximum efficiency some seven daylight hours are the minimum necessary between the decision to bomb a given target and take-off of aircraft.

The target cannot be altered during that period without involving a new start. If the preparatory work has to be done in darkness the minimum period would be extended to nine or ten hours.

It is not proposed to whittle Bomber Command away by operations against 'fleeting targets'. In the main, tactical results will be achieved as a result against 'OVERLORD' strategical targets. The statement appears to refer to the 'turn-round' period. For operations against important transient targets connected with 'OVERLORD' during the critical period, Bomber Command forces could be standing by and some simplified briefing procedure arranged. Under these circumstances it would seem that the period between the order to attack and the take-off could be reduced by day to something more of the order of 60 minutes.

This paragraph gives an exaggerated impression of the time necessary to bomb up for the attack of targets of the type likely to be attacked during the period of two weeks before and after D day. Standard bomb loads will be used and these can be prepared in advance at dispersal points. It is not correct to say that the target cannot be altered during the period of seven hours without involving a new start and consequent further delay. In bombing by marker technique the target can be changed at short notice.

No occasion has arisen for testing the C-in-C's pessimistic statement on the time taken to bomb up for the attack of targets in connection with 'OVERLORD'. The comments of the Air Staff are, however, substantiated by the fact that standardised bomb loads have been employed against tactical targets and by the fact that main force attacks have almost exclusively been on markers and therefore have called for little or no briefing.

16–17 *'Programme Bombing'*

'Programme Bombing', except over a long period and in the most general terms is ruled out altogether as an operation of war. A planned schedule of heavy bomber operations to give immediate assistance to

It is not accepted that 'programme bombing' cannot be undertaken in the 'OVERLORD' theatre of operations. This statement would appear to have been made without full knowledge of the tasks which

The drenching of beaches by heavy bomber attack will not necessarily involve the cratering of a large area of coast to an extent imposing limitations on our own troop movements. 500 lb. bombs with instan-

Bomber Command were most successfully employed on 'programme bombing' in relation to 'OVERLORD' and their attacks on gun positions were highly effective.

The C-in-C's statement that

Paras of Memorandum	Statements in C-in-C's Memorandum	Comments by AEAF	Comments by the Air Staff (27 January 1944)	Comments by the Air Staff (28 June 1944)
	ground forces would be extremely unreliable and almost wholly futile. Beach drenching could be regarded only as a contingent possibility and could not form an integral part of any plan. In no circumstances would heavy bombers be relied on to destroy gun emplacements, nor are they suitable for cutting railway communications.	the heavy bomber force would be called upon to perform in support of the Operation.	taneous or air burst fuses should be used, and little cratering will in fact result. The effect of bombing attacks on gun emplacements has been exhaustively examined by an Inter-Service Committee, and they agreed that if guns are not provided with overhead cover a high degree of neutralisation can be effected. Similarly with air burst and instantaneous fused bombs appreciable casualties and lowering of morale can be caused to defenders in slit trenches. Professor Zuckerman's Report on bombing of communications in Sicily and Italy shows exclusively that great effect can be achieved by heavy bombers, and that if it is to have immediate effect in the battle area the targets selected must be close to that area and not hundreds of miles away as is suggested in the C-in-C's memorandum.	the heavy bomber force could in no circumstances be relied on to cut railway communications could not have been further from the truth. Whether the attacks have been on marshalling yards, junctions, tunnels or bridges in nearly every case most successful results have been achieved.

18–20 *Cost of Changing Bomber Policy*
States the case for continuing the heavy bomber offensive on GERMANY and the consequences of a six-months break in this offensive.

The cost of diverting the whole or part of the heavy bomber effort to the direct support of 'OVERLORD' would certainly receive the fullest consideration, and the decision to do so will be taken at the highest level.

The general contentions of these paragraphs that the effects of strategical bombing are cumulative and that there is recovery rate as well as destructive rate, and that therefore any cessation of attacks on Germany is to be avoided is accepted. It is incorrect, however, to suggest that these arguments apply to an interruption of say two weeks or even to a temporary diminution of effort due to the needs of 'OVERLORD'. Weather conditions have many times imposed periods of interruption of the attack of Germany. It is incorrect to suggest that a relatively short interruption even of several weeks of the bombing of Germany would enable the enemy to redispose the major part of his air and ground defences and move them from central Germany to the Invasion Area.

It is true that 'OVERLORD' commitments have caused some diversion of effort from the bombing of German targets. This has not been considerable, however, since Bomber Command are in any case severely limited in their attacks on Germany by moonlight and by the short nights now being experienced. Bomber Command reverted at D + 6 to strategical bombing, when they attacked the synthetic oil plants in the Ruhr. 'OVERLORD' has provided an abundance of profitable targets for attack by Bomber Command during the recent moonlight periods.

The Air Staff view that relatively short interruptions, even of several weeks of the bombing of Germany would not enable the enemy to redispose the major part of his air and ground defences was correct. Any major movement by the enemy of ground defences or night fighters to the West has been influenced chiefly by the knowledge that Bomber Command were un-

Paras of Memorandum	Statements in C-in-C's Memorandum	Comments by AEAF	Comments by the Air Staff (27 January 1944)	Comments by the Air Staff (28 June 1944)
				likely to operate further East than the Ruhr during the short periods of darkness.
21	*Morale* Germany would go wild with a sense of relief and reborn hope with a cessation or ponderable reduction of the bombing of GERMANY proper.	Failure of Operation 'OVERLORD' would result in far graver repercussions than a temporary cessation in the bombing of German centres.	Whilst it is entirely practicable for Bomber Command during certain phases of 'OVERLORD' materially to assist land operations, this can be done without allowing the German population to receive any appreciable respite from bombing attack. It should be possible even with the needs of 'OVERLORD' to maintain a sufficient degree of pressure on Germany so as to allow of no recovery in morale. Indeed, some such constant pressure will be necessary in order to compel the enemy to maintain fighter forces in Germany and prevent a complete concentration in the 'OVERLORD' area.	There is no indication 'that Germany has gone wild with a sense of relief and reborn hope with a cessation or ponderable reduction of the bombing of Germany proper'. The threat to the German population is still as great as ever, and is maintained by such attacks as Bomber Command has made upon the Ruhr and the Americans upon Berlin in recent weeks. On the contrary, the knowledge of the enormous air effort which has been devoted to the support of 'OVERLORD' must have been viewed with considerable apprehension by the German population; an apprehension which will grow with success of the invasion. The German population fully realise their troops are being subjected to the very heavy

419

	Conclusions		
22	The Bomber Command Memorandum concludes by stating that it is clear that the best, and indeed the only, effective support Bomber Command can give to Operation 'OVERLORD' is the intensification of the attacks against suitable industrial targets in GERMANY. bombing attacks normally directed at them and that these attacks, by playing their part in the successful establishment of the bridgehead, may be even more injurious in securing the defeat of Germany than if directed at the population.	The desirability of maintaining the Bomber Command offensive against industrial centres in GERMANY is fully appreciated. Bomber Command must, however, be diverted in whole or part as required to the attack of suitable targets in support of Operation 'OVERLORD' in the preparatory phase, during the assault, and subsequently. The comments of A.E.A.F. are agreed. The extent to which the support of Bomber Command will be required in the various phases of 'OVERLORD' will be determined by the C.C.O.S. after they have had General Eisenhower's recommendations. The C.O.S. and the C.C.O.S. are in a position to balance the respective needs of 'OVERLORD' and 'POINTBLANK' and can adjust the degree of support required from the strategical air forces, in accordance with the particular requirements at the time.	Generally, the conclusions of the Bomber Command memorandum have proved entirely incorrect. The support which Bomber Command has, in fact, been capable of affording has played an outstanding part in the successful establishment of the bridgehead. The statement that 'the only effective support Bomber Command could give to operation 'OVERLORD' was the intensification of attacks against industrial targets in Germany' has proved to be very far indeed from the truth.

APPENDIX 5

(see p. 337)

The Strategic Air War against Germany, 1939–1945
Overall Report B.B.S.U. 1946
Preface

This Unit was in being from the end of June 1945, to the middle of September 1946, and was established on the recommendation of a Committee that was set up by the Secretary of State for Air, under the Chairmanship of Sir Geoffrey Vickers, V.C. It had headquarters both in London and in Germany and, with the exception of the eastern zone of Germany, its field staffs moved freely on the Continent in search of relevant information. The Unit was administered by the Royal Air Force, but its central and field staffs were drawn from all the Services, and from civilian Departments of State (the Ministry of Home Security and the Ministry of Aircraft Production) which were concerned in the field of work under investigation. It also included a number of independent observers. A skeleton Air Ministry organisation that had been established in October 1944, under the name of the British Bombing Research Mission, was taken over by the B.B.S.U. on its formation, as was also the Bombing Analysis Unit [the BAU] of the Allied Expeditionary Forces and S.H.A.E.F.

In accordance with the recommendations of the Vickers Committee, it had been intended that the report of the British Bombing Survey Unit should be reviewed by an 'interdepartmental board' before publication. Owing, however, to the accurate and voluminous contemporary statistical German data that proved to be available, the facts about the influence of air bombardment on Germany's war effort have turned out to be far less controversial, and the need for a formal 'board' consequently less, than had been originally anticipated. Its place has been filled by informal consultation with Government departments over the past two years.

For the collection of its primary data, the British Bombing Survey Unit was divided into the following Panels, each of which has been responsible for its own report. Towns, Aircraft Industry, Shipbuilding, Sea-Communications, Inland Communications, Weapon Effectiveness, Underground Structures, Civil Defence, U-Boat Industry.

In its study of the offensive against German oil supplies, the B.B.S.U. joined forces with the Technical Sub-Committee on Axis Oil of the J.I.C. [Joint Intelligence Committee] and the Oil Committee of the Combined Strategic Targets Committee. A report of this enquiry was published separately in 1946 by the Technical Sub-Committee on Axis Oil under the title 'Oil as a Factor in the German War Effort, 1933–1945'.

The British Bombing Survey Unit was the counterpart of a 'United States Strategic Bombing Survey' (U.S.S.B.S.). This organisation was set up under the authority of the President of the United States before the British Bombing Survey Unit had been established, but at a time when both the British Bombing Research Mission and the Bombing Analysis Unit were already functioning. U.S.S.B.S. was a much bigger organisation than the B.B.S.U., and employed as many as a thousand personnel, including specialists in all fields of industry. Throughout the period of field work, the most cordial relations existed between our two organisations, and every help was given by U.S.S.B.S. to the central staff and to the field parties of the B.B.S.U. The B.B.S.U. deliberately avoided overlapping with U.S.S.B.S. in collecting figures relating to German production and consumption. Here we have drawn freely upon the American material, to which we have added by further enquiry where it seemed useful or necessary. In its analysis of the material, however, the B.B.S.U. has worked independently of the U.S.S.B.S. The fact that both organisations have reached similar conclusions on the major issues involved is mainly a reflection of the objectivity, and of the lack of ambiguity, of contemporary records of events in Germany during the war years.

The B.B.S.U. was wound up before its main report, and some of the Panel reports, had been completed. The following are the more important papers which were used in the preparation of the present 'Overall' Report. No consistent attempt has been made to cite the sources for many of the factual data which it incorporates. Where they are not stated, they can be found in the Panel Reports of the B.B.S.U. or in the reports of the U.S.S.B.S.

British Bombing Survey Unit
  1. Report on the Effects of Strategic Air Attacks on German Towns.
  2. Potential and Actual Output of German Armaments in Relation to the Combined Bomber Offensive.
  3. The Effects of Air Attack on Inland Communications.
  4. Oil as a Factor in the German War Effort, 1939–1945 (Technical Sub-Committee on Axis Oil).
  5. The Effects of Bombing the German Aircraft Industry.
  6. The Effects of Strategic Bombing on the Production of German U-Boats.
  7. The Effects of Air Attacks on German Sea-Communications in North-West European Waters.
  8. German Experience in the Underground Transfer of War Industries.
  9. Report on Weapon Effectiveness.

United States Strategic Bombing Survey
  1. Overall Report (European War).
  2. Summary Report (Pacific War).
  3. The Effects of Strategic Bombing on the German Economy.
  4. Overall Economic Effects Division Report.
  5. Oil Division—Final Report.
     Oil Division—Final Report, Appendices.
  6. The German Oil Industry (Team 78, Ministerial Report).
  7. The Effects of Strategic Bombing on German Transportation.

APPENDIX 6

(see p. 337)

The Strategic Air War against Germany, 1939-1945
Overall Report B.B.S.U. 1946
Conclusions

The initial attacks on the enemy's oil supplies and transportation systems in 1940 and 1941 were as much the failure as the 1944 and 1945 offensives against the same target systems were the outstanding successes of the whole bomber offensive. By comparison with the latter, the area attacks against German industrial cities paradoxically reveal themselves as an inconclusive offensive. In spite of the extensive material destruction which they caused, those that were delivered before the early autumn of 1944 had only an irritant effect on German production. On the other hand, collateral effects of those that took place in the final six months of the war were an important factor in depressing the Ruhr steel industry, and if the war had lasted six months longer than it did, armament production would in consequence have been seriously affected. The fourth major offensive of the strategic air forces, the attack against aircraft assembly plants, failed almost completely in its primary purpose. On the other hand, the tactical employment of heavy bombers, which was usually regarded as a diversionary employment, was sometimes associated with successful ground operations, although when we leave the field of morale, one cannot say in what specific material way it assisted the advance of the armies. Air action was also very successful in disrupting the enemy's sea communications and in defeating the U-boat—although attacks on the U-boat industry achieved significant results only after the submarine menace had been defeated at sea.

This is the first picture that emerges when one rapidly surveys the field, target system by target system. It is somewhat distorted, not only because it fails to take into account differences in the effective weight of attack delivered against different target systems, but because it glosses over the fundamental fact that freedom of target selection, which could only be provided by effective air superiority over Germany, did not exist in the earlier part of the war. Before dealing with this question it is, however, necessary to consider, in general, first the way in which the results of the bombing of different target systems interacted, and second the interaction of the entire bomber offensive with the land battle.

For as events materialised, three major factors were associated in Germany's defeat. The first and most obvious was the over-running of her territory by the armies of the Allies. The second was the breakdown of her war industry, which was mainly a consequence of the bombing of her communications system. The third was the drying-up of her resources of liquid fuel, and the disruption of her chemical industry, which resulted from the bombing of synthetic oil plants and refineries. If it could be assumed that any one of these factors had operated in isolation without the assistance of the other two, Germany would still have been defeated—although the time of her capitulation might well have been different from what it was. If none of these factors had operated, another less decisive, but nevertheless potential war-winning event was looming on the horizon—the damage to the Ruhr steel plants, which would have shown itself in a decline in the output of armaments in the second half of 1945.

It is an unreal abstraction, however, to consider these factors in mutual isolation. For example, it is quite clear that the blows that were struck at the enemy's transport system in the western occupied territories and western Germany were a major contribution to our successful lodgement in Normandy, and to the German failure to marshal the forces with which she could have driven us out. Equally it is certain that the land battle would not have progressed as favourably as it did after France had been liberated if bombing had not depleted the enemy's oil supplies. On the other side of the picture we have the fact that from September 1944, onwards the bomber offensive was facilitated by land advances which not only helped to defeat the enemy's early warning system, but which also made it possible to establish on the German frontier radio stations to assist navigation and bombing.

This broad picture of interaction between the air and land war applies predominantly to the western front. By comparison, the influence of the strategic bomber offensive on the eastern front was neither direct nor, until the last months of the war, of critical significance. Opposed to any contrary view is the fact that the tide was running hard against the Germans in the east before our own landings in Normandy, and before Germany's war production or her oil supplies had been seriously affected by our air offensive. What can be said with certainty is that the subsequent occurrence of these two events considerably eased the task of our Russian allies and hastened Germany's final collapse, and that earlier on, the diversion of air strength to the defence of the Reich reduced the German air forces on the eastern front.

The role of mutual interaction emerges more plainly when we consider the strategic air war on its own, and in this light the over-riding importance of the offensive against communications becomes very clear. The story of the relation of this offensive to the attacks that were delivered against Germany's oil industry begins, as we have seen, in the planning phase. The first point we should note is that the end of the war might well have been disastrously delayed, and our own part in it much diminished, if the 'Overlord Transportation Plan' had been set aside in favour of the alternative pre-D-Day proposals to bomb synthetic oil plants in Germany and to cut a specific number of railway links to the bridgehead area during a few days immediately before and after the period of the landings. On the one hand oil stocks in France were sufficient, by German standards, to counter an invasion, while on the other, weather conditions over western France during the first fortnight of the invasion were so bad that air operations were reduced to a minimum in the very period when our land forces were most vulnerable. Had the French railway system not already been thoroughly dislocated by our strategic air forces, the mobility which the German forces would have enjoyed might well have turned the scales against us—as it might equally well have done even later in the lodgement phase of our invasion. Both the landing in Normandy and the subsequent battle in France were thus in every sense a 'Combined Operation', and it is difficult to see how they could have succeeded if the integral air plan had not been executed.

Correspondingly, as we have seen, the disruption of communications interacted strongly with the offensive against the oil industry. For although it is quite clear that the far-reaching initial success of the latter campaign was entirely the result of the specific attacks made on the oil plants themselves during the summer of 1944, it is improbable that equal success would have attended the attacks that were made during the bad weather of the autumn and winter of 1944, in particular, attacks on distant plants such as Leuna and Poelitz, if flying operations had not been made easier by the liberation of France and Belgium. Further, the information we now have makes it clear that after the initial shock, subsequent effects of the oil offensive would have been partly buffered by the execution of the Geilenberg programme of repairs and dispersal, had this programme itself not been defeated by the industrial chaos that was simultaneously resulting from the bombing of communications. Not even complete immunity from air attack, still less the palliative effect of the Geilenberg programme, would have enabled the oil industry to do more than limp along if the rail and water transport had been disrupted.

The serious dislocation incurred by the Ruhr steel industry in the winter of 1944 and spring of 1945, as a result of the damage inflicted by nearby 'area attacks' to such plant facilities as water, electric power, and gas supplies, and to the means for carrying out short-haul transport, also cannot be considered independently of the increasing and general industrial chaos. For if one were to assume that these attacks had taken place in a period when the communications system was not being disrupted, it would be reasonable to suppose that the damage they caused, which in general did not affect vital and scarce plant equipment, could have been at least partly repaired and held in check—as was the equivalent, even if less severe, damage suffered by the industry in the first half of 1943. It would hardly seem that the set-back to the German steel industry would have been critical had it occurred in isolation.

An opposite conclusion is suggested only in the case of the bombing of the communications system, mainly because the effects of the resultant dislocation pervaded all current national activity, including that of the railways themselves. For while it is probable that repairs would have been more effective if no other target systems were being simultaneously attacked, it is very unlikely that they could have kept pace with an ever-increasing scale of destruction that engulfed the repair facilities, including means of transport, themselves. Further, when we consider the question of independence of effects, we see that the critical results of the bomber-offensive against communications had begun to manifest themselves both in the economic and military spheres before the time of the invasion of the west, before the offensive against oil, and before the Ruhr steel plants were seriously damaged. For example, such bombing of the railways as was carried out in eastern France, Belgium and Luxembourg prior to D-Day not only suppressed the traffic of minette ore to the Saar and crippled the industry of the areas they served, but also slowed down the fortification of the French channel coast and the building of V-weapon installations. Again, the precipitous decline which began in German war production later in the year was for all practical purposes undetermined by events other than the decline in transport operations, which affected not only production but also distribution in every industrial field. The more intense and widely-distributed the damage to the communications system, the more wholesale and more dispersed was its effect upon industry and upon military activity.

When allowances are made for territorial losses, and for such declines in armament output as would have been caused by the loss of raw materials, it follows that the direct occupation of industrial areas would not have affected the overall production of finished munitions by more than about one percent in the third quarter of 1944, and that the corresponding losses for the last quarter of the year, and the first quarter of 1945 were of the order of three and thirteen percent respectively.

APPENDIX 7

(see p. 365)

Memorandum on the need for a central Governmental Science Secretariat, submitted by the author to Herbert Morrison, Lord President of the Council, on 16 September, 1945

Scientific affairs in Great Britain are badly integrated and planned. Yet the economic condition of the country today is such that it demands the fullest possible use and extension of our scientific resources in the restoration of industry and agriculture, in the development of social services and in the determination of defence policies—which in turn calls for a large measure of forward-thinking and bold and energetic planning. The matter is of such importance that it should be made the charge of a full-time working Secretariat answerable to the highest Cabinet level.

The Lord President of the Council is the Minister under whom the D.S.I.R., the M.R.C. and the A.R.C. are set up. The control which these bodies exercise over their respective fields varies, that of the D.S.I.R. and A.R.C. probably being stronger today than that of the M.R.C. In no case is their activity on the scale that is required by modern conditions. In addition to these Government scientific bodies, the Service Departments all possess scientific technical branches and, in a few cases, Scientific Advisers who also deal with operational planning. Some other Ministries have scientific advisers and scientific advisory committees. For example, the Ministry of Works has a scientific staff and a Scientific Advisory Council, whose function it is to consider matters of all kinds related primarily to the housing problem. The Chief Scientific Adviser of the Ministry of Works is also the Chief Adviser on Civil Defence matters to the Home Office.

The co-ordination of these activities was recognised to be defective in the war. Attempts to remedy the situation were made by the appointment of the Scientific Advisory Committee of the War Cabinet. This body, formed of representatives of the Royal Society and of Government scientific agencies, was found in practice to lack both initiative and authority, and its achievements were negligible. Its failure was virtually recognised in the appointment of three scientific advisers to the Ministry of Production, but they were provided with insufficient staff and such limited powers that they proved effective only in dealing with a few detailed problems.

These were wartime measures which will presumably now lapse. The present situation, however, demands a greater organisation of science than was necessary in war, since the aims to be achieved are more various, and the overriding priorities of war cannot any longer be invoked. To revert to the pre-war position would be disastrous. Already Industries, Universities and Government Departments are bidding against each other for our very limited supply of good scientists. In the absence of a scientific general staff, the Lord President's office is seriously handicapped in advising the Cabinet on the furtherance of our scientific resources as a whole. For this reason it is suggested that there be established a Science Secretariat, attached to the Lord President's Office, with functions as follows:

Governmental:

(i) To initiate and recommend action towards the development and use of our scientific resources for our economic and defence requirements (agriculture, industry, etc. etc.), based on a rapid survey of the distribution of our present scientific strength.

(ii) To collect and keep up to date statistics and information on our scientific potential, and to provide estimates of our quantitative and qualitative needs for scientists.

(iii) To advise *ad hoc* on scientific problems put before it by the Cabinet Office.

(iv) To arrange, where necessary, scientific advice in governmental departments and to co-ordinate the use of scientists in governmental work.

Scientific:

(i) To prepare plans for the better co-ordination and extension of the University, Industrial and Governmental scientific activities of the country.

Educational:

(i) To plan for the supply of the much larger number of University trained scientists necessary for the full development of our national resources.

(ii) To ensure that an appreciation of science is adequately provided for in our schemes for general education.

International Relations:

(i) To arrange, where necessary, for the proper representation of British science in the United Nations Organisations.

(ii) To assure facilities for the international exchange of knowledge.

(iii) To keep in touch with the Advisory Committee on Atomic Research.

(iv) To keep informed about, and to advise on the restoration and direction of educational and scientific activities in Germany.

The Secretariat would report directly to the Lord President in the same way as do the Joint Planning Committee and the Joint Intelligence Sub-Committee to the Chiefs of Staff Committee, and the Central Statistical Bureau to the Cabinet. Like the latter three in their own spheres, it should have powers to call for information from any governmental or public scientific organisations but, again like them, the Secretariat would in no sense supersede the functions of its counterpart bodies within Ministries. The proposed Science Secretariat should work in parallel with the Central Statistical Bureau. The Government scientific organisations such as the D.S.I.R., M.R.C. and A.R.C. would continue to report directly to the Lord President.

It is considered that the Secretariat should be composed of about four senior scientists of acknowledged scientific repute, and some six junior scientists. Scientific merit being equal, they should be men who could be relied upon to give active and strong support to the Government's policies, and who would take a forward view of what should, and could be done in this very important field of national activity.

INDEX

Where a subject has been treated in a separate note at the end of the book, this is indicated by, e.g. (1) 390 *n* 12, or (2) 381 *ch* 11 *n* 3.
(1) means note 12 on page 390. (2) means note 3 to chapter 11 on page 381.
fn. = footnote appearing on page cited.

Dickinson, H. D., 60, 394
Dieppe, surrender of, 281–2
Dieppe raid, 156–7
  casualty survey of, 157–8, 170
diffusionist theory, 19, 20, 40, 70
Dingwall, Eric, 139
Dobell, Clifford, 97
Dodds, Charles, 100
Donovan, Maj.-Gen. William (Wild
  Bill), 157 and fn.
Doolittle, Maj.-Gen. J. H., 358
  and *Overlord* planning, 230
  in N. Africa, 175, 176
Douglas, J. W. B., 98
Douglas, Air Chief Marshal Sir Wil-
  liam Sholto, 162, 170–1,176, 347
Drennan, Prof. M. R., 12, 15–16, 18
Dresden, reaction to bomber attacks
  on, 224–5, 351–2, 382 *n* 15
Driberg, Tom, 400 and fn.
Drummond, Jack, 401–2
Drury, Gp Capt. E. S. Dru,
  and Bombing Analysis Unit, 286–7,
    291, 324–6
  and *Overlord* air plan, 261
Dundas, R. H. (Robin), 89
Dunkirk evacuation, casualty survey
  of, 119, 124

Eaker, Lt-Gen. Ira, 204–5, 218
Economic Warfare Department, *see*
  United States Economic Warfare
  Department
Eden, Anthony, 104 fn., 214
  and *Overlord* air plan, 247, 250
Egerton, Alfred, 396–7
Eisenhower, Gen. Dwight D., 199,
  296, 351, 368, 369–70
  and Ardennes offensive, 315, 357,
    387 *ch* 16 *n* 1
  and battle for Caen, 283–5, 348
  and communications v. oil offensive,
    297, 388 *n* 4
  and control of strategic air forces,
    222, 245, 297–8
  and inter-Allied rivalry, 297, 349
  and *Overlord* air plan, 199, 219, 225,

Eisenhower, Gen. Dwight D.—*cont.*
  226, 228, 231, 243–5, 254–7, 287,
    332, 339, 357, 385 *n* 11
  and Pantelleria operations, 183, 190,
    195
  S.Z. commended in Official Dispatch
    on, 195
  and plan for final assault on Ger-
    many, 306, 345, 348
  and relations with other com-
    manders, 199, 284–5, 346, 369
  and Sicilian operations, 196, 197,
    198–9, 381 *ch* 11 *n* 2
  Supreme Commander, Allied Ex-
    peditionary Force, 214, 265, 291,
    320, 326
Elliot, Air Cdre William, 213 and fn.
Elliot Smith, Sir Grafton, 18–20, 61–3
  and diffusionist theory, 20, 40
  and interpretation of fossil remains,
    20–1, 61, 62, 65
  and S.Z., 19, 25, 27–8, 39, 41, 50, 51,
    62, 65, 68, 77, 84
Ellis, Prof. Charles, 237–8
Ellis Committee, *see* War Cabinet
  Joint Technical Warfare . . .
Emmens, C. W. (Cliff), 144 and fn.,
  146, 207, 282, 335
endocrinology, development of studies
  of, in Britain, 100
  Journal of, 99–101
Ephrussi, Boris, 291, 294, 321, 333
Erleigh, Michael (Viscount Erleigh),
  103–4
evolution, *see* man, physical evolution
  of
Ezra, Maj. Derek, and communications
  offensives planning, 314–16
  and German railway records, 298
    and fn., 301

Fairbanks, Douglas, jr., 151
'Falaise pocket', 281, 282–3
Faringdon, Lord (Gavin Henderson),
  93
Fickel, Gen. J., 291, 332
Fish Hoek fossil remains, 14, 46